FINITE MATHEMATICS

WITH BUSINESS APPLICATIONS

PRENTICE-HALL QUANTITATIVE METHODS SERIES

Dr. W. Allen Spivey, *editor*

Cyert and Davidson *Statistical Sampling for Accounting Information*

Kemeny, Schleifer, Snell and Thompson *Finite Mathematics with Business Applications*

Massé *Optimal Investment Decisions: Rules for Action and Criteria for Choice*

PRENTICE-HALL INTERNATIONAL

London · Tokyo · Sydney · Paris

PRENTICE-HALL OF CANADA LTD.

PRENTICE-HALL OF MEXICO, S.A.

FINITE MATHEMATICS

WITH BUSINESS APPLICATIONS

John G. Kemeny

Professor of Mathematics
Dartmouth College

Arthur Schleifer, Jr.

Associate Professor of Business Administration
Amos Tuck School of Business Administration
Dartmouth College

J. Laurie Snell

Professor of Mathematics
Dartmouth College

Gerald L. Thompson

Associate Professor of Applied Mathematics
and Industrial Administration
Carnegie Institute of Technology

Prentice-Hall, Inc. Englewood Cliffs, N.J.

Library of Congress Catalog Card Number: 62-18305

Fifth printing .... June. 1965

PRINTED IN THE UNITED STATES OF AMERICA
48383—C

Preface

Mathematics has, in recent years, been widely applied to the fields of business and industrial administration. The growth and development of such mathematically oriented subjects as operations research, statistical decision theory, management science, and mathematical programming, and the application of these subjects to business problems, make it desirable that students of business and industrial administration take courses in applied mathematics in their undergraduate training. The Gordon and Howell[1] and Pierson[2] reports, and a number of articles and symposia[3] have reviewed the current state of mathematics training for business students and have suggested the directions in which such training might proceed in the future. While most agree that students of business should be exposed to some traditional mathematics, such as is given in pre-calculus and calculus courses, they all have called for a course which would provide a sophisticated introduction for the non-mathematician to topics in modern mathematical analysis—what has come to be known as finite mathematics.

The book, *Introduction to Finite Mathematics*, written by three of us, was conceived as an answer to a similar gap in the mathematical training of behavioral and social scientists. Another version of that book, *Finite Mathematical Structures*, written by three of us together with H. Mirkil, was directed to the mathematical training of students in the physical sciences. These two books, together with the present one, have used the same central theme: to develop material from the *finite* point of view, that

---

[1] R. A. Gordon and J. E. Howell, *Higher Education for Business*, New York: Columbia University Press, 1959, pp. 159–163.

[2] F. C. Pierson *et al.*, *The Education of American Businessmen*, New York: McGraw-Hill Book Co., Inc., 1959, pp. 186–190.

[3] See, for example, S. Goldberg, "Mathematics for Business Students" in *Views on Business Education*, School of Business Administration, Chapel Hill, University of North Carolina, 1960; R. K. Gaumnitz and O. H. Brownlee, "Mathematics for Decision Makers," *Harvard Business Review*, 34, 3 (May–June 1956), p. 48; G. A. W. Boehm, "Mathematics II: The New Uses of the Abstract," *Fortune*, LVIII, 1 (July 1958), p. 124.

v

is, without resorting to infinite sets, limiting processes, continuity, etc. We have found that the basic ideas of finite mathematics are easier to state and theorems about them considerably easier to prove than is the case with their infinite counterparts. And we believe that, for the class of problems with which we are here concerned, the task of abstracting from the real world to a mathematical model is much easier with finite mathematics.

In the present book we have treated topics in finite mathematics in the context of business and industrial administration. The basic mathematics core of the book remains as in the previous books, but most of the applied exercises and examples have been set in the context of business. In addition, more than one-third of the book is completely new. The new material consists partly of new mathematical ideas, but it also treats a large number of applications of mathematics to business and administration problems. Among the applications discussed are computer circuits, critical path analysis, flow diagrams for computing and accounting procedures, Monte Carlo simulation of decision processes, reliability, decision theory, waiting line theory, a simple approach to mathematics of finance, and the simplex method for solving linear programming problems and matrix games.

Besides "tree diagrams," a pedagogical device found to be of great usefulness in *Introduction to Finite Mathematics*, we have utilized other diagrammatic devices. For instance, the graph of the jobs in a project is used in the critical path analysis of Chapter II. And in Chapter III there is a discussion of flow diagrams, which permit the easy description of complicated computational processes, such as the Monte Carlo simulation calculations of Chapter IV, the accounting procedures of Chapter VI, and the simplex calculations of Chapter VII. In addition, the ability to construct a good flow diagram is perhaps seventy per cent of the work of writing a computer program in one of the algebraic languages commonly used to program modern computers.

The basic core of the book consists of the unasterisked sections of the first five chapters. This material should be covered in every introductory course and constitutes a basic mathematics course. The optional (asterisked) sections of these chapters, together with Chapters VI, VII, and VIII, can be used to enrich the basic course in various directions, depending upon the interests of the instructor and class. These additional sections can also be used for supplementary material in the functional business courses, for seminar study, and for self-study on the part of a student. The entire book can be used for a year's course in mathematics and its applications to business and administration problems. Furthermore, the optional material contains many of the topics which are taught under such titles as Operations Research, Quantitative Methods, etc.

In organizing the book, we have included major applications within each chapter. We hope that the ordering of material in this book will motivate the student by demonstrating immediately the relevance of the mathematical theory contained herein to applied problems.

Recognizing the possibility that some instructors may want to skip some sections of the book and take up topics in an order different from that in which the book was laid out, however, we have included in the Contents the prerequisites for each section. Generally, we have listed only immediate prerequisites. We have, however, permitted for emphasis a certain amount of redundancy in our listing. It is hoped that this listing of prerequisites will also help the student who has difficulty with a particular section to trace back to the source of his difficulty.

It occasionally happens that a detail which is not crucial to the assimilation of the principal subject matter of a section depends on some previous section. For example, in Section 4 of Chapter VI, we discuss how to interpolate in Table III by using approximate formulae developed from the binomial theorem (Section 8 of Chapter III). This discussion is not, however, crucial for an understanding of the main theme of the section, although it permits wider application of the theory. Dependencies of this sort are shown by putting in parentheses the number of the prerequisite section.

The only prerequisite for this book itself is the mathematical maturity obtained from two and a half or more years of high school mathematics. It can, therefore, be used at any stage in the curriculum from the beginning of the freshman year on. Most of the material in the book has been tested in some version at Dartmouth College, Carnegie Institute of Technology, and a number of other institutions.

We would like to thank H. Mirkil who kindly permitted us to utilize parts of the book three of us wrote with him. The Dartmouth Computation Center provided help in preparing the Appendix Tables and in obtaining solutions for some of the examples in the text. Also, the following people have been kind enough to read and criticize parts of the manuscript or have suggested problem material to us: N. Churchill, G. Cooke, R. M. Cyert, H. J. Davidson, D. Dearborn, M. W. Herriott, R. H. Klein, M. Miller, L. E. Morrissey, Jr., R. Schlaifer, R. Trueblood, and P. R. Winters. We are grateful to them for their suggestions. We would also like to thank the production staff of Prentice-Hall for their usual careful attention to editing and printing.

J. G. K.

A. S., Jr.

J. L. S.

G. L. T.

Contents

Prerequisites

I. Compound Statements

1. Purpose of the theory	1	
2. The most common connectives	4	I.1
3. Other connectives	9	I.2
4. Logical possibilities	13	I.3
5. Tree diagrams	19	I.4
6. Decision trees	25	I.5
7. Logical relations	29	I.4
*8. A systematic analysis of logical relations	33	I.7
*9. Statements having given truth tables	37	I.3, (I.7)
*10. Applications to switching circuits	40	I.9
*11. Binary numbers	44	I.2
*12. Computer circuits	47	I.10, I.11
Suggested Reading	52	

II. Sets and Subsets

1. Introduction	53	I.4
2. Operations on subsets	57	II.1
3. The relationship between sets and compound statements	62	II.2, I.7
*4. The abstract laws of set operations	66	II.2
*5. Voting coalitions	68	II.2
*6. Critical path analysis	72	II.1
Suggested Reading	82	

III. Partitions and Counting

1. Partitions	84	II.2
*2. Applications	90	III.1

3. The number of elements in a set   95   III.1, II.2
4. Permutations   98   I.5, III.3
5. Counting partitions   102   III.4
6. Two-cell partitions of two-valued sets   106   III.5
7. Some properties of binomial coefficients   110   III.5
8. Binomial and multinomial theorems   114   III.5
*9. Voting power   117   III.4
*10. Flow diagrams   120
*11. Flow diagrams for counting problems   126   III.4, III.7, III.10
     Suggested Reading   133

IV. Probability Theory

1. Introduction   134   I.1, II.1
2. Properties of a probability measure   137   IV.1, I.2, I.4, II.2
3. The equiprobable measure   141   IV.2
4. Probability of a sample from a finite two-
   valued set   145   IV.3, III.6
*5. Two nonintuitive examples   148   IV.3, III.4
6. Conditional probability and Bayes' theorem   152   IV.2
7. Finite stochastic processes   160   IV.6, I.5
8. Independent trials with two outcomes   169   IV.7, III.5
*9. The law of large numbers   177   IV.8
*10. Independent trials with more than two
     outcomes   183   IV.7, IV.8, III.5
11. Expected value   186   IV.8
12. Markov chains   193   IV.7
*13. Monte Carlo simulation   199   III.10, IV.7, IV.8, IV.12
*14. Monte Carlo analysis of decision rules   207   IV.9, IV.11, IV.13
*15. Reliability of components   215   IV.7
*16. Decision theory   221   IV.6, IV.7, IV.8, IV.11
     Suggested Reading   228

V. Vectors and Matrices

1. Column and row vectors   229
2. The product of vectors; examples   234   V.1
3. Matrices and their combination with vectors   240   V.2, (IV.12)
4. The addition and multiplication of matrices   248   V.3
5. The solution of linear equations   254   V.4
6. The inverse of a square matrix   262   V.5

*7. The parts requirements listing problem   268   V.6
 8. Applications of matrix theory to Markov
        chains   274   V.4, IV.12
 9. Absorbing Markov chains   282   V.6, V.8
*10. An example from waiting line theory   289   V.8
*11. Charge accounts   295   V.9
*12. Further applications of Markov chains   299   V.9
*13. Max and min operations   304   V.4, IV.11
     Suggested Reading   311

VI. *Mathematics of Finance and Accounting*

A. Mathematics of Finance
 1. A finite difference equation   312
 2. Some important special cases   319   VI.1
 3. Solving for interest rate and number of
        payments   325   VI.2
 4. Nominal and effective interest rates   330   VI.3, (III.8)
*5. Tax offsets on depreciation   334   VI.2
*6. Formulas for present value of depreciation
        charges   339   VI.5

B. Mathematics of Accounting
 7. Double classification bookkeeping   346   V.4
 8. Financial reports   352   VI.7
*9. Flow diagrams for double classification
        bookkeeping   358   VI.8, III.10
    Suggested Reading   363

VII. *Linear Programming*

 1. Polyhedral convex sets   364   I.4, II.3, V.5
 2. Extreme points; maxima and minima of
        linear functions   370   VII.1, (V.2)
 3. Linear programming problems   379   VII.2
 4. The simplex method for solving linear pro-
        gramming problems   384   VII.3, (V.6)
 5. Dual linear programming problems   394   VII.4
    Suggested Reading   401

VIII. *The Theory of Games*

 1. Introduction: strictly determined games   402   V.3, (V.13)
 2. Nonstrictly determined games   407   VIII.1, IV.11

3. Matrix games 414 VIII.2
4. More on matrix games: the fundamental
   theorem 422 VIII.3, V.4
5. Two-row and two-column matrix games 425 VIII.4
6. Simplified poker 432 VIII.5
*7. Model of an expanding economy 436 V.3
*8. Existence of an economic equilibrium 442 VIII.7, VIII.4
*9. The simplex method for solving matrix
   games 448 VIII.4, VII.4, VII.5
*10. Two-person nonzero-sum games 455 VIII.5
   Suggested Reading 464

Appendix Tables

I. Binomial probabilities 466
II. Random numbers 468
III. Single payment compound amount factor 472
IV. Uniform payment present value factor 474

Index

477

FINITE MATHEMATICS

WITH BUSINESS APPLICATIONS

|

Compound Statements

---

1. Purpose of the theory

We propose in this first chapter to study ways of putting statements together to form other statements. For example, from the statement "I have a pair of aces" and the statement "You have a straight flush" we can form the more complicated statement "Either I have a pair of aces or else you do not have a straight flush." This new statement is called a *compound* statement, while the statements out of which it is compounded are called its *simple* parts. Any statement (even though already compound) can be used as one of the simple parts of another compound statement.

It might seem natural first to make a thorough study of statements themselves, before one studies ways of putting them together. But we have chosen not to undertake an investigation of the inner nature of statements because (1) such an investigation would be difficult, belonging more to linguistics than to mathematics, and (2) we do not need to know very much about statements in order to understand the various methods of compounding them. It has been found in mathematics that it is often fruitful to take such a by-pass—to assume temporarily that a difficult first

1

problem has been solved, and then go on to show how the solution of the next problem would depend on the various possible solutions of the first.

Hence all we will care to know about a statement is whether it is true or false, and we will proceed then to show how the truth or falsity of a compound statement depends on the truth or falsity of its simple parts. We will also allow for the fact that a statement like "I have a pair of aces" is sometimes true and sometimes false, depending on what hand I hold. The possible five-card poker hands I might hold (and we will see in the next chapter that there are 2,598,960 of these) are an instance of what we will call *logical possibilities* in Section 4 of the present chapter. Before considering any statement we determine in advance the logical possibilities to which it applies. For each of these possibilities the statement is definitely either true or false. Usually it will be true when applied to some possibilities, false when applied to others, though there exist statements that are true in all cases and statements that are false in all cases.

Our problem now is twofold: (1) What are the various ways in which statements can be *compounded*? (2) How do we determine the *truth value* (i.e., the truth or falsity) of a compound statement, given the truth values of its simple parts? While the first systematic treatment of ideas related to this twofold problem is found in the writings of Aristotle, mathematical methods were first employed by George Boole about 100 years ago. The more polished techniques now available are the product of twentieth-century mathematical logicians.

> **Examples.** As examples of simple statements let us take "Business is good" and "Stock prices are high." We will let p stand for the former and q for the latter.
>
> Suppose we wish to make the compound statement that both are true: "Business is good *and* stock prices are high." We shall symbolize this statement by $p \wedge q$. The symbol $\wedge$, which can be read "and," is our first connective.
>
> In place of the strong assertion above we might want to make the weak (cautious) assertion that one or the other of the statements is true: "Business is good *or* stock prices are high." We symbolize this assertion by $p \vee q$. The symbol $\vee$, which can be read "or," is the second connective which we shall use.
>
> Suppose we believed that one of the statements above was false, for example, "Stock prices are *not* high." Symbolically we would write $\sim q$. Our third connective is then $\sim$, which can be read "not."
>
> More complex compound statements can now be made. For example, $p \wedge \sim q$ stands for "Business is good *and* stock prices are *not* high."

EXERCISES

1. The following are compound statements or may be so interpreted. Find their simple components.

    (a) Business is bad and stock prices are high.

    (b) Business is good but stock prices are not high.

    (c) Business will improve or stock prices will decline.

    (d) Stock prices and bond prices are high.

    (e) We should sell common or preferred stock.

    (f) We should sell neither common nor preferred stock.

    (g) Either business is going to improve or we should liquidate our inventories now.

2. In Exercise 1 assign letters to the various components, and write the statements in symbolic form.   [*Ans.* (b) $p \wedge \sim q$.]

3. Write the following statements in symbolic form, letting p be "Jones' productivity is higher than Smith's" and q be "Jones earns more money than Smith."

    (a) Jones' productivity is higher than Smith's but Jones earns no more money than Smith.

    (b) Jones' productivity is no higher than Smith's, but he earns more money than Smith.

    (c) Jones' wages and productivity are both lower than Smith's.

    (d) Either Jones produces more than Smith or Smith earns more money than Jones.

    (e) Jones neither produces more nor earns more money than Smith.

    (f) Jones does not produce more than Smith but he earns less money.

    (g) It is not true that Jones both produces less and earns less money than Smith.

4. Assume that Jones' productivity is higher than Smith's and that he earns more money. Which of the seven compound statements in Exercise 3 are true?   [*Ans.* (d), (g).]

5. Write the following in symbolic form.

    (a) The Acme Company sells to Brown and Company (statement p).

    (b) Brown and Company sells to the Acme Company (statement q).

    (c) Acme and Brown sell to each other.

    (d) Acme and Brown do not sell to each other.

    (e) Brown buys from Acme but Acme does not reciprocate.

    (f) Brown buys from Acme but Acme does not buy from Brown.

    (g) Neither Acme nor Brown fails to sell to the other.

    (h) It is not true that Acme and Brown fail to sell to one another.

6. Suppose Acme sells to Brown but Brown does not sell to Acme. Which of the eight statements in Exercise 5 are true?

7. For each statement in Exercise 5 give a condition under which it is false.   [*Ans.* (c) Acme does not sell to Brown.]

8. Let p be "Stock prices are high," and q be "Stocks are rising." Give a verbal translation for each of the following.

    (a) $p \wedge q$.

    (b) $p \wedge \sim q$.

  (c) $\sim p \wedge \sim q$.
  (d) $p \vee \sim q$.
  (e) $\sim(p \wedge q)$.
  (f) $\sim(p \vee q)$.
  (g) $\sim(\sim p \vee \sim q)$.

9. Using your answers to Exercise 8, parts (e), (f), (g), find simpler symbolic statements expressing the same idea.

10. Let p be "Jones is Treasurer" and q be "Smith is Controller." Translate into English and simplify:

$$\sim[\sim p \vee \sim\sim q] \wedge \sim\sim p.$$

2. The most common connectives

The truth value of a compound statement is determined by the truth values of its components. When discussing a connective we will want to know just how the truth of a compound statement made with this connective depends upon the truth of its components. A very convenient way of tabulating this dependency is by means of a *truth table*.

Let us consider the compound $p \wedge q$. Statement p could be either true or false and so could statement q. Thus there are four possible pairs of truth values for these statements and we want to know in each case whether or not the statement $p \wedge q$ is true. The answer is straightforward: If p and q are both true, then $p \wedge q$ is true, and otherwise $p \wedge q$ is false. This seems reasonable since the assertion $p \wedge q$ says no more and no less than that p and q are both true.

Figure 1 gives the truth table for $p \wedge q$, the *conjunction* of p and q. The truth table contains all the information that we need to know about the connective $\wedge$, namely it tells us the truth value of the conjunction of two statements given the truth values of each of the statements.

p	q	$p \wedge q$
T	T	T
T	F	F
F	T	F
F	F	F

Figure 1

p	q	$p \vee q$
T	T	?
T	F	T
F	T	T
F	F	F

Figure 2

We next look at the compound statement $p \vee q$, the *disjunction* of p and q. Here the assertion is that one or the other of these statements is true. Clearly, if one statement is true and the other false, then the disjunction is true, while if both statements are false, then the disjunction is

certainly false. Thus we can fill in the last three rows of the truth table
for disjunction (see Figure 2).

Observe that one possibility is left unsettled, namely, what happens if
both components are true? Here we observe that the everyday usage of
"or" is ambiguous. Does "or" mean "one or the other or both" or does it
mean "one or the other but not both"?

Let us seek the answer in examples. The sentence "Brown or Smith is
a foreman" allows for the possibility that both men may be foremen.
However the sentence "I will go to Dartmouth or to Princeton" indicates
that only one of these schools will be chosen. "I will buy a TV set or a
phonograph next year" could be used in either sense; the speaker may mean
that he is trying to make up his mind which one of the two to buy, but he
could also mean that he will buy *at least one* of these—possibly both. We
see that sometimes the context makes the meaning clear but not always.

A mathematician would never waste his time on a dispute as to which
usage "should" be called the disjunction of two statements. Rather he
recognizes two perfectly good usages, and calls one the *inclusive disjunction*
(*p* or *q* or both) and the other the *exclusive disjunction* (*p* or *q* but not both).
The symbol $\vee$ will be used for inclusive disjunction, and the symbol $\underline{\vee}$
will be used for exclusive disjunction. The truth tables for these are found
in Figures 3 and 4 below. Unless we state otherwise, our disjunctions will
be inclusive disjunctions.

p	q	$p \vee q$
T	T	T
T	F	T
F	T	T
F	F	F

Figure 3

p	q	$p \underline{\vee} q$
T	T	F
T	F	T
F	T	T
F	F	F

Figure 4

The last connective we shall discuss in this section is *negation*. If *p* is a
statement, the symbol $\sim p$, called the negation of *p*, asserts that *p* is false.
Hence $\sim p$ is true when *p* is false, and false when *p*
is true. The truth table for negation is shown in
Figure 5.

Besides using these basic connectives singly to form
compound statements, several can be used to form
a more complicated compound statement, in much the
same way that complicated algebraic expressions can

p	$\sim p$
T	F
F	T

Figure 5

be formed by means of the basic arithmetic operations. For example,
$\sim(p \wedge q)$, $p \wedge \sim p$, and $(p \vee q) \vee \sim p$ are all compound statements.
They are to be read "from the inside out" in the same way that algebraic

expressions are, namely, quantities inside the innermost parentheses are first grouped together, then these parentheses are grouped together, etc. Each compound statement has a truth table which can be constructed in a routine way. The following examples show how to construct truth tables.

Example 1. Consider the compound statement $p \lor \sim q$. We begin the construction of its truth table by writing in the first two columns the four possible pairs of truth values for the statements p and q. Then we write the proposition in question, leaving plenty of space between symbols so that we can fill in columns below. Next we copy the truth values of p and q in the columns below their occurrences in the proposition. This completes step 1 of the construction, see Figure 6.

p	q	$p \lor \sim q$	
T	T	T	T
T	F	T	F
F	T	F	T
F	F	F	F
Step No.		1	1

Figure 6

Next we treat the innermost compound, the negation of the variable q, completing step 2, see Figure 7.

p	q	p	$\lor$	$\sim$	q
T	T	T		F	T
T	F	T		T	F
F	T	F		F	T
F	F	F		T	F
Step No.		1		2	1

Figure 7

Finally we fill in the column under the disjunction symbol, which gives us the truth value of the compound statement for various truth values of its variables. To indicate this we place two parallel lines on each side of the final column, completing step 3 as in Figure 8.

p	q	p	V	~	q
T	T	T	T	F	T
T	F	T	T	T	F
F	T	F	F	F	T
F	F	F	T	T	F
Step No.		1	3	2	1

Figure 8

The next two examples show truth tables of more complicated compounds worked out in the same manner. There are only two basic rules which the student must remember when working these: first, work from the "inside out"; and second, the truth values of the compound statement are found in the last column filled in during this procedure.

Example 2. The truth table for the statement $(p \lor \sim q) \land \sim p$ together with the numbers indicating the order in which the columns are filled in appears in Figure 9.

p	q	(p	V	~	q)	∧	~	p
T	T	T	T	F	T	F	F	T
T	F	T	T	T	F	F	F	T
F	T	F	F	F	T	F	T	F
F	F	F	T	T	F	T	T	F
Step No.		1	3	2	1	4	2	1

Figure 9

Example 3. The truth table for the statement $\sim[(p \land q) \lor (\sim p \land \sim q)]$, together with the numbers indicating the order in which the columns are filled in, appears in Figure 10.

p	q	~	[(p	∧	q)	V	(~	p	∧	~	q)]
T	T	F	T	T	T	T	F	T	F	F	T
T	F	T	T	F	F	F	F	T	F	T	F
F	T	T	F	F	T	F	T	F	F	F	T
F	F	F	F	F	F	T	T	F	T	T	F
Step No.		5	1	3	1	4	2	1	3	2	1

Figure 10

EXERCISES

1. Give a compound statement which symbolically states "p or q but not both," using only $\sim$, $\vee$, and $\wedge$.

2. Construct the truth table for your answer to Exercise 1, and compare this with Figure 4.

3. Construct the truth table for the symbolic form of each statement in Exercise 3 of Section 1. How does Exercise 4 of Section 1 relate to these truth tables?

4. Construct a truth table for each of the following:
   (a) $\sim(p \wedge q)$.   [Ans. FTTT.]
   (b) $p \wedge \sim p$.   [Ans. FF.]
   (c) $(p \vee q) \vee \sim p$.   [Ans. TTTT.]
   (d) $\sim[(p \vee q) \wedge (\sim p \vee \sim q)]$.   [Ans. TFFT.]

5. Let p stand for "Jones passed the course" and q stand for "Smith passed the course" and translate into symbolic form the statement "It is not the case that Jones and Smith both failed the course." Construct a truth table for this compound statement. State *in words* the circumstances under which the statement is true.

6. Construct a simpler statement about Jones and Smith that has the same truth table as the one in Exercise 5.

7. Let $p \mid q$ express that "p and q are not both true." Write a symbolic expression for $p \mid q$ using $\sim$ and $\wedge$.

8. Write a truth table for $p \mid q$.

9. Write a truth table for $p \mid p$.   [Ans. Same as Figure 5.]

10. Write a truth table for $(p \mid q) \mid (p \mid q)$.   [Ans. Same as Figure 1.]

11. Construct a truth table for each of the following:
    (a) $\sim(p \vee q) \vee \sim(q \vee p)$.   [Ans. FFFT.]
    (b) $\sim(p \vee q) \wedge p$.   [Ans. FFFF.]
    (c) $\sim(p \veebar q)$.   [Ans. TFFT.]
    (d) $\sim(p \mid q)$.   [Ans. TFFF.]

12. Construct two symbolic statements, using only $\sim$, $\vee$, and $\wedge$, which have the truth tables (a) and (b), respectively:

p	q	(a)	(b)
T	T	T	T
T	F	F	F
F	T	T	F
F	F	T	T

3. *Other connectives*

Suppose we did not wish to make an outright assertion but rather an assertion containing a condition. As examples consider the following sentences. "If they do not improve the quality, we will not continue to buy from them." "If the following statement is true, then I can prove the theorem." "If the cost of living continues to rise, then the government will impose rigid curbs." Each of these statements is of the form *"if p then q."* The *conditional* is then a new connective which is symbolized by the arrow →.

Of course the precise definition of this new connective must be made by means of a truth table. If both p and q are true, then $p \to q$ is certainly true, and if p is true and q false, then $p \to q$ is certainly false. Thus the first two lines of the truth table can easily be filled in, see Figure 11a. Suppose now that p is false; how shall we fill in the last two lines of the

p	q	$p \to q$
T	T	T
T	F	F
F	T	?
F	F	?

Figure 11a

p	q	$p \to q$
T	T	T
T	F	F
F	T	T
F	F	T

Figure 11b

truth table in Figure 11a? At first thought one might suppose that it would be best to leave it completely undefined. However, to do so would violate our basic principle that a statement is either true or false.

Therefore we make the completely arbitrary decision that the conditional, $p \to q$, is *true* whenever p is false, regardless of the truth value of q. This decision enables us to complete the truth table for the conditional and it is given in Figure 11b. A glance at this truth table shows that the conditional $p \to q$ is considered false only if p is true and q is false. If we wished we might rationalize the arbitrary decision made above by saying that if statement p happens to be false then we give the conditional $p \to q$ the "benefit of the doubt" and consider it true (see Exercise 1).

In everyday conversation it is customary to combine simple statements only if they are somehow related. Thus we might say "It is raining today and I will take an umbrella," but we would not say "I read a good book and I will take an umbrella." However, the rather ill-defined concept of relatedness is difficult to enforce. Concepts related to each other in one person's mind need not be related in another's. In our study of compound statements no requirement of relatedness is imposed on two statements in order that they be compounded by any of the connectives. This freedom sometimes produces strange results in the use of the conditional. For example, according to the truth table in Figure 11b the statement "If

$2 \times 2 = 5$, then black is white" is true, while the statement "If $2 \times 2 = 4$, then cows are monkeys" is false. Since we use the "if . . . then . . ." form usually only when there is a causal connection between the two statements, we might be tempted to label both of the above statements as nonsense. At this point it is important to remember that no such causal connection is intended in the usage of $\rightarrow$; the meaning of the conditional is contained in Figure 11b and nothing more is intended. This point will be discussed again in Section 6 with regard to implication.

Closely related to the conditional connective is the *biconditional* statement, $p \leftrightarrow q$, which may be read *"p if and only if q."* The biconditional statement asserts that if p is true, then q is true, and if p is false, then q is false. Hence the biconditional is true in these cases and false in the others so that its truth table can be filled in as in Figure 12.

p	q	$p \leftrightarrow q$
T	T	T
T	F	F
F	T	F
F	F	T

Figure 12

The biconditional is the last of the five connectives which we shall use in this chapter. The table below gives a summary of them together with the numbers of the figures giving their truth tables. Remember that the

Name	Symbol	Translated as	Truth Table
Conjunction	$\wedge$	"and"	Figure 1
Disjunction (inclusive)	$\vee$	"or"	Figure 3
Negation	$\sim$	"not"	Figure 5
Conditional	$\rightarrow$	"if . . . then . . ."	Figure 11b
Biconditional	$\leftrightarrow$	". . . if and only if . . ."	Figure 12

complete definition of each of these connectives is given by its truth table. The examples below show the use of the two new connectives.

Examples. In Figures 13 and 14 the truth tables of two statements are worked out following the procedure of Section 2. The statement in Figure 13 is said

p	q	p	$\rightarrow$	$(p$	$\vee$	$q)$
T	T	T	T	T	T	T
T	F	T	T	T	T	F
F	T	F	T	F	T	T
F	F	F	T	F	F	F
Step No.		1	3	1	2	1

Figure 13

to be *logically true* (see Section 4). The statement in Figure 14 has the same truth table as $p \rightarrow q$ and is said to be *equivalent* to it (see Section 7).

p	q	$\sim$	p	$\leftrightarrow$	$(p$	$\rightarrow$	$\sim$	$q)$
T	T	F	T	T	T	F	F	T
T	F	F	T	F	T	T	T	F
F	T	T	F	T	F	T	F	T
F	F	T	F	T	F	T	T	F
Step No.		2	1	4	1	3	2	1

Figure 14

It is also possible to form compound statements from three or more simple statements. The next example is a compound formed from three simple statements p, q, and r. Notice that there will be a total of eight possible triples of truth values for these three statements so that the truth table for our compound will have eight rows as shown in Figure 15.

p	q	r	$[p$	$\rightarrow$	$(q$	$\vee$	$r)]$	$\wedge$	$\sim$	$[p$	$\leftrightarrow$	$\sim$	$r]$
T	T	T	T	T	T	T	T	T	T	T	F	F	T
T	T	F	T	T	T	T	F	F	F	F	T	T	F
T	F	T	T	T	F	T	T	T	T	T	F	F	T
T	F	F	T	F	F	F	F	F	F	F	T	T	F
F	T	T	F	T	T	T	T	F	F	F	F	T	T
F	T	F	F	T	T	T	F	T	T	T	F	F	F
F	F	T	F	T	F	T	T	F	F	F	F	T	T
F	F	F	F	T	F	F	F	T	T	T	F	T	F
Step No.			1	3	1	2	1	5	4	1	3	2	1

Figure 15

EXERCISES

1. One way of filling in the question-marked squares in Figure 11a is given in Figure 11b. There are three other possible ways.
   (a) Write the three other truth tables.
   (b) Show that each one of these truth tables has an interpretation in terms of the connectives now available to us.

2. Write truth tables for $q \vee p$, $q \wedge p$, $q \rightarrow p$, $q \leftrightarrow p$. Compare these with the truth tables in Figures 3, 1, 11b, and 12, respectively.

3. Construct truth tables for:
   (a) $p \rightarrow (q \lor r)$.   [*Ans.* TTTFTTTT.]
   (b) $(p \lor r) \land (p \rightarrow q)$.   [*Ans.* TTFFTFTF.]
   (c) $(p \lor q) \leftrightarrow (q \lor p)$.   [*Ans.* TTTT.]
   (d) $p \land \sim p$.   [*Ans.* FF.]
   (e) $(p \rightarrow p) \lor (p \rightarrow \sim p)$.   [*Ans.* TT.]
   (f) $(p \lor \sim q) \land r$.   [*Ans.* TFTFFFTF.]
   (g) $[p \rightarrow (q \rightarrow r)] \rightarrow [(p \rightarrow q) \rightarrow (p \rightarrow r)]$. [*Ans.* TTTTTTTT.]

4. For each of the following statements (i) find a symbolic form, and (ii) construct the truth table. Use the notation: p for "Murray is a good salesman," q for "Adams is a poor salesman," r for "Murray will get the account."
   (a) If Murray is a good salesman and Adams is a poor salesman, then Murray will get the account.   [*Ans.* TFTTTTTT.]
   (b) Murray will get the account if and only if either he is a good salesman or Adams is a poor salesman.   [*Ans.* TFTFTFFT.]
   (c) If Adams is a poor salesman and Murray fails to get the account, then Murray is not a good salesman.   [*Ans.* Same as (a).]

5. Construct truth tables for each of the following, and give an interpretation.
   (a) $(p \rightarrow q) \land (q \rightarrow p)$. (Compare with Figure 12.)
   (b) $(p \land q) \rightarrow p$.
   (c) $q \rightarrow (p \lor q)$.
   (d) $(p \rightarrow q) \leftrightarrow (\sim p \lor q)$.

6. The truth table for a statement compounded from two simple statements has four rows, and the truth table for a statement compounded from three simple statements has eight rows. How many rows would the truth table for a statement compounded from four simple statements have? How many for five? For n? Devise a systematic way of writing down these latter truth tables.

7. Let p be "We are going to make a cheaper product," and q be "We are going to lose business." Translate each of the following into symbolic form.
   (a) If we make a cheaper product, then we will lose business.
   (b) If we lose business, then we will make a cheaper product.
   (c) We will lose business if and only if we make a cheaper product.
   (d) If we lose business, then we will not make a cheaper product.
   (e) It is not the case that we will lose business if and only if we do not make a cheaper product.

8. Construct truth tables for the statements in Exercise 7.
   [*Ans.* TFTT, TTFT, TFFT, FTTT, TFFT.]

9. Construct a truth table for
   (a) $(p \lor q) \leftrightarrow (\sim r \land \sim s)$.
   (b) $(p \land q) \rightarrow \sim[\sim p \land (r \lor s)]$.

10. Construct a truth table for $\sim[(\sim p \wedge \sim q) \wedge (p \vee r)]$.

[*Ans.* TTTTTTFT.]

11. Find a simpler statement having the same truth table as the one found in Exercise 10.

4. *Logical possibilities*

In using ordinary language we often write or speak the same sentence many times, each time applying it to a different situation. To know whether or not "you have a straight flush" we must know what hand you have been dealt. It is proper that we try to incorporate this feature of ordinary language into the structure of elementary logic. Hence we make each statement relative to certain *logical possibilities*. These we think of as fixed in advance, and we agree that a sentence does not "make sense," is not in fact a statement at all, until its possibilities are specified. When we are considering several statements at once (and we usually are, since our main business in this chapter is the compounding of statements) we must arrange to have each of these statements apply to exactly the same logical possibilities. And in solving a scientific problem we regularly draw up a list of logical possibilities first, before considering the various statements relative to these possibilities.

Example 1. Let us analyze the logical possibilities for the following situation, one that arises in the theory of probability. Suppose there are two urns, the

Possibility	Urn	First Ball	Second Ball
1	1	black	black
2	1	black	white
3	1	white	black
4	2	black	white
5	2	white	black
6	2	white	white

Figure 16

first containing two black balls and one white ball, the second containing one black ball and two white balls, all balls of different sizes. We are to select an urn at random and draw two balls in succession from it. Figures 16 and 17 show two different ways of analyzing the logical possibilities.

In Figure 16 we have analyzed the possibilities as far as colors of balls drawn was concerned. Such an analysis may be sufficient for many purposes. In Figure 17 we have carried out a finer analysis, in which we distinguish between sizes of balls when they are of the same color. For some purposes the finer analysis may be necessary.

Possibility	Urn	First Ball	Second Ball
1′	1	small black	large black
2′	1	large black	small black
3′	1	small black	white
4′	1	large black	white
5′	1	white	small black
6′	1	white	large black
7′	2	black	small white
8′	2	black	large white
9′	2	small white	black
10′	2	large white	black
11′	2	small white	large white
12′	2	large white	small white

Figure 17

It is important to realize that the possibilities in a given problem may be analyzed in many different ways, from a very rough grouping to a highly refined one. The *main requirement* on an analysis of logical possibilities is that under any conceivable circumstances one and only one of these possibilities must be the case.

Possibility	Truth Value of "Two black balls are drawn from the first urn"
1	T
2	F
3	F
4	F
5	F
6	F

Figure 18

Once the logical possibilities are listed we can then make statements relative to them. "Two black balls are drawn from the first urn" makes sense both for the regular analysis above, and also for the finer analysis. Its truth tables for the two analyses are shown in Figures 18 and 19. On the other hand, "the small white ball is drawn after the large white ball from the second urn" makes sense only relative to the finer analysis of possibilities. It is true for case 12′ of this analysis, and false in the other eleven cases. Thus if we intend to study a certain statement in connection

Possibility	Truth Value of "Two black balls are drawn from the first urn"
1′	T
2′	T
3′	F
4′	F
5′	F
6′	F
7′	F
8′	F
9′	F
10′	F
11′	F
12′	F

Figure 19

with a scientific problem we must be sure to make our analysis of possibilities fine enough so that the truth value of the statement will be determined for each possibility. It is clear that if a given English sentence makes sense for a rough analysis of possibilities it will still make sense for any finer analysis. The last sentence quoted above, on the other hand, provides an example of a statement relative to a fine analysis that does not make sense relative to a rougher analysis.

Although a typical statement is true in some cases and false in others, we can have a statement that is true for all possible cases under consideration. Such a statement is called *logically true* (or a *tautology*). Its logical truth in general follows from the meaning of the words and the form of the statement, together with the context of the problem about which the statement is made. For instance, "At most two black balls are drawn" is logically true for either list of possibilities in Example 1 above. And in fact a sentence that is logically true for one analysis of possibilities in a given problem will be logically true for any other analysis of possibilities in this problem. Similarly, a statement that is false in every possible case under consideration is said to be *logically false* (or a *self-contradiction*). The statement that "the sum of the spots is 13" applied to all possible rolls of a pair of dice is always false.

The (horizontal) rows of a truth table provide an especially important example of logical possibilities. Suppose that we have three simple statements p, q, r. Then for the truth values of these statements we have 8 possibilities. Any statement s compounded from p, q, r can be looked at as a statement relative to these possibilities. For instance if s is the compound statement $p \rightarrow (\sim q \vee r)$ then Figure 20 is simply a disguise for the truth table of $p \rightarrow (\sim q \vee r)$.

Possibility	Truth Value of s
TTT	T
TTF	F
TFT	T
TFF	T
FTT	T
FTF	T
FFT	T
FFF	T

Figure 20

There is no reason to suppose, however, that every combination of truth values for p, q, r can always occur. Suppose, for instance, that in the urns and balls situation of Example 1, and with the rough analysis of possibilities listed in Figure 16, we have the following three statements p, q, r: "Urn 1 is selected" is p. "The first ball drawn is white" is q. And "The second ball drawn is black" is r. Figure 21 lists the truth values of p, q, r for each of the six rough possibilities of Example 1.

Possibility	p	q	r
1	T	F	T
2	T	F	F
3	T	T	T
4	F	F	F
5	F	T	T
6	F	T	F

Figure 21

Here the truth table rows TTF and FFT never occur. Hence for these particular statements p, q, r we must delete the possibilities TTF and FFT from Figure 20, leaving only the six rows shown in Figure 22. Now the compound statement s is logically true, since its only F occurs in a row that no longer corresponds to a logical possibility.

Possibility	Truth Value of s
TTT	T
TFT	T
TFF	T
FTT	T
FTF	T
FFF	T

Figure 22

When three statements p, q, r are such that all eight truth-table rows are logical possibilities, we say that these three statements are (logically) *independent*. This property of statements will be investigated more thoroughly in Section 8. In situations where we lack precise knowledge of the interrelatedness of p, q, r it is usual to assume p, q, r *independent* in carrying out a truth-table analysis of a statement compounded from them. And, in fact, if a compound expression involving (say) the letters p and q and r turns out to be a logically true statement for just one choice of independent simple statements p and q and r, then it is logically true by virtue of its form alone, and will be logically true for every other choice of statements p and q and r, independent or not. For instance the compound statement "If I have a pair of aces and you have a straight flush, then I have a pair of aces," is logically true regardless of what relation may exist between the simple statement "I have a pair of aces" and the simple statement "You have a straight flush."

Example 2. As a more complicated example let us consider the classification of consumers of a product according to income, education, and sex that is carried out in Figure 23. Whether this analysis into 24 cases or the listing of

Case	Income	Education	Sex
1	high	college	male
2	high	college	female
3	high	high school	male
4	high	high school	female
5	high	grammar school	male
6	high	grammar school	female
7	high	none	male
8	high	none	female
9	medium	college	male
10	medium	college	female
11	medium	high school	male
12	medium	high school	female
13	medium	grammar school	male
14	medium	grammar school	female
15	medium	none	male
16	medium	none	female
17	low	college	male
18	low	college	female
19	low	high school	male
20	low	high school	female
21	low	grammar school	male
22	low	grammar school	female
23	low	none	male
24	low	none	female

Figure 23

three variables is adequate will depend on the problem. For example, if we want to allow for people with graduate degrees, we must have more cases, and if we believe that consumer use of the product in question depends on a person's age as well as income, education, and sex, we must have more variables.

The statement "This consumer is a high-income man" is true in cases 1, 3, 5, and 7 and false in others. "This consumer is a woman whose income is not low and who has had some education" will be true in cases 2, 4, 6, 10, 12, and 14. The statement "This consumer's income is high, medium, or low," however, furnishes no information. It is true in every case, hence logically true. Analogously, the statement "This consumer is a man with less than medium income, who has gone neither to college, high school, nor grammar school, but is not a low-income man with no education" is a self-contradiction.

Of all the logical possibilities, one and only one represents the facts as they are. That is, for a given person one and only one of the 24 cases is a correct description. To know which one, we need factual information. When we say that a certain statement is "true," without qualifying it, we mean that it is true in this one case. But, as we have said before, what the case actually is lies outside the domain of logic. Logic can tell us what the circumstances (logical possibilities) are for which a statement is true.

EXERCISES

1. Prove that the negation of a logically true statement is logically false, and the negation of a logically false statement is logically true.

2. Classify the following as (i) logically true, (ii) a self-contradiction, (iii) neither.
   (a) $p \leftrightarrow p$.   [*Ans.* Logically true.]
   (b) $p \rightarrow \sim p$.
   (c) $(p \lor q) \leftrightarrow (p \land q)$.   [*Ans.* Neither.]
   (d) $(p \rightarrow \sim q) \rightarrow (q \rightarrow \sim p)$.
   (e) $(p \rightarrow q) \land (q \rightarrow r) \land \sim(p \rightarrow r)$.   [*Ans.* Self-contradiction.]
   (f) $(p \rightarrow q) \rightarrow p$.
   (g) $[(p \rightarrow q) \rightarrow p] \rightarrow p$.

3. Figure 23 gives the possible classifications of one consumer according to income, education, and sex. How many cases do we get if we classify two consumers jointly?   [*Ans.* 576.]

4. For each of the 24 cases in Figure 23 state whether the following statement is true: "The person has no formal education, and, if the person is a woman, then her income is low."

5. In Example 1, with the logical possibilities given by Figure 16, state the cases in which the following statements are true.
   (a) Urn one is selected.
   (b) At least one white ball is drawn.
   (c) At most one white ball is drawn.

(d) If the first ball drawn is white, then the second is black.

(e) Two balls of different color are drawn if and only if urn one is selected.

6. In Example 1 give two logically true and two logically false statements (other than those in the text).

7. In a college using grades A, B, C, D, and F, how many logically possible report cards are there for a student taking four courses? [*Ans.* 625.]

8. A man has nine coins totaling 78 cents. What are the logical possibilities for the distribution of the coins? [*Hint:* There are three possibilities.]

9. In Exercise 8, which of the following statements are logically true and which are logically false?
   (a) He has at least one penny.   [*Ans.* Logically true.]
   (b) He has at least one nickel.   [*Ans.* Neither.]
   (c) He has exactly two nickels.   [*Ans.* Logically false.]
   (d) He has exactly three nickels if and only if he has exactly one dime.
                                        [*Ans.* Logically true.]

10. In Exercise 8, we are told that the man has no nickel in his possession. What can we infer from this?

11. Two dice are rolled. Which of the following analyses satisfy the main requirement for logical possibilities? What is wrong with the others? The sum of the numbers shown is:
   (a): (1) 6, (2) not 6.
   (b): (1) an even number, (2) less than 6, (3) greater than 6.
   (c): (1) 2, (2) 3, (3) 4, (4) more than 4.
   (d): (1) 7 or 11, (2) 2, 3, or 12, (3) 4, 5, 6, 8, 9, or 10.
   (e): (1) 2, 4, or 6, (2) an odd number, (3) 10 or 12.
   (f): (1) less than 5 or more than 8, (2) 5 or 6, (3) 7, (4) 8.
   (g): (1) more than 5 and less than 10, (2) at most 4, (3) 7, (4) 11 or 12.
             [*Ans.* (a), (c), (d), (f) satisfy the condition.]

12. Assume that p and q are so related that they must have the same truth value. Retest the compound statements in Exercise 2(c) and in 2(f) under this assumption.

13. Let p be the statement "Jones sold more than 11 units yesterday," q be "Jones sold less than 23 units yesterday," and r be "Jones sold exactly 17 units yesterday." Write down the eight truth-table cases and eliminate those that are not possible. How many cases remain?

14. Give a verbal interpretation for the statement s whose truth table is shown in Figure 22. Verify from the interpretation that s is logically true.

5. Tree diagrams

A very useful tool for analyzing logical possibilities is the drawing of a "tree." This device will be illustrated by several examples.

Example 1. Consider again the example in Figure 23. Suppose we let the classification proceed as follows: first consider all consumers before classification as being all in one class; next split this large class into three subclasses by putting the low-income consumers in one class, the medium-income in another, and the high-income consumers in the third; next split up each of these subclasses into four smaller subclasses (making a total of twelve in all) according

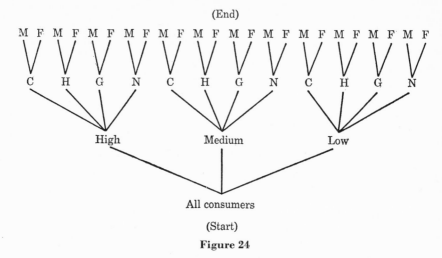

(End)

High   Medium   Low

All consumers

(Start)

Figure 24

to education; finally, split each of these subclasses into two parts by grouping males together and females together. The final classification then divides the class of all consumers into 24 subclasses. Figure 24 gives a graphical representation of the process described above.

For obvious reasons we shall call a figure like Figure 24, which starts at a point and branches out, a *tree*.

Observe that the tree contains all the information relevant for the classification problem. Each *path* through the tree from the start to the end (bottom to top) represents a logical possibility. There are 24 in all, one for each end point of the tree, and similarly there are 24 cases in Figure 23. The order in which we performed the classification is arbitrary, that is, we might equally well have first classified consumers according to education, then sex, and finally income. We would still get 24 logical possibilities but the tree that we would obtain would differ from that of Figure 24 (see Exercise 1).

Example 2. Next let us consider the example of Figure 16. This is a three-stage process: first we select an urn, then draw a ball and then draw a second ball. The tree of logical possibilities is shown in Figure 25. We note that six is the correct number of logical possibilities. The reason for this is: if we choose the first urn (which contains two black balls and one white ball) and draw from

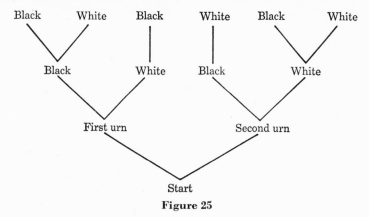

Figure 25

it a black ball, then the second draw may be of either color; however, if we draw a white ball first, then the second ball drawn is necessarily black. Similar remarks apply if the second urn is chosen.

The reader should observe that in the tree of Figure 24 each point on the same level has the same number of *branches* leading out of it (for instance, four branches for each point on the second level), while in the tree of Figure 25 this is not the case.

Example 3. As a final example let us construct the tree of logical possibilities for the outcomes of a World Series played between the Dodgers and the Yankees. In Figure 26 is shown half of the tree, corresponding to the case

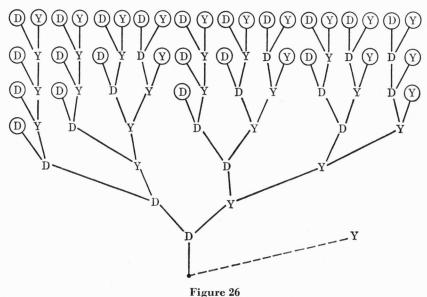

Figure 26

when the Dodgers win the first game (the dotted line at the bottom leads to the other half of the tree). In the figure a "D" stands for a Dodger win and "Y" for a Yankee win. There are 35 possible outcomes (corresponding to the circled letters) in the half-tree shown, so that the World Series can end in 70 ways.

This example is different from the previous two in that the paths of the tree end at different levels, corresponding to the fact that the World Series ends whenever one of the teams has won four games.

Not always do we wish as detailed an analysis as that provided in the examples above. If, in Example 2, we wanted to know only the color and order in which the balls were drawn and not which urn they came from, then there would be only four logical possibilities instead of six. Then in Figure 25 the second and fourth paths (counting from the left) represent the same outcome, namely, a black ball followed by a white ball. Similarly the third and fifth paths represent the same outcome. Finally, if we cared only about the color of the balls drawn, not the order, then there are only three logical possibilities: two black balls, two white balls, or one black and one white ball.

A less detailed analysis of the possibilities for the World Series is also possible. For example we can analyze the possibilities as follows: Dodgers in 4, 5, 6, or 7 games; and Yankees in 4, 5, 6, or 7 games. The new classification reduced the number of possibilities from 70 to 8. The other possibilities have not been eliminated but merely grouped together. Thus the statement "Dodgers in 4 games" can happen in only one way, while "Dodgers in 7 games" can happen in 20 ways (see Figure 26). A still less detailed analysis would be a classification according to the number of games in the series. Here there are only four logical possibilities.

The reader will find that it often requires several trials before the "best" way of listing logical possibilities is found for a given problem.

EXERCISES

1. Construct the tree for Example 1 if the order of classification is education, sex, and income. Do the same if the order of classification is sex, income, and education. Are there any other ways of performing this classification?

2. In 1955 the Dodgers lost the first two games of the World Series, but won the series in the end. In how many ways can the series go so that the losing team wins the first two games?   [*Ans.* 10.]

3. In how many ways can the World Series be played (see Figure 26) if the Dodgers win the first game and
   (a) No team wins two games in a row.   [*Ans.* 1.]
   (b) The Dodgers win at least the odd-numbered games.   [*Ans.* 5.]
   (c) The winning team wins four games in a row.   [*Ans.* 4.]
   (d) The losing team wins four games.   [*Ans.* 0.]

4. A man is considering the purchase of one of three types of stocks. Each stock may go up, go down, or stay the same after his purchase. Draw the tree of logical possibilities.

5. For the tree constructed in Exercise 4 give a statement which:
   (a) Is true in two-thirds of the cases.
   (b) Is false in all but one case.
   (c) Is true in all but one case.
   (d) Is logically true.
   (e) Is logically false.

6. We set up an experiment similar to that of Figure 16, but urn one has two black balls and two white balls, while urn two has one white ball and four black balls. We select an urn, and draw three balls from it. Construct the tree of logical possibilities. How many cases are there?   [*Ans.* 10.]

7. From the tree constructed in Exercise 6 answer the following questions.
   (a) In how many cases do we draw three black balls?
   (b) In how many cases do we draw two black balls and one white ball?
   (c) In how many cases do we draw three white balls?
   (d) How many cases does this leave?   [*Ans.* 3.]

8. In Exercise 6 we wish to make a rougher classification of logical possibilities. What branches (in the tree there constructed) are identified if:
   (a) We do not care about the order in which the balls are drawn.
   (b) We care neither about the order of balls, nor about the number of the urn selected.
   (c) We care only about what urn is selected, and whether the balls drawn are all the same color.

9. Work Exercise 7 of the last section by sketching a tree diagram.

10. Let us define three arithmetical operations. The operation A adds 2 to a given number. The operation R raises the number to the second power, and D divides the number by 2. Draw a tree showing the possible orders in which the operations can be applied (using each operation once). How many orders are there?   [*Ans.* 6.]

11. Use the tree constructed in Exercise 10 to show the result of applying all three operations to the number 0, in various orders.

12. Use the tree of Exercise 10 to show what happens if the tree operations are applied to a number x, in various orders. For each of the six cases decide whether there is an x which is left unchanged after the three operations.

13. Demand for an item on a particular day can vary between 0 and 3 units. Draw a tree diagram to show the possible demands on each of two successive days.

14. An item can be *sold* if it is *demanded* and if there is sufficient stock to *supply* the demand. For the tree constructed in Exercise 13, what are the possible sales in each of the two days if the initial stock is: (a) 4 units? (b) 6 units?

15. Suppose the initial inventory of the item of Exercise 13 is 2 units, but that after the first day an additional 2 units arrive from the factory. Now what are the possible sales at the end of two days?

16. The inventory at the end of a period is the inventory at the beginning of the period diminished by the sales during the period and augmented by new stock that arrives prior to the end of the period. In Exercise 15 list the inventory at the end of the first day and at the end of the second day for each of the possible combinations of two days' demand.

17. Sampling to determine which of two courses of action to take is often performed according to a "decision rule." In acceptance sampling to determine whether a lot purchased from a vendor is acceptable, for example, a decision rule may be of the form: "Take a sample of size n from the lot and determine how many pieces in the sample are defective and how many are good. If the number of defectives is less than or equal to some number c, accept the lot; otherwise reject the lot." Such a decision rule can be characterized simply by the sample size n and the "acceptance number" c; it is called an (n, c) decision rule.

Draw a tree diagram for the decision rule $(7, 3)$, given that the first item in the sample is good, and that each item can be classified as either "good" or "defective." Indicate those outcomes which lead to acceptance of the lot and those which lead to rejection.

18. In the decision tree of Exercise 17, it is often possible to apply the decision rule and conclude what to do with the lot before all seven items have been sampled. If, for example, the first four items are classified as defective, the lot will be rejected according to the decision rule, and hence the sampling operation may as well be curtailed at this earlier stage.

Redraw the tree diagram of Exercise 17, curtailing the sampling operation as soon as a decision about the lot can be reached. Compare this diagram with Figure 26.

19. An electric utility bills its residential customers bimonthly. Reminders or warnings are issued on overdue accounts on the basis of the amount of the uncollected balance, number of days overdue, the customer's credit rating, and whether or not the customer has a deposit. Classify these variables as follows:

$$\text{Uncollected balance} \begin{cases} \text{under \$25} \\ \text{\$25 or over} \end{cases}$$

$$\text{Days overdue} \begin{cases} \text{30 to 60} \\ \text{over 60} \end{cases}$$

$$\text{Credit rating} \begin{cases} \text{good} \\ \text{fair} \\ \text{poor} \end{cases}$$

$$\text{Deposit} \begin{cases} \text{yes} \\ \text{no} \end{cases}$$

Construct the tree of logical possibilities.

20. In Exercise 19 it is desired to send a reminder to all overdue accounts whose uncollected balance is less than \$25 except for (a) poor credit risks with no deposit and (b) fair credit risks with no deposit whose accounts are overdue more than 60 days; the latter two exceptions will receive strong warnings. For overdue accounts whose uncollected balance is \$25 or more, warnings are to be sent to all except (a) the good credit risks and (b) accounts that are overdue 60 days or less and that are covered by deposits; these exceptions will receive reminders.

Are these criteria logically consistent? If so, indicate which of the logical possibilities receive warnings and which receive reminders.

6. Decision trees

One important application of tree diagrams is in the logical analysis of decision making. The decisions made by a businessman often form a time sequence, and hence are particularly well illustrated by a tree diagram.

Example 1. A wholesaler distributes a single item whose purchase cost and selling price vary according to a known seasonal pattern. These costs and prices are shown for the next four months in Figure 27. Let us suppose that

Month	Purchase Cost	Selling Price
1	\$4	\$9
2	\$5	\$6
3	\$8	\$3
4	\$4	\$7

Figure 27

in any one month he either sells his entire stock, or restocks his warehouse, or decides to do nothing. We refer to these three types of acts as "sell," "buy," or "hold." If he starts with a full warehouse, the possible sequence of acts is shown in Figure 28 for the next four months.

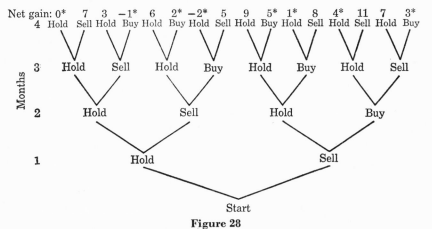

Figure 28

We can compute his net gain over the four months from Figures 27 and 28. For example, on the sixth branch his acts are hold-sell-hold-buy. He sells his wares in the second month, at $6 per unit, and refills his warehouse in the fourth month at $4 per unit. Thus he makes a net gain of $2 per unit, which we show at the top of Figure 28. The asterisk indicates that he ends up with a full warehouse.

A quick look at the net gains shows us that only two combinations of actions can be considered rational. Of the eight paths that leave him with a full warehouse, sell-hold-hold-buy is best, since this leaves him with the largest net profit ($5 per unit). Of the eight paths leaving him with an empty warehouse, the maximum net gain of $11 per unit is realized in sell-buy-hold-sell. Which of the two alternatives he prefers will depend on whether he feels a full warehouse at the end of four months is worth more than a difference of $6 per unit. But even without this knowledge we can make certain decisions, e.g., he should definitely sell in the first month and hold in the third. By looking at Figure 27 we can make these decisions intuitively plausible.

The first example had the very simple feature that all the relevant facts were known. This is described as *decision making under certainty*. The making of decisions under *uncertainty* is both more interesting and more difficult to treat. In this section we consider only the logical analysis of such problems. In Chapter IV we shall consider certain techniques for actually making the decisions.

Uncertainty is caused because the decision maker does not have knowledge or control of all relevant facts. We shall refer to procedures over which he has control as *acts*, while factors that he cannot control will be called *events*. An event may be the outcome of an act of another person, or it may be a natural occurrence. These two possibilities will be illustrated in Examples 3 and 2, respectively.

Example 2. An oil wildcatter must decide whether to drill a well or to sell his rights in a given location. The desirability of drilling depends on whether there

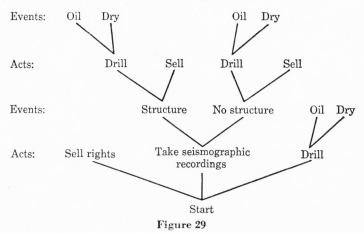

Figure 29

is oil beneath the surface. Before drilling, the wildcatter may obtain geological and geophysical information by taking seismographic recordings, from which deductions can be made concerning the existence of subsurface structure usually associated with oil pools. The information obtained from the recordings does not provide perfect predictions, however: sometimes oil is found where no subsurface structure has been detected, and vice versa. Figure 29 shows the tree of logically possible act-event combinations.

To make a rational decision, the planner would need additional information in this example. First of all, he would have to know how much he can realize in a sale and how much oil would be worth. He would also have to know the probabilities of various events. For example, how likely is it that a well in which no structure is found will nevertheless produce oil?

Example 3. The Walker Company, a manufacturer of electronic components and equipment, has been requested by an aircraft manufacturer to develop a special component which may be used in one of two subassemblies, which we shall designate A and B, in a new type of experimental aircraft. A sample of the developed components is to be sent to the aircraft manufacturer and if found acceptable, Walker may then undertake development of one of the two subassemblies. Upon completion, this will be tested for acceptability, and if it is found satisfactory Walker may then attempt to develop the other subassembly.

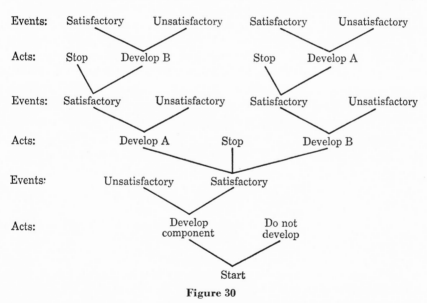

Figure 30

Walker has the option of refusing to undertake any or all of the three development contracts, although refusal to develop the basic component will, of course, preclude the possibility of developing either of the subassemblies. If an unsatisfactory product is produced at any of the three stages, Walker's contract will be automatically canceled. Walker may undertake development of A or B in either order. Figure 30 shows the sequence of possible act-event combinations.

EXERCISES

1. Identify the possible and relevant acts and events in the following situations:
   (a) An investor may buy stocks or bonds. If business conditions are good he will make more money with stocks, but if a recession occurs he will be better off with bonds.
   (b) A department store owner may insure his store against fire.
   (c) A manufacturer receives from a vendor a lot containing 1000 pieces of a particular part, of which an unknown number are defective. He may accept or reject the lot.
   (d) Three applicants are interviewed for a job, which will be offered to one of them.
   (e) A manufacturer of a new product must decide on a price, although he does not know how price will affect demand.
   (f) A manufacturer may replace a machine tool that is now in his factory with a newer model, but a radically new and improved model may be developed and placed on the market in the next two years.
   (g) A company may market its product in a foreign country, but the success of the enterprise may depend on whether and how long the present government of the foreign country remains in power.

2. Suppose in Example 1 that the wholesaler can make a profit of $3 per item in a quick turnover if his warehouse is not in use in the fourth period. Recompute the cash consequences of acts and determine the best sequences.

3. Draw a tree diagram for the situation of Example 1 if the wholesaler can deal in two items, A and B, where the price and cost schedule for A is given by Figure 27 and the price and cost schedule for B is:

Month	Purchase cost	Selling price
1	$15	$13
2	$15	$12
3	$13	$11
4	$14	$19

The warehouse can stock the same number of units of either A or B. As of now (Month 0) it is filled with A. Why does it not make sense to stock some of A and some of B simultaneously?

4. Evaluate each sequence of acts in Exercise 3 in terms of their cash consequences to the wholesaler. Classify the cash consequences of sequences according to the state of the warehouse in Month 4. What are the possible rational decisions?   [*Partial Ans.* Sell A in first month, hold in second.]

5. What additional information is needed in Exercise 3 for a rational decision? Discuss the way this information would be used to make the decision.

6. An investor has an opportunity of buying either of two stocks, or he may decide not to buy. The stocks may go up or down during the next month. Draw the decision tree. What decision seems best if the first stock is equally likely to go up \$2 per share or go down \$3, while the second stock has a very small chance of going up \$10 and will otherwise drop \$1 per share? Give an intuitive discussion of how such a decision should be made.

7. A personnel manager must screen applicants for a job. All applicants have already filled out an application form, on the basis of which they may be accepted or rejected at once. The personnel manager may, at his discretion, subject individual applicants to an interview, an aptitude test, or both; if both, they may be administered in either order. Draw a tree showing the possible sequences of acts.

8. A coffee roasting company must plan its purchases of green beans for roasting 90 days hence. Because it has no excess warehouse space, it must plan either to buy the beans 90 days hence or to buy 90-day futures now for delivery in three months. Before deciding between these alternatives, it can have the company economist make a forecast of the anticipated price movement of coffee over the next three months. The economist's forecast can be reported in one of two categories: "the price will increase" and "the price will decline or remain the same." The forecast may, of course, be wrong. Draw a tree showing the possible act-event combinations.

9. Machinists must get tools from a tool crib that is serviced by clerks. If all the clerks are busy, then a machinist who needs tools will join a queue waiting in front of the crib. There are two clerks (who may or may not be busy) and the queue is empty. If four machinists arrive, draw the tree of logical possibilities and find the length of the queue in each case.

7. Logical relations

Until now we have considered statements in isolation. Sometimes, however, we want to consider the relationship between pairs of statements. The most interesting such relation is that one statement (logically) *implies* the other one. If p implies q we also say that q follows from p, or that q is (logically) deducible from p. For example, in any mathematical theorem the hypothesis implies the conclusion.

If we have listed all logical possibilities for a pair of statements p and q, then we shall characterize implication as follows: p implies q if q is true whenever p is true, i.e., if q is true in all the logically possible cases in which p is true.

For compound statements having the same simple parts truth tables provide a convenient method for testing this relation. In Figure 31 we

p	q	$p \leftrightarrow q$	$p \rightarrow q$	$p \vee q$
T	T	T	T	T
T	F	F	F	T
F	T	F	T	T
F	F	T	T	F

Figure 31

illustrate this method. Let us take $p \leftrightarrow q$ as our hypothesis. Since it is true only in the first and fourth cases and $p \rightarrow q$ is true in both these cases we see that the statement $p \leftrightarrow q$ implies $p \rightarrow q$. On the other hand the statement $p \vee q$ is false in the fourth case and hence it is not implied by $p \leftrightarrow q$. Again, a comparison of the last two columns of Figure 31 shows that the statement $p \rightarrow q$ does not imply and is not implied by $p \vee q$.

The relation of implication has a close affinity to the conditional statement, but it is important not to confuse the two. The conditional is a new *statement* compounded from two given statements, while implication is a *relation* between the two statements. The connection is the following: p *implies* q if and only if the conditional $p \rightarrow q$ *is logically true.*

That this is the case is shown by a simple argument. The statement p implies the statement q if q is true whenever p is true. This means that there is no case in which p is true and q false, i.e., no case in which $p \rightarrow q$ is false. But this in turn means that $p \rightarrow q$ is logically true. In Exercise 1 this result will be applied to Figure 31.

Let us now take up the "paradoxes" of the conditional. Conditional statements sound paradoxical when the components are not related. For example, it sounds strange to say that "If it is a nice day, then chalk is made of wood" is true on a rainy day. It must be remembered that the conditional statement just quoted means no more and no less than that one of the following holds: (1) It is a nice day and chalk is made of wood, or (2) It is not a nice day and chalk is made of wood, or (3) It is not a nice day and chalk is not made of wood. [See Figure 11b.] And on a rainy day number 3 happens to be correct.

But it is by no means true that "It is a nice day" implies that "Chalk is made of wood." It is logically possible for the former to be true and for the latter to be false (indeed, this is the case on a nice day, with the usual method of chalk manufacture), hence the implication does not hold. Thus while the conditional quoted in the previous paragraph is true on a given day, it is not logically true.

In common parlance "if . . . then . . ." is usually asserted on logical grounds. Hence any usage in which such an assertion happens to be true, but is not logically true, sounds paradoxical. Similar remarks apply to the common usage of "if and only if."

If the biconditional $p \leftrightarrow q$ is not only true but logically true, then this establishes a relation between p and q. Since $p \leftrightarrow q$ is true in every logically possible case, the statements p and q have the same truth value in every case. We say, under these circumstances, that p and q are (logically) *equivalent*. For compound statements having the same simple parts, the truth table provides a convenient means of testing for equivalence. We merely have to verify that the compounds have the same truth table. Figure 32 establishes that $p \rightarrow q$ is equivalent to $\sim p \vee q$.

p	q	$p \rightarrow q$	$\sim p \vee q$
T	T	T	T
T	F	F	F
F	T	T	T
F	F	T	T

Figure 32

A pair of statements p and q are said to be *inconsistent* if knowing that one of them is true assures us that the other is false. In other words, p and q are inconsistent if it is impossible for both of them to be true. This concept can be extended to the case of any number of statements: The statements $p_1, p_2, \ldots, p_n$ are inconsistent if it is impossible for all of them to be true. In particular a single statement $(n = 1)$ is inconsistent when it is self-contradictory.

If the statements are compounded from the same simple parts, then there is an easy method for testing the consistency of the statements. We construct a truth table for each statement and examine the truth tables one case at a time. If there is a case in which all statements are true (a row of all T's) then the statements are consistent, otherwise they are inconsistent. This method is illustrated in Figure 31. If we examine the three truth tables, we find that they are all T in the first case, hence $p \leftrightarrow q$, $p \rightarrow q$, and $p \vee q$ are consistent. But if we add any statement that is false in the first case, e.g., $\sim p$, then the resulting four statements will be inconsistent.

EXERCISES

1. Show that $(p \leftrightarrow q) \rightarrow (p \rightarrow q)$ is logically true, but that $(p \leftrightarrow q) \rightarrow (p \vee q)$ is not logically true.

2. Prove that p is equivalent to q just in case p implies q and q implies p.

3. Construct truth tables for the following compounds, and test for implications and equivalences.

(a) $p \wedge q$.

(b) $p \rightarrow \sim q$.

(c) $\sim p \vee \sim q$.

(d) $\sim p \vee q$.

(e) $p \wedge \sim q$.   [*Ans.* (b) equiv. (c); (a) impl. (d); (e) impl. (b), (c).]

4. Construct truth tables for the following compounds, and arrange them in order so that each compound implies all the following ones.

(a) $\sim p \leftrightarrow q$.

(b) $p \rightarrow (\sim p \rightarrow q)$.

(c) $\sim [p \rightarrow (q \rightarrow p)]$.

(d) $p \vee q$.

(e) $\sim p \wedge q$.   [*Ans.* (c), (e), (a), (d), (b).]

5. At most how many of the following assertions can one person consistently believe?

(a) The quality of Product Z is good.

(b) Product Z is overpriced.

(c) Product Z is not overpriced but its quality is poor.

(d) If Product Z's quality is good, then it is overpriced.

(e) The quality of Product Z is good if and only if it is not overpriced.

(f) Either the quality of Product Z is good, or it is not overpriced, but not both.   [*Ans.* 4.]

6. Show that the five statements in Exercise 3 are not consistent. Are any four of these five statements consistent?

7. Given nine compound statements containing only the letters p and q, prove that if they are consistent then there must be at least one equivalent pair among them.

8. If p is logically true, prove that:

(a) $p \vee q$ is logically true.

(b) $\sim p \wedge q$ is logically false.

(c) $p \wedge q$ is equivalent to q.

(d) $\sim p \vee q$ is equivalent to q.

9. If p and q are logically true and r is logically false, what is the status of $(p \vee \sim q) \wedge \sim r$?   [*Ans.* Logically true.]

10. Prove that the conjunction or disjunction of a statement with itself is equivalent to the statement.

11. Prove that the double negation of a statement is equivalent to the statement.

12. Prove that a statement which implies its own negation is a self-contradiction.

13. What is the status of a statement equivalent to its own negation?

14. What relation exists between two logically true statements? Between two self-contradictions?

15. Prove that a logically true statement is implied by every statement, and that a self-contradiction implies every statement.

*8. A systematic analysis of logical relations

The relation of implication is characterized by the fact that it is impossible for the hypothesis to be true and the conclusion to be false. If two statements are equivalent, it is impossible for one to be true and the other to be false. Thus we see that for an implication one truth table case must not occur, and for an equivalence two of the four truth table cases must not occur. The absence of one or more truth table cases is thus characteristic of logical relations. In this section we shall investigate all conceivable relations that can exist between two statements.

We shall say that two statements are *independent* if each of the four truth table cases (see Figure 33) can occur. The two statements are *dependent* if one or more of the four cases in Figure 33 cannot occur. [See Section 4.]

If p and q are statements such that exactly one of the cases in Figure 33 is excluded, then we say that there is a *onefold* relation between them. Obviously there are four possible onefold relations which we list below. (a) If case 1 is excluded, the two statements cannot both be true. In this case p and q are *inconsistent*. [See Section 7.] Traditional logic calls them

p	q	Case No.
T	T	1
T	F	2
F	T	3
F	F	4

Figure 33

a pair of "contraries." (b) If case 2 is excluded, then [see Section 7] p *implies q.* (c) If case 3 is excluded, it is false that q is true and p is false, that is, q *implies p.* (d) If case 4 is excluded, both statements cannot be false, i.e., one of them must be true. Such a pair of statements is called a pair of *subcontraries.*

If p and q are statements such that exactly two of the cases in Figure 33 are excluded, then we say that there is a *twofold* relation between them. There are six ways in which two cases can be selected from four, but several of these do not produce interesting relations. For example, suppose cases 1 and 2 are excluded; then p cannot be true, i.e., it is logically false. Similarly, if cases 1 and 3 are excluded, then q is logically false. On the other hand, if cases 3 and 4 are excluded, then p is logically true; and if 2 and 4 are excluded, then q is logically true. Hence we see that these choices do not give us new relations; they merely indicate that one of the two statements is logically true or false. We now have only two alternatives remaining: (A) cases 2 and 3 are excluded which means that the two statements are equivalent; and (B) cases 1 and 4 are excluded, which means that the two statements cannot both be true and cannot both be false; in other words, one must be true and the other false. We shall then say that p and q are *contradictories*.

It is not hard to see that there are no threefold relations, for if three of the cases in Figure 33 are excluded, then there is only one possibility for each of the two statements, so that each must be either logically true or logically false.

We have already noted the connection of implication and equivalence to the conditional and biconditional, respectively. We can do the same for the three remaining relations. If p and q are subcontraries, then they cannot both be false; since this is the only case in which their disjunction is false, we see that p and q are subcontraries if and only if $p \vee q$ is logically true. If p and q are inconsistent, then they cannot both be true; since this is the only case in which their conjunction is true, we see that p and q are inconsistent if and only if $p \wedge q$ is logically false. Finally, if p and q are contradictories, then cases 1 and 4 of Figure 33 are excluded, hence $p \leftrightarrow q$ is logically false. (Note also that, if p and q are contradictories, then $p \veebar q$ is logically true.) The table in Figure 34 gives a summary of the relevant facts about the six relations we have derived.

Case(s) Excluded	Relation	Alternate Definition
T-T	Inconsistent	$p \wedge q$ logically false
F-F	Subcontraries	$p \vee q$ logically true
T-F	First implies second	$p \rightarrow q$ logically true
F-T	Second implies first	$q \rightarrow p$ logically true
T-F and F-T	Equivalents	$p \leftrightarrow q$ logically true
T-T and F-F	Contradictories	$p \leftrightarrow q$ logically false

Figure 34

Subcontraries are not of great theoretical interest, but inconsistent statements and contradictories are very important. Each of these relations can be generalized to hold for more than two statements. We have already defined the notion of inconsistency for n statements. They cannot all be true simultaneously, i.e., their conjunction must be false. On the other hand, if we have n different statements such that one and only one of them can be true, then we say they form a *complete set of alternatives*. If $n = 1$, then we have a single logically true statement; and if $n = 2$, then we have a pair of contradictories.

Truth tables again furnish a method for recognizing when relations hold between statements. The examples below show how the method works.

Examples. Consider the five compound statements, all having the same components, which appear in Figure 35. Find all relations which exist between pairs of these statements.

p	q	$p \wedge q$	$\sim p \vee \sim q$	$\sim p \vee q$	$\sim p$	$p \to q$
T	T	T	F	T	F	T
T	F	F	T	F	F	F
F	T	F	T	T	T	T
F	F	F	T	T	T	T
Statement number:		1	2	3	4	5

Figure 35

First of all we note that statements 3 and 5 have identical truth tables, hence they are equivalent. Therefore we need consider only one of them, say statement 3. Statements 1 and 2 have exactly opposite truth tables, hence they are contradictories. Upon comparing statements 1 and 3 we find no T-F case, so that 1 implies 3. Since numbers 1 and 4 are never both true they are inconsistent, while numbers 2 and 3 are never both false, so they are subcontraries. Finally, upon comparing either 2 or 3 to 4 we find no T-F case and hence both are implied by 4. Thus the six relations we found above are all exemplified in Figure 35. Observe also that statements p and q give an example of a pair of independent statements. [See Section 4.]

EXERCISES

1. Construct truth tables for the following four statements and state what relation (if any) holds between each of the six pairs formable.
   (a) $\sim p$.
   (b) $\sim q$.
   (c) $p \wedge \sim q$.
   (d) $\sim(\sim p \vee q)$.
   [Ans. (a) and (b) independent; (a) and (c), (d) inconsistent;
(c), (d) imply (b); (c) equiv. (d).]

2. Construct truth tables for each of the following six statements. Give an example of an independent pair, and an example of each of the six possible relations among these.
   (a) $p \leftrightarrow q$.
   (b) $p \to q$.
   (c) $\sim p \wedge \sim q$.

   (d) $(p \wedge q) \vee (\sim p \wedge \sim q)$.
   (e) $\sim q$.
   (f) $p \wedge \sim q$.

3. Prove the following assertions:
   (a) The disjunction of two contradictory statements is logically true.
   (b) Two statements are equivalent if and only if either one implies the other one.
   (c) The negations of two inconsistent statements are subcontraries.

4. What is the relation between the following pair of statements?
   (a) $p \rightarrow [p \wedge \sim(q \vee r)]$.
   (b) $\sim p \vee (\sim q \wedge \sim r)$.   [*Ans.* Equivalent.]

5. Suppose that any two of the statements p, q, and r are independent. And let us further suppose that there are only four possible truth table cases for the three statements. Prove that either r is equivalent to $p \leftrightarrow q$, or r is equivalent to $p \vee q$.

6. Prove the following assertions:
   (a) The negations of two equivalent statements are equivalent.
   (b) In a complete set of alternatives any two statements are inconsistent.
   (c) If p and q are subcontraries, and if each implies r, then r is logically true.

7. Pick out a complete set of (four) alternatives from:
   (a) It is raining but the wind is not blowing.
   (b) It rains if and only if the wind blows.
   (c) It is not the case that it rains and the wind blows.
   (d) It is raining and the wind is blowing.
   (e) It is neither raining nor is the wind blowing.
   (f) It is not the case that it is raining or the wind is not blowing.
                                           [*Ans.* (a), (d), (e), (f).]

8. What is the relation between $[p \vee \sim(q \vee r) \vee (p \wedge s)]$ and $\sim(p \wedge q \wedge r \wedge s)$?   [*Ans.* Subcontraries.]

9. Suppose that p and q are inconsistent. What is the relation between
   (a) p and $\sim q$.
   (b) $\sim p$ and q.
   (c) $\sim p$ and $\sim q$.
   (d) p and $\sim p$.

10. Let p, q, and r be three statements such that any two of them are independent. Discuss the possible relations among the three statements. [*Hint:* If we ignore the order of the statements, there are 16 such relations. The relations are at most fourfold. There are two fourfold relations, and 12 other relations are found from these by excluding fewer cases. In addition, there are two other twofold relations.]

11. Construct the set of logical possibilities which classify a person with respect to sex and marital status.

(a) Show that "if the person is a bachelor then he is unmarried" is logically true.
(b) Find the relation between "the person is a man" and "the person is a bachelor."
(c) Find a simple statement that is a subcontrary of "the person is a man," and is consistent with it.

*9. Statements having given truth tables

In Sections 2 and 3 we showed how to construct the truth table for any compound statement. It is also interesting to consider the converse problem, namely, given a truth table to find one or more statements having this truth table. The converse problem always has a solution, and in fact, a solution using only the connectives $\wedge$, $\vee$, and $\sim$. The discussion which we give here is valid only for a truth table in three variables but can easily be extended to cover the case of n variables.

As we have observed in Section 3, a truth table with three variables has eight rows, one for each of the eight possible triples of truth values. Suppose that our given truth table has its last column consisting entirely of F's. Then it is easy to check that the truth table of the statement $p \wedge \sim p$ also has only F's in its last column, so that this statement serves as an answer to our problem. We now need consider only truth tables having one or more T's. The method that we shall use is to construct statements that are true in one case only, and then to construct the desired statement as a disjunction of these.

It is not hard to construct statements that are true in only one case. In Figure 36 are listed eight such statements, each true in exactly one case.

p	q	r	Basic Conjunctions
T	T	T	$p \wedge q \wedge r$
T	T	F	$p \wedge q \wedge \sim r$
T	F	T	$p \wedge \sim q \wedge r$
T	F	F	$p \wedge \sim q \wedge \sim r$
F	T	T	$\sim p \wedge q \wedge r$
F	T	F	$\sim p \wedge q \wedge \sim r$
F	F	T	$\sim p \wedge \sim q \wedge r$
F	F	F	$\sim p \wedge \sim q \wedge \sim r$

Figure 36

We shall call such statements *basic conjunctions*. Such a basic conjunction contains each variable or its negation, depending on whether the line on which it appears in Figure 36 has a T or an F under the variable. Observe that the disjunction of two such basic conjunctions will be true in exactly two cases, the disjunction of three in three cases, etc. Therefore, to find a statement having a given truth table simply form the disjunction of those basic conjunctions which occur in Figure 36 on the rows where the given truth table has T's.

Example 1. Find a statement whose truth table has T's in the first, second, and last rows, and F's in the other rows. The required statement is the disjunction of the first, second, and eighth basic conjunctions, that is,

$$(p \wedge q \wedge r) \vee (p \wedge q \wedge \sim r) \vee (\sim p \wedge \sim q \wedge \sim r).$$

In Exercise 2 you will show that this statement has the required truth table.

Example 2. A logician is captured by a tribe of savages and placed in a jail having two exits. The savage chief offers the captive the following chance to escape: "One of the doors leads to certain death and the other to freedom. You can leave by either door. To help you in making a decision, two of my warriors will stay with you and answer any one question which you wish to ask of one of them. I must warn you, however, that one of my warriors is completely truthful while the other always lies." The chief then leaves, believing that he has given his captive only a sporting chance to escape.

After thinking a moment, our quick-witted logician asks one question and then chooses the door leading to freedom. What question did he ask?

Let p be the statement "The first door leads to freedom," and q be the statement "You are truthful." It is clear that p and q are useless questions in themselves, so let us try compound statements. We want to ask a single question for which a "yes" answer means that p is true and a "no" answer means that p is false, regardless of which warrior is asked the question. The answers desired to these questions are listed in Figure 37.

The next thing to consider is, what would be the truth table of a question having the desired answers? If the warrior answers "yes" and if he is truthful, that is if q is true, then the truth value is T. But if he answers "yes" and he is a liar, that is if q is false, then the truth value is F. A similar analysis holds if the answer is "no." The truth values of the desired question are shown in Figure 37.

p	q	Desired Answer	Truth Table of Question
T	T	yes	T
T	F	yes	F
F	T	no	F
F	F	no	T

Figure 37

Therefore we have reduced the problem to that of finding a statement having the truth table of Figure 37. Following the general method outlined above, we see that the statement

$$(p \wedge q) \vee (\sim p \wedge \sim q)$$

will do. Hence the logician asks the question: "Does the first door lead to freedom and are you truthful, or does the second door lead to freedom and are you lying?" The statement $p \leftrightarrow q$ also has the truth table given in Figure 37, hence a shorter equivalent question would be: "Does the first door lead to freedom if and only if you are truthful?"

As can be seen in Example 2, the method does not necessarily yield the simplest possible compound statement. However it has two advantages: (1) It gives us a mechanical method of finding a statement that solves the problem. (2) The statement appears in a standard form. The latter will be made use of in designing switching circuits (see Section 10).

EXERCISES

1. Show that each of the basic conjunctions in Figure 36 has a truth table consisting of one T appearing in the row in which the statement appears in Figure 36, and all the rest F's.

2. Find the truth table of the compound statement constructed in Example 1.

3. In Example 2 there is a second question, having a different truth table from that in Figure 37, which the logician can ask. What is it?

4. Construct one or more compound statements having each of the following truth tables, (a), (b), and (c).

p	q	r	(a)	(b)	(c)
T	T	T	T	F	T
T	T	F	F	F	T
T	F	T	T	F	T
T	F	F	F	T	F
F	T	T	F	F	T
F	T	F	F	F	T
F	F	T	T	F	F
F	F	F	F	F	T

5. Using only $\vee$, $\wedge$ and $\sim$, write a statement equivalent to each of the following:
   (a) $p \leftrightarrow q$.
   (b) $p \rightarrow q$.
   (c) $\sim(p \rightarrow q)$.

6. Using only $\vee$ and $\sim$ write down a statement equivalent to $p \wedge q$. Use this result to prove that any truth table can be represented by means of the two connectives $\vee$ and $\sim$.

   In Exercises 7-10 we will study the new connective $\downarrow$, where $p \downarrow q$ expresses "neither p nor q."

7. Construct the truth table of $p \downarrow q$.

8. Construct the truth table for $p \downarrow p$. What other compound has this truth table? [*Ans.* Same as Figure 5.]

9. Construct the truth table for $(p \downarrow q) \downarrow (p \downarrow q)$. What other compound has this truth table? [*Ans.* Same as Figure 3.]

10. Use the results of Exercises 6, 8, and 9 to show that any truth table can be represented by means of the single connective $\downarrow$.

11. Use the results of Exercises 9 and 10 of Section 2 to show that any truth table can be represented by means of the single connective $|$.

12. Write down a compound of p, q, r which is true if and only if exactly one of the three components is true.

13. The "basic conjunctions" for statements having only one variable are p and $\sim p$. Discuss the various compound statements that can be formed by disjunctions of these. How do these relate to the possible truth tables for statements of one variable? What can be asserted about an arbitrary compound, no matter how long, that contains only the variable p?

[*Ans.* There are four possible truth tables.]

14. A student is confronted with a true-false exam, consisting of five questions. He knows that his instructor always has more true than false questions, and that he never has three questions in a row with the same answer. From the nature of the first and last questions he knows that these must have the opposite answer. The only question to which he knows the answer is number two. And this *assures* him of having all answers correct. What did he know about question two? What is the answer to the five questions? [*Ans.* TFTTF.]

*10. Applications to switching circuits

The theory of compound statements has many applications to subjects other than pure mathematics. As an example we shall develop a theory of simple switching networks.

A switching network is an arrangement of wires and switches which connect together two terminals T_1 and T_2. Each switch can be either "open" or "closed." An open switch prevents the flow of current, while a closed switch permits flow. The problem that we want to solve is the following: given a network and given the knowledge of which switches are closed, determine whether or not current will flow from T_1 to T_2.

$T_1 \bullet\!\!\!-\!\!\!-\!\!\!-\!\!\!- \text{P} -\!\!\!-\!\!\!-\!\!\!-\!\!\!\bullet T_2 \qquad\qquad T_1 \bullet\!\!-\!\!\!- \text{P} -\!\!\!-\!\!\!- \text{Q} -\!\!\!-\!\!\!-\!\!\!\bullet T_2$

Figure 38   **Figure 39**

Figure 38 shows the simplest kind of network in which the terminals are connected by a single wire containing a switch P. If P is closed, then current will flow between the terminals, and otherwise it will not. The network in Figure 39 has two switches P and Q in "series." Here the current flows only if both P and Q are closed.

To see how our logical analysis can be used to solve the problem stated above let us associate a statement with each switch. Let p be the statement "Switch P is closed" and let q be the statement "Switch Q is closed." Then in Figure 38 current will flow if and only if p is true. Similarly in Figure 39 the current will flow if and only if both p and q are true, that is, if and only if $p \wedge q$ is true. Thus the first circuit is represented by p and the second by $p \wedge q$.

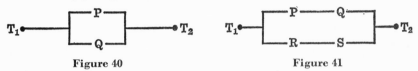

Figure 40　　　　　　　　　　　　**Figure 41**

In Figure 40 is shown a network with switches P and Q in "parallel." In this case the current flows if either of the switches is closed, so the circuit is represented by the statement $p \vee q$.

The network in Figure 41 combines the series and parallel types of connections. The upper branch of the network is represented by the statement $p \wedge q$ and the lower by $r \wedge s$; hence the entire circuit is represented by $(p \wedge q) \vee (r \wedge s)$. Since there are four switches and each one can be either open or closed, there are $2^4 = 16$ possible settings for these switches. Similarly, the statement $(p \wedge q) \vee (r \wedge s)$ has four variables, so that its truth table has 16 rows in it. The switch settings for which current flows correspond to the entries in the truth table for which the above compound statement is true.

Switches need not always act independently of each other. It is possible to couple two or more switches together so that they open and close simultaneously, and we shall indicate this in diagrams by giving all such switches the same letter. It is also possible to couple two switches together, so that if one is closed, the other is open. We shall indicate this by giving the first switch the letter P and the second the letter P'. Then the statement "P is closed" is true if and only if the statement "P' is closed" is false. Therefore if p is the statement "P is closed," then $\sim p$ is the statement representing "P' is closed."

Such a circuit is illustrated in Figure 42. The associated compound statement is $[p \vee (\sim p \wedge \sim q)]$ $\vee [p \wedge q]$. Since the statement is

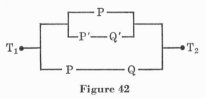

Figure 42

false only if p is false and q is true, the current will flow unless P is open and Q is closed. We can also check this directly. If P is closed, current will flow through the top branch regardless of Q's setting. If both switches are open, then P' and Q' will be closed, so that current will flow through the middle branch. But if P is open and Q is closed, none of the branches will pass current.

Notice that we never had to consider current flow through the bottom branch. The logical counterpart of this fact is that the statement associated with the network is equivalent to $[p \vee (\sim p \wedge \sim q)]$ whose associated network is just the upper two branches of Figure 42. Thus the electrical properties of the circuit of Figure 42 would be the same if the lower branch were omitted.

As a last problem we shall consider the design of a switching network having certain specified properties. An equivalent problem, which we solved in Section 9, is that of constructing a compound statement having a given truth table. As in that section, we shall limit ourselves to statements having three variables, although our methods could easily be extended.

In Section 9 we developed a general method for finding a statement having a given truth table not consisting entirely of F's. (The circuit which corresponds to a statement whose truth table consists entirely of F's is one in which current never flows, and hence is not of interest.) Each such statement could be constructed as a disjunction of basic conjunctions. Since the basic conjunctions were of the form $p \wedge q \wedge r$, $p \wedge q \wedge \sim r$, etc., each will be represented by a circuit consisting of three switches in series and will be called a *basic series circuit*. The disjunction of certain of these basic conjunctions will then be represented by the circuit obtained by putting several basic series circuits in parallel. The resulting network will not, in general, be the simplest possible such network fulfilling the requirements, but the method always suffices to find one.

p	q	r	Desired Truth Value	Corresponding Basic Conjunction
T	T	T	T	$p \wedge \quad q \wedge \quad r$
T	T	F	T	$p \wedge \quad q \wedge \sim r$
T	F	T	T	$p \wedge \sim q \wedge \quad r$
T	F	F	F	$p \wedge \sim q \wedge \sim r$
F	T	T	T	$\sim p \wedge \quad q \wedge \quad r$
F	T	F	F	$\sim p \wedge \quad q \wedge \sim r$
F	F	T	F	$\sim p \wedge \sim q \wedge \quad r$
F	F	F	F	$\sim p \wedge \sim q \wedge \sim r$

Figure 43

Example. A three-man committee wishes to employ an electric circuit to record a secret simple majority vote. Design a circuit so that each member can push a button for his "yes" vote (not push it for a "no" vote), and so that a signal light will go on if a majority of the committee members vote yes.

Let p be the statement "committee member 1 votes yes," let q be the statement "member 2 votes yes," and let r be "member 3 votes yes." The truth table of the statement "majority of the members vote yes" appears in Figure 43. From that figure we can read off the desired compound statement as

$$(p \wedge q \wedge r) \vee (p \wedge q \wedge \sim r) \vee (p \wedge \sim q \wedge r) \vee (\sim p \wedge q \wedge r).$$

The circuit desired for the voting procedure appears in Figure 44. (See Exercise 7.)

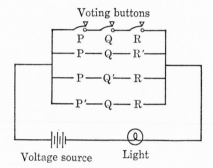

Voting buttons

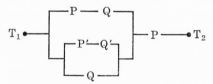

Voltage source   Light

Figure 44

EXERCISES

1. What kind of a circuit has a logically true statement assigned to it? Give an example.

2. Construct a network corresponding to
$$[(p \wedge \sim q) \vee (\sim p \wedge q)] \vee (\sim p \wedge \sim q).$$

3. What compound statement represents:

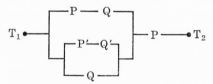

4. Work out the truth table of the statement in Exercise 3. What does this tell us about the circuit?

5. Design a simpler circuit than the one in Exercise 3, having the same properties.

6. Construct a network corresponding to
$$[(p \vee q) \wedge \sim r] \vee [(\sim p \wedge r) \vee q].$$

7. Find the simplest circuit equivalent to that in Figure 44.

8. Design a circuit for an electrical version of the game of matching pennies: At a given signal each of the two players either opens or closes a switch under his control. If they both do the same, A wins; if they do the opposite, then B wins. Design the circuit so that a light goes on if A wins.

9. In a large hall it is desired to turn the lights on or off from any one of four switches on the four walls. This can be accomplished by designing a circuit which turns the light on if an even number of switches are closed, and off if an odd number are closed. (Why does this solve the problem?) Design such a circuit.

10. A committee has five members. It takes a majority vote to carry a measure, except that the chairman has a veto (i.e., the measure carries only if he votes for it). Design a circuit for the committee, so that each member votes for a measure by pressing a button, and the light goes on if and only if the measure is carried.

11. A group of candidates is asked to take a true-false exam, with four questions. Design a circuit such that a candidate can push the buttons of those questions to which he wants to answer "true," and that the circuit will indicate the number of correct answers. [*Hint:* Have five lights, corresponding to 0, 1, 2, 3, 4 correct answers, respectively.]

12. Devise a scheme for working truth tables by means of switching circuits.

*11. Binary numbers

In the decimal system the numeral "3825" represents the number 3 thousand 8 hundred twenty-5, or

$$3 \times 10^3 + 8 \times 10^2 + 2 \times 10^1 + 5 \times 1.$$

The convention is that, starting at the right, successive digits represent multiples of increasing powers of ten. We therefore speak of the system as being to the *base 10*. The choice of 10 as a base is due to a historical accident, presumably because man has ten fingers. Any other integer greater than 1 would serve just as well. For example, if we choose 8 as a base (octal system), then "325" represents the number which in the decimal system could be written as

$$3 \times 8^2 + 2 \times 8^1 + 5 \times 1 = 213.$$

Thus the numeral "325" in the octal system represents the same number as the numeral "213" in the decimal system.

The smallest possible base is 2, and the resulting system for representing numbers is known as the *binary number system*. In the decimal system we must use ten different digits, from 0 to 9, to represent the possible multiples of a power of 10 up to the next power. In general if the base is

b, we need the digits $0, 1, \ldots, b - 1$. This means that in the binary system the only digits used are 0 and 1. A one in the right-hand position stands for 1, in the next position for $2^1 = 2$, in the next for $2^2 = 4$, and in the next for $2^3 = 8$. Figure 45 shows some binary numbers and their decimal equivalents. Each digit in the binary system is known as a *bit*.

Binary number	1	10	11	100	101	110	111	1000	10000	100000
Decimal equivalent	1	2	3	4	5	6	7	8	16	32

Figure 45

The addition and multiplication tables for binary arithmetic are particularly simple; they are shown, respectively, in Figure 46 (a) and (b).

+	0	1
0	0	1
1	1	10

·	0	1
0	0	0
1	0	1

(a)   (b)

Figure 46

All the entries in the multiplication table and three entries in the addition table are like the corresponding entries in the decimal tables. The one surprising entry is $1 + 1 = 10$; but this is also clear when we recall that "10" in the binary system represents the number two.

Example 1. Let us perform the addition "$6 + 7 = 13$" in the binary system. From Figure 45 we see that the binary representation of the integer six is 110, and that for seven is 111. Then:

$$\begin{array}{r} 110 \\ + 111 \\ \hline 1101 \end{array}$$

where 1101 in binary is

$$1 \cdot 2^3 + 1 \cdot 2^2 + 0 \cdot 2^1 + 1 \cdot 1 = 13$$

in decimal, the answer we expected to get.

Example 2. Let us now perform the multiplication "$6 \cdot 7 = 42$" in binary

$$\begin{array}{r} 110 \\ \times 111 \\ \hline 110 \\ 110 \\ 110 \\ \hline 101010 \end{array}$$

The number 101010 in binary is equivalent to

$$1 \cdot 2^5 + 0 \cdot 2^4 + 1 \cdot 2^3 + 0 \cdot 2^2 + 1 \cdot 2^1 + 0 \cdot 1 = 42,$$

the answer which we expected to get.

We will have occasion in the next section to represent truth table cases by strings of zeros and ones. Our convention will be that the bit 0 corresponds to F, and the bit 1 to T. We have carried this out for a truth table of three statements in Figure 47. We note that the resulting binary numbers represent the integers $0, 1, 2, \ldots, 7$ in decreasing order. This is one way to prove that the number of cases in a truth table with n variables is 2^n. (See Exercise 9.)

p	q	r	Binary Number	Number Represented
T	T	T	111	seven
T	T	F	110	six
T	F	T	101	five
T	F	F	100	four
F	T	T	011	three
F	T	F	010	two
F	F	T	001	one
F	F	F	000	zero

Figure 47

EXERCISES

1. Translate each of the following numbers into the binary system.
   (a) 20.   [*Ans.* 10100.]
   (b) 75.
   (c) 128.
   (d) 80.   [*Ans.* 1010000.]
   (e) 200.

2. Using the results of Exercise 1, carry out the following additions in the binary system. Check your results.
   (a) 20 + 80.
   (b) 75 + 80.
   (c) 128 + 128.
   (d) 128 + 200.
   (e) 80 + 200.   [*Ans.* (e) 100011000.]

3. Using the results of Exercise 1, carry out the following multiplications in the binary system. Check your results.
   (a) 20 × 20.
   (b) 20 × 80.
   (c) 128 × 128.

4. Using the results of Exercise 1, carry out the subtraction 200 − 128 in the binary system.

5. If a number is written in the binary number system, how can one tell whether it is even or odd?

6. In a multiple choice test, in which each question has four possible answers, the answers are numbered 1, 2, 4, and 8. The students are told that in each question there may be no correct answer, one correct answer, or several correct answers. They are told to add together the numbers of the correct answers (or to write 0 if there is no correct answer).

   (a) Show that the resulting number gives the instructor all the information he desires.

   (b) On a given question the correct sum was 7. Three students put down 4, 8, and 15 respectively. Which answer was most nearly correct? Which was the worst?   [Ans. 15 best, 8 worst.]

7. Express the numbers 80 and 200 in the number system using base 8 (called the *octal* number system). Add the resulting numbers in the octal system, and check your result.   [Ans. 430.]

8. Compare the addition in Exercise 7 with that in Exercise 2(e). From this describe how the octal system can be used as a shorthand for the binary system. [*Hint:* Each octal digit takes the place of three binary digits.]

9. Use the correspondence between truth table cases and binary numbers to prove that for n statements there are exactly 2^n truth table cases.

10. Suppose that in Figure 47 we let 0 correspond to T and 1 to F; what numbers do the eight cases represent?

11. Suppose that in Figure 1 we replace T by 1 and F by 0; give an arithmetical interpretation of the resulting table. Do the same for Figure 3.

12. Carry out Exercise 11, but under the convention that T corresponds to 0 and F to 1.

*12. Computer circuits

In high-speed computers numbers are represented in the binary system. We shall now consider how binary numbers can be represented in computers and what types of circuits are needed to carry out the arithmetical operations. Although the components of modern electronic computers are vacuum tubes or transistors, these components play the same roles as switches in switching circuits. Hence the logic of electronic circuits may equally well be studied in terms of simple switching circuits.

Since a switch has only two positions, it is ideally suited to represent a bit in a binary number. An open switch will represent 0, while a closed switch stands for 1. In Section 10 we associated truth tables to switching circuits; we now let binary numbers correspond to the truth table cases by letting 1 stand for T (the switch is closed) and 0 for F (it is false that the switch is closed, hence it is open). Thus we have the correspondence illustrated in Figure 47 in the last section.

At any moment the computer has many numbers stored in its "memory." It may be called upon to take one or more of these numbers, to carry out an arithmetical operation, and to store the result. For example, it may be asked to take two numbers, to multiply them together, and to store the product for future use. Thus we have a pair of binary numbers in memory, with each bit of each number controlling a switch. These are the input switches, and they will be denoted by the letters P, Q, and R. The result of the multiplication will be a new binary number, each of whose bits is again represented by a switch. These output switches will be labeled A, B, or C. We presume that these switches are open to start with, and that if we want them closed (to represent a 1 in the answer), we must send a signal to the output switch. Thus, for a typical arithmetical operation one must design a circuit consisting of the input switches, which sends a signal to those output switches which are 1's in the answer, and only to those.

Example 1. In the multiplication of two numbers, in any system, we always multiply a digit of one number by a digit of the other number, and then we add these products. Hence we never need to multiply more than one digit at a time. Thus for binary numbers we need a circuit only for the product of one bit by another bit. Let us call the switches corresponding to these bits P and Q. The answer will be a single bit, represented by switch A.

First we construct a table representing the arithmetical operation. This is shown in Figure 48. We then construct the corresponding truth table, replacing 0 by F and 1 by T. This is shown in Figure 49. Now we have reduced the problem to the type treated in Section 10. Since the truth table contains a single T, we need only one basic series circuit, and hence multiplication of two bits is accomplished by the very simple circuit of Figure 50. If an electric

First Bit	Second Bit	Product Bit
0	0	0
0	1	0
1	0	0
1	1	1

Figure 48

p	q	a
F	F	F
F	T	F
T	F	F
T	T	T

Figure 49

Figure 50

impulse is sent from the terminal T, the signal will reach the output switch A if and only if both switches P and Q are closed. In other words, the answer bit is 1 if and only if both of the original bits are 1's, which is what Figure 48 states.

Example 2. For the addition of two binary numbers we need a more complicated circuit. While we still add one bit of one number to a bit of the other number, we must remember that we may have a "carry." Hence our circuit must be designed for the addition of three bits at a time. These bits will control switches P, Q, and R. We have as an output both an answer bit and a carry, to be represented by A and C respectively. Figures 51, 52, and 53 show the arithmetical operations, the truth table, and the resulting circuit. The

First Bit	Second Bit	Third Bit	Sum Bit	Carry
0	0	0	0	0
0	0	1	1	0
0	1	0	1	0
0	1	1	0	1
1	0	0	1	0
1	0	1	0	1
1	1	0	0	1
1	1	1	1	1

Figure 51

p	q	r	a	c
F	F	F	F	F
F	F	T	T	F
F	T	F	T	F
F	T	T	F	T
T	F	F	T	F
T	F	T	F	T
T	T	F	F	T
T	T	T	T	T

Figure 52

circuit of Figure 53, given by our automatic method, is quite complicated. A simpler circuit, accomplishing the same result, is shown in Figure 54. Let us check, for example, the third line of our tables. This is the line $0 + 1 + 0$. Since Q is the only closed input switch, no current can flow through the P switches in Figure 54, nor can the current pass the R switches. This means that the only current flowing will be through the P'-R'-Q-branch, which turns A on, but not C. Hence the answer is 1 and there is no carry.

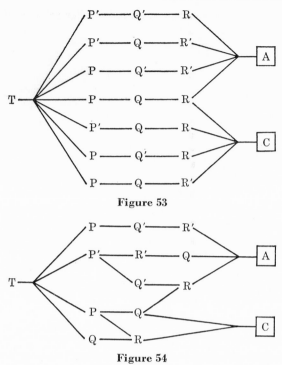

Figure 53

Figure 54

Example 3. As our final example we will consider a circuit for the difference of two bits, represented by P and Q. We have a single bit answer (represented by A), but the answer may be negative, hence we need a bit to serve as a possible minus sign. This "sign bit" will be represented by output switch B. The

First Bit	Second Bit	Answer Bit	Sign Bit
0	0	0	+
0	1	1	−
1	0	1	+
1	1	0	+

Figure 55

p	q	a	b
F	F	F	F
F	T	T	T
T	F	T	F
T	T	F	F

Figure 56

arithmetical table is shown in Figure 55, the truth table in 56, and the circuit in 57. In the truth table b asserts that the sign is negative, i.e., the switch B (corresponding to the sign bit) is closed if and only if the sign is negative.

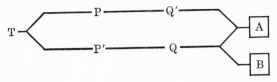

Figure 57

EXERCISES

1. Check the circuit in Figure 53. Verify that the circuit in Figure 54 serves the same purpose.

2. Check the circuit in Figure 57.

3. Most high-speed computers have a "logical or," which forms the maximum of two bits (i.e., the answer is equal to the larger one). Form the arithmetical and truth tables, and design a circuit to carry out the operation. Where does the name "logical or" come from?

4. Carry out the instructions of Exercise 3 for the "logical and," which forms the minimum of two bits.

5. Design a circuit which will add a one-bit number to a two-bit number. [*Hint:* There are three input and three output switches.]

6. Design a circuit for the addition of two two-bit numbers.

7. Simplify the circuit obtained in Exercise 6 to as few components as possible.

8. Design a circuit for the subtraction of one two-bit number from another. [*Hint:* There are two answer bits and a sign bit in the output.]

9. Simplify as much as possible the circuit obtained in Exercise 8.

10. How many bits are needed to represent all decimal integers up to 1000?

11. "Business" as distinguished from "scientific" computers often are designed to represent numbers in a form more closely allied to our familiar decimal number system. One system which combines some of the advantages of binary with some of the advantages of decimal representation is a form of "binary coded decimal." In this system, each integer from 0 through 9 is represented by its (4 bit) binary equivalent, and the position of each block of four bits corresponds to the position of the equivalent decimal digit in the decimal representation of a number. Thus 0001 in binary represents the digit 1 in decimal, 1001 in binary represents 9 in decimal, and 10010001 in binary coded decimal represents 91 in decimal.

(a) Express in binary coded decimal the numbers corresponding to the decimal integers:

$$11, \quad 52, \quad 64, \quad 98, \quad 128, \quad 144.$$

(b) What decimal integers correspond to the following binary coded decimal integers:

$$1000, \quad 01010101, \quad 100000010101?$$

(c) Do the following numbers have any meaning in binary coded decimal:

$$11010001, \quad 10101010, \quad 00101100?$$

(d) How many bits are needed to represent all decimal integers up to 1000 as binary coded decimals?

(e) Discuss some of the advantages and disadvantages of the binary coded decimal representation in comparison with pure binary representation of numbers.

SUGGESTED READING

Tarski, A., *Introduction to Logic*, Oxford, New York, 2d rev. ed., 1946, Chapters I, II.

Cohen, M. R., and E. Nagel, *An Introduction to Logic and Scientific Method*, Harcourt, Brace, New York, 1934.

Church, A., *Introduction to Mathematical Logic*, Volume I, Princeton University Press, 1956.

Suppes, P., *Introduction to Mathematical Logic*, Van Nostrand, Princeton, 1957.

Hilbert, D., and W. Ackermann, *Principles of Mathematical Logic*, Chelsea, New York, 2d ed., 1950.

Allendoerfer, C. B., and C. O. Oakley, *Principles of Mathematics*, McGraw-Hill, New York, 1955, Chapter I.

Johnstone, H. W., Jr., *Elementary Deductive Logic*, Crowell, New York, 1954, Parts One and Two.

Hohn, Franz, "Some Mathematical Aspects of Switching," *The American Mathematical Monthly*, **62** (1955), pp. 75–90.

||

Sets and Subsets

1. Introduction

A well-defined collection of objects is known as a *set*. This concept, in its complete generality, is of great importance in mathematics since all of mathematics can be developed by starting from it.

The various pieces of furniture in a given room form a set. So do the books in a given library, or the integers between 1 and 1,000,000, or all the ideas that mankind has had, or the human beings alive between one billion B.C. and ten billion A.D., or the machine tools in a factory, or the members of the board of directors of a company, or the products which a company sells. These examples are all examples of *finite* sets, that is, sets having a finite number of elements. All the sets discussed in this book will be finite sets.

There are two essentially different ways of specifying a set. One can give a rule by which it can be determined whether or not a given object is a member of the set, or one can give a complete list of the elements in the set. We shall say that the former is a *description* of the set and the latter is a *listing* of the set. For example, we can define a set of four people as

(a) the members of the executive committee of the XYZ Corporation, or (b) the people whose names are Jones, Smith, Brown, and Green. It is customary to use braces to surround the listing of a set; thus the set above should be listed {Jones, Smith, Brown, Green}.

We shall frequently be interested in sets of logical possibilities, since the analysis of such sets is very often a major task in the solving of a problem. Suppose, for example, that we were interested in the successes of three companies which compete with one another in four territories, which we shall designate simply as North, South, East, and West. We are interested in determining the possibilities for market leadership in each territory, where a company is the market leader if its share of the market is larger than that of any competitor. Assume that Company A markets in all territories, that B does not market in the East, and C does not market in the North. A list of the logical possibilities is given in Figure 1. Since there are only two possible market leaders in the East and in the North, while there are three possibilities in the South and three in the West, there are in all $2 \cdot 2 \cdot 3 \cdot 3 = 36$ different logical possibilities as listed in Figure 1.

A set that consists of some members of another set is called a *subset* of that set. For example, the set of those logical possibilities in Figure 1 for which the statement "Company A is the market leader in at least three territories" is true, is a subset of the set of all logical possibilities. This subset can also be defined by listing its members:

$$\{P1, P2, P3, P4, P7, P13, P19\}.$$

In order to discuss all the subsets of a given set, let us introduce the following terminology. We shall call the original set the *universal set*, one-element subsets will be called *unit sets*, and the set which contains no members the *empty set*. We do not introduce special names for other kinds of subsets of the universal set. As an example, let the universal set $\mathfrak{U}$ consist of the three elements $\{a, b, c\}$. The *proper subsets* of $\mathfrak{U}$ are those sets containing some but not all of the elements of $\mathfrak{U}$. The proper subsets consist of three two-element sets, namely, $\{a, b\}$, $\{a, c\}$, and $\{b, c\}$ and three unit sets, namely, $\{a\}$, $\{b\}$, and $\{c\}$. To complete the picture we also consider the universal set a subset (but not a proper subset) of itself, and we consider the empty set $\mathcal{E}$, that contains no elements of $\mathfrak{U}$, as a subset of $\mathfrak{U}$. At first it may seem strange that we should include the sets $\mathfrak{U}$ and $\mathcal{E}$ as subsets of $\mathfrak{U}$, but the reasons for their inclusion will become clear later.

We saw that the three-element set above had $8 = 2^3$ subsets. In general, a set with n elements has 2^n subsets, as can be seen in the following manner. We form subsets P of $\mathfrak{U}$ by considering each of the elements of $\mathfrak{U}$ in turn and deciding whether or not to include it in the subset P. If we decide to put every element of $\mathfrak{U}$ into P we get the universal set, and

Possibility Number	Market Leader in the East	Market Leader in the South	Market Leader in the North	Market Leader in the West
P1	A	A	A	A
P2	A	A	A	B
P3	A	A	A	C
P4	A	A	B	A
P5	A	A	B	B
P6	A	A	B	C
P7	A	B	A	A
P8	A	B	A	B
P9	A	B	A	C
P10	A	B	B	A
P11	A	B	B	B
P12	A	B	B	C
P13	A	C	A	A
P14	A	C	A	B
P15	A	C	A	C
P16	A	C	B	A
P17	A	C	B	B
P18	A	C	B	C
P19	C	A	A	A
P20	C	A	A	B
P21	C	A	A	C
P22	C	A	B	A
P23	C	A	B	B
P24	C	A	B	C
P25	C	B	A	A
P26	C	B	A	B
P27	C	B	A	C
P28	C	B	B	A
P29	C	B	B	B
P30	C	B	B	C
P31	C	C	A	A
P32	C	C	A	B
P33	C	C	A	C
P34	C	C	B	A
P35	C	C	B	B
P36	C	C	B	C

Figure 1

if we decide to put no element of $\mathcal{U}$ into P we get the empty set. In most cases we will put some but not all the elements into P and thus obtain a proper subset of $\mathcal{U}$. We have to make n decisions, one for each element of the set, and for each decision we have to choose between two alternatives. We can make these decisions in $2 \cdot 2 \cdot \ldots \cdot 2 = 2^n$ ways, and hence this is the number of different subsets of $\mathcal{U}$ that can be formed. Observe that our formula would not have been so simple if we had not included the universal set and the empty set as subsets of $\mathcal{U}$.

In the example of market leadership above there are 2^{36} or about 70 billion subsets. Of course, we cannot deal with this many subsets in a practical problem, but fortunately we are usually interested in only a few of the subsets. The most interesting subsets are those which can be defined by means of a simple rule such as "The set of all logical possibilities in which C is not the leader in at least two territories." It would be difficult to give a simple description for the subset containing the elements

$$\{P1, P4, P14, P30, P34\}.$$

On the other hand, we shall see in the next section how to define new subsets in terms of subsets already defined.

Examples. We illustrate the two different ways of specifying sets in terms of the market leadership example. Let the universal set $\mathfrak{U}$ be the logical possibilities given in Figure 1.

1. What is the subset of $\mathfrak{U}$ in which Company B is the leader in more territories than either of the other companies?

Answer: $\{P11, P12, P17, P23, P26, P28, P29\}$.

2. What is the subset in which the leadership is split two and two?

Answer: $\{P5, P8, P10, P15, P21, P30, P31, P35\}$.

3. Describe the set $\{P1, P4, P19, P22\}$.

Answer: The set of possibilities for which A is the leader in the South and the West.

4. How can we describe the set $\{P18, P24, P27\}$?

Answer: The set of possibilities for which C is the leader in the West, and the leadership in the three other territories is split three ways.

EXERCISES

1. In the market leadership example, give a listing for each of the following sets.
   (a) The set in which C is the market leader in at least two territories.
   (b) The set in which the same company is the market leader in the East, South, and North.
   (c) The set in which B is the market leader in all four territories.

2. A company is considered to dominate the market if it is the market leader in three territories, or if it is the leader in two territories including the West. List the sets in which there is a dominating company.

3. Give simple descriptions for the following sets (referring to the market leadership example).
   (a) $\{P33, P36\}$.
   (b) $\{P10, P11, P12, P28, P29, P30\}$.
   (c) $\{P6, P20, P22\}$.

4. A company wishes to run three different advertisements of product A, which we shall designate A1, A2, and A3, and two different advertisements,

B1 and B2 of product B, in successive issues of a weekly magazine. If it is decided to alternate advertisements of product A and product B, list the set of all possibilities.

5. In Exercise 4, list the following subsets. Let the words "is next to" mean either "immediately precedes" or "immediately follows."
   (a) The set in which A1 is next to B2.
   (b) The set in which B2 is next to A2 and A3.
   (c) The set in which A2 is the third advertisement.
   (d) The set in which B1 is the third advertisement.
   (e) The set in which an advertisement of product A starts and ends the series.

6. Pick out all pairs in Exercise 5 in which one set is a subset of the other.

7. A TV producer is planning a half-hour show. He wants to have a combination of comedy, music, and commercials. If each is allotted a multiple of five minutes, construct the set of possible distributions of time. (Consider only the total time allotted to each.)

8. In Exercise 7, list the following subsets.
   (a) The set in which more time is devoted to comedy than to music.
   (b) The set in which no more time is devoted to commercials than to either music or comedy.
   (c) The set in which exactly five minutes is devoted to music.
   (d) The set in which all three of the above conditions are satisfied.

   9. In Exercise 7, find two sets, each of which is a proper subset of the set in 8(a) and also of the set in 8(c).

2. *Operations on subsets*

In Chapter I we considered the ways in which one could form new statements from given statements. Now we shall consider an analogous procedure, the formation of new sets from given sets. We shall assume that each of the sets that we use in the combination is a subset of some universal set, and we shall also want the newly formed set to be a subset of the same universal set. As usual we can specify a newly formed set either by a description or by a listing.

If P and Q are two sets we shall define a new set $P \cap Q$, called the *intersection* of P and Q, as follows: $P \cap Q$ is the set which contains those and only those elements which belong to both P and Q. As an example, consider the logical possibilities listed in Figure 1. Let P be the subset in which Company A is the market leader in at least three territories, i.e., the set

$$\{P1, P2, P3, P4, P7, P13, P19\}.$$

Let Q be the subset in which A is the leader in the East and the South, i.e., the set

$$\{P1, P2, P3, P4, P5, P6\}.$$

Then the intersection $P \cap Q$ is the set in which both events take place, i.e., where A is the leader in the East and the South *and* is the leader in at least three territories. Thus $P \cap Q$ is the set

$$\{P1, P2, P3, P4\}.$$

If P and Q are two sets we shall define a new set $P \cup Q$, called the *union* of P and Q, as follows: $P \cup Q$ is the set that contains those and only those elements that belong either to P or to Q (or to both). In the example in the paragraph above, the union $P \cup Q$ is the set of possibilities for which either A is the leader in the East and the South *or* is the leader in at least three territories, i.e., the set

$$\{P1, P2, P3, P4, P5, P6, P7, P13, P19\}.$$

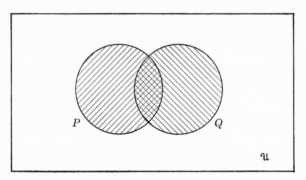

Figure 2

To help in visualizing these operations we shall draw diagrams, called Venn diagrams, which illustrate them. We let the universal set be a rectangle and let subsets be circles drawn inside the rectangle. In Figure 2 we show two sets P and Q as shaded circles. Then the doubly crosshatched area is the intersection $P \cap Q$ and the total shaded area is the union $P \cup Q$.

If P is a given subset of the universal set $\mathfrak{U}$, we can define a new set $\tilde{P}$, called the *complement* of P, as follows: $\tilde{P}$ is the set of all elements of $\mathfrak{U}$ that are *not* contained in P. For example, if, as above, Q is the set in which Company A is the market leader in the East and the South, then $\tilde{Q}$ is the set $\{P7, P8, \ldots, P36\}$. The shaded area in Figure 3 is the complement of the set P. Observe that the complement of the empty set $\mathcal{E}$ is the universal set $\mathfrak{U}$, and also that the complement of the universal set is the empty set.

Sometimes we shall be interested in only part of the complement of a set. For example, we might wish to consider the part of the complement of the set Q that is contained in P, i.e., the set $P \cap \tilde{Q}$. The shaded area in Figure 4 is $P \cap \tilde{Q}$.

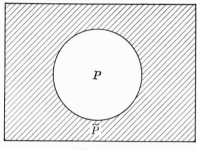

Figure 3

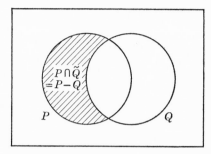

Figure 4

A somewhat more suggestive definition of this set can be given as follows: let $P - Q$ be the *difference* of P and Q, that is, the set that contains those elements of P that do not belong to Q. Figure 4 shows that $P \cap \tilde{Q}$ and $P - Q$ are the same set. In the market leadership example above the set $P - Q$ can be listed as {P7, P13, P19}.

The complement of a set is a special case of a difference set, since we can write $\tilde{Q} = \mathfrak{u} - Q$. If P and Q are nonempty sets whose intersection is the empty set, i.e., $P \cap Q = \mathcal{E}$, then we say that they are *disjoint* sets.

Examples. In the market leadership example, consider the four territories in the order East, South, North, West, and let R be the set in which A is the leader in the first three territories, i.e., the set {P1, P2, P3}; let S be the set in which A is the leader in the last two territories, i.e., the set

{P1, P7, P13, P19, P25, P31}.

Then $R \cap S = $ {P1} is the set in which A is the leader in the first three territories and also the last two, that is he is the leader in all the territories. We also have

$R \cup S = $ {P1, P2, P3, P7, P13, P19, P25, P31},

which can be described as the set in which A is the leader in the first three territories or the last two. The set in which A is not the leader in the first three territories is

$\tilde{R} = $ {P4, P5, . . . , P36}.

Finally, we see that the difference set $R - S$ is the set in which A is the market leader in the first three territories but not both of the last two. This set can be found by taking from R the element {P1} which it has in common with S, so that

$R - S = $ {P2, P3}.

EXERCISES

1. Draw Venn diagrams for $P \cap Q$, $P \cap \tilde{Q}$, $\tilde{P} \cap Q$, $\tilde{P} \cap \tilde{Q}$.

2. Give a step-by-step construction of the diagram for $(P - Q) \cup (P \cap \tilde{Q})$.

3. Venn diagrams are also useful when three subsets are given. Construct such a diagram, given the subsets P, Q, and R. Identify each of the eight resulting areas in terms of P, Q, and R.

4. In testing blood, three types of antigens are looked for: A, B, and Rh. Every person is classified doubly. He is Rh positive if he has the Rh antigen, and Rh negative otherwise. He is type AB, A, or B depending on which of the other antigens he has, with type O having neither A nor B. Draw a Venn diagram, and identify each of the eight areas.

5. Considering only two subsets, the set X of people having antigen A, and the set Y of people having antigen B, define (symbolically) the types AB, A, B, and O.

6. A person can receive blood from another person if he has all the antigens of the donor. Describe in terms of X and Y the sets of people who can give to each of the four types. Identify these sets in terms of blood types.

7.

	Liked Very Much	Liked Slightly	Disliked Slightly	Disliked Very Much
Men	1	3	5	10
Women	6	8	3	1
Boys	5	5	3	2
Girls	8	5	1	1

This tabulation records the reaction of a number of spectators to a television show. All the categories can be defined in terms of the following four: M (male), G (grown-up), L (liked), Vm (very much). How many people fall into each of the following categories:

(a) M.   [*Ans.* 34.]

(b) $\tilde{L}$.

(c) Vm.

(d) $M \cap \tilde{G} \cap \tilde{L} \cap Vm$.   [*Ans.* 2.]

(e) $\tilde{M} \cap G \cap L$.

(f) $(M \cap G) \cup (L \cap Vm)$.

(g) $\widetilde{(M \cap G)}$.   [*Ans.* 48.]

    (h) $(M \cup \tilde{G})$.

    (i) $(M - G)$.

    (j) $[\tilde{M} - (G \cap L \cap \widetilde{Vm})]$.

8. In a survey of 100 families, the numbers that read the most recent issues of various magazines were found to be: *Look*, 28; *Time*, 30; *Life*, 42; *Look* and *Time*, 8; *Look* and *Life*, 10; *Time* and *Life*, 5; all three magazines, 3.

    (a) How many read none of the three magazines?   [*Ans.* 20.]

    (b) How many read *Life* as their only magazine?   [*Ans.* 30.]

    (c) How many read *Time* if and only if they read *Life*?   [*Ans.* 38.]

9. In another survey of 100 families, the numbers that had read recent issues of a certain monthly magazine were found to be: September only, 18; September but not August, 23; September and July, 8; September, 26; July, 48; July and August, 8; none of the three months, 24.

    (a) How many read the August issue?   [*Ans.* 18.]

    (b) How many read two consecutive issues?   [*Ans.* 8.]

    (c) How many read the July issue if and only if they did not read the August issue?   [*Ans.* 50.]

    (d) How many read the September and August issues but not the July issue?   [*Ans.* None.]

10. The report of an inspector who inspected a lot of 100 pieces and reported the number of hardness, finish, and dimensional defects of pieces in the last lot was as follows: all three defects, 5; hardness and finish, 10; dimensional and finish, 8; dimensional and hardness, 20; finish, 30; hardness, 23; dimensional, 50. The inspector was fired. Why?

11. The workers in a factory were classified according to skill, number of years in the employ of the factory, and whether they performed direct or indirect labor. If they had worked less than three years in the factory, they were categorized as short-term workers; if they had worked ten years or more, they were considered long-term, and all others were medium-term employees. The data are summarized in the following table:

	Skilled and Direct	Unskilled and Direct	Skilled and Indirect	Unskilled and Indirect
Short	6	9	10	20
Medium	7	11	15	9
Long	2	3	8	0

Let SH = Short, M = Medium, L = Long, SK = Skilled, I = Indirect. Determine the number of workers in the following classes.

    (a) $SH \cap SK \cap I$.   [*Ans.* 10.]

    (b) M.

    (c) $L \cap I$.

    (d) $(M \cup L) \cap (SK \cup I)$.   [*Ans.* 41.]

    (e) $\widetilde{SH} \cup (\widetilde{SK \cap I})$.

12. In Exercise 11, which set of each of the following pairs has more workers as members?

(a) $(\widetilde{SH \cup M})$ or L.

(b) $I \cap \widetilde{SK}$ or $SH - (I \cap \widetilde{SK})$.

(c) $\mathcal{E}$ or $L \cap \widetilde{SK} \cap I$.

3. The relationship between sets and compound statements

The reader may have observed several times in the preceding sections that there was a close connection between sets and statements, and between set operations and compounding operations. In this section we shall formalize these relationships.

If we have a number of statements under consideration there is a natural way of assigning a set to each one of these statements. First we form the set of all logical possibilities for the statements under consideration and call this set the universal set. Then to each statement we assign the subset of logical possibilities of the universal set for which that statement is true. This idea is so important that we embody it in a formal definition.

DEFINITION. Let p, q, r, ... be statements and let $\mathcal{U}$ be their set of logical possibilities; let P, Q, R, ... be the subsets of $\mathcal{U}$ for which statements p, q, r, ... are respectively true; then we call P, Q, R, ... the *truth sets* of statements p, q, r, ...

If p and q are statements, then $p \vee q$ and $p \wedge q$ are also statements and hence must have truth sets. To find the truth set of $p \vee q$ we observe that it is true whenever p is true or q is true (or both). Therefore we must assign to $p \vee q$ the logical possibilities which are in P or in Q (or both); that is, we must assign to $p \vee q$ the set $P \cup Q$. On the other hand, the statement $p \wedge q$ is true only when both p and q are true, so that we must assign to $p \wedge q$ the set $P \cap Q$.

Thus we see that there is a close connection between the logical operation of disjunction and the set operation of union, and also between conjunction and intersection. A careful examination of the definitions of union and intersection shows that the word "or" occurs in the definition of union and the word "and" occurs in the definition of intersection. Thus the connection between the two theories is not surprising.

Since the connective "not" occurs in the definition of the complement of a set, it is not surprising that the truth set of $\sim p$ is $\tilde{P}$. This follows since $\sim p$ is true when p is false, so that the truth set of $\sim p$ contains all logical possibilities for which p is false, that is, the truth set of $\sim p$ is $\tilde{P}$.

The truth sets of two statements p and q are shown in Figure 5. Also marked on the diagram are the various logical possibilities for these two statements. The reader should pick out in this diagram the truth sets of the statements $p \vee q$, $p \wedge q$, $\sim p$, and $\sim q$.

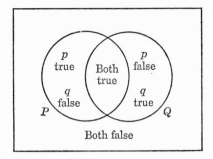

Figure 5

The connection between a statement and its truth set makes it possible to "translate" a problem about compound statements into a problem about sets. It is also possible to go in the reverse direction. Given a problem about sets, think of the universal set as being a set of logical possibilities and think of a subset as being the truth set of a statement. Hence we can "translate" a problem about sets into a problem about compound statements.

So far we have discussed only the truth sets assigned to compound statements involving $\vee$, $\wedge$, and $\sim$. All the other connectives can be defined in terms of these three basic ones, so that we can deduce what truth sets should be assigned to them. For example, we know that $p \to q$ is equivalent to $\sim p \vee q$ (see Figure 32 of Chapter I). Hence the truth set of $p \to q$ is the same as the truth set of $\sim p \vee q$, that is, it is $\tilde{P} \cup Q$. The

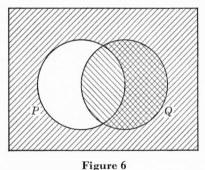

Figure 6

Venn diagram for $p \to q$ is shown in Figure 6, where the shaded area is the truth set for the statement. Observe that the unshaded area in Figure 6 is the set $P - Q = P \cap \tilde{Q}$ which is the truth set of the statement $p \wedge \sim q$. Thus the shaded area is the set $\widetilde{(P - Q)} = \widetilde{P \cap \tilde{Q}}$ which is the truth set of the statement $\sim [p \wedge \sim q]$. We have thus discovered the fact $(p \to q)$, $(\sim p \vee q)$, and $\sim (p \wedge \sim q)$ are equivalent. It is always the case that two compound statements are equivalent if and only if they have the same truth sets. We also see that Venn diagrams can be used to discover relations between statements.

Suppose now that p is a statement that is logically true. What is its truth set? Now p is logically true if and only if it is true in every logically possible case, so that the truth set of p must be $\mathfrak{U}$. Similarly, if p is logically false, then it is false for every logically possible case, so that its truth set is the empty set $\mathcal{E}$.

Finally, let us consider the implication relation. Recall that p implies q if and only if the conditional $p \rightarrow q$ is logically true. But $p \rightarrow q$ is logically true if and only if its truth set is $\mathfrak{U}$, that is $\widetilde{(P - Q)} = \mathfrak{U}$, or $(P - Q) = \mathcal{E}$. From Figure 4 we see that if $P - Q$ is empty, then P is contained in Q. We shall symbolize the containing relation as follows: $P \subset Q$ means "P is a subset of Q." We conclude that $p \rightarrow q$ is logically true if and only if $P \subset Q$.

Let us briefly summarize the above discussion. To each statement there corresponds a truth set. To each logical connective there corresponds a set operation. To each relation between statements there corresponds a relation between the truth sets. The truth sets of the statements $p \vee q$, $p \wedge q$, $\sim p$, and $p \rightarrow q$ are $P \cup Q$, $P \cap Q$, $\tilde{P}$, and $\widetilde{(P - Q)}$, respectively. Statement p is logically true if $P = \mathfrak{U}$ and logically false if $P = \mathcal{E}$. Statements p and q are equivalent if and only if $P = Q$, and p implies q if and only if $P \subset Q$.

Example 1. Prove by means of a Venn diagram that the statement $[p \vee (\sim p \vee q)]$ is logically true. The assigned set of this statement is $[P \cup (\tilde{P} \cup Q)]$, and its Venn diagram is shown in Figure 7. In that figure the set P is shaded vertically, and the set $\tilde{P} \cup Q$ is shaded horizontally. Their union is the entire shaded area, which is $\mathfrak{U}$, so that the compound statement is logically true.

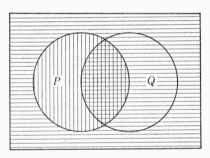

Figure 7

Example 2. Prove by means of Venn diagrams that $p \vee (q \wedge r)$ is equivalent to $(p \vee q) \wedge (p \vee r)$. The truth set of $p \vee (q \wedge r)$ is the entire shaded area of Figure 8, and the truth set of $(p \vee q) \wedge (p \vee r)$ is the doubly shaded area in Figure 9. Since these two sets are equal, we see that the two statements are equivalent.

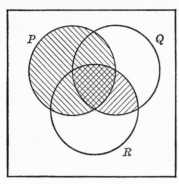

Figure 8   **Figure 9**

Example 3. Show by means of a Venn diagram that q implies $p \to q$. The truth set of $p \to q$ is the shaded area in Figure 6. Since this shaded area includes the set Q we see that q implies $p \to q$.

EXERCISES

Note: In Exercises 1, 2, and 3, find first the truth set of each statement.

1. Use Venn diagrams to test which of the following statements are logically true or logically false.
   - (a) $p \lor \sim p$.
   - (b) $p \land \sim p$.
   - (c) $p \lor (\sim p \land q)$.
   - (d) $p \to (q \to p)$.
   - (e) $p \land \sim(q \to p)$.   [*Ans.* (a), (d) logically true; (b), (e) logically false.]

2. Use Venn diagrams to test the following statements for equivalences.
   - (a) $p \lor \sim q$.
   - (b) $\sim(p \land q)$.
   - (c) $\sim(q \land \sim p)$.
   - (d) $p \to \sim q$.
   - (e) $\sim p \lor \sim q$.
        [*Ans.* (a) and (c) equivalent; (b) and (d) and (e) equivalent.]

3. Use Venn diagrams for the following pairs of statements to test whether one implies the other.
   - (a) $p;\ p \land q$.
   - (b) $p \land \sim q;\ \sim p \to \sim q$.
   - (c) $p \to q;\ q \to p$.
   - (d) $p \land q;\ p \land \sim q$.

4. A pair of statements is said to be *inconsistent* if they cannot both be true. Devise a test for inconsistency.

5. Three or more statements are said to be inconsistent if they cannot all be true. What does this state about their truth sets?

6. In the following three compound statements (a) assign variables to the components, (b) bring the statements into symbolic form, (c) find the truth sets, and (d) test for consistency.

If this is a good course, then I will work hard in it.

If this is not a good course, then I shall get a bad grade in it.

I will not work hard, but I will get a good grade in this course.

[*Ans.* Inconsistent.]

Note: In Exercises 7-9 assign to each set a statement having it as a truth set.

7. Use truth tables to find which of the following sets are empty.
   (a) $(P \cup Q) \cap (\tilde{P} \cup \tilde{Q})$.
   (b) $(P \cap Q) \cap (\tilde{Q} \cap R)$.
   (c) $(P \cap Q) - P$.
   (d) $(P \cup R) \cap (\tilde{P} \cup \tilde{Q})$.   [*Ans.* (b) and (c).]

8. Use truth tables to find out whether the following sets are all different.
   (a) $P \cap (Q \cup R)$.
   (b) $(R - Q) \cup (Q - R)$.
   (c) $(R \cup Q) \cap \widetilde{(R \cap Q)}$.
   (d) $(P \cap Q) \cup (P \cap R)$.
   (e) $(P \cap Q \cap \tilde{R}) \cup (P \cap \tilde{Q} \cap R) \cup (\tilde{P} \cap Q \cap \tilde{R}) \cup (\tilde{P} \cap \tilde{Q} \cap R)$.

9. Use truth tables for the following pairs of sets to test whether one is a subset of the other.
   (a) $P; P \cap Q$.
   (b) $P \cap \tilde{Q}; Q \cap \tilde{P}$.
   (c) $P - Q; Q - P$.
   (d) $\tilde{P} \cap \tilde{Q}; P \cup Q$.

10. Show, both by the use of truth tables and by the use of Venn diagrams, that $p \wedge (q \vee r)$ is equivalent to $(p \wedge q) \vee (p \wedge r)$.

*4. The abstract laws of set operations

The set operations which we have introduced obey some very simple abstract laws, which we shall list in this section. These laws can be proved by means of Venn diagrams or they can be translated into statements and checked by means of truth tables.

The abstract laws given below bear a close resemblance to the elementary algebraic laws with which the student is already familiar. The resemblance can be made even more striking by replacing $\cup$ by $+$, $\cap$ by $\times$, $\mathfrak{u}$ by 1, and ε by 0. For this reason, a set, its subsets, and the laws of combination of subsets are considered an algebraic system, called a Boolean algebra—after the British mathematician George Boole who was the first person to study them from the algebraic point of view. Any other system obeying these laws, for example the system of compound statements studied in Chapter I, is also known as a Boolean algebra. We can study any of these systems from either the algebraic or the logical point of view.

Below are the basic laws of Boolean algebras. The proofs of these laws will be left as exercises.

The laws governing union and intersection:

A1. $A \cup A = A$.
A2. $A \cap A = A$.
A3. $A \cup B = B \cup A$.
A4. $A \cap B = B \cap A$.
A5. $A \cup (B \cup C) = (A \cup B) \cup C$.
A6. $A \cap (B \cap C) = (A \cap B) \cap C$.
A7. $A \cap (B \cup C) = (A \cap B) \cup (A \cap C)$.
A8. $A \cup (B \cap C) = (A \cup B) \cap (A \cup C)$.
A9. $A \cup \mathfrak{U} = \mathfrak{U}$.
A10. $A \cap \mathcal{E} = \mathcal{E}$.
A11. $A \cap \mathfrak{U} = A$.
A12. $A \cup \mathcal{E} = A$.

The laws governing complements:

B1. $\tilde{\tilde{A}} = A$.
B2. $A \cup \tilde{A} = \mathfrak{U}$.
B3. $A \cap \tilde{A} = \mathcal{E}$.
B4. $\widetilde{(A \cup B)} = \tilde{A} \cap \tilde{B}$.
B5. $\widetilde{(A \cap B)} = \tilde{A} \cup \tilde{B}$.
B6. $\tilde{\mathfrak{U}} = \mathcal{E}$.

The laws governing set-differences:

C1. $A - B = A \cap \tilde{B}$.
C2. $\mathfrak{U} - A = \tilde{A}$.
C3. $A - \mathfrak{U} = \mathcal{E}$.
C4. $A - \mathcal{E} = A$.
C5. $\mathcal{E} - A = \mathcal{E}$.
C6. $A - A = \mathcal{E}$.
C7. $(A - B) - C = A - (B \cup C)$.
C8. $A - (B - C) = (A - B) \cup (A \cap C)$
C9. $A \cup (B - C) = (A \cup B) - (C - A)$.
C10. $A \cap (B - C) = (A \cap B) - (A \cap C)$.

EXERCISES

1. Test laws in the group A1–A12 by means of Venn diagrams.

2. "Translate" the A-laws into laws about compound statements. Test these by truth tables.

3. Test the laws in groups B and C by Venn diagrams.

4. "Translate" the B- and C-laws into laws about compound statements. Test these by means of truth tables.

5. Derive the following results from the 28 basic laws.
   (a) $A = (A \cap B) \cup (A \cap \tilde{B})$.
   (b) $A \cup B = (A \cap B) \cup (A \cap \tilde{B}) \cup (\tilde{A} \cap B)$.
   (c) $A \cap (A \cup B) = A$.
   (d) $A \cup (\tilde{A} \cap B) = A \cup B$.

6. From the A- and B-laws and from C1, derive C2–C6.

7. Use A1–A12 and C2–C10 to derive B1, B2, B3, and B6.

*5. Voting coalitions

As an application of our set concepts we shall consider the significance of voting coalitions in voting bodies. Here the universal set is a set of human beings which form a decision-making body. For example, the universal set might be the members of a committee, or of a city council, or of a convention, or of the House of Representatives, etc. Each member can cast a certain number of votes. The decision as to whether or not a measure is passed can be decided by a simple majority rule, or a two-thirds majority, etc.

Suppose now that a subset of the members of the body forms a coalition in order to pass a measure. The question is whether or not they have enough votes to guarantee passage of the measure. If they have enough votes to carry the measure, then we say they form a *winning coalition*. If the members *not* in the coalition can pass a measure of their own, then we say that the original coalition is a *losing coalition*. Finally, if the members of the coalition cannot carry their measure, and if the members not in the coalition cannot carry their measure, then the coalition is called a *blocking coalition*.

Let us restate these definitions in set-theoretic terms. A coalition C is winning if they have enough votes to carry an issue; coalition C is losing if the coalition $\tilde{C}$ is winning; and coalition C is blocking if neither C nor $\tilde{C}$ is a winning coalition.

The following facts are immediate consequences of these definitions. The complement of a winning coalition is a losing coalition. The complement of a losing coalition is a winning coalition. The complement of a blocking coalition is a blocking coalition.

Example 1. A committee consists of six men each having one vote. A simple majority vote will carry an issue. Then any coalition of four or more members is winning, any coalition with one or two members is losing, and any three-person coalition is blocking.

Example 2. Suppose in Example 1 one of the six members (say the chairman) is given the power to break ties. Then any three-person coalition of which he is a member is winning, while the other three-person coalitions are losing; hence there are no blocking coalitions. The other coalitions are as in Example 1.

Example 3. Let the universal set $\mathfrak{U}$ be the set $\{x, y, w, z\}$, where x and y each has one vote, w has two votes, and z has three votes. Suppose it takes five votes to carry a measure. Then the winning coalitions are: $\{z, w\}$, $\{z, x, y\}$, $\{z, w, x\}$, $\{z, w, y\}$, and $\mathfrak{U}$. The losing coalitions are the complements of these sets. Blocking coalitions are: $\{z\}$, $\{z, x\}$, $\{z, y\}$, $\{w, x\}$, $\{w, y\}$, and $\{w, x, y\}$.

The last example shows that it is not always necessary to list all members of a winning coalition. For example, if the coalition $\{z, w\}$ is winning, then it is obvious that the coalition $\{z, w, y\}$ is also winning. In general, if a coalition C is winning, then any other set that has C as a subset will also be winning. Thus we are led to the notion of a *minimal winning coalition*. A minimal winning coalition is a winning coalition which contains no winning coalition as a proper subset. Another way of stating this is that a minimal winning coalition is a winning coalition such that, if any member is lost from the coalition, then it ceases to be a winning coalition.

If we know the minimal winning coalitions, then we know everything that we need to know about the voting problem. The winning coalitions are all those sets that contain a minimal winning coalition, and the losing coalitions are the complements of the winning coalitions. All other sets are blocking coalitions.

In Example 1 the minimal winning coalitions are the sets containing four members. In Example 2 the minimal winning coalitions are the three-member coalitions that contain the tie-breaking member and the four-member coalitions that do not contain the tie-breaking member. The minimal winning coalitions in the third example are the sets $\{z, w\}$ and $\{z, x, y\}$.

Sometimes there are committee members who have special powers or lack of power. If a member can pass any measure he wishes without needing anyone else to vote with him, then we call him a *dictator*. Thus member x is a dictator if and only if $\{x\}$ is a winning coalition. A somewhat weaker

but still very powerful member is one who can by himself block any measure. If x is such a member, then we say that x has *veto power*. Thus x has
veto power if and only if {x} is a blocking coalition. Finally if x is not a
member of any minimal winning coalition, we shall call him a *powerless*
member. Thus x is powerless if and only if any winning coalition of which
x is a member is a winning coalition without him.

Example 4. An interesting example of a decision-making body is the Security
Council of the United Nations. The Security Council has eleven members
consisting of the five permanent large nation members called the Big Five,
and six small nation members. In order that a measure be passed by the
Council, seven members including all of the Big Five must vote for the measure. Thus the seven-member sets made up of the Big Five plus two small
nations are the minimal winning coalitions. Then the losing coalitions are the
sets that contain at most four small nations. The blocking coalitions are the
sets that are neither winning nor losing. In particular, a unit set that contains one of the Big Five as a member is a blocking coalition. This is the sense
in which a Big Five member has a veto. [The possibility of "abstaining" is
immaterial in the above discussion.]

Example 5. Some companies have directors elected by a system known as
cumulative voting. The system operates as follows. Suppose there are s
shares of stock voting, and that there are d directorships to be filled at an
election. Each share of stock is given d votes, which can be cast without any
restrictions. Thus, in particular, the d votes of a share can be distributed
with one vote for each of d candidates, or they may be cumulated, so that all
d votes go to a single candidate. The candidates are ranked according to the
number of votes received, the d highest candidates winning the election.

Let us raise the problem: What is the minimal winning coalition that will
elect a given person as director?

Suppose that the coalition has t shares to vote; hence the coalition's candidate will receive at least td votes. The other shareholders have $s - t$ shares,
hence may cast $(s - t)d$ votes. For our candidate to fail to win, each of d
other candidates must receive at least td votes. This is only possible if

$$(s - t)d \geq (td) \cdot d \quad \text{or} \quad dt \leq (s - t).$$

Hence the coalition can guarantee the election if $dt > s - t$ or

$$t > \frac{1}{d + 1} s,$$

that is, if they control more than a fraction $1/(d + 1)$ of the shares. If they
have $s/(d + 1)$ shares or less, then the formula $(s - t)d \geq (td) \cdot d$ shows that
the opposition could split its votes evenly among d other candidates and either
defeat our candidate or create a tie.

Thus, for example, if there are 6 directors to be elected, and there are
700,000 shares, then 100,001 shares form a minimal winning coalition.

EXERCISES

1. A committee has w, x, y, and z as members. Member w has two votes, the others have one vote each. List the winning, losing, and blocking coalitions.

2. A committee has n members, each with one vote. It takes a majority vote to carry an issue. What are the winning, losing, and blocking coalitions?

3. The Board of Estimate of New York City consists of eight members with voting strength as follows:

    s. Mayor .... 4 votes
    t. Controller 4
    u. Council President 4
    v. Brooklyn Borough President 2
    w. Manhattan Borough President 2
    x. Bronx Borough President 2
    y. Richmond Borough President 2
    z. Queens Borough President 2

    A simple majority is needed to carry an issue. List the minimal winning coalitions. List the blocking coalitions. Do the same if we give the mayor the additional power to break ties.

4. A company has issued 100,000 shares of common stock and each share has one vote. How many shares must a stockholder have to be a dictator? How many to have a veto?   [*Ans.* 50,001; 50,000.]

5. In Exercise 4, if the company requires a two-thirds majority vote to carry an issue, how many shares must a stockholder have to be a dictator or to have a veto?   [*Ans.* At least 66,667; at least 33,334.]

6. Prove that if a committee has a dictator as a member, then the remaining members are powerless.

7. We can define a maximal losing coalition in analogy to the minimal winning coalitions. What is the relation between the maximal losing and minimal winning coalitions? Do the maximal losing coalitions provide all relevant information?

8. Prove that any two minimal winning coalitions have at least one member in common.

9. Find all the blocking coalitions in the Security Council example.

10. Prove that if a man has veto power and if he together with any one other member can carry a measure, then the distribution of the remaining votes is irrelevant.

11. The XYZ Company has cumulative voting for directors. If five directorships are to be filled at an election and 1000 shares are voting, what is the minimal winning coalition needed to elect a director?

12. Show that the number of shares t_n needed to elect $n \leq d$ directorships with cumulative voting is the smallest t_n for which $t_n > ns/(d + 1)$. (For simplicity, we allow the casting of fractional votes.)

13. Show that if the number of directorships for which votes are being cast is odd, a minimal winning coalition for obtaining a majority of the director-ships is a block of more than half the shares, but that this is not so if the number of directorships is even.

14. In "straight" voting for directors, one vote per share is permitted, and a vote is cast for an entire slate of candidates, the number of candidates on a slate being equal to the number of directorships to be filled. Under "straight" voting, what is a minimal winning coalition to elect a single director? A majority of the directors? An entire slate of directors?

*6. Critical path analysis

Whenever tasks are performed by many different people, or groups of people, perhaps with the aid of machines, planning and coordination of their activities is required. Some pairs of tasks can be carried on simul-taneously (in parallel), while other pairs of tasks must be done in a certain order (in series). Commonly, the planning is left to some person who is director of the project, and it is he who keeps track of the progress of the job.

If all goes well with the project, this method of coordination is satis-factory. But if the project is falling behind schedule, or if for some reason it must be speeded up, a better approach is desirable.

The basic tool for such an approach is a project graph, which we will describe below. The entire approach is known as *critical path analysis*. We first need to introduce a number of technical terms.

DEFINITION. A *project* is a nonempty set of jobs $\{a, b, c, \ldots\}$ to each of which a *time* is assigned, and a relationship of being a *predecessor* of other jobs is determined.

For example, the jobs may be all the individual tasks that have to be completed in building a house or constructing an airplane. The time of a job is the number of time units (in some conveniently chosen units) that are required to finish the job, and a is a predecessor of b (or b is a *successor* of a) if a must be completed before b can be started. For instance, in constructing a house, pouring the foundation is a predecessor of putting up the roof.

To specify the predecessors of a given job, it suffices to specify the *immediate predecessors*, which is the smallest set of jobs such that once they are completed the given job may be started. The predecessors of a job are its immediate predecessors, the immediate predecessors of these, etc.

DEFINITION. A *project graph* is a set of boxes in the plane with arrows connecting some of the boxes. There is one box for each job, and if *a* is an immediate predecessor of *b*, then there is an arrow from *a* to *b*. Predecessors appear at a lower level than their successors.

It is also helpful to introduce the following convention: We add to the list of jobs the pseudo-jobs "start" and "finish." Each requires 0 time to carry out, and "start" is a predecessor of all other jobs, while "finish" is a successor of all other jobs. These will be very convenient for bookkeeping purposes.

Example 1. Our project is the manufacture of a machine component which consists of two parts, P and Q. Each part must be turned on a lathe and Q must also be polished. Two types of raw materials, A and B, are needed. The project is specified by Figure 10. Its project graph is shown in Figure 11.

Job	Description	*Immediate* *Predecessors*	*Time*
a	Start	none	0
b	Order A	$\{a\}$	2
c	Order B	$\{a\}$	1
d	Turn P	$\{b, c\}$	2
e	Turn Q	$\{b, c\}$	1
f	Polish Q	$\{e\}$	2
g	Assemble component	$\{d, f\}$	1
h	Finish	$\{g\}$	0

Figure 10

As may be seen in Figure 11, the project graph is a convenient and concise way of tabulating all the relevant information. In fact, such a graph represents a common language that can be understood not only by foremen, superintendents, and project directors, but also by workmen and even by someone not involved in the project. We shall now show that a great deal more may be learned from a project graph.

As a first task we shall try to find the earliest possible completion date for our project. To do this, we carry out the following simple computations, beginning at "start," and working our way up one level at a time: (1) Write 0 to the right of "start." (2) Take a new job, and write to the *left* of it the largest number written to the right of any immediate predecessor.

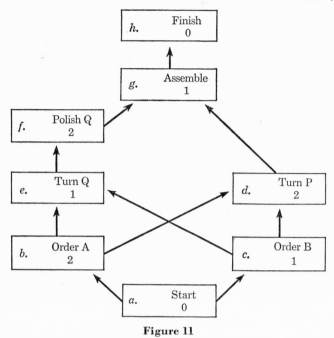

Figure 11

(3) Add to this number the time of the project, and record this to the *right* of the job. (4) Stop when "finish" is reached.

The interpretation of this simple routine is as follows: The number to the left of a job is the earliest that it can be started, and the number to the right of it is the earliest that it can be completed. We begin by saying that "start" comes at time 0, and then we compute the other figures using the fact that a project can start as soon as its immediate predecessors have been completed. We call the times computed the *early start time* (e.s.t.) and *early finish time* (e.f.t.) for the various jobs. The e.s.t. for "finish" (or e.f.t., which is the same) is the answer to our problem, namely the earliest time at which the project can be completed. We refer to this as the *target time.*

Example 1 (continued). Figure 12 shows the e.s.t. and e.f.t. of all the jobs. These may be computed by the four-step method described above. The target time turns out to be 6.

We would next like to know how much freedom we have in scheduling various tasks. For this we want the latest times at which a project can be started or finished without delaying the target time. These will be the *late start times* (l.s.t.) and *late finish times* (l.f.t.) of various jobs. We again put the starting times to the left and the finish times to the right of jobs, sepa-

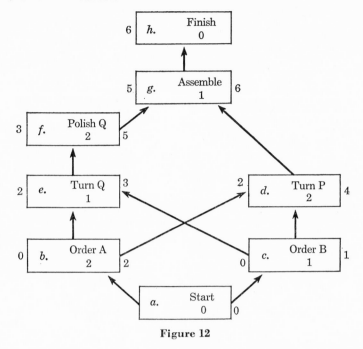

Figure 12

rating e.s.t. from l.s.t. and e.f.t. from l.f.t. by a hyphen. Our computation is very similar to the other four-step method, but this time we start with "finish" and work down one level at a time: (1) The l.s.t. of "finish" is the target time. (2) Take a new job, and assign to it as l.f.t. the smallest of the l.s.t.'s of its immediate successors. (3) Obtain the l.s.t. by subtracting the time of the project. (4) Stop when "start" is reached. Note that all that we have really used is the fact that a job must be finished before any of its successors are started.

> **Example 1 (continued).** Figure 13 shows the results of the new four-step computation. We note that we ended up with 0 as the late starting time for "start." This must always be the case, since the target time is the earliest possible target assuming that we start at 0. If a later starting time were possible for the project, then we should have been able to find an earlier target time.

DEFINITION. The *slack time* of a job is the difference between its l.s.t. and its e.s.t. A job with 0 slack time is a *critical job*.

The slack time may be thought of as the amount of freedom we have in scheduling that particular job, if all other jobs are scheduled suitably. Of course this could also be computed by taking the difference between

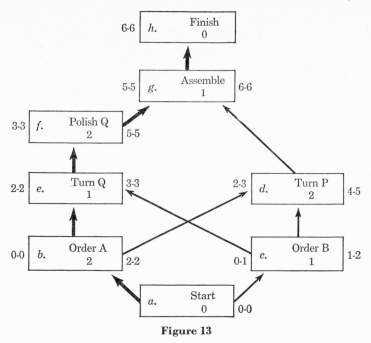

Figure 13

l.f.t. and e.f.t. A critical job is a bottleneck in the project. The target date can be decreased only by decreasing the time required for one or more critical jobs (see Exercise 1).

DEFINITION. A *critical path* is a path (following the arrows) from "start" to "finish" that consists entirely of critical jobs.

THEOREM. Every critical job (not counting "start" and "finish") has at least one critical immediate predecessor and at least one critical immediate successor. Every project has at least one critical path, and every critical job lies on one or more critical paths.

Proof. Let us first show that "finish" has at least one critical immediate predecessor. If it did not, then each of its immediate predecessors would have an e.f.t. less than the l.f.t. Hence each of these could be finished at least one unit before its l.f.t. But the l.f.t. of an immediate predecessor of "finish" is the target time, hence the target time could be reduced, which is impossible.

In exactly the same way we show that we get a contradiction by assuming that all immediate predecessors of any critical job have slacks. Thus we conclude that a critical job must have at least one critical immediate predecessor.

We can also show that "start" and all critical jobs have critical immediate successors. (See Exercise 3.) This completes the first part of the theorem. It also shows that there are critical jobs other than "start" or "finish." Take any such job a, and pick an immediate predecessor of a and an immediate successor of a that are critical. Continue this process in both directions till "start" and "finish" are reached, yielding a critical path which contains a. This completes the proof.

Example 1 (continued). The darkened path in Figure 13 shows the one critical path of our example. All critical jobs lie on this path. Thus, reducing job d to one time unit will not speed the project, since this job had a slack of 1, anyway. Job g would still have to wait for the completion of the critical predecessors b, e, and f, which are not helped by a change in d.

Example 2. In Figure 14 we redraw the figure of Example 1, but with a changed job time for d. Here the critical jobs are b, d, and g, and the critical

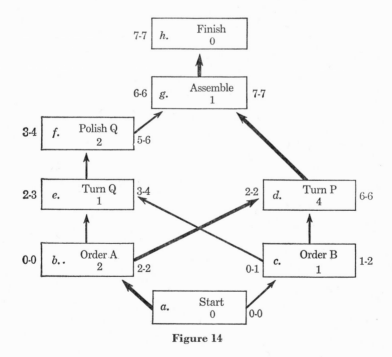

Figure 14

path is shown darkened in the figure. The noncritical jobs, which are c, e, and f, each have total slack equal to 1. Note that we cannot use up the slack in jobs e and f both, without delaying the finish time of the project. For if e is delayed by one unit, then the early start time for f becomes 4 and hence f becomes a critical job.

There are other kinds of slack that can be defined for jobs, and these are discussed in the exercises (see Exercises 9–11).

Example 3. A student wishes to major in mathematics and minor in physics. He must take seven mathematics courses, two statistics courses, and two physics courses, plus a mathematical physics course. These are all one-term courses. What is the minimum number of terms it will take for him to finish his requirements, ignoring all other course requirements and constraints? The twelve courses are listed with their immediate predecessors (usually called prerequisites) in Figure 15. Except for "start" and "finish," which take no

No.	*Courses*	*Immediate Predecessors* *(Prerequisites)*
	Start	None
M101	Calculus I	Start
M102	Calculus II	M101
M103	Finite Mathematics	Start
M104	Calculus III	M102, M103
S1	Elementary Statistics	M103
S2	Advanced Statistics	S1, M102
P1	Elementary Physics	M101
P2	Advanced Physics	P1, M102
M108	Advanced Calculus	M104
M109	Mathematical Physics	M108, P2
M110	Complex Variable	M108
M111	Real Variable	M110
	Finish	M109, M111, S2

Figure 15

time, each course takes one unit of time (a term). The project graph is shown in Figure 16. In the figure the early and late start and completion for each job, as well as the slack ($s = \ldots$) are marked. The minimum time to complete the project is six terms. The critical path, which in this case is unique, is shown as a darkened line. The critical courses (jobs) are seen to be M101, M102, M104, M108, M110, and M111. Delaying the taking of any critical course will delay the completion of the major. On the other hand, some courses have quite a bit of slack. Statistics 1 and 2 have three units of slack each. M103 has one term slack, but if it is delayed for that term, then both statistics

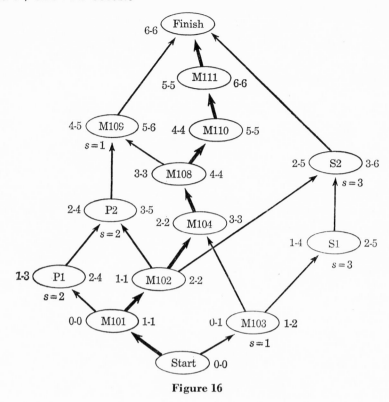

Figure 16

courses have one less unit of slack. Many other observations can be made from the figure.

Example 4. One of the important uses for critical path analysis is in the planning and monitoring of the development of new kinds of equipment. Figure 17 shows an example of such a plan for the development of a new piece of electronics equipment. It is assumed that the design involves some quite standard kinds of circuits that take little time, plus the development of some new kinds of circuits, and the design of the chassis and panel racks for the completed product. The times in weeks are given, as well as the early and late times, and the slack times for noncritical jobs. We see that the design and testing of the special circuits form the bottleneck in the project.

EXERCISES

1. Prove that reducing the time of a noncritical job does not reduce the target time.

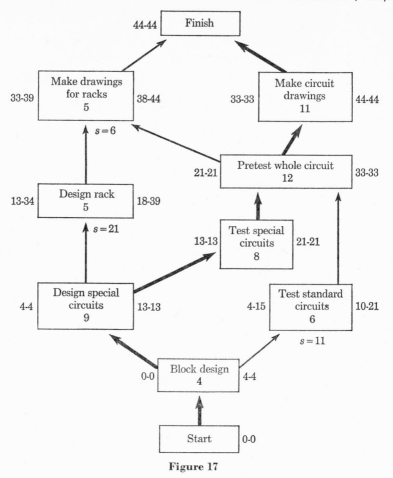

Figure 17

2. The *dual project* of a given project is the project carried out in reverse. That is, we make the successors of each job its predecessors in the dual project. Describe a simple method for obtaining the project graph of the dual project given the graph of the original project. How do the various times change?

3. In the section it was shown that every critical job has at least one critical immediate predecessor. Use the idea of the dual project to derive from this that every critical job has at least one critical immediate successor.

4. Winters, a house contractor, has listed the jobs needed to build a house. They are shown below together with their predecessors and their times. Draw the project graph. Compute the e.s.t., e.f.t., l.f.t., and e.f.t. for each job. Mark critical paths and show slacks.

Job	Description	Predecessors	Time (Days)
a	Start	None	0
b	Lay foundation	{a}	6
c	Wooden frame including rough roof	{b}	4
d	Brickwork	{b}	4
e	Basement drains and plumbing	{b}	1
f	Pour basement floor	{e}	2
g	Rough plumbing	{c, f}	3
h	Rough wiring	{c, f}	2
i	Heating and ventilating	{c, f}	4
j	Plaster board and plaster (drying)	{i, h, g}	10
k	Install finish flooring	{j}	3
l	Install kitchen fixtures	{j}	2
m	Install finish plumbing	{j}	2
n	Finish carpentry	{j}	3
o	Roofing and flashing	{d, c, f}	2
p	Gutters and downspouts	{o}	1
q	Storm drains for rain water	{p}	1
r	Sand and varnish flooring	{k, l, m, n}	2
s	Paint	{r}	3
t	Finish electrical work	{s}	2
u	Finish grading	{q}	2
v	Walks and landscaping	{u}	5
w	Finish	{v, t}	0

5. In Example 3 assume that the student delays the following courses by the amounts indicated, but elects all other courses as early as possible. By how much is the final completion time of his major delayed?
   (a) M103 one term.
   (b) M103 one term and S1 four terms.
   (c) M101 two terms and M108 one term.
   (d) P2 two terms and M109 one term.   [*Ans.* (a) 0; (b) 2; (c) 3; (d) 1.]

6. Draw a project graph for the task of cooking a meal in a kitchen with two stove burners and one oven, assuming that the menu will consist of: soup, roast, baked potato, vegetables, pie, and coffee. Assume reasonable times for each job. Find critical jobs and paths and total slack for each job.

7. Plan the following job: repair an automobile engine, installing new rings and pistons, grinding valves, replacing spark plugs, etc.

8. Which of the following projects are suitable for critical path analysis?
   (a) Mowing a lawn.
   (b) Writing a letter.
   (c) Moving out of a house.
   (d) Repairing a watch.
   (e) Servicing an airplane.
   (f) Building a bridge.
   (g) Getting dressed in the morning.

   9. The *free slack* of a job is defined to be the smallest of the early start times
   of the successors of a minus the early finish time of a. For instance, in
   Figure 14 job e has 0 free slack while job f has 1 free slack. Free slack
   measures the amount a job can be displaced assuming all other jobs are
   started as early as possible.
   (a) Find the free slacks of the noncritical jobs in Figure 16.
   (b) Find the free slacks of the noncritical jobs in Figure 17.
   [*Partial Ans.* In Figure 16, M109 has free slack of 1, and S2 has free slack
   of 3.]

   10. The *independent slack* of a job a is defined to be the minimum of the early
   start times of successors of a minus the maximum of the late finish times
   of predecessors of a minus the time for a, *providing* this quantity is nonnegative; otherwise the independent slack of a is defined to be zero. Independent slack measures the amount a job can be displaced regardless of
   all other jobs, providing only that the other jobs remain within their early
   and late times.
   (a) In Figure 13 show that job d has independent slack 1.
   (b) In Figure 14 show that jobs e and f each have independent slack of
   zero.
   (c) Find the independent slacks for noncritical jobs in Figure 16.
   (d) Find the independent slacks of noncritical jobs in Figure 17.

   11. Devise a project having at least one job that has different slack, free
   slack, and independent slacks.

   12. A group of authors laid out the following plans for writing a book jointly.
   The project is still not completed. Why?

Job	Description	Immediate Predecessors	Time (Weeks)
a	Start	none	0
b	Write Chapter 1	$\{a\}$	2
c	Write Chapter 2	$\{a\}$	1
d	Write Chapter 3	$\{b, c\}$	4
e	Write Chapter 4	$\{c\}$	2
f	Draw diagrams	$\{d, e, h\}$	1
g	Compile index	$\{f\}$	2
h	Write preface	$\{d, e, i\}$	1
i	Compile bibliography	$\{g\}$	2
j	Finish	$\{h, i\}$	0

SUGGESTED READING

Birkhoff, G., and S. MacLane, *A Survey of Modern Algebra*, Macmillan, New
York, 1953, Chapter XI.

Tarski, A., *Introduction to Logic*, Oxford, New York, 2d rev. ed., 1946, Chapter
IV.

Mathematical Association of America, Committee on Undergraduate Program, *Universal Mathematics*, Tulane Book Store, Tulane University, New Orleans, 1955, Part II, Chapter I.

Allendoerfer, C. B., and C. O. Oakley, *Principles of Mathematics*, McGraw-Hill, New York, 1955, Chapter V.

Johnstone, H. W., Jr., *Elementary Deductive Logic*, Crowell, New York, 1954, Part Three.

Williams, C. M., *Cumulative Voting for Directors*, Division of Research, Harvard Graduate School of Business Administration, Boston, 1951, Chapter III.

Levy, F. K., G. L. Thompson, and J. D. Wiest, "A Mathematical Development of Critical Path Scheduling," in *Industrial Scheduling*, edited by J. F. Muth and G. L. Thompson, Prentice-Hall, Englewood Cliffs, N.J., 1963, 387 pp.

III

Partitions and Counting

---

1. Partitions

The problem to be studied in this chapter can be most conveniently described in terms of partitions of a set. A *partition* of a set $\mathfrak{U}$ is a subdivision of the set into subsets that are disjoint and exhaustive, i.e., every element of $\mathfrak{U}$ must belong to one and only one of the subsets. The subsets A_i in the partition are called *cells*. Thus $[A_1, A_2, \ldots, A_r]$ is a partition of $\mathfrak{U}$ if two conditions are satisfied: (1) $A_i \cap A_j = \mathcal{E}$ if $i \neq j$ (the cells are disjoint) and (2) $A_1 \cup A_2 \cup \ldots \cup A_r = \mathfrak{U}$ (the cells are exhaustive).

Example 1. If $\mathfrak{U} = \{a, b, c, d, e\}$, then $[\{a, b\}, \{c, d, e\}]$ and $[\{b, c, e\}, \{a\}, \{d\}]$ and $[\{a\}, \{b\}, \{c\}, \{d\}, \{e\}]$ are three different partitions of $\mathfrak{U}$. The last is a partition into unit sets.

The process of going from a fine to a less fine analysis of a set of logical possibilities is actually carried out by means of a partition. For example, let us consider the logical possibilities for the first three games of the

84

World Series if the Yankees play the Dodgers. We can list the possibilities in terms of the winner of each game as

$$\{YYY, YYD, YDY, DYY, YDD, DYD, DDY, DDD\}.$$

We form a partition by putting all the possibilities with the same number of wins for the Yankees in a single cell,

$$[\{YYY\}, \{YYD, YDY, DYY\}, \{YDD, DYD, DDY\}, \{DDD\}].$$

Thus, if we wish the possibilities to be Yankees win three games, win two, win one, win zero, then we are considering a less detailed analysis obtained from the former analysis by identifying the possibilities in each cell of the partition.

If $[A_1, A_2, \ldots, A_r]$ and $[B_1, B_2, B_3, \ldots, B_s]$ are two partitions of the same set $\mathfrak{U}$, we can obtain a new partition by considering the collection of all subsets of $\mathfrak{U}$ of the form $A_i \cap B_j$ (see Exercise 7). This new partition is called the *cross-partition* of the original two partitions.

> **Example 2.** A common use of cross-partitions is in the problem of classification. For example, from the set $\mathfrak{U}$ of a salesman's visits over the last month we can form the partition $[S, \tilde{S}]$ where S is the set of all visits that culminated in a sale. We may also form the partition $[P, N]$ where P is the set of prospects who were called on previously and N is the set of new prospects. The cross-partition
>
> $$[P \cap S, \quad P \cap \tilde{S}, \quad N \cap S, \quad N \cap \tilde{S}]$$
>
> gives a complete classification according to the two separate classifications.

Many of the examples with which we shall deal in the future will relate to processes which take place in stages. It will be convenient to use partitions and cross-partitions to represent the stages of the process. The graphical representation of such a process is, of course, a tree. For example, suppose that the process is such that we learn in succession the truth values of a series of statements relative to a given situation. If $\mathfrak{U}$ is the set of logical possibilities for the situation, and p is a statement relative to $\mathfrak{U}$, then the knowledge of the truth value of p amounts to knowing which cell of the partition $[P, \tilde{P}]$ contains the actual possibility. Recall that P is the truth set of p, and $\tilde{P}$ is the truth set of $\sim p$. Suppose now we discover the truth value of a second statement q. This information can again be described by a partition, namely, $[Q, \tilde{Q}]$. The two statements together give us information which can be represented by the cross-partition of these two partitions,

$$[P \cap Q, \quad P \cap \tilde{Q}, \quad \tilde{P} \cap Q, \quad \tilde{P} \cap \tilde{Q}].$$

That is, if we know the truth values of p and q, we also know which of the cells of this cross-partition contain the particular logical possibility describing the given situation. Conversely, if we knew which cell contained the possibility, we would know the truth values for the statements p and q.

The information obtained by the additional knowledge of the truth value of a third statement r, having a truth set R, can be represented by the cross-partition of the three partitions $[P, \tilde{P}]$, $[Q, \tilde{Q}]$, $[R, \tilde{R}]$. This cross-partition is

$$[P \cap Q \cap R, \quad P \cap Q \cap \tilde{R}, \quad P \cap \tilde{Q} \cap R, \quad \tilde{P} \cap Q \cap R,$$
$$P \cap \tilde{Q} \cap \tilde{R}, \quad \tilde{P} \cap Q \cap \tilde{R}, \quad \tilde{P} \cap \tilde{Q} \cap R, \quad \tilde{P} \cap \tilde{Q} \cap \tilde{R}].$$

Notice that now we have the possibility narrowed down to being in one of $8 = 2^3$ possible cells. Similarly, if we knew the truth values of n statements, our partition would have 2^n cells.

If the set $\mathfrak{U}$ were to contain 2^{20} (approximately one million) logical possibilities, and if we were able to ask yes-no questions in such a way that the knowledge of the truth value of each question would cut the number of possibilities in half each time, then we could determine in 20 questions any given possibility in the set $\mathfrak{U}$. We could accomplish this kind of questioning, for example, if we had a list of all the possibilities and were allowed to ask "Is it in the first half?," and, if the answer is yes, then "Is it in the first one-fourth?," etc. In practice we ordinarily do not have such a list, and we can only approximate this procedure.

Example 3. "Key sort" cards are cards containing a series of punched holes along the upper edge. A card may contain information about an employee, an account, a part number, a stockholder, a sales order, etc. A set of cards is kept in a box, and each card is classified by assigning it to a cell of one or more partitions of the set. To make it easy to find all the members of a cell of a particular partition, or of a cross-partition, the following mechanical procedure is used. A subset of the set of holes along the upper edge of the card is assigned to each partition. The holes so assigned are called a "field." The cells of a partition can be distinguished by cutting slots through some of the holes in the field. A rod can be inserted through the set of cards at a particular hole location and then lifted. The cards that are slotted at that location will remain in the box and those that are not will be lifted out with the rod.

The number of hole locations assigned to a field depends on the number of cells in the partition that the field represents. We can think of each hole location as a bit, letting a slot represent a 0 and an unslotted hole a 1. If there are n hole locations in a field, they can be made to correspond to as many as 2^n cells, since with n bits we can represent the 2^n decimal integers 0 through $2^n - 1$. Thus a four-bit field can represent a 16-cell partition.

Suppose, for example, we have a card for each worker in a factory. The workers are classified by sex, job classification, and department number. A single bit can be arbitrarily assigned to indicate a worker's sex; for example, let 0 represent female, 1 represent male. If there are 13 job classifications, we need a four-bit field for them; we may assign 0001 for classification 1, up to

1101 for classification 13. Let there be 25 departments; then we need a five-bit field for them, assigning 00001 to department 1 up to 11001 for department 25.

Now suppose we want to find all the male workers in job classification 6 working in department 11. These will be identified by the binary number 1011001011, the first bit identifying sex, the next four bits the job, and the last five bits the department. We first partition the set by withdrawing those cards with unslotted holes in hole location 1. These are all the male workers in the factory. We withdraw from this subset all cards with unslotted holes in location 2; these correspond to workers in job classification 8 and higher, while those that are left represent job classifications 7 or lower. Of those which are left, we now withdraw those with unslotted holes in locations 3 and 4, and remove from this subset the cards with slotted holes in location 5. We now have the subset of male workers in job classification 6. The procedure is continued in this fashion to find the subset of *this* subset which contains workers in department 11.

Observe that the procedure works independently of the original order of the cards in the box.

Example 4. In a computer numbers are "stored" in numbered "memory addresses," one number to each address. Sometimes an entire table is stored in a computer by putting into successive memory addresses successive tabled values. Consider, for instance, the table in Figure 1, in which each value is

Memory Address	Tabled Value	Memory Address	Tabled Value
1	24	5	2000
2	100	6	2002
3	101	7	5179
4	197	8	5280

Figure 1

larger than its immediate predecessor. The set of instructions by which we can communicate with the computer permits us to ask, "What number is located in a particular memory address?" We cannot, however, directly ask the inverse questions, "In what memory address is a particular number located?" or "Between what two tabled values does a particular number fall?"

Suppose, for example, we would like to know between what two numbers in the table a nontabulated number such as 4096 lies. We can quickly scan the table by eye and see that it lies between the numbers in addresses 6 and 7. But what systematic procedure should be used to locate such a number? We first observe that in a table of ascending values a given number lies between the number in address a and the number in address $a + 1$ if it is larger than the number in a and smaller than the number in $a + 1$. Thus we could locate the position of the number 4096 by systematically scanning the memory addresses, starting with address 1, and asking whether the number in each address is larger than 4096. We would obtain a series of "no" answers until we reached address 7, and this would tell us that 4096 is between the numbers in addresses 6 and 7.

A procedure that requires fewer steps is systematically to partition the set of memory addresses. We first split the set in half, and ask whether 4096 is larger than the largest number in the first cell, i.e., 197, the number in address 4. The answer is yes, so we next consider the second cell as our universal set and partition it into two cells, the first consisting of the numbers in addresses 5 and 6, the second of the numbers in addresses 7 and 8. Once again, we ask whether the number 4096 is larger than the largest number in the first cell, i.e., 2002, the number in address 6. Since the answer is again yes, we again consider the second cell, i.e., the numbers in addresses 7 and 8, as our universal set, partition it into unit sets, and ask whether 4096 is larger than the number in the first cell, i.e., 5179. Since the answer is no, we now know that 4096 is larger than the number in address 6 but smaller than the number in address 7, and we have therefore found its place in the table.

Note that the second procedure required three questions while the first procedure took seven. The difference in the number of questions required is even more startling for longer lists. For instance, it is possible to locate a given number's position in a list of a million numbers by asking only 20 questions.

EXERCISES

1. If $\mathfrak{U}$ is the set of integers from 1 to 6, find the cross-partitions of the following pairs of partitions:
   (a) $[\{1, 2, 3\}, \{4, 5, 6\}]$ and $[\{1, 4\}, \{2, 3, 5, 6\}]$.
   (b) $[\{1, 2, 3, 4, 5\}, \{6\}]$ and $[\{1, 3, 5\}, \{2, 6\}, \{4\}]$.
   $\qquad\qquad\qquad\qquad$ [*Ans.* (a) $\{1\}, \{2, 3\}, \{4\}, \{5, 6\}$.]

2. A coin is thrown three times. List the possibilities according to which side turns up each time. Give the partition formed by putting in the same cell all those possibilities for which the same number of heads occur.

3. Let p and q be two statements with truth sets P and Q. What can be said about the cross-partition of $[P, \tilde{P}]$ and $[Q, \tilde{Q}]$ in the case that:
   (a) p implies q. $\qquad\qquad\qquad\qquad$ [*Ans.* $P \cap \tilde{Q} = \varepsilon$.]
   (b) p is equivalent to q.
   (c) p and q are inconsistent.

4. Consider the set of eight states consisting of Illinois, Colorado, Michigan, New York, Vermont, Texas, Alabama, and California.
   (a) Show that in three "yes" or "no" questions one can identify any one of the eight states.
   (b) Design a set of three "yes" or "no" questions which can be answered independently of each other and which will serve to identify any one of the states.

5. An unabridged dictionary contains about 600,000 words and 3000 pages. If a person chooses a word from such a dictionary, is it possible to identify this word by twenty "yes" or "no" questions? If so, describe the procedure that you would use and discuss the feasibility of the procedure.

[*Ans.* One solution is the following. Use 12 questions to locate the page, but then you may need 9 questions to locate the word.]

6. Mr. Jones has two parents, each of his parents had two parents, each of these had two parents, etc. Tracing a person's family tree back 40 generations (about 1000 years) gives Mr. Jones 2^{40} ancestors, which is more people than have been on the earth in the last 1000 years. What is wrong with this argument?

7. Let $[A_1, A_2, A_3]$ and $[B_1, B_2]$ be two partitions. Prove that the cross-partition of the two given partitions really is a partition, that is, it satisfies requirements (1) and (2) for partitions.

8. The cross-partition formed from the truth sets of n statements has 2^n cells. As seen in Chapter I, the truth table of a statement compounded from n statements has 2^n rows. What is the relationship between these two facts?

9. Let p and q be statements with truth sets P and Q. Form the partition

$$[P \cap Q, \quad P \cap \tilde{Q}, \quad \tilde{P} \cap Q, \quad \tilde{P} \cap \tilde{Q}].$$

State in each case below which of the cells must be empty in order to make the given statement a logically true statement.

(a) $p \to q$.

(b) $p \leftrightarrow q$.

(c) $p \lor \sim p$.

(d) p.

10. A partition $[A_1, A_2, \ldots, A_n]$ is said to be a *refinement* of the partition $[B_1, B_2, \ldots, B_m]$ if every A_j is a subset of some B_k. Show that a cross-partition of two partitions is a refinement of each of the partitions from which the cross-partition is formed.

11. Consider the partition of the people in the United States determined by classification according to states. The classification according to county determines a second partition. Show that this is a refinement of the first partition. Give a third partition which is different from each of these and is a refinement of both.

12. What can be said concerning the cross-partition of two partitions, one of which is a refinement of the other?

13. Given nine objects, of which it is known that eight have the same weight and one is heavier, show how, in two weighings with a pan balance, the heavy one can be identified.

14. Suppose that you are given thirteen objects, twelve of which are the same, but one is either heavier or lighter than the others. Show that, with three

weighings using a pan balance, it is possible to identify the odd object.
[A complete solution to this problem is given on page 59 of *Mathematical Snapshots*, 1960 edition, by H. Steinhaus.]

15. A subject can be completely classified by introducing several simple subdivisions and taking their cross-partition. Thus, courses in college may be partitioned according to subject, level of advancement, number of students, hours per week, interests, etc. For each of the following subjects, introduce five or more partitions. How many cells are there in the complete classification (cross-partition) in each case?

(a) United States corporations.

(b) A company's assets.

(c) Workers in a plant.

(d) Consumers of a product.

*2. Applications

Here we shall give four applications showing how partitions can be used to describe four different situations in mathematical terms. Examples like these will be more fully developed in later chapters.

Example 1. *A simple game.* Smith and Jones play the following game: Jones is to hold concealed in his hand either a $1 or a $2 bill. Smith is to guess which it is, and gets the bill if he guesses correctly. We shall consider in a later chapter the amount Smith should pay to play the game in order to make it fair, but at the moment we are interested only in describing the possibilities for the play of the game. The game develops in two stages. First Jones chooses a $1 or a $2 bill, and second Smith guesses either 1 or 2. We can represent the ways that these stages can be carried out by a tree with four branches shown in Figure 2. The four ways that the game can be played are represented by the four paths of the tree which we denote by a_1, a_2, a_3, a_4.

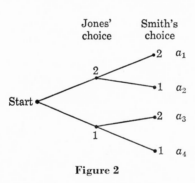

Figure 2

We can also represent the progress of the game by a sequence of three partitions,

Start	$[\{a_1, a_2, a_3, a_4\}]$
Jones' Choice	$[\{a_1, a_2\}, \{a_3, a_4\}]$
Smith's Choice	$[\{a_1\}, \{a_2\}, \{a_3\}, \{a_4\}]$.

Notice that we have associated a partition with each level of the tree. A cell of the partition associated with a particular level contains all paths going through one branching point at this level.

We can also use partitions to indicate the amount of control which each player has on the outcome. The control of Jones can be indicated by the partition $[\{a_1, a_2\}, \{a_3, a_4\}]$. That is, Jones can determine which of the two cells of this partition will contain the play of the game. Similarly, Smith can control the cell of the partition $[\{a_1, a_3\}, \{a_2, a_4\}]$ that will contain the play. The final partition is the cross-partition of these two partitions.

Example 2. *Consumer purchasing behavior.* Housewives on some consumer panels are asked to report over a period of years all of their purchases of some common grocery items, such as coffee, frozen orange juice, bread, soap, etc. Among the data collected for each such purchase are the date, size of each item in the purchase, number of units purchased, and brand name. Thus, for each housewife in the panel a complete sequential listing of purchases by brand of these items over a period of time can be obtained.

Suppose we are interested in housewives' patterns of purchasing Brand A of frozen orange juice. We can then partition the set $\mathfrak{U}$ of all panel members' frozen orange juice purchases by putting purchases of Brand A in one cell, and purchases of any other brand in the other cell. The resulting partition is $[A, \bar{A}]$, where A is the set of purchases of Brand A. We may then see whether the panel is *representative* of the marketing region from which it is drawn by seeing whether the number of elements of A, compared with the number of elements of $\mathfrak{U}$, is in roughly the same proportion as the *market share* of Brand A in the region in question.

For other purposes we may let $\mathfrak{U}$ be the set of all *housewives* in the panel, which can be partitioned into $[A, B, C, X]$, where the set A consists of those housewives who purchase more of Brand A than any other brand, and the sets B and C are defined analogously, while the set X consists of housewives who purchase more of some brand other than A, B, or C. We may also partition the set of all housewives into $[H, L]$, where H is the set whose family incomes exceed $6000 a year and L is the set for which family income is $6000 or less per year. We may then look at the cross-partition

$$[H \cap A, \ H \cap B, \ H \cap C, \ H \cap X, \ L \cap A, \ L \cap B, \ L \cap C, \ L \cap X].$$

From this partition we may find, for example, that $H \cap A$ is practically equal to A, while $L \cap B$ is practically equal to B, which would imply that Brand A is bought principally by high-income families and B by relatively low-income families.

Example 3. *Small-group behavior.* Some sociologists study the behavior of a small group of people which has been given the job of jointly solving a problem. An example of this is a committee trying to decide whether or not to market a new product. Before a decision is reached, there is a good deal of discussion and argument among the members of the group, and experiments have been designed to study the role of each person in such a situation. For these experiments, observers record the name of the person making each remark together with the name of the person to whom the remark is directed. Sometimes the nature of the remark is recorded and also the time when it is made.

☞   Consider an experiment of the above kind performed with four people, a, b, c, d. Let $\mathfrak{U}$ be the set of all remarks made. Form the partition $[S_a, S_b, S_c, S_d]$ of $\mathfrak{U}$ where S_a is the set of all remarks made by a, S_b the set of all remarks made by b, etc. Form also the partition $[T_a, T_b, T_c, T_d]$ of $\mathfrak{U}$ where T_a is the set of all remarks received by a, T_b is the set of all remarks received by b, etc. A sociologist is interested, for example, in the following question. Order the cells of the S partition according to the number of elements in each cell. If we do the same for the T partition, will the order be the same? That is, does the person who makes the most remarks also receive the most, and the one who makes the second most receive the second most, etc.?

A second problem is the following. Suppose that a partition $[U_1, U_2, U_3]$ of $\mathfrak{U}$ is made, where U_1 is the set of remarks made in a first interval of time, U_2 those made in a second interval of time, and U_3 those made in a third and final interval of time. Then if we form the cross-partition of this partition with each of the previous two partitions we will have a finer analysis which shows how the discussion changes in time. It might show, for instance, that the discussion had changed from a three-way to a two-way discussion. It could also happen that eventually one person had made many remarks and received few. The nature of the partitions will of course depend upon the particular group of subjects and the particular experiment.

Example 4. *Scaling techniques.* A scaling technique, which is sometimes used in marketing research, can be explained in terms of partitions. Before describing its use in marketing research, we shall first consider the method in relation to a simple test of a specialized ability of a set of respondents.

Let $\mathfrak{U}$ be a set of respondents to whom a two-question "test" is administered. We may then form the partition $[R_1, W_1]$, in which R_1 is the set who answered the first question right and W_1 is the set who were wrong on the first question. Similarly, we may form the partition $[R_2, W_2]$, where the subscript 2 refers to the second question. We then examine the cross-partition

$$[R_1 \cap R_2, \quad R_1 \cap W_2, \quad W_1 \cap R_2, \quad W_1 \cap W_2].$$

Clearly, members of the cell $R_1 \cap R_2$, who were right on both questions, deserve to be ranked in the highest group, members of $W_1 \cap W_2$ in the lowest group, and the rest in the middle. But should those who were right on one question and wrong on the other be ranked the same, regardless of which question was answered correctly?

One way to avoid the problem implied by this question is to design the test questions so that one of the two ambiguous cross-partitions is empty or nearly empty. If, for example, the test is designed to measure spelling ability, we might ask the respondent to spell the words "cat" and "cataclysm." Of those who correctly spelled only one word, we would expect that "cataclysm" would invariably be the misspelled word, i.e., the cell $W_1 \cap R_2$ would be empty. To put it in equivalent but slightly different language, the set of respondents who can spell both words correctly would be expected to be a proper subset of the set who can spell "cat" correctly, and identical with the set who can spell "cataclysm" correctly. The extension of this concept to "tests" involving more than two questions is obvious.

In marketing research this method is sometimes used to measure consumer attitudes. Suppose, for example, that a coffee marketer sends a questionnaire to a number of housewives and, among other things, would like to ascertain the intensity of each respondent's liking for coffee. One method for doing this is to ask a single question, in which the respondent scales himself. For example, the questionnaire might ask the housewife whether she likes coffee "very much," "fairly much," "not so much," or "not at all." The problem with this technique is that different respondents with roughly the same attitudes may rate themselves quite differently simply because of the different interpretations of the possible responses. To avoid this difficulty we may use a multi-question scaling device much like our "spelling test." In a two-question version, for instance, we might ask

1. Do you like coffee better than tea?

Yes_____ No_____

2. Apart from breakfast, do you drink hot coffee in hot weather?

Yes_____ No_____

Partitioning the set of respondents into $[Y, N]$ with appropriate subscripts, where Y is the set answering "yes" to a question and N is the set answering "no," we may find empirically that one of the two cells $Y_1 \cap N_2$ or $N_1 \cap Y_2$, say $N_1 \cap Y_2$, is virtually empty, in which case the two questions are considered good determinants of attitude towards coffee: the respondents are ranked from high to low according to whether they belong to cell

$$Y_1 \cap Y_2, \quad Y_1 \cap N_2, \quad \text{or} \quad N_1 \cap N_2.$$

EXERCISES

1. Jones has two pennies and Smith has one. They agree to match pennies three times or until one of them has no pennies, whichever happens first. Draw a tree to represent the possible plays for the game. Show the progress of the game by a sequence of partitions. [*Ans.* There are four paths.]

2. In Example 2, what information is obtained from the cross-partition of the partitions $[A, \tilde{A}]$ and $[H, L]$?

3. In Example 1 of Section 6, Chapter I, partition the set $\mathfrak{U}_i$ of possible acts in the ith month into $[H_i, B_i, S_i]$, where H_i is the set of acts labeled "Hold" in the ith month, and similarly B and S stand for "Buy" and "Sell." Looking at the set $\mathfrak{U} = \mathfrak{U}_i \cap \mathfrak{U}_{i+1}$ partitioned in this manner, what can we say about the cells $B_i \cap B_{i+1}$ and $S_i \cap S_{i+1}$? About the cell $H_i \cap H_{i+1}$?

4. In Exercise 3, let the set $\mathfrak{U}_i$ of possible acts in the ith month be partitioned into $[E_i, F_i]$, where E_i is the set of acts that leave the warehouse empty at the *end* of the ith month, and F_i is the set that leave it full. What can we say about the cells $F_i \cap S_i$ and $E_i \cap B_i$ of the cross-partition of the partitions $[H_i, B_i, S_i]$ and $[E_i, F_i]$?

5. In Exercises 3 and 4, suppose $E_{i+1} \cap H_{i+1} = \varepsilon$. What can we say about the cells of the partition $[E_i, F_i]$?

6. In Example 3, what information can be obtained from the cross-partition of $[S_a, S_b, S_c, S_d]$ and $[T_a, T_b, T_c, T_d]$?

7. Suppose that in Example 3, a partition $[V, \tilde{V}]$ of $\mathfrak{u}$ is made, where V is the set of all remarks that were made in the form of a question. What information can be obtained from the cross-partition of $[V, \tilde{V}]$ and $[S_a, S_b, S_c, S_d]$? From the cross-partition of $[V, \tilde{V}]$ and $[U_1, U_2, U_3]$?

8. In Example 2, let the ith purchase of frozen orange juice by a housewife be partitioned according to whether it was or was not Brand A, that is, according to $[A_i, \tilde{A}_i]$. What information is obtained from the cross-partition of the partitions

$$[A_i, \tilde{A}_i] \quad \text{and} \quad [A_{i+1}, \tilde{A}_{i+1}]?$$

9. Suppose that, in Example 2, the following assumptions are made concerning the behavior of all housewives in purchasing frozen orange juice. For each housewife, on her next purchase after a purchase of Brand A she purchases Brand A again 60% of the time, and some other brand 40% of the time. Following a purchase of some brand other than A, she buys Brand A 20% of the time and some other brand 80% of the time.
   (a) If the last purchase of half of the housewives was Brand A, what fraction should we predict will buy Brand A on the next purchase? Two purchases from now? Three purchases from now?
   (b) If the last purchase of one-third of the housewives was Brand A, what fraction should we predict will buy Brand A on the next purchase? Two purchases from now? One hundred purchases from now?

10. In a three-word spelling test (see Example 4), the set of respondents is partitioned into $[R_i, W_i]$ according to whether the ith word ($i = 1, 2, 3$) was spelled correctly or not. If the first word is the hardest and the third is the easiest to spell, which cells of the cross-partition of $[R_1, W_1]$, $[R_2, W_2]$, and $[R_3, W_3]$ must be empty in order that the test provide an unambiguous method of scaling the respondents?

11. Have ten of your classmates answer the two questions designed to measure attitude towards coffee in Example 4. Are you able to scale your classmates' attitudes?

12. Try to design a three-question scale of attitude towards coffee, and test it on ten classmates. You may use one or both of the questions of Example 4 if you like, or design new questions.

13. Design and test on ten classmates two-question attitude scales to measure attitude towards:
   (a) airplane travel.
   (b) Japanese cameras.
   (c) compact automobiles.
   (d) cash dividend rates on common stocks.

3. *The number of elements in a set*

The remainder of this chapter will be devoted to certain counting problems. For any set X we shall denote by $\mathbf{n}(X)$ the number of elements in the set.

Suppose we know the number of elements in certain given sets and wish to know the number in other sets related to these by the operations of unions, intersections, and complementation. As an example, consider the following problem.

Suppose that we are told that 10 men are on the board of directors of the ABC Corporation, and 15 are on the board of the XYZ Corporation. Can we then tell how many are on the board either of ABC or XYZ? The answer is "no," since clearly we would also need to know how many are members of both boards. If we know that no man is a member of both boards, i.e., if we know that the two sets of directors are disjoint, then the answer would be the sum of the two numbers, or 25 directors.

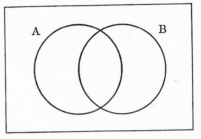

Figure 3

In general, if we are given disjoint sets A and B, then it is true that $\mathbf{n}(A \cup B) = \mathbf{n}(A) + \mathbf{n}(B)$. Suppose now that A and B are not disjoint as shown in Figure 3. We can divide the set A into disjoint sets $A \cap \tilde{B}$ and $A \cap B$. Similarly we can divide B into the disjoint sets $\tilde{A} \cap B$ and $A \cap B$. Thus,

$$\mathbf{n}(A) = \mathbf{n}(A \cap \tilde{B}) + \mathbf{n}(A \cap B)$$
$$\mathbf{n}(B) = \mathbf{n}(\tilde{A} \cap B) + \mathbf{n}(A \cap B).$$

Adding these two equations, we obtain

$$\mathbf{n}(A) + \mathbf{n}(B) = \mathbf{n}(A \cap \tilde{B}) + \mathbf{n}(\tilde{A} \cap B) + 2\mathbf{n}(A \cap B).$$

Since the sets $A \cap \tilde{B}$, $\tilde{A} \cap B$, and $A \cap B$ are disjoint sets whose union is $A \cup B$, we obtain the formula

$$\mathbf{n}(A \cup B) = \mathbf{n}(A) + \mathbf{n}(B) - \mathbf{n}(A \cap B)$$

which is valid for any two sets A and B.

Example 1. Let p and q be statements relative to a set $\mathfrak{U}$ of logical possibilities. Denote by P and Q the truth sets of these statements. The truth set of $p \vee q$ is $P \cup Q$ and the truth set of $p \wedge q$ is $P \cap Q$. Thus the above formula enables us to find the number of cases where $p \vee q$ is true if we know the number of cases for which p, q, and $p \wedge q$ are true.

Example 2. *More than two sets.* It is possible to derive formulas for the number of elements in a set which is the union of more than two sets (see Exercise 8), but usually it is easier to work with Venn diagrams. For example,

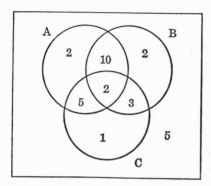

Figure 4

suppose that the following statistics are reported about a group of 30 corporation directors:

19 are directors of Company A.
17 are directors of Company B.
11 are directors of Company C.
12 are directors of A and B.
7   are directors of A and C.
5   are directors of B and C.
2   are directors of A, B, and C.

We draw the Venn diagram in Figure 4 and fill in the numbers for the number of elements in each subset, working from the bottom of our list to the top. That is, since 2 men are directors of all three companies, and 5 are directors of B and C, then 3 are directors of B and C but not A, etc. Once the diagram is completed we can read off the number which are directors of any combination of the companies. For example, the number which are directors of C but not A is $3 + 1 = 4$.

Example 3. *Implications of test information.* Consider once again Example 2 of Section 6, Chapter I, but let us restrict our attention to those cases in which a test in the form of a seismographic recording was taken but in which, regardless of the outcome of the test, the decision was made to drill. We may then partition the set $\mathfrak{U}$ of holes drilled under these conditions into $[S, \tilde{S}]$, where S is the set for which the test indicated subsurface structure; we may also partition the set of holes drilled into $[O, D]$, where O is the set of holes yielding oil, and D is the set of dry holes. We may then look at the cross-partition

$$[S \cap O, S \cap D, \tilde{S} \cap O, \tilde{S} \cap D]$$

of these partitions.

Suppose that a study has shown that the fraction of holes for which the test revealed structure is greater among holes with oil than among dry holes. It is then asserted that

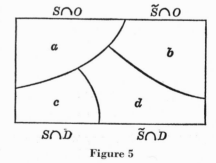

Figure 5

information about structure is relevant to the finding of oil, i.e., that the fraction of holes yielding oil is greater among holes revealing structure than among the other holes.

Let $a = \mathbf{n}(S \cap O)$, $b = \mathbf{n}(\tilde{S} \cap O)$, $c = \mathbf{n}(S \cap D)$, $d = \mathbf{n}(\tilde{S} \cap D)$, as indicated in Figure 5. The fractions in which we are interested are

$$p_1 = \frac{a}{a+b}, \quad p_2 = \frac{c}{c+d}, \quad p_3 = \frac{a}{a+c}, \quad p_4 = \frac{b}{b+d},$$

where p_1 is the fraction among holes that yield oil for which the test revealed structure, p_2 the fraction among dry holes for which the test revealed structure, p_3 the fraction of holes yielding oil among those for which the test revealed structure, and p_4 is the fraction of holes yielding oil among those for which the test indicated no subsurface structure.

The argument above states that if $p_1 > p_2$, then $p_3 > p_4$. The hypothesis,

$$\frac{a}{a+b} > \frac{c}{c+d},$$

is true if and only if $ac + ad > ac + bc$, that is, if and only if $ad > bc$. The conclusion,

$$\frac{a}{a+c} > \frac{b}{b+d},$$

is true if and only if $ab + ad > ab + bc$, that is, if and only if $ad > bc$. Thus the two statements $p_1 > p_2$ and $p_3 > p_4$ are in fact equivalent statements, so that the argument is valid.

EXERCISES

1. In Example 2 find:
   (a) The number of men that are directors of Company A but not C.
   (b) The number that are directors of exactly two of the three companies.
   (c) The number that are directors of one or none of the companies.

   [*Ans.* (b) 18.]

2. A radio station broadcasts identical commercial advertisements at 10 A.M. and at 11 A.M. A sample survey indicates that there are 10,700 listeners at 10 A.M. and 12,400 at 11 A.M. How many different people hear the commercial in the morning if:
   (a) No one listens to the station for as long as one hour?
   (b) 2300 of the people who were listening at 10 A.M. are also listening at 11 A.M.?

3. If the truth set of a statement p has 10 elements, and the truth set of a statement q has 20 elements, find the number of elements in the truth set of $p \vee q$ if:
   (a) p and q are inconsistent.
   (b) p and q are consistent and there are 2 elements in the truth set of $p \wedge q$.

   [*Ans.* (b) 28.]

4. If p is a statement that is true in ten cases, and q is a statement that is true in five cases, find the number of cases that both p and q are true if $p \lor q$ is true in ten cases. What relation holds between p and q?

5. Assume that a particular oil wildcatter finds that of holes drilled without regard to the outcome of seismological recordings, 30% produce oil. Suppose that half of the holes in which the test reveals subsurface structure are dry and five-sixths of those in which the test reveals no subsurface structure are dry. Find the fraction of holes in which the test reveals structure and which produce oil, and the fraction in which the test reveals no structure but which produce oil.

6. In a survey of anticipated consumer expenditures, 35% of all families interviewed said they expected to buy a new car within a year. In a follow-up series of interviews, 80% of those who actually did buy cars within the year had previously said they would do so, while 20% of those who did not buy cars had previously indicated that they expected to buy.
   (a) What fraction of the group actually bought cars?
   (b) Of the total group, what fraction acted differently from its expectations?   [*Ans.* 20%.]
   (c) Comment on the effectiveness of the interviews on anticipated expenditures as predictors of actual expenditures.

7. Of 10,000 parts screened twice by an automatic inspection machine, 8100 were classified as good both times, 100 as defective both times, and 900 were classified as good the first time and defective the second. Comment on the effectiveness of the inspection machine.

8. Let A, B, and C be any three subsets of a universal set $\mathfrak{U}$. Draw a Venn diagram and show that

$$\mathbf{n}(A \cup B \cup C) = \mathbf{n}(A) + \mathbf{n}(B) + \mathbf{n}(C) - \mathbf{n}(A \cap B)$$
$$- \mathbf{n}(B \cap C) - \mathbf{n}(A \cap C) + \mathbf{n}(A \cap B \cap C).$$

9. If p and q are equivalent statements and $\mathbf{n}(P) = 10$, what is $\mathbf{n}(P \cup Q)$?

10. If p implies q, prove that $\mathbf{n}(P \cup \tilde{Q}) = \mathbf{n}(P) + \mathbf{n}(\tilde{Q})$.

11. On a transcontinental airliner, there are 9 boys, 5 American children, 9 men, 7 foreign boys, 14 Americans, 6 American males, and 7 foreign females. What is the number of people on the plane?   [*Ans.* 33.]

4. Permutations

We wish to consider here the number of ways in which a group of n different objects can be arranged. An arrangment of n different objects *in a given order* is called a *permutation* of the n objects. We consider first the case of three objects, a, b, and c. We can exhibit all possible permutations of these three objects as paths of a tree, as shown in Figure 6. Each path exhibits a possible permutation, and there are six such paths. We could also list these permutations as follows:

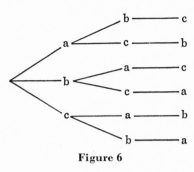

Figure 6

abc,	bca,
acb,	cab,
bac,	cba.

If we were to construct a similar tree for n objects, we would find that the number of paths could be found by multiplying together the numbers n, $n - 1$, $n - 2$, continuing down to the number 1. The number obtained in this way occurs so often that we give it a symbol, namely $n!$, which is read "n factorial." Thus, for example,

$$3! = 3 \cdot 2 \cdot 1 = 6, \qquad 4! = 4 \cdot 3 \cdot 2 \cdot 1 = 24, \qquad \text{etc.}$$

For reasons which will be clear later, we define $0! = 1$. Thus we can say *there are $n!$ different permutations of n distinct objects.*

Example 1. Seven different machining operations are to be performed on a part, but they may be performed in any sequence. We may then consider $7! = 5040$ different orders in which the operations may be performed.

Example 2. Ten workers are to be assigned to 10 different jobs. In how many ways can the assignments be made? The first worker may be assigned in 10 possible ways, the second in any of the 9 remaining ways, the third in 8, and so forth: there are $10! = 3,628,800$ possible ways of assigning the workers to the jobs.

Example 3. A company has n directors. In how many ways can they be seated around a circular table at a board meeting if two arrangements are considered different only if at least one person has a different person sitting on his right in the two arrangements. To solve the problem, consider one director in a fixed position. There are $(n - 1)!$ ways in which the other people may be seated. We have now counted all the arrangements we wish to consider different. Thus there are also $(n - 1)!$ possible seating arrangements.

A GENERAL PRINCIPLE. There are many counting problems for which it is not possible to give a simple formula for the number of possible cases. In many of these the only way to find the number of cases is to draw a tree and count them (see Exercise 4). In some problems, the following general principle is useful.

If one thing can be done in exactly r different ways, for each of these a second thing can be done in exactly s different ways, for each of the first two, a third can be done in exactly t ways, etc., then the sequence of things can be done in r·s·t . . . ways.

The validity of the above general principle can be established by thinking of a tree representing all the ways in which the sequence of things can be done. There would be r branches from the starting position. From the ends of each of these r branches there would be s new branches, and from each of these t new branches, etc. The number of paths through the tree would be given by the product $r·s·t$. . . .

Example 4. The number of permutations of n distinct objects is a special case of this principle. If we were to list all the possible permutations, there would be n possibilities for the first, for each of these $n-1$ for the second, etc., until we came to the last object, and for which there is only one possibility. Thus there are $n(n-1) \ldots 1 = n!$ possibilities in all.

Example 5. An automobile manufacturer produces 4 different models; models A and B can come in any of four body styles—sedan, hardtop, convertible, and station wagon—while models C and D come only as sedans or hardtops. Each car can come in one of 9 colors. Thus models A and B each have $4·9 = 36$ distinguishable types, while C and D have $2·9 = 18$ types, so that there are in all

$$2·36 + 2·18 = 108$$

different car types produced by the manufacturer.

Example 6. Suppose there are n applicants for a certain job. Three interviewers are asked independently to rank the applicants according to their suitability for the job. It is decided that an applicant will be hired if he is ranked first by at least two of the three interviewers. What fraction of the possible reports would lead to the acceptance of some candidate? We shall solve this problem by finding the fraction of the reports which do not lead to an acceptance and subtract this answer from 1. Frequently an indirect attack of this kind on a problem is easier than the direct approach. The total number of reports possible is $(n!)^3$ since each interviewer can rank the men in $n!$ different ways. If a particular report does not lead to the acceptance of a candidate, it must be true that each interviewer has put a different man in first place. This can be done in $n(n-1)(n-2)$ different ways by our general principle. For each possible first choice, there are $[(n-1)!]^3$ ways in which the remaining men can be ranked by the interviewers. Thus the number of reports which do not lead to acceptance is

$$n(n-1)(n-2)[(n-1)!]^3.$$

Dividing this number by $(n!)^3$ we obtain

$$\frac{(n-1)(n-2)}{n^2}$$

as the fraction of reports which fail to accept a candidate. The fraction which leads to acceptance is found by subtracting this fraction from 1 which gives

$$\frac{3n - 2}{n^2}.$$

For the case of three applicants, we see that $\frac{7}{9}$ of the possibilities lead to acceptance. Here the procedure might be criticized on the grounds that even if the interviewers are completely ineffective and are essentially guessing, there is a good chance that a candidate will be accepted on the basis of the reports. For n equal to ten, the fraction of acceptances is only .28, so that it is possible to attach more significance to the interviewers' ratings, if they reach a decision.

EXERCISES

1. A salesman is going to call on five customers. In how many different sequences can he do this if he
   (a) calls on all five in one day?
   (b) calls on three one day and two the next? [*Ans.* 120; 120.]

2. A machine shop has two milling machines, four lathes, seven drill presses, and three grinders. In how many ways can a part be routed that must first be ground, then milled, then turned on a lathe, and then drilled? In how many ways can it be routed if these four operations can be performed in any order?

3. Show the possible arrangements of machines A, B, C, and D in a circle. How many are there?

4. How many possible ways are there of seating six people, A, B, C, D, E, and F, at a circular table if
   (a) A must always have B on his right? [*Ans.* 24.]
   (b) A must always have either B or C on his right? [*Ans.* 48.]
   (c) A must always have either B or C on his right, and B either C or D? [*Ans.* 18.]

5. In seating n people around a circular table, suppose we distinguish between two arrangements only if at least one person has at least one different person sitting next to him in the two arrangements. That is, we do not regard two arrangements as different simply because the right-hand and left-hand neighbors of a person have interchanged places. Now how many distinguishable arrangements are there?

6. In how many ways can six people be assigned to offices if
   (a) there are six offices, and one person is assigned to each office?
   (b) there are three offices, and two people are assigned to each?
   (c) there are four offices, two accommodating two people and two one person each?

7. A company has six officers and six directors; two of the directors are officers. List the possible memberships of a committee of four men who are either officers or directors in terms of the number of members who are (a) just officers, (b) just directors, and (c) both officers and directors.

8. In Exercise 7, how many ways are there of obtaining a committee of four consisting of
   (a) two who are just officers, one who is just a director, and one who is an officer and a director? [*Ans.* 48.]
   (b) two who are just officers and two who are officers and directors? [*Ans.* 6.]
   (c) two who are just officers and two who are just directors? [*Ans.* 36.]

9. In Exercise 7, suppose a committee of four is to consist of at least two officers and at least two directors, where a man who is both an officer and a director satisfies both quotas. In how many ways can such a committee be formed?

10. Modify Example 6 so that, to be accepted, an applicant must be first in two of the interviewer's ratings and must be either first or second in the third interviewer's rating. What fraction of the possible reports lead to acceptance in the case of three applicants? In the case of n? [*Ans.* $\frac{4}{9}$; $4/n^2$.]

11. Find the number of arrangements of the five symbols that can be distinguished. (The same letters with different subscripts indicate distinguishable objects.)
   (a) A_1, A_2, B_1, B_2, B_3. [*Ans.* 120.]
   (b) A, A, B_1, B_2, B_3. [*Ans.* 60.]
   (c) A, A, B, B, B. [*Ans.* 10.]

12. Show that the number of distinguishable arrangements possible for n objects, n_1 of type 1, n_2 of type 2, etc., for r different types is

$$\frac{n!}{n_1!n_2!\ldots n_r!}.$$

5. Counting partitions

Up to now we have not had occasion to consider the partitions $[(1, 2), (3, 4)]$ and $[(3, 4), (1, 2)]$ of the integers from 1 to 4 as being different partitions. Here it will be convenient to do so, and to indicate this distinction we shall use the term ordered partition. An *ordered partition with r cells* is a partition with r cells (some of which may be empty), with a particular order specified for the cells.

We are interested in counting the number of possible ordered partitions with r cells that can be formed from a set of n objects having a prescribed number of elements in each cell. We consider first a special case to illustrate the general procedure.

Suppose that we have eight customers, A, B, C, D, E, F, G, and H, and we wish to assign these to three salesmen, three to Salesman 1, three to Salesman 2, and two to Salesman 3. In how many different ways can the assignment be made? One way to assign the customers is to put them in some arbitrary sequence, assigning the first three to Salesman 1, the next three to Salesman 2, and the last two to Salesman 3. There are 8! ways in which the customers can be ordered, but not all of these lead to different assignments. We can represent the assignment corresponding to a particular order as follows,

$$|BCA|DFE|HG|.$$

In this case, B, C, and A are assigned to Salesman 1, D, F, and E to Salesman 2, and H and G to Salesman 3. Notice that orders which simply change the sequence for a particular salesman lead to the same assignment. The number of different orders which lead to the same assignment as the one above is the number of arrangements which differ from the given one only in that the sequence for a particular salesman is different. There are $3!\cdot3!\cdot2!$ such orders, since we can arrange the three customers of Salesman 1 in 3! different ways, for each of these, the customers of Salesman 2 in 3! different ways, and for each of these, the customers of Salesman 3 in 2! ways. Thus we can divide the 8! different sequences into groups of $3!\cdot3!\cdot2!$ different orders such that all the sequences in a single group lead to the same assignment of customers. Since there are $3!\cdot3!\cdot2!$ elements in each group and 8! elements altogether, there are $8!/(3!3!2!)$ groups, or this many different assignments of customers.

The same argument could be carried out for r salesmen and n customers with n_1 assigned to the first salesman, n_2 assigned to the second, etc. This would lead to the following result. Let $n_1, n_2, \ldots, n_r$ be nonnegative integers with

$$n_1 + n_2 + \ldots + n_r = n.$$

Then,

The number of ordered partitions with r cells $[A_1, A_2, A_3, \ldots, A_r]$ of a set of n elements with n_1 in the first cell, n_2 in the second, etc. is

$$\frac{n!}{n_1!n_2!\ldots n_r!}.$$

We shall denote this number by the symbol

$$\binom{n}{n_1, n_2, \ldots, n_r}.$$

The special case of two cells is particularly important. Here the problem can be stated equivalently as the problem of finding the number of subsets with r elements that can be chosen from a set of n elements. This is true because any choice defines a partition $[A, \tilde{A}]$, where A is the set of elements chosen and $\tilde{A}$ is the set of remaining elements. The number of such partitions is $\dfrac{n!}{r!(n-r)!}$ and hence this is also the number of subsets with r elements. Our notation $\begin{pmatrix} n \\ r, n-r \end{pmatrix}$ for this case is shortened to $\begin{pmatrix} n \\ r \end{pmatrix}$. These numbers are known as *binomial coefficients*.

Notice that $\begin{pmatrix} n \\ n-r \end{pmatrix}$ is the number of subsets with $n-r$ elements which can be chosen from n, which is the number of partitions of the form $[\tilde{A}, A]$ above. Clearly, this is the same as the number of $[A, \tilde{A}]$ partitions. Hence

$$\binom{n}{r} = \binom{n}{n-r}.$$

Example 1. A company buys a certain electronic component from three vendors. In how many sequences can it place six orders, two with A, three with B, and one with C? From each possible sequence, we form a partition with three cells of the six purchases. In the first cell we put the purchases from A, in the second those from B, and in the third those from C. There are $\begin{pmatrix} 6 \\ 2, 3, 1 \end{pmatrix} = 60$ such partitions, and hence 60 sequences in which two orders can be placed with A, three with B, and one with C.

Example 2. On July 14, 1961, 1257 different stock issues were traded on the New York Stock Exchange. Of these, 576 advanced, 429 declined, and 252 closed unchanged from the previous day. This determines a partition of the 1257 stocks into three cells with 576, 429, and 252 elements. Thus there are $\dfrac{1257!}{576!429!252!}$ different ways in which this particular result could come about. This number is approximately equal to $2 \cdot 10^{568}$.

Example 3. The following example will be important in probability theory, which we take up in the next chapter. If a coin is thrown six times, there are 2^6 possibilities for the outcome of the six throws, since each throw can result in either a head or a tail. How many of these possibilities result in four heads and two tails? Each sequence of six heads and tails determines a two-cell partition of the numbers from one to six as follows: in the first cell put the numbers corresponding to throws which resulted in a head, and in the second put the numbers corresponding to throws which resulted in tails. We require that the first cell should contain four elements and the second two elements. Hence the number of the 2^6 possibilities which lead to four heads and two tails is the number of two-cell partitions of six elements which have four elements in the first cell and two in the second cell. The answer is $\begin{pmatrix} 6 \\ 4 \end{pmatrix} = 15$.

For n throws of a coin, a similar analysis shows that there are $\binom{n}{r}$ different sequences of H's and T's of length n which have exactly r heads and $n - r$ tails.

EXERCISES

1. Compute the following numbers.

(a) $\binom{7}{5}$ [*Ans.* 21.]   (e) $\binom{5}{0}$

(b) $\binom{3}{2}$ (f) $\binom{5}{1, 2, 2}$

(c) $\binom{7}{2}$ (g) $\binom{4}{2, 0, 2}$ [*Ans.* 6.]

(d) $\binom{250}{249}$ [*Ans.* 250.]   (h) $\binom{2}{1, 1, 1}$

2. Give an interpretation for $\binom{n}{0}$ and also for $\binom{n}{n}$. Can you now give a reason for making $0! = 1$?

3. How many ways can nine accounts be assigned to three different salesmen so that each one gets three accounts? How many ways if one particular pair of accounts cannot be assigned to the same salesman?
[*Ans.* 1680; 1260.]

4. A group of seven workers is to be assigned to seven of ten available jobs. If all of the workers are assigned jobs, in how many ways can the jobs be assigned to the workers? How many possibilities are there for the un-assigned jobs, if three of the jobs are sure to be assigned?

5. Customers of the ABC Company may have their orders delivered from one of three field warehouses. If fifteen customers place orders,
   (a) How many possibilities are there for assigning the warehouses from which the orders are delivered?   [*Ans.* 3^{15}.]
   (b) How many of these possibilities would result in the assignment of the same number of orders from each warehouse?   [*Ans.* 756,756.]

6. A brewing company contracts with a television station to show three spot commercials a week for 35 weeks. The commercials consist of a series of cartoons. It is decided that in no two weeks will exactly the same three cartoons be shown. What is the minimum number of cartoons that will accomplish this? What is the minimum number if it is determined never to show the same commercial twice?

7. In how many ways can a machine produce ten pieces, half of which are good and half defective? In how many ways if no two consecutive pieces are both good or both defective?

8. From a lot containing six pieces, three good and three defective, a sample of three pieces is drawn. If we distinguish each piece, find the number of possible samples that can be formed,

(a) with no restrictions.   [*Ans.* 20.]
(b) with three good pieces and no defectives.   [*Ans.* 1.]
(c) with two good pieces and one defective.   [*Ans.* 9.]
(d) with one good piece and two defectives.   [*Ans.* 9.]
(e) with no good pieces and three defectives.   [*Ans.* 1.]

What is the relation between your answer in part (a) and the answers to the remaining four parts?

9. Exercise 8 suggests that the following should be true:

$$\binom{2n}{n} = \binom{n}{0}\binom{n}{n} + \binom{n}{1}\binom{n}{n-1} + \binom{n}{2}\binom{n}{n-2} + \ldots + \binom{n}{n}\binom{n}{0}$$
$$= \binom{n}{0}^2 + \binom{n}{1}^2 + \ldots + \binom{n}{n}^2.$$

Show that it is true.

10. Show that

$$\binom{a}{b} = \frac{a \cdot (a-1) \cdot (a-2) \cdot \ldots \cdot (a-b+2) \cdot (a-b+1)}{b \cdot (b-1) \cdot (b-2) \cdot \ldots \cdot 2 \cdot 1}$$

where there are exactly b terms in both the numerator and the denominator.

6. *Two-cell partitions of two-valued sets*

In this section we shall discuss a particular partitioning problem which is especially applicable to the theory of sampling finite two-valued populations, which will be discussed in Chapter IV. We shall restrict our discussion to counting the number of partitions of a certain kind.

We shall consider two-valued sets, that is, sets $\mathcal{U}$ which can be partitioned into exactly two cells $[A, \tilde{A}]$. For instance, let $\mathcal{U}$ be a lot of 1000 pieces partitioned into $[G, D]$, where G is the subset of good pieces and D the subset of defectives. Or let $\mathcal{U}$ be the set of residents of a city partitioned into $[T, \tilde{T}]$, where T is the subset of residents who have a television receiver in their home. Or let $\mathcal{U}$ be the set of employees of a company, partitioned into $[U, \tilde{U}]$, where U is the subset of employees who are union members.

Suppose now that we form a new two-celled partition $[S, \tilde{S}]$ of $\mathcal{U}$. For example, if $\mathcal{U}$ is a lot of 1000 pieces, it may be partitioned into a subset which is inspected and a subset which is not inspected, the inspected subset commonly being called a "sample." Similarly, if $\mathcal{U}$ is the set of residents of a city, we may form a partition according to whether or not a particular resident is sent a questionnaire inquiring about access to a television receiver; the subset which receives the questionnaire is again commonly called a "sample." If the set $\mathcal{U}$ consists of employees of a company, we may form a partition according to whether a particular employee is or is not a member of a certain committee of employees.

The problem we wish to consider in this section is the following. Given a set $\mathcal{U}$ containing N elements partitioned into $[A, \tilde{A}]$, where A contains R elements, in how many ways can we form the partition $[S, \tilde{S}]$ of $\mathcal{U}$ where S contains n elements, subject to the condition that $A \cap S$ contains r elements? These relations are more readily seen if we look at the "2 $\times$ 2 table" shown as Figure 7. The letters in the body of the table indicate the

	S	$\tilde{S}$	
A	r	$R - r$	R
$\tilde{A}$	$n - r$	$N - R - n + r$	$N - R$
	n	$N - n$	N

Figure 7

number of elements in each of the cells of the cross-partition, while the letters in the margins indicate the number of elements in the cells of the partitions. Since

$$\mathbf{n}(A \cap S) + \mathbf{n}(A \cap \tilde{S}) = \mathbf{n}(A), \quad \mathbf{n}(A \cap S) + \mathbf{n}(\tilde{A} \cap S) = \mathbf{n}(S), \quad \text{etc.}$$

the sum of the numbers in a row must equal the number in the margin of that row, and similarly the sum of the numbers in a column must equal the number in the margin of that column. Hence, given the column totals and row totals and the fact that $\mathbf{n}(A \cap S) = r$, we can easily obtain the number of elements in the other cells of the cross-partition as shown. From the facts that all of the entries in the body of the table and in the margins must be integers greater than or equal to 0, we obtain the following restrictions:

(1) $0 \leq r \leq n \leq N, \qquad 0 \leq r \leq R \leq N, \qquad 0 \leq R - r \leq N - n \leq N.$

Example. Suppose the set $\mathcal{U}$ is a lot containing six pieces (see Exercise 8, Section 5), of which three are good and three defective. We would like to know the number of ways we can draw a sample of three pieces containing two defectives. The set $\mathcal{U}$ is thus partitioned into $[D, G]$, where $N = \mathbf{n}(\mathcal{U}) = 6$, $R = \mathbf{n}(D) = 3$, $N - R = \mathbf{n}(G) = 3$, and into $[S, \tilde{S}]$, where $n = \mathbf{n}(S) = 3$ and $N - n = \mathbf{n}(\tilde{S}) = 3$. We are interested in the number of ways in which we can form the partition $[S, \tilde{S}]$ subject to the restriction that $r = \mathbf{n}(D \cap S) = 2$. The statement of the problem is summarized in the 2 $\times$ 2

	S	$\tilde{S}$	
D	2	1	3
G	1	2	3
	3	3	6

Figure 8

table of Figure 8, the entries of which you should verify.

The counting problem is now very simple. We want to know the number of ways of forming the partition $[S, \tilde{S}]$ such that $\mathbf{n}(S) = n$ and $\mathbf{n}(A \cap S) = r$. Observe that these conditions imply that

$$\mathbf{n}(\tilde{S}) = N - n, \quad \mathbf{n}(\tilde{A} \cap S) = n - r, \text{ etc.}$$

We saw in the last section that there are $\binom{R}{r}$ subsets with r elements which can be chosen from R, and similarly there are $\binom{N - R}{n - r}$ subsets with $n - r$ elements which can be chosen from $N - R$. For *each* of the $\binom{R}{r}$ subsets which result in r elements in the cell $A \cap S$ there are $\binom{N - R}{n - r}$ subsets which result in $n - r$ elements in the cell $\tilde{A} \cap S$. Accordingly, by the principle of Section 4, there are $\binom{R}{r} \cdot \binom{N - R}{n - r}$ ways of partitioning $\mathfrak{U}$ into $[S, \tilde{S}]$ such that

$$\mathbf{n}(S) = n \quad \text{and} \quad \mathbf{n}(A \cap S) = r.$$

Example (continued). In the problem summarized by Figure 8, $N = 6$, $R = 3$, $n = 3$, and $r = 2$, so that there are $\binom{3}{2} \cdot \binom{6 - 3}{3 - 2} = 9$ ways to form the partition, as we observed in Exercise 8 of the last section. Let

$$\mathfrak{U} = \{d_1, d_2, d_3, g_1, g_2, g_3\}$$

where d_i is an element of D for $i = 1, 2, 3$, and g_j is an element of G for $j = 1$, 2, 3. Then we may partition $\mathfrak{U}$ into $[S, \tilde{S}]$ where $\mathbf{n}(S) = 3$ and $\mathbf{n}(\tilde{S}) = 3$, and where the first cell contains two elements of D, in the ways shown in Figure 9.

$$\{d_1, d_2, g_1 \mid d_3, g_2, g_3\} \quad \{d_1, d_2, g_2 \mid d_3, g_1, g_3\} \quad \{d_1, d_2, g_3 \mid d_3, g_1, g_2\}$$
$$\{d_1, d_3, g_1 \mid d_2, g_2, g_3\} \quad \{d_1, d_3, g_2 \mid d_2, g_1, g_3\} \quad \{d_1, d_3, g_3 \mid d_2, g_1, g_2\}$$
$$\{d_2, d_3, g_1 \mid d_1, g_2, g_3\} \quad \{d_2, d_3, g_2 \mid d_1, g_1, g_3\} \quad \{d_2, d_3, g_3 \mid d_1, g_1, g_2\}$$

Figure 9

EXERCISES

1. A lot of N pieces contains R defectives. A sample of n pieces is drawn from the lot and the number r of defectives in the lot is determined. What are the possible values of r if
   (a) $n = 10$, $R = 5$, $N = 100$?
   (b) $n = 10$, $R = 5$, $N = 12$?
   (c) $n = 5$, $R = 10$, $N = 100$?
   (d) $n = 5$, $R = 10$, $N = 12$?

2. In the context of Exercise 1, interpret the restrictions given by the inequalities (1). [For example, $r \leq R$ means that there can be no more defectives in the sample than there are in the lot.]

3. A committee consists of five union and four nonunion men. In how many ways can a subcommittee of five be formed consisting of three union and two nonunion men? [*Ans.* 60.]

4. Answer Exercise 3 for subcommittees of five containing
   (a) five union men.
   (b) four union men.
   (c) two union men.
   (d) one union man.
   (e) no union men.
   Why can you not use the formula to answer part (e)?

5. In how many ways can a subcommittee of five be formed from a committee of nine? How does this answer relate to the answers of Exercises 3 and 4?

6. Let $f(r; n, R, N) = \binom{R}{r}\binom{N-R}{n-r}$. Show that

$$f(r+1; n, R, N) = \frac{(n-r)(R-r)}{(r+1)[(N-R)-(n-r-1)]}\, f(r; n, R, N).$$

Show that if $n \leq N - R$,

$$f(0; n, R, N) = \binom{N-R}{n},$$

while if $n \leq R$,

$$f(n; n, R, N) = \binom{R}{n}.$$

Use these relationships to obtain the answers to Exercises 3 and 4.

7. A lot of six pieces contains three good pieces and three defectives. In how many ways can a sample of two containing one good piece and one defective be drawn from the lot? List the partitions that satisfy these criteria. [*Partial Ans.* 9.]

8. In Exercise 7 we can label each piece according to whether it is an element of the sample S or of $\tilde{S}$. Thus if s_i, $i = 1, 2$, is an element of S, and s_j' is an element of $\tilde{S}$, $j = 1, 2, 3, 4$,

$$\mathfrak{U} = \{s_1, s_2, s_1', s_2', s_3', s_4'\}.$$

We may then form an ordered partition of the elements of $\mathfrak{U}$ according to whether they are or are not defective. Thus

$$[D, G] = \{s_1, s_1', s_2' \mid s_2, s_3', s_4'\}$$

is one ordered partition that satisfies the criteria of Exercise 7—one of the defectives is an element of S and two of the defectives are elements of $\tilde{S}$, while one of the good pieces is an element of S and two are elements of $\tilde{S}$. How many such partitions are there? List them.

9. In Exercise 7 we did not distinguish partitions according to the order of the elements within a cell; for example, we considered

$$\{d_1, g_1 \mid d_2, d_3, g_2, g_3\} \quad \text{and} \quad \{g_1, d_1 \mid g_2, g_3, d_2, d_3\}$$

to be the same partition. To calculate the number of ways to obtain a sample of two with one good piece and one defective, where one distinguishes among orders within each cell of the partition, show:

(a) the number of ways of obtaining any specified order within cells—e.g.,

$\{gd \mid ggdd\}$—is $3 \cdot 3 \cdot 2 \cdot 1 \cdot 2 \cdot 1 = 3! \cdot 3! = 36$.

(b) the number of ways of obtaining any other specified order is also $3! \cdot 3! = 36$.

(c) the number of orders in which a g and a d are in the first cell and two g's and two d's are in the second is $\binom{2}{1}\binom{4}{2} = 12$.

(d) the total number of ways of obtaining one d and one g in the first cell and two d's and two g's in the second is $36 \cdot 12 = 432$.

10. How many ways are there of drawing a sample of two from a lot of six?
[$Ans.$ 15.]

11. Show that the ratio of the number of ways the sample of Exercise 7 can be drawn to the total number of ways a sample can be drawn from a lot of six is the same as the ratio of the number of ways of obtaining one d and one g in the first cell and two d's and two g's in the second to the number of ways of arranging six distinguishable items.

12. Let $n = 5$ and $R/N = .8$. Calculate the ratio of the number of possible samples with $r = 3$ to the total number of possible samples with $n = 5$ if

(a) $N = 5$.   [$Ans.$ 0.]

(b) $N = 10$.   [$Ans.$ $\frac{2}{9} = .2222$.]

(c) $N = 50$.   [$Ans.$ $\dfrac{1,067,040}{5,085,024} = .20984$.]

(d) $N = 1000$.   [$Ans.$ .205056.]

(e) What number does the ratio approach as N becomes very large?
[$Ans.$ .2048.]

7. Some properties of binomial coefficients

The binomial coefficients $\binom{n}{j}$ introduced in Section 5 will play an important role in our future work. We give here some of the more important properties of these numbers.

A convenient way to obtain these numbers is given by the famous Pascal triangle, shown in Figure 10. To obtain the triangle we first write the 1's down the sides. Any of the other numbers in the triangle has the property that it is the sum of the two adjacent numbers in the row just above. Thus the next row in the triangle is 1, 6, 15, 20, 15, 6, 1. To find the binomial coefficient $\binom{n}{j}$ we look in the row corresponding to the number

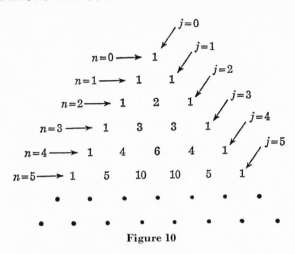

Figure 10

n and see where the diagonal line corresponding to the value of j intersects this row. For example, $\binom{4}{2} = 6$ is in the row marked $n = 4$ and on the diagonal marked $j = 2$.

The property of the binomial coefficients upon which the triangle is based is

$$\binom{n+1}{j} = \binom{n}{j-1} + \binom{n}{j}.$$

This fact can be verified directly (see Exercise 6), but the following argument is interesting in itself. The number $\binom{n+1}{j}$ is the number of subsets with j elements that can be formed from a set of $n+1$ elements. Select one of the $n+1$ elements, x. The $\binom{n+1}{j}$ subsets can be partitioned into those that contain x, and those that do not. The latter are subsets of j elements formed from n objects, and hence there are $\binom{n}{j}$ such subsets. The former are constructed by adding x to a subset of $j-1$ elements formed from n elements, and hence there are $\binom{n}{j-1}$ of them. Thus

$$\binom{n+1}{j} = \binom{n}{j-1} + \binom{n}{j}.$$

If we look again at the Pascal triangle, we observe that the numbers in a given row increase for a while, and then decrease. We can prove this fact in general by considering the ratio of two successive terms,

$$\frac{\binom{n}{j+1}}{\binom{n}{j}} = \frac{n!}{(j+1)!(n-j-1)!} \cdot \frac{j!(n-j)!}{n!} = \frac{n-j}{j+1}.$$

The numbers increase as long as the ratio is greater than 1, i.e., $n - j > j + 1$. This means that $j < \frac{1}{2}(n - 1)$. We must distinguish the case of an even n from an odd n. For example, if $n = 10$, j must be less than $\frac{1}{2}(10 - 1) = 4.5$. Hence the last increase is in going from $j = 4$ to $j = 5$. Thus $\binom{10}{5}$ is the largest term and from $j = 5$ on the terms decrease. For $n = 11$, j must be less than $\frac{1}{2}(11 - 1) = 5$. For $j = 5$, $(n - j)/(j + 1) = 1$. Hence, up to $j = 5$ the terms increase, then $\binom{11}{5} = \binom{11}{6}$, and then the terms decrease.

EXERCISES

1. Extend the Pascal triangle to $n = 16$. Save the result for later use.

2. Prove that

$$\binom{n}{0} + \binom{n}{1} + \binom{n}{2} + \ldots + \binom{n}{n} = 2^n,$$

using the fact that a set with n elements has 2^n subsets.

3. For a set of ten elements prove that there are more subsets with five elements than there are subsets with any other fixed number of elements.

4. Using the fact that

$$\binom{n}{j+1} = \frac{n-j}{j+1} \cdot \binom{n}{j},$$

compute $\binom{30}{s}$ for $s = 1, 2, 3, 4$ from the fact that $\binom{30}{0} = 1$.

[*Ans.* 30; 435; 4060; 27,405.]

5. There are $\binom{52}{13}$ different possible bridge hands. Assume that a list is made showing all these hands, and that in this list the first card in every hand is crossed out. This leaves us with a list of twelve-card hands. Prove that at least two hands in the latter list contain exactly the same cards.

6. Prove that

$$\binom{n+1}{j} = \binom{n}{j-1} + \binom{n}{j},$$

using only the fact that

$$\binom{n}{j} = \frac{n!}{j!(n-j)!}.$$

7. Construct a triangle in the same way that the Pascal triangle was constructed, except that instead of writing numbers, write only "even" or "odd." Construct the triangle for 16 rows. What does this triangle tell you about the numbers in the Pascal triangle? Use this result to check your triangle in Exercise 1.

8. In the triangle obtained in Exercise 7, what property do the rows 1, 2, 4, 8, and 16 have in common? What does this say about the numbers in the corresponding rows of the Pascal triangle? What would you predict for the terms in the 32nd row of the Pascal triangle?

9. For the following table state how one row is obtained from the preceding row and give the relation of this table to the Pascal triangle.

1	1	1	1	1	1	1
1	2	3	4	5	6	7
1	3	6	10	15	21	28
1	4	10	20	35	56	84
1	5	15	35	70	126	210
1	6	21	56	126	252	462
1	7	28	84	210	462	924

10. Referring to the table in Exercise 9, number the columns starting with 0, 1, 2, . . . and number the rows starting with 1, 2, 3, ... Let $f(n, r)$ be the element in the nth column and the rth row. The table was constructed by the rule

$$f(n, r) = f(n - 1, r) + f(n, r - 1)$$

for $n > 0$ and $r > 1$, and $f(n, 1) = f(0, r) = 1$ for all n and r. Verify that

$$f(n, r) = \binom{n + r - 1}{n}$$

satisfies these conditions and is in fact the only choice for $f(n, r)$ which will satisfy the conditions.

11. Consider a set $\{a, a, a\}$ of three objects which cannot be distinguished from one another. Then the ordered partitions with two cells which could be distinguished are

$$[\{a, a, a\}, \quad \varepsilon]$$
$$[\{a, a\}, \quad \{a\}]$$
$$[\{a\}, \quad \{a, a\}]$$
$$[\varepsilon, \quad \{a, a, a\}].$$

List all such ordered partitions with three cells. How many are there?

[*Ans.* 10.]

12. Let $f(n, r)$ be the number of distinguishable ordered partitions with r cells which can be formed from a set of n indistinguishable objects. Show that $f(n, r)$ satisfies the conditions

$$f(n, r) = f(n - 1, r) + f(n, r - 1)$$

for $n > 0$ and $r > 1$, and $f(n, 1) = f(0, r) = 1$ for all n and r.

[*Hint:* Show that $f(n, r - 1)$ is the number of partitions which have the last cell empty and $f(n - 1, r)$ is the number which have at least one element in the last cell.]

13. Using the results of Exercises 10 and 12 show that the number of distinguishable ordered partitions with r cells which can be formed from a set of n indistinguishable objects is

$$\binom{n + r - 1}{n}.$$

14. Assume that a mailman has seven letters to put in three mail boxes. How many ways can this be done if the letters are not distinguished?

[*Ans.* 36.]

15. By an ordered partition with r elements of n we mean a sequence of r nonnegative integers, possibly some 0, written in a definite order, and having sum n. For example, $\{1, 0, 3\}$ and $\{3, 0, 1\}$ are two different ordered partitions with 3 elements of 4. Show that the number of ordered partitions with r elements of n is

$$\binom{n + r - 1}{n}.$$

8. Binomial and multinomial theorems

It is sometimes necessary to expand products of the form $(x + y)^3$, $(x + 2y + 11z)^5$, etc. In this section we shall consider systematic ways of carrying out such expansions.

Consider first the special case $(x + y)^3$. We write this as

$$(x + y)^3 = (x + y)(x + y)(x + y).$$

To perform the multiplication, we choose either an x or a y from each of the three factors and multiply our choices together; we do this for all possible choices and add the results. We represent a particular set of choices by a two-cell partition of the numbers 1, 2, 3. In the first cell we put the numbers which correspond to factors from which we chose an x. In the second cell we put the numbers which correspond to factors from which we chose a y. For example, the partition $[\{1, 3\}, \{2\}]$ corresponds to a choice of x from the first and third factors and y from the second. The product so obtained is $xyx = x^2y$. The coefficient of x^2y in the expansion of $(x + y)^3$ will be the number of partitions which lead to a choice of two x's and one y. That is, the number of two-cell partitions of three elements with two elements in the first cell and one in the second, which is $\binom{3}{2} = 3$.

More generally the coefficient of the term of the form x^iy^{3-i} will be $\binom{3}{j}$

for $j = 0, 1, 2, 3$. Thus we can write the desired expansion as

$$(x + y)^3 = \binom{3}{3}x^3 + \binom{3}{2}x^2y + \binom{3}{1}xy^2 + \binom{3}{0}y^3$$

$$= x^3 + 3x^2y + 3xy^2 + y^3.$$

The same argument carried out for the expansion $(x + y)^n$ leads to the binomial theorem of algebra. This motivates the name *binomial coefficient*.

BINOMIAL THEOREM. The expansion of $(x + y)^n$ is given by

$$(x + y)^n = x^n + \binom{n}{n-1}x^{n-1}y + \binom{n}{n-2}x^{n-2}y^2 + \ldots + \binom{n}{1}xy^{n-1} + y^n.$$

Example 1. Let us find the expansion for $(a - 2b)^3$. To fit this into the binomial theorem, we think of x as being a and y as being $-2b$. Then we have

$$(a - 2b)^3 = a^3 + 3a^2(-2b) + 3a(-2b)^2 + (-2b)^3$$

$$= a^3 - 6a^2b + 12ab^2 - 8b^3.$$

We turn now to the problem of expanding the trinomial $(x + y + z)^3$. Again we write

$$(x + y + z)^3 = (x + y + z)(x + y + z)(x + y + z).$$

This time we choose either an x or y or z from each of the three factors. Our choice is now represented by a three-cell partition of the set of numbers $\{1, 2, 3\}$. The first cell has the numbers corresponding to factors from which we choose an x, the second cell the numbers corresponding to factors from which we choose a y, and the third those from which we choose a z. For example, the partition $[\{1, 3\}, \varepsilon, \{2\}]$ corresponds to a choice of x from the first and third factors, no y's, and z from the second factor. The term obtained is $xzx = x^2z$. The coefficient of the term x^2z in the expansion is thus the number of three-cell partitions with two elements in the first cell, none in the second, and one in the third. There are $\binom{3}{2, 0, 1} = 3$ such partitions. In general the coefficient of the term of the form $x^ay^bz^c$ in the expansion of $(x + y + z)^3$ will be

$$\binom{3}{a, b, c} = \frac{3!}{a!b!c!}.$$

Finding this way the coefficient for each possible a, b, and c we obtain

$$(x + y + z)^3 = x^3 + y^3 + z^3 + 3x^2y + 3xy^2$$
$$+ 3yz^2 + 3y^2z + 3xz^2 + 3x^2z + 6xyz.$$

The same method can be carried out in general for finding the expansion of $(x_1 + x_2 + \ldots + x_r)^n$. From each factor we choose either an x_1, or x_2, or x_3, $\ldots$, or x_r, form the product and add these products for all possible n choices. We will have r^n products, but many will be equal. A particular choice of one term from each factor determines an r-cell partition of the numbers from 1 to n. In the first cell we put the numbers of the factors from which we choose an x_1, in the second cell those from which we choose x_2, etc. A particular choice gives us a term of the form $x_1^{n_1} x_2^{n_2} \ldots x_r^{n_r}$ with $n_1 + n_2 + \ldots + n_r = n$. The corresponding partition has n_1 elements in the first cell, n_2 in the second, etc. For each such partition we obtain one such term. Hence the number of these terms which we obtain is the number of such partitions, which is

$$\binom{n}{n_1, n_2, \ldots, n_r} = \frac{n!}{n_1! n_2! \ldots n_r!}$$

Thus we have the multinomial theorem.

MULTINOMIAL THEOREM. The expansion of $(x_1 + x_2 + \ldots + x_r)^n$ is found by adding all terms of the form

$$\binom{n}{n_1, n_2, \ldots, n_r} x_1^{n_1} x_2^{n_2} \ldots x_r^{n_r}$$

where $n_1 + n_2 + \ldots + n_r = n$.

EXERCISES

1. Expand by the binomial theorem
   (a) $(x + y)^4$.
   (b) $(1 + x)^5$.
   (c) $(x - y)^3$.
   (d) $(2x + a)^4$.
   (e) $(2x - 3y)^3$.
   (f) $(100 - 1)^5$.

2. Expand
   (a) $(x + y + z)^4$.
   (b) $(2x + y - z)^3$.
   (c) $(2 + 2 + 1)^3$. (Evaluate two ways.)

3. (a) Find the coefficient of the term $x^2 y^3 z^2$ in the expansion of $(x + y + z)^7$.
       [*Ans.* 210.]
   (b) Find the coefficient of the term $x^6 y^3 z^2$ in the expression $(x - 2y + 5z)^{11}$.
       [*Ans.* −924,000.]

4. Using the binomial theorem, prove that

   (a) $\binom{n}{0} + \binom{n}{1} + \binom{n}{2} + \ldots + \binom{n}{n} = 2^n$.

   (b) $\binom{n}{0} - \binom{n}{1} + \binom{n}{2} - \binom{n}{3} + \ldots \pm \binom{n}{n} = 0$.

5. Using an argument similar to the one in Section 7, prove that

$$\binom{n+1}{i,\ j,\ k} = \binom{n}{i-1,\ j,\ k} + \binom{n}{i,\ j-1,\ k} + \binom{n}{i,\ j,\ k-1}.$$

6. Let $f(n, r)$ be the number of terms in the multinomial expansion of

$$(x_1 + x_2 + \ldots + x_r)^n,$$

and show that

$$f(n, r) = \binom{n+r-1}{n}.$$

[*Hint:* Show that the conditions of Section 7, Exercise 10, are satisfied by showing that $f(n, r - 1)$ is the number of terms which do not have x_r and $f(n - 1, r)$ is the number which do. Alternatively, use Exercise 15 of Section 7 by showing that each term in the expansion determines an ordered sequence of r integers whose sum is n.]

7. How many terms are there in each of the expansions:
   (a) $(x + y + z)^6$? [*Ans.* 28.]
   (b) $(a + 2b + 5c + d)^4$? [*Ans.* 35.]
   (c) $(r + s + t + u + v)^6$? [*Ans.* 210.]

8. Prove that k^n is the sum of the numbers $\binom{n}{r_1, r_2, \ldots, r_k}$ for all choices of $r_1, r_2, \ldots, r_k$ such that $r_1 + r_2 + \ldots + r_k = n$.

*9. Voting power

We return to the problem raised in Section 5 of Chapter II. Now we are interested not only in coalitions, but also in the power of individual members. We will develop a numerical measure of voting power that was suggested by L. S. Shapley and M. Shubik. While the measure will be explained in detail below, for the reasons for choosing this particular measure the reader is referred to the original paper.

First of all we must realize that the number of votes a man controls is not in itself a good measure of his power. If x has three votes and y has one vote, it does not necessarily follow that x has three times the power that y has. Thus if the committee has just three members {x, y, z} and z also has one vote, then x is a dictator and y is powerless.

The basic idea of the power index is found in considering various alignments of the committee members on a number of issues. The n members are ordered $x_1, x_2, \ldots, x_n$ according to how likely they are to vote for the measure. If the measure is to carry, we must persuade x_1 and x_2 up to x_i to vote for it until we have a winning coalition. If {$x_1, x_2, \ldots, x_i$} is a winning coalition but {$x_1, x_2, \ldots, x_{i-1}$} is not winning, then x_i is the crucial member of the coalition. We must persuade him to vote for the measure, and he is the one hardest to persuade of the i necessary members. We call x_i the *pivot*.

For a purely mathematical measure of the power of a member we do not consider the views of the members. Rather we consider all possible ways that the members could be aligned on an issue, and see how often a given member would be the pivot. That means considering all permutations, and there will be $n!$ of them. In each permutation one member will be the pivot. The frequency with which a man is the pivot of an alignment is a good measure of his voting power.

DEFINITION. The voting power of a member of a committee is the number of alignments in which he is pivotal divided by the total number of alignments. (The total number of alignments, of course, is $n!$, for a committee of n members.)

Example 1. If all n members have one vote each, and it takes a majority vote to carry a measure, it is easy to see (by symmetry) that each member is pivot in $1/n$ of the alignments. Hence each member has power $= 1/n$. Let us illustrate this for $n = 3$. There are $3! = 6$ alignments. It takes two votes to carry a measure; hence the second member is always the pivot. The alignments are: 1**2**3, 1**3**2, 2**1**3, 2**3**1, 3**1**2, 3**2**1. The pivots are in **boldface**. Each member is pivot twice, hence has power $\frac{2}{6} = \frac{1}{3}$.

Example 2. Reconsider Chapter II, Section 5, Example 3 from this point of view. There are 24 permutations of the four members. We will list them, with the pivot in **boldface**:

w**x**yz	w**x**zy	w**y**xz	w**y**zx	w**z**xy	w**z**yx
x**w**yz	x**w**zy	x**y**wz	xy**z**w	x**z**wy	xz**y**w
y**x**wz	y**x**zw	y**w**xz	yw**z**x	y**z**xw	yz**w**x
z**x**yw	z**x**wy	z**y**xw	zy**w**x	z**w**xy	z**w**yx

We see that z has power of $\frac{14}{24}$, w has $\frac{6}{24}$, x and y have $\frac{2}{24}$ each. (Or, simplified, they have $\frac{7}{12}$, $\frac{3}{12}$, $\frac{1}{12}$, $\frac{1}{12}$ power, respectively.) We note that these ratios are much further apart than the ratio of votes which is 3:2:1:1. Here three votes are worth seven times as much as the single vote and more than twice as much as two votes.

Example 3. Reconsider Chapter II, Section 5, Example 4. By an analysis similar to the ones used so far (see Exercises 12 and 13) it can be shown that in the Security Council of the United Nations each of the Big Five has $\frac{76}{385}$ or approximately 0.197 power, while each of the small nations has approximately 0.002 power. This reproduces our intuitive feeling that, while the small nations in the Security Council are not powerless, nearly all the power is in the hands of the Big Five.

Example 4. In a committee of five each member has one vote, but the chairman has veto power. Hence the minimal winning coalitions are three-member coalitions including the chairman. There are $5! = 120$ permutations. The pivot cannot come before the chairman, since without the chairman we do not have a winning coalition. Hence, when the chairman is in place number 3, 4, or 5, he is the pivot. This happens in $\frac{3}{5}$ of the permutations. When he is in position 1 or 2, then the number 3 man is pivot. The number of permutations in which the chairman is in one of the first two positions and a given man is third is $2 \cdot 3! = 12$. Hence the chairman has power $\frac{3}{5}$, and each of the others has power $\frac{1}{10}$.

EXERCISES

1. A committee of three makes decisions by majority vote. Write out all permutations, and calculate the voting powers if the three members have:
   (a) one vote each.   [*Ans.* $\frac{1}{3}, \frac{1}{3}, \frac{1}{3}$.]
   (b) one vote for two of them, two votes for the third.   [*Ans.* $\frac{1}{6}, \frac{1}{6}, \frac{2}{3}$.]
   (c) one vote for two of them, three votes for the third.   [*Ans.* $0, 0, 1$.]
   (d) one, two, and three votes, respectively.   [*Ans.* $\frac{1}{6}, \frac{1}{6}, \frac{2}{3}$.]
   (e) two votes each for two of them, and three votes for the third.
                                       [*Ans.* $\frac{1}{3}, \frac{1}{3}, \frac{1}{3}$.]

2. Prove that in any decision-making body the sum of powers of the members is 1.

3. What is the power of a dictator? What is the power of a "powerless" member? Prove that your answers are correct.

4. A large company issued 100,000 shares. These are held by three stockholders, who have 50,000, 49,999, and 1 share, respectively. Calculate the powers of the three members.   [*Ans.* $\frac{2}{3}, \frac{1}{6}, \frac{1}{6}$.]

5. A committee consists of 100 members having one vote each, plus a chairman who can break ties. Calculate the power distribution. (Do *not* try to write out all permutations!)

6. In Exercise 5, give the chairman a veto instead of the power to break ties. How does this change the power distribution?
                [*Ans.* The chairman has power $\frac{50}{101}$.]

7. How are the powers in Exercise 1 changed if the committee requires a $\frac{3}{4}$ vote to carry a measure?

8. If, in a committee of five requiring majority decisions, each member has one vote, then each has power $\frac{1}{5}$. Now let us suppose that two members team up, and always vote the same way. Does this increase their power? (The best way to represent this situation is by allowing only those permutations in which these two members are next to each other.)
            [*Ans.* Yes, the pair's power increases from .4 to .5.]

9. Given the votes that each member of a decision-making body controls, show that the minimal winning coalitions can be determined. If the minimal winning coalitions are known, show that the power of each member can be determined without knowing anything about the number of votes that each member controls.

10. Answer the following questions for a three-man committee:
    (a) Find all possible sets of minimal winning coalitions.
    (b) For each set of minimal winning coalitions find the distribution of voting power.
    (c) Verify that the various distributions of power found in Exercises 1 and 7 are the only ones possible.

11. In Exercise 1, parts (a) and (e) have the same answer, and parts (b) and (d) and Exercise 4 also have the same answer. Use the results of Exercise 9 to find a reason for these coincidences.

12. Compute the voting power of one of the Big Five in the Security Council of the United Nations as follows:
    (a) Show that for the nation to be pivotal it must be in the number 7 spot or later.
    (b) Show that there are $\binom{6}{2}6!4!$ permutations in which the nation is pivotal in the number 7 spot.
    (c) Find similar formulas for the number of permutations in which it is pivotal in the number 8, 9, 10, or 11 spot.
    (d) Use this information to find the total number of permutations in which it is pivotal, and from this compute the power of the nation.

13. Use the result of Exercise 12 to find the voting power of a small nation in the Security Council.

*10. Flow diagrams

A flow diagram is a graphical device for showing the logical structure of a computation. A good flow diagram enables anyone familiar with arithmetical operations to carry out a computation, without the necessity of understanding the problem that gives rise to the computation. Thus, for example, it is easy to convert a flow diagram into a detailed set of instructions for a computing machine.

Flow diagrams have many advantages. Although a set of instructions (program) for one computer would be meaningless to a different kind of machine, the same flow diagram may be used to prepare a program for a variety of machines. It also enables a nonexpert to use computers, since he may hand his flow diagram to a professional programmer. This division of labor, having the customer write a flow diagram and having an expert change this to a program, is endorsed by many businesses.

But flow diagrams are extremely useful even in the absence of computing machines. They are an ideal way of clarifying a systematic or computational procedure.

A flow diagram consists of four types of components. The basic component is a *box*, which contains an arithmetical order. For example, the box

instructs one to take x (some given or previously computed quantity), to add 2 to it, and assign this value to y. The quantity y may be one of the desired answers, or a quantity to be used in a later step in the computation. In general a box orders us to carry out arithmetical operations on known quantities, and to assign the answer to some variable. Note that a statement such as $x + 2 \rightarrow y$ is an *imperative* sentence since it commands the carrying out of an instruction. This should be contrasted with a statement such as $x + 2 = y$ which is a *declarative* sentence indicating that a certain relation holds. These two statements are entirely different and should not be confused.

The next component in a flow diagram is the *circle*, which contains a question to be answered. These questions normally ask whether two known quantities are equal, or whether a certain inequality holds between them. For example, the circle

$$\left(y > 5? \right)$$

asks whether the number y is now bigger than 5. The outcome of a circle is a "yes" or "no," and we use circles to create a fork in the flow diagram. That is, we may have one set of instructions if the answer is "yes," and a different set for a "no" answer.

We are now almost ready to write a simple flow diagram, but we must make provisions for starting and stopping. For this we use *terminals*, which are indicated by dashed boxes. Thus

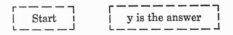

are typical terminals. The logical flow in the diagram will be indicated by arrows, which must start with a terminal and end in a terminal on each branch of the diagram.

Example 1. Suppose that we wish to compute $\sqrt{|a - 2|}$, for some given number a. We wish to write a flow diagram that will work for any value of a. Such a diagram is shown in Figure 11. In this problem a is given, and we have

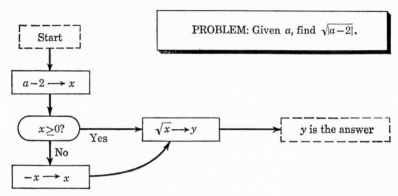

Figure 11

chosen y to represent the answer; i.e., $y = \sqrt{|a - 2|}$. We have introduced x for convenience, as a name for a partial answer. The flow diagram may be replaced by the following verbal instructions: "Subtract 2 from a. If the result is nonnegative, then take its square root, and this will be the answer. But if the result is negative, first replace the answer by minus the answer, and then take its square root." Even in so simple a problem the advantages of the flow diagram are clear.

This example illustrates a major need for flow diagrams. The formula $\sqrt{|a - 2|}$ is static. It does not carry with it instructions on how the formula should be evaluated. This becomes more obvious in a more complex formula; a high school student may be baffled as to "where to start" in a formula like

$$\frac{\sqrt{-(a + 3b)(5 - 7)}}{((a - 2b)^2 + 3)^3}.$$

But the flow diagram is dynamic; it gives step-by-step procedural directions.

Although a flow diagram of this sort may at first appear rather unfamiliar, one of the most useful ways to gain an understanding of a particular diagram is to replace the symbols with numbers and actually carry out the instructions in the diagram. By choosing numbers that will cause each possible path to be followed, the adequacy of a flow diagram can be informally checked. Thus, we can try $a = 100$. The flow diagram says set $100 - 2 = 98$ equal to x. It then asks is $x = 98 \geq 0$? The answer is "yes." Therefore set $\sqrt{x} = \sqrt{98}$ equal to y. Then $y = \sqrt{98}$ is the answer. Try the same step-by-step analysis with $a = \frac{1}{2}$; with $a = -17.43$.

The great advantage of a computing machine is its tremendous speed in repetitive processes, that is, in carrying out essentially the same instructions a large number of times. Such repetitive patterns, or "loops," are diagrammed by means of the *diamond*, the fourth type of component. For example, the diamond

instructs us to let $i = 1$, and carry out the instructions below till these bring us back to the diamond. Then let $i = 2$, and carry out the same instructions. We keep repeating this procedure until we have carried the instructions out for $i = 100$, then we go on to the instructions to the right of the diamond. The letter i in the diamond is known as an *index*.

Example 2. Let us illustrate this in terms of finding the sum of 100 given numbers. The flow diagram is shown in Figure 12. We start with 0, and keep adding the 100 numbers one at a time (since adding a single number to a given number is one of the basic operations of any computer), till we have added all 100. Then we have the desired sum.

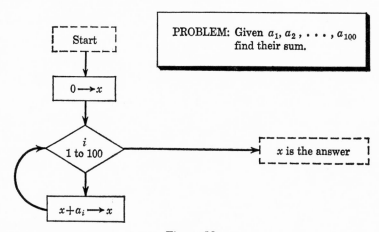

Figure 12

It is instructive to follow Figure 12 step by step. First we set $x = 0$. This step is called "initializing." Then we enter the diamond, and choose $i = 1$. Hence in the box below the diamond we compute $0 + a_1 = a_1$, and assign this to x. Then we return to the diamond, and let $i = 2$. This time in the box below we compute $a_1 + a_2$, and assign this to x. The next time we let $i = 3$, and compute $(a_1 + a_2) + a_3$, etc. Clearly, after looping 100 times, x will have assigned to it the sum of all the numbers.

Example 3. A similar but slightly more complicated diagram is shown in Figure 13. This computation will play a key role in Chapter V. The figure

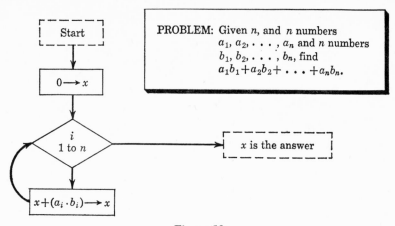

Figure 13

shows an interesting variation in the use of the diamond. We do not have to specify in the diagram how many times the computation should loop; we simply state that i goes from 1 to n, where n will be one of the numbers supplied to us. This gives us much greater flexibility. Not only may we vary the values of the a's and b's, but we may also vary their number, and still the same flow diagram will apply.

Example 4. Figure 14 illustrates a very important procedure, in which no arithmetical operation needs to be carried out. Given the n numbers a_1, a_2, $\ldots$, a_n we are interested in finding the largest number. Of course there may be repetitions in the sequence, but there is always a unique largest one—which may occur more than once. Thus, for example, the *maximum* (or *max*) of the sequence 1, 5, 11, 8, 11, 9, 0, 10, 5, 4, 5 is 11. Similarly, the *minimum* (or *min*) is 0. Figure 14 gives directions for finding the max of n given numbers. The

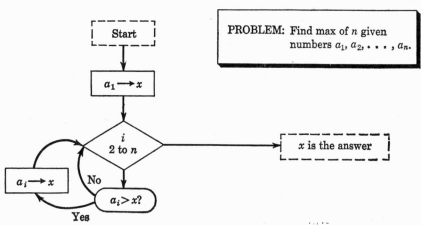

Figure 14

basic idea is very simple: Start with the first number and look at the remaining numbers one at a time. For each, check whether it is larger than the largest previous number, till you have checked all n. In the flow diagram x stands for the largest number found up to that step in the computation, so that at the end x is equal to the max.

Example 5. The full power of flow diagramming can best be seen in a problem that requires a loop within a loop. Let us consider the problem of taking n given numbers $a_1, a_2, \ldots, a_n$ and arranging them in decreasing order, that is, so that in the new order $a_1 \geq a_2$, $a_2 \geq a_3$, etc. Figure 15 describes one such method. We go through our list of numbers, and compare each number with the preceding one. If it is greater than the preceding one, we interchange them. Since we must go through the entire list, this is one loop, and it is accomplished by the diamond in Figure 15. At the end of the loop we have

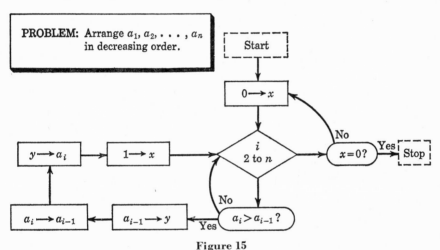

Figure 15

a "better" order, but we are probably not done. We must now go through the same loop again, getting a further improvement, and repeat the loop till we find that no change is necessary. This repetition of loops cannot be achieved by a diamond, since we do not know how many times we have to go through the list. Instead, we keep track of whether any change occurred during the loop, and keep on until we get through the list for the first time without a change. This "keeping track" is accomplished by a *signal*, which in Figure 15 is the variable x. Variable x is set equal to 0 at the beginning of each loop, but is changed to 1 if the order of two of the numbers in the list is changed.

EXERCISES

1. Write a flow diagram to compute $(2a + 5)^2$ for an arbitrary a.

2. In Figure 11, for what values of a will we get a "no" in the circle?

3. Write a flow diagram to find the geometric mean of five numbers, that is, $\sqrt[5]{a_1 a_2 a_3 a_4 a_5}$.

4. In Figure 13, let $n = 3$, and $a_1 = 1$, $a_2 = 0$, $a_3 = -1$, $b_1 = 2$, $b_2 = 5$, $b_3 = 2$. Follow the flow diagram step by step to find the answer. Check your answer.

5. Write a flow diagram to find the min of n numbers.

6. Write a flow diagram to find the arithmetic mean (or average) of n numbers, i.e., $(a_1 + a_2 + \ldots + a_n)/n$.

7. Write a flow diagram for arranging 100 given numbers in increasing order.

8. Write a flow diagram for taking n given numbers in increasing order, and removing duplications. The answer should be a number m, giving how many different numbers there were, and an increasing sequence a_1, a_2, $\ldots$, a_m.

9. Use the results of Exercises 7 and 8 to write a flow diagram for removing duplicates from 100 given numbers.

10. Why is the variable y introduced in Figure 15? Why not interchange a_{i-1} and a_i by the two boxes given below?

11. Show that a diamond can always be replaced by a combination of boxes and a circle.

*11. Flow diagrams for counting problems

The purpose of this section is to give further examples of flow diagrams, applying this technique to the types of computational problems treated earlier in the chapter.

Example 1. The computation of $n!$ is ideally suited for flow diagramming. It requires just a simple loop, as shown in Figure 16.

Let us raise the question of what happens in Figure 16 if we ask for 0!. Inside the diamond we then ask for i to go from 1 to 0. For this one needs a convention, and the standard convention is that if we ask i to go from a up to b, but $a > b$, then the loop is simply omitted. Thus our program will yield $0! = 1$. If we let $n = 1$, then the diamond instructs us to go from 1 to 1, hence we loop just once, with $i = 1$. Thus $1! = 1 \cdot 1 = 1$.

Example 2. A more interesting problem is the computation of the binomial coefficients $\binom{n}{j}$. We shall use the method of the Pascal triangle, computing

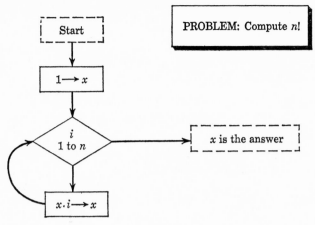

Figure 16

one row of the triangle at a time. This is shown in Figure 17. In this example we again make use of the convention that when $1 > n - 1$, the second diamond's loop is omitted. (See Exercise 3.)

Let us next consider three types of averages. Given a sequence of numbers $a_1, a_2, \ldots, a_n$, by their "average" we usually mean the *arithmetic mean*, which is $(a_1 + a_2 + \ldots + a_n)/n$. But many other types of averages are in common use. For example, the *median* is the "middle number" if we arrange our numbers in decreasing order. If there are an odd number

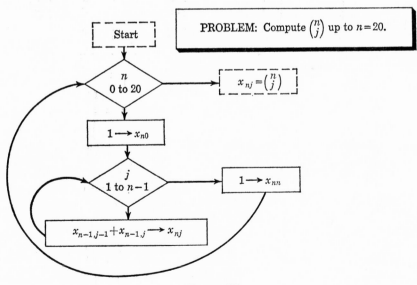

Figure 17

of numbers, then this is precisely defined, but with an even number of a's, there are two candidates for the median. Thus, more precisely, we arrange our numbers in decreasing order and then one of three things can happen: (1) There are an odd number of a's, in which case the median is the middle one. (2) There are an even number and the two middle numbers are the same, then this number is the median. (3) The two middle numbers are different, then both are called medians. Often, in this case, one defines the set of medians to be the interval having the two middle numbers as end points.

Another commonly used "average" is the mode. This is defined as the commonest number in the sequence, that is, the number occurring the largest number of times in the sequence. In case of a tie we may have several modes.

Before diagramming the computation of the three types of averages, let us introduce an important short cut in flow diagrams. It often occurs that a previously diagrammed computation occurs as part of a larger computation. Instead of duplicating the previous diagram, we simply insert an instruction to carry out that computation at the specified place in the new diagram. (On a computing machine this usually requires only a single instruction.) We then refer to the small computation as a *subroutine* of the larger one. In the diagram we indicate this by inserting a box or circle containing a verbal instruction to use a previously defined routine.

Example 3. To diagram the arithmetic mean we need only compute the sum and divide by n. Suppose that we want the arithmetic mean of the given numbers $a_1, a_2, \ldots, a_{100}$. We can easily accomplish this by using Figure 12 of the last section as a subroutine. The diagram is shown in Figure 18.

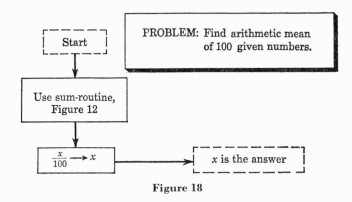

Figure 18

Example 4. To find the median of n numbers we will have to test whether the positive integer n is even or odd. Some computers have automatic tests for this. But just in case this is not available, we will write a subroutine for testing evenness. This is shown in Figure 19. Here the output is "yes" or "no," and the subroutine is used as a circle in Figure 20.

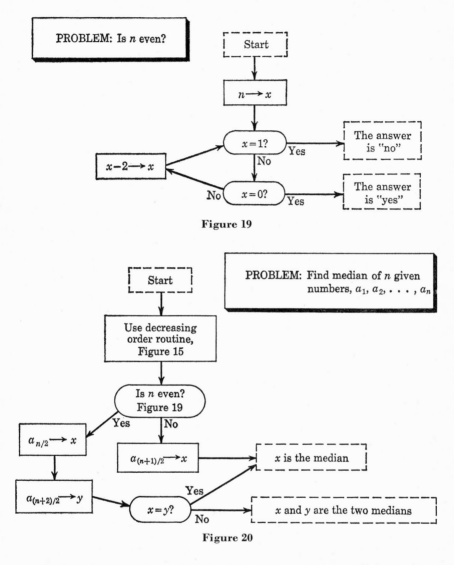

Figure 19

Figure 20

Example 5. To find a routine for determining modes, we will first write a very useful subroutine which counts the frequency (number of occurrences) of all numbers in a sequence. This is shown in Figure 21. The basic idea of the routine is the following: We first write $a_1, a_2, \ldots, a_n$, the given numbers, in decreasing order. Then we run through this list (using index i), noting whether we have hit a new number. Since the numbers have been ordered,

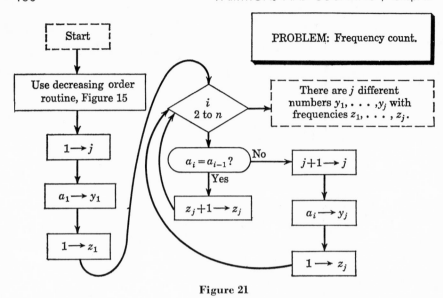

Figure 21

a number different from the previous one is new. If we find a new number, we assign this to a new variable y_j (where j indexes the *different* numbers) and set up a counter z_j. But if the number is not new, then we increase z_j by 1. This explains the fork in Figure 21. The three instructions preceding the loop simply get us started, i.e., these are initializing instructions.

Given the frequency count routine, it is easy to find the modes. We need only pick out the number or numbers having the largest frequency. The flow diagram is drawn in Figure 22.

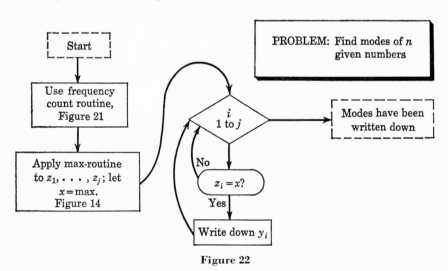

Figure 22

EXERCISES

1. Write a flow diagram for the computation of 2^n. Does it give the correct answer for $n = 0$ and $n = 1$?

2. Suppose that a machine can do only sums and not products. Write a flow diagram for computing na, where n is an integer and a any number. Does it give the correct answer for $n = 0$ and $n = 1$?

3. Check Figure 17 for the cases of $n = 0$ and $n = 1$, by following the diagram step by step.

4. Write a flow diagram for computing $\binom{n}{j}$ using the factorial routine as a subroutine.

5. Find the arithmetic mean, the medians, and the modes of each of the following sequences. Use the flow diagrams in Figures 18–21.
   (a) 1, 2, 2, 2, 3, 3, 8.
   (b) 1, 1, 1, 2, 2, 3, 3, 3.
   (c) 1, 2, 2, 2, 3.
   (d) 1, 2, 3, 4, 5, 6.
   (e) 2, 5, 0, 9, 2, 1.

6. Write a flow diagram to test whether n is divisible by 3.

7. Write a flow diagram to test whether a given integer n is a perfect square.

8. Write a routine which for given positive number a will find the greatest integer whose cube is less than a. What does your routine do if $a < 1$?

9. Given the n numbers $a_1, a_2, \ldots, a_n$, what does the following routine do?

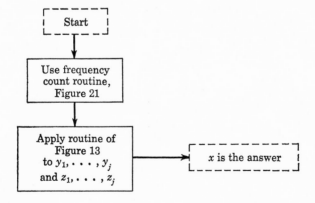

10. Write a flow diagram for testing whether among n given numbers there are at least two that are equal. Make the diagram as simple as possible, without using subroutines.

11. Let x be any positive number and carry out each of the following programs. In each case determine y.

(a)   (b)

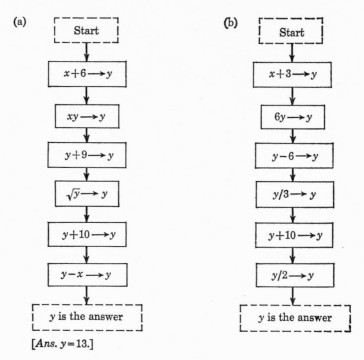

[*Ans.* $y = 13$.]

12. Let a, b, c, and x be given numbers. Carry out the following program and identify the result.

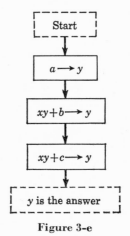

Figure 3-e

13. Let x and y be given numbers and carry out the following program. Note that the program terminates by indicating either a yes or a no answer. What is the significance of each answer?

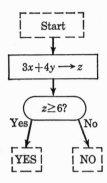

SUGGESTED READING

Mathematical Association of America, Committee on the Undergraduate Program, *Universal Mathematics*, Part II, Tulane Book Store, Tulane University, New Orleans, 1955, Chapters III, IV.

Shapley, L. S., and M. Shubik, "A Method for Evaluating the Distribution of Power in a Committee System," *The American Political Science Review*, XLVIII (1954), pp. 787–792.

Whitworth, W. A., *Choice and Chance, with 1000 Exercises*, Stechert, New York, 1934.

Probability Theory

1. Introduction

We often hear statements of the following kind: "The missile is likely to fire successfully," "We have a fair chance of making the sale," "There is an even chance that a coin will come up heads," etc. In each case our statement refers to a situation in which we are not certain of the outcome, but we express some degree of confidence that our prediction will be verified. The theory of probability provides a mathematical framework for such assertions.

Consider an experiment whose outcome is not known. Suppose that someone makes an assertion p about the outcome of the experiment, and we want to assign a probability to p. When statement p is considered in isolation, we usually find no natural assignment of probabilities. Rather, we look for a method of assigning probabilities to all conceivable statements concerning the outcome of the experiment. At first this might seem to be a hopeless task, since there is no end to the statements we can make about the experiment. However, we are aided by a basic principle:

FUNDAMENTAL ASSUMPTION. Any two equivalent statements will be assigned the same probability.

As long as there are a finite number of logical possibilities, there are only a finite number of truth sets, and hence the process of assigning probabilities is a finite one. We proceed in three steps: (1) we first determine $\mathfrak{U}$, the possibility set, that is, the set of all logical possibilities, (2) to each subset X of $\mathfrak{U}$ we assign a number called the measure $\mathbf{m}(X)$, (3) to each statement p we assign $\mathbf{m}(P)$, the measure of its truth set, as a probability. The probability of statement p is denoted by $\mathbf{Pr}[p]$.

The first step, that of determining the set of logical possibilities, is one that we considered in the previous chapters. It is important to recall that there is no unique method for analyzing logical possibilities. In a given problem we may arrive at a very fine or a very rough analysis of possibilities, causing $\mathfrak{U}$ to have many or few elements.

Having chosen $\mathfrak{U}$, the next step is to assign a number to each subset X of $\mathfrak{U}$, which will in turn be taken to be the probability of any statement having truth set X. We do this in the following way.

Assignment of a measure. Assign a positive number (weight) to each element of $\mathfrak{U}$, so that the sum of the weights assigned is 1. Then the measure of a set is the sum of the weights of its elements. The measure of the set $\mathcal{E}$ is 0.

In applications of probability to business problems, the assignment of measures and the analysis of the logical possibilities may sometimes depend upon masses of data which are best obtained, analyzed, and interpreted by a professional statistician; at other times, the task depends more on qualitative knowledge and judgment of facts with which the businessman himself is most familiar, so that he is the person best qualified to assign measures and analyze the logical possibilities. Very often a combination of objective fact and subjective judgment makes it important for the statistician and the businessman to work together on this job.

Once the weights are assigned, to find the probability of a particular statement we must find its truth set and find the sum of the weights assigned to elements of the truth set. This problem, which might seem easy, can often involve considerable mathematical difficulty. The development of techniques to solve this kind of problem is the main task of probability theory.

Example 1. An ordinary die is thrown. What is the probability that the number which turns up is less than 4? Here the possibility set is $\mathfrak{U} = \{1, 2, 3, 4, 5, 6\}$. The symmetry of the die suggests that each face should have the same probability of turning up. To make this so we assign weight $\frac{1}{6}$ to each of the outcomes. The truth set of the statement, "The number which turns up is less than 4," is $\{1, 2, 3\}$. Hence the probability of this statement is $\frac{3}{6} = \frac{1}{2}$, the sum of the weights of the elements in its truth set.

Example 2. Three computer manufacturers, A, B, and C, are trying to contract for the installation of a computer system with the X Company. The sales manager of A feels that his company has the same chance of winning the contract as B, but that A (and hence also B) is twice as likely to win it as C is. What is the probability that A or C wins the contract? We take as $\mathfrak{U}$ the set $\{A, B, C\}$. If we were to assign weight a to the outcome C, then we would assign weight $2a$ to each of the outcomes A and B. Since the sum of the weights must be 1, we have $2a + 2a + a = 1$, or $a = \frac{1}{5}$. Hence we assign weights $\frac{2}{5}$, $\frac{2}{5}$, $\frac{1}{5}$ to the outcomes A, B, and C, respectively. The truth set of the statement "Company A or Company C wins the contract" is $\{A, C\}$. The sum of the weights of the elements of this set is $\frac{2}{5} + \frac{1}{5} = \frac{3}{5}$. Hence the probability that A or C wins the contract is $\frac{3}{5}$.

EXERCISES

1. Assume that there are n possibilities for the outcome of a given experiment. How should the weights be assigned if it is desired that all outcomes be assigned the same weight?

2. Let $\mathfrak{U} = \{a, b, c\}$. Assign weights to the three elements so that no two have the same weight, and find the measures of the eight subsets of $\mathfrak{U}$.

3. In an election Jones has probability $\frac{1}{2}$ of winning, Smith has probability $\frac{1}{3}$, and Black has probability $\frac{1}{6}$.
   (a) Construct $\mathfrak{U}$.
   (b) Assign weights.
   (c) Find the measures of the eight subsets.
   (d) Give a pair of nonequivalent predictions which have the same probability.

4. Give the possibility set $\mathfrak{U}$, for each of the following experiments.
   (a) An election between candidates A and B is to take place.
   (b) A number between 1 and 5 is chosen at random.
   (c) A two-headed coin is thrown.
   (d) A student is asked for the day of the year on which his birthday falls.
   (e) A sample of 5 pieces is taken from a lot of 1000 and inspected to see how many defectives there are.
   (f) An item is offered for sale on a day when there are four units in inventory.

5. For which of the cases in Exercise 4 might it be appropriate to assign the same weight to each outcome?

6. Job applicants are given an aptitude test to determine their qualifications for performing a certain skilled task. For an applicant selected at random the following probabilities have been assigned to the results of taking the

test and of actual job performance: The probability that the applicant would perform unsatisfactorily both on the test and on the job is $\frac{1}{2}$. The probability that his performance would be satisfactory either on the test or on the job (but not both) is $\frac{1}{3}$.

(a) What is the probability that the applicant would perform satisfactorily both on the test and on the job?

(b) From the information given, is it possible to find the probability that the applicant would perform satisfactorily on the job? [*Ans.* No.]

7. A die is loaded in such a way that the probability of each face is proportional to the number of dots on that face. (For instance, a 6 is three times as probable as a 2.) What is the probability of getting an even number in one throw? [*Ans.* $\frac{4}{7}$.]

8. If a coin is thrown three times, list the eight possibilities for the outcomes of the three successive throws. A typical outcome can be written (HTH). Determine a probability measure by assigning an equal weight to each outcome. Find the probabilities of the following statements:

(r) The number of heads that occur is greater than the number of tails. [*Ans.* $\frac{1}{2}$.]

(s) Exactly two heads occur. [*Ans.* $\frac{3}{8}$.]

(t) The same side turns up on every throw. [*Ans.* $\frac{1}{4}$.]

9. For the statements given in Exercise 8, which of the following equalities are true?

(a) $\mathbf{Pr}[r \vee s]\ \ = \mathbf{Pr}[r] + \mathbf{Pr}[s]$.
(b) $\mathbf{Pr}[s \vee t]\ \ = \mathbf{Pr}[s] + \mathbf{Pr}[t]$.
(c) $\mathbf{Pr}[r \vee \sim r] = \mathbf{Pr}[r] + \mathbf{Pr}[\sim r]$.
(d) $\mathbf{Pr}[r \vee t]\ \ = \mathbf{Pr}[r] + \mathbf{Pr}[t]$.

10. Which of the following pairs of statements (see Exercise 8) are inconsistent? (Recall that two statements are inconsistent if their truth sets have no element in common.)

(a) r, s.   (c) $r, \sim r$.
(b) s, t.   (d) r, t.   [*Ans.* (b) and (c).]

11. State a theorem suggested by Exercises 9 and 10.

2. *Properties of a probability measure*

Before studying special probability measures, we shall consider some general properties of such measures which are useful in computations and in the general understanding of probability theory.

Three basic properties of a probability measure are:

(A) $\mathbf{m}(X) = 0$ if and only if $X = \mathcal{E}$.
(B) $0 \le \mathbf{m}(X) \le 1$ for any set X.
(C) For two sets X and Y,

$$\mathbf{m}(X \cup Y) = \mathbf{m}(X) + \mathbf{m}(Y)$$

if and only if X and Y are disjoint, i.e., have no elements in common.

The proofs of properties (A) and (B) are left as an exercise (see Exercise 16). We shall prove (C).

We observe first that $\mathbf{m}(X) + \mathbf{m}(Y)$ is the sum of the weights of the elements of X added to the sum of the weights of Y. If X and Y are disjoint, then the weight of every element of $X \cup Y$ is added once and only once, and hence $\mathbf{m}(X) + \mathbf{m}(Y) = \mathbf{m}(X \cup Y)$.

Assume now that X and Y are not disjoint. Here the weight of every element contained in both X and Y, i.e., in $X \cap Y$, is added twice in the sum $\mathbf{m}(X) + \mathbf{m}(Y)$. Thus this sum is greater than $\mathbf{m}(X \cup Y)$ by an amount $\mathbf{m}(X \cap Y)$. By (A) and (B), if $X \cap Y$ is not the empty set, then $\mathbf{m}(X \cap Y) > 0$. Hence in this case we have $\mathbf{m}(X) + \mathbf{m}(Y) > \mathbf{m}(X \cup Y)$. Thus if X and Y are not disjoint, the equality in (C) does not hold. Our proof shows that in general we have

(C') For any two sets X and Y,

$$\mathbf{m}(X \cup Y) = \mathbf{m}(X) + \mathbf{m}(Y) - \mathbf{m}(X \cap Y).$$

Since the probabilities for statements are obtained directly from the probability measure $\mathbf{m}(X)$, any property of $\mathbf{m}(X)$ can be translated into a property about the probability of statements. For example, the above properties become, when expressed in terms of statements:

(a) $\mathbf{Pr}[p] = 0$ if and only if p is logically false.
(b) $0 \le \mathbf{Pr}[p] \le 1$ for any statement p.
(c) The equality
$$\mathbf{Pr}[p \vee q] = \mathbf{Pr}[p] + \mathbf{Pr}[q]$$

holds if and only if p and q are inconsistent.

(c') For any two statements p and q,

$$\mathbf{Pr}[p \vee q] = \mathbf{Pr}[p] + \mathbf{Pr}[q] - \mathbf{Pr}[p \wedge q].$$

Another property of a probability measure which is often useful in computation is

(D) $$\mathbf{m}(\tilde{X}) = 1 - \mathbf{m}(X)$$

or, in the language of statements,

(d) $$\mathbf{Pr}[\sim p] = 1 - \mathbf{Pr}[p].$$

The proofs of (D) and (d) are left as an exercise (see Exercise 17).

It is important to observe that our probability measure assigns probability 0 only to statements which are logically false, i.e., which are false for every logical possibility. Hence, a prediction that such a statement will be true is certain to be wrong. Similarly a statement is assigned probability 1 only if it is true in every case, i.e., logically true. Thus the prediction that a statement of this type will be true is certain to be correct. (While these properties of a probability measure seem quite natural, it is necessary, when dealing with infinite possibility sets, to weaken them slightly. We consider in this book only the finite possibility sets.)

We shall now discuss the interpretation of probabilities that are not 0 or 1. We shall give only some intuitive ideas that are commonly held concerning probabilities. While these ideas can be made mathematically more precise, we offer them here only as a guide to intuitive thinking.

Suppose that, relative to a given experiment, a statement has been assigned probability p. From this it is often inferred that if a sequence of such experiments is performed under identical conditions, the fraction of experiments which yield outcomes making the statement true would be approximately p. The mathematical version of this is the "law of large numbers" of probability theory (which will be treated in Section 9). In cases where there is no natural way to assign a probability measure, the probability of a statement is estimated experimentally. A sequence of experiments is performed and the fraction of the experiments which make the statement true is taken as the approximate probability for the statement.

A second and related interpretation of probabilities is concerned with betting. Suppose that a certain statement has been assigned probability p. We wish to offer a bet that the statement will in fact turn out to be true. We agree to give r dollars if the statement does not turn out to be true, provided that we receive s dollars if it does turn out to be true. What should r and s be to make the bet fair? If it were true that in a large number of such bets we would win s a fraction p of the time and lose r a fraction $1 - p$ of the time, then our average winning per bet would be $sp - r(1 - p)$. To make the bet fair we should make this average winning 0. This will be the case if $sp = r(1 - p)$ or if $r/s = p/(1 - p)$. Notice that this determines only the ratio of r and s. Such a ratio, written $r:s$, is said to give *odds* for the bet.

Example. Assume that a probability of $\frac{3}{4}$ has been assigned to a certain horse winning a race. Then the odds for a fair bet would be $\frac{3}{4}:\frac{1}{4}$. These odds could be equally well written as $3:1$, $6:2$, or $12:4$, etc. A fair bet would be to agree to pay \$3 if the horse loses and receive \$1 if the horse wins. Another fair bet would be to pay \$6 if the horse loses and win \$2 if the horse wins.

EXERCISES

1. Let p and q be statements such that $\mathbf{Pr}[p \wedge q] = \frac{1}{4}$, $\mathbf{Pr}[\sim p] = \frac{1}{3}$, and $\mathbf{Pr}[q] = \frac{1}{2}$. What is $\mathbf{Pr}[p \vee q]$?   [*Ans.* $\frac{11}{12}$.]

2. Using the result of Exercise 1, find $\mathbf{Pr}[\sim p \wedge \sim q]$.

3. Let p and q be statements such that $\mathbf{Pr}[p] = \frac{1}{2}$ and $\mathbf{Pr}[q] = \frac{2}{3}$. Are p and q consistent?   [*Ans.* Yes.]

4. Show that, if $\mathbf{Pr}[p] + \mathbf{Pr}[q] > 1$, then p and q are consistent.

5. The Acme Company has submitted bids on two projects. The Controller assigns a probability of .4 to being awarded the first project, a probability of .6 to obtaining at least one, and a probability of .1 to obtaining both. What is the probability that the company will be awarded the second project?

6. An automobile dealer believes that within the next week he will sell at least four cars with probability .9, but less than seven cars with probability .6. What is the probability that he will sell four, five, or six?   [*Ans.* .5.]

7. What odds should a person give on a bet that a six will turn up when a die is thrown?

8. Referring to Example 2 of Section 1, what odds should the sales manager of Company A be willing to give for a bet that either A or B will win the contract?

9. Prove that if the odds relative to a given statement are $r:s$, then the probability that the statement will be true is $r/(r + s)$.

10. Using the result of Exercise 9 and the definition of "odds," show that if the odds are $r:s$ that a statement is true, then the odds are $s:r$ that it is false.

11. A man is willing to give 5:4 odds that the Dodgers will win the World Series. What must the probability of a Dodger victory be for this to be a fair bet?   [*Ans.* $\frac{5}{9}$.]

12. It has been found through long experience that 85 per cent of the pieces which a certain machine produces are good. What odds should be given that the next piece produced will be good?

13. A man offers 1:3 odds that A will occur, 1:2 odds that B will occur. He knows that A and B cannot both occur. What odds should he give that A or B will occur?   [*Ans.* 7:5.]

14. A man offers 3:1 odds that A will occur, 2:1 odds that B will occur. He knows that A and B cannot both occur. What odds should he give that A or B will occur?

15. Show from the definition of a probability measure that $\mathbf{m}(X) = 1$ if and only if $X = \mathfrak{U}$.

16. Show from the definition of a probability measure that properties (A), (B) of the text are true.

17. Prove property (D) of the text. Why does property (d) follow from this property?

18. Prove that if R, S, and T are three sets that have no element in common,
$$\mathbf{m}(R \cup S \cup T) = \mathbf{m}(R) + \mathbf{m}(S) + \mathbf{m}(T).$$

19. If X and Y are two sets such that X is a subset of Y, prove that $\mathbf{m}(X) \leq \mathbf{m}(Y)$.

20. If p and q are two statements such that p implies q, prove that $\mathbf{Pr}[p] \leq \mathbf{Pr}[q]$.

21. Suppose that you are given n statements and each has been assigned a probability equal to r. Prove that the probability of the disjunction of these statements is less than or equal to nr.

22. The following is an alternative proof of property (C′) of the text. Give a reason for each step.
    (a) $X \cup Y = (X \cap \tilde{Y}) \cup (X \cap Y) \cup (\tilde{X} \cap Y)$.
    (b) $\mathbf{m}(X \cup Y) = \mathbf{m}(X \cap \tilde{Y}) + \mathbf{m}(X \cap Y) + \mathbf{m}(\tilde{X} \cap Y)$.
    (c) $\mathbf{m}(X \cup Y) = \mathbf{m}(X) + \mathbf{m}(Y) - \mathbf{m}(X \cap Y)$.

23. If X, Y, and Z are any three sets, prove that, for any probability meas ure
$$\mathbf{m}(X \cup Y \cup Z) = \mathbf{m}(X) + \mathbf{m}(Y) + \mathbf{m}(Z) - \mathbf{m}(X \cap Y)$$
$$- \mathbf{m}(Y \cap Z) - \mathbf{m}(X \cap Z) + \mathbf{m}(X \cap Y \cap Z).$$

24. Translate the result of Exercise 23 into a result concerning three statements p, q, and r.

25. Prove that for any two statements p and q,
    (a) $\mathbf{Pr}[p \wedge q] = \mathbf{Pr}[q \wedge p]$.
    (b) $\mathbf{Pr}[p \wedge q] + \mathbf{Pr}[p \wedge \sim q] = \mathbf{Pr}[p]$.
    (c) $\mathbf{Pr}[p \wedge q] + \mathbf{Pr}[\sim p \wedge q] = \mathbf{Pr}[q]$.

3. The equiprobable measure

We have already seen several examples where it was natural to assign the same weight to all possibilities in determining the appropriate probability measure. The probability measure determined in this manner is called the *equiprobable measure*. The measure of sets in the case of the equiprobable measure has a very simple form. In fact, if $\mathfrak{U}$ has n elements and if the equiprobable measure has been assigned, then for any set X, $\mathbf{m}(X)$ is r/n, where r is the number of elements in the set X. This is true since the weight of each element in X is $1/n$, and hence the sum of the weights of elements of X is r/n.

The particularly simple form of the equiprobable measure makes it easy to work with. In view of this it is important to observe that a particular choice for the set of possibilities in a given situation may lead to the equiprobable measure, while some other choice will not. For example, consider the case of two throws of an ordinary coin. Suppose that we are interested in statements about the number of heads which occur. If we take for the possibility set the set $\mathfrak{U} = \{HH, HT, TH, TT\}$, then it is reasonable to assign the same weight to each outcome, and we are led to the equiprobable measure. If, on the other hand, we were to take as possible outcomes the set $\mathfrak{U} = \{no\ H,\ one\ H,\ two\ H\}$, it would not be natural to assign the same weight to each outcome, since one head can occur in two different ways, while each of the other possibilities can occur in only one way.

The phrase "at random" is often associated with the equiprobable measure. Strictly speaking, one out of a set of possibilities is chosen "at random" provided *any* probability measure whatsoever has been assigned to the set of possibilities. When there is no further qualification, however, a choice "at random" from a set of possibilities usually means that the set has assigned to it the equiprobable measure. Thus, if we say, for example, that a number has been chosen "at random" from the set of integers from 1 through 100, we imply that the equiprobable measure has been assigned to the set, i.e., that the probability of choosing any particular number—say 29—is .01.

Example 1. Suppose that we throw two ordinary dice. Each die can turn up a number from 1 to 6; hence there are $6 \cdot 6$ possibilities. We assign weight $\frac{1}{36}$ to each possibility. A prediction that is true in j cases will then have probability $j/36$. For example, "The sum of the dice is 5," will be true if we get $1 + 4$, $2 + 3$, $3 + 2$, or $4 + 1$. Hence the probability that the sum of the dice is 5 is $\frac{4}{36} = \frac{1}{9}$. The sum can be 12 in only one way, $6 + 6$. Hence the probability that the sum is 12 is $\frac{1}{36}$.

Example 2. A lot contains 80 good pieces and 20 defectives. A sample of two is drawn at random from the lot. What is the probability that both pieces are defective? There are 100 possibilities for the first piece, and for each of these there are 99 possibilities for the second. Hence there are $100 \cdot 99$ possibilities for the result of two draws. We assign the equiprobable measure. The statement "both pieces are defective" is true in $20 \cdot 19$ of the $100 \cdot 99$ possibilities. Hence the probability of the statement is $20 \cdot 19/100 \cdot 99$ or .0384.

Example 3. Assume that, on the basis of a predictive index applied to salesmen A, B, and C when applying for a job, it is predicted that after one year the sales of A will be the highest, C the second highest, and B the lowest of the three. Suppose, in fact, that these predictions turn out to be exactly correct. If the predictive index has no merit at all, and hence the predictions were made simply at random, what is the probability that such a prediction will be correct? There are $3! = 6$ orders in which the men might finish. If the predictions were really made at random, then we would assign an equal weight to each of the six outcomes. In this case the probability that a particular prediction is true is $\frac{1}{6}$. Since this probability is reasonably large, we would hesitate to conclude that the predictive index is in fact useful, on the basis of this one experiment. Suppose, on the other hand, it predicted the order of six men correctly. Then a similar analysis would show that, by guessing, the probability is $\frac{1}{6!} = \frac{1}{720}$ that such a prediction would be correct. Hence, we might conclude here that there is strong evidence that the index has some merit.

EXERCISES

1. A letter is chosen at random from the word "random." What is the probability that it is an n? That it is a vowel?   [*Ans.* $\frac{1}{6}$; $\frac{1}{3}$.]

2. An integer between 3 and 12 inclusive is chosen at random. What is the probability that it is an even number? That it is even and divisible by three?

3. A card is drawn at random from a pack of playing cards.
   (a) What is the probability that it is either a heart or the king of clubs?
                                                                          [*Ans.* $\frac{7}{26}$.]
   (b) What is the probability that it is either the queen of hearts or an honor card (i.e., ten, jack, queen, king, or ace)?   [*Ans.* $\frac{5}{13}$.]

4. A word is chosen at random from the set of words $\mathfrak{U} = \{$men, bird, ball, field, book$\}$. Let p, q, and r be the statements:

   p: The word has two vowels.
   q: The first letter of the word is "b."
   r: The word rhymes with "cook."

   Find the probability of the following statements:
   (a) p.   (d) $p \wedge q$.
   (b) q.   (e) $(p \vee q) \wedge \sim r$.
   (c) r.   (f) $p \rightarrow q$.   [*Ans.* (f) $\frac{4}{5}$.]

5. A single die is thrown. Find the probability that
   (a) An odd number turns up.
   (b) The number which turns up is greater than two.
   (c) A seven turns up.

6. In the market leadership example of Chapter II, Section 1, assume that all 36 possibilities for leadership in the four territories are equally likely. Find the probability:
   (a) That Company A is the leader in more territories than either of its rivals.   [*Ans.* $\frac{7}{18}$.]
   (b) That the same company is the leader in all the territories.   [*Ans.* $\frac{1}{36}$.]
   (c) That every territory has a different market leader.   [*Ans.* 0.]

7. A single die is thrown twice. What value for the sum of the two outcomes has the highest probability? What value or values of the sum has the lowest probability of occurring?

8. In December, 1960, the E. I. duPont de Nemours Company had 210,840 common stockholders, and General Motors Corporation had 830,873

common stockholders. Assume that there were 50,000 investors who held common stock in both companies. If a person is selected at random from the list of common stockholders of duPont, what is the probability that he is also a stockholder of General Motors? If a General Motors stockholder is selected at random, what is the probability that he is *not* a duPont stockholder?

9. A certain part can be defective because it has one or more out of three possible defects: insufficient tensile strength, a burr, or a diameter outside tolerance limits. In a lot of 1000 pieces it is known that

120 have a tensile strength defect.
80 have a burr.
60 have an unacceptable diameter.
22 have tensile strength and burr defects.
16 have tensile strength and diameter defects.
20 have burr and diameter defects.
8 have all three defects.

If a piece is drawn at random from the lot, what is the probability that the piece
(a) Is not defective?   [*Ans.* .79.]
(b) Has exactly two defects?   [*Ans.* .034.]

10. Parts A, B, C, D, E, and F are to be produced one after the other on a machine. If all permutations are equally likely, what is the probability that
(a) The permutation will be D, B, F, A, E, C?
(b) Part A will directly precede part B?
(c) Part D will directly either follow or be followed by part F?

11. In Exercise 10, answer questions (a), (b), and (c) if part A must be directly followed by either B or C and all permissible permutations are equally likely.

12. A lot contains 20 pieces, of which 14 are good and 6 are defective. If the equiprobable measure is assigned to all possible samples of given size, what is the probability of obtaining a sample of five with
(a) No defectives?   [*Ans.* .129.]
(b) One defective?
(c) Two defectives?
(d) Three defectives?   [*Ans.* .117.]
(e) Four defectives?
(f) Five defectives?
(g) Three or more defectives?
(h) Less than two defectives?
(i) Between two and four (inclusive) defectives?
(j) Less than six defectives?
(k) Two good pieces?
(l) Between one and three (inclusive) good pieces? [*Ans.* .483.]

13. A room contains a group of n people who are wearing badges numbered from 1 to n. If two people are selected at random, what is the probability that the larger badge number is a 3? Answer this problem assuming that $n = 5, 4, 3, 2$. [*Ans.* $\frac{1}{5}$; $\frac{1}{3}$; $\frac{2}{3}$; 0.]

14. In Exercise 13, suppose that we observe two men leaving the room and that the larger of their badge numbers is 3. What might we guess as to the number of people in the room?

15. Find the probability that a bridge hand will have suits of:

    (a) 5, 4, 3, and 1 cards. $\left[Ans.\ \dfrac{4!\binom{13}{5}\binom{13}{4}\binom{13}{3}\binom{13}{1}}{\binom{52}{13}} \cong .129. \right]$

    (b) 6, 4, 2, and 1 cards. [*Ans.* .047.]
    (c) 4, 4, 3, and 2 cards. [*Ans.* .216.]
    (d) 4, 3, 3, and 3 cards. [*Ans.* .105.]

16. There are $\binom{52}{13} = 6.35 \times 10^{11}$ possible bridge hands. Find the probability that a bridge hand dealt at random will be all of one suit. Estimate *roughly* the number of bridge hands dealt in the entire country in a year. Is it likely that a hand of all one suit will occur sometime during the year in the United States?

17. Find the probability of obtaining each of the following poker hands. (A poker hand is a set of five cards chosen at random from a deck of 52 cards.)
    (a) Royal flush (ten, jack, queen, king, ace in a single suit.)
    $[Ans.\ 4/\binom{52}{5} = .0000015.]$
    (b) Straight flush (five in a sequence in a single suit, but not a royal flush).
    $[Ans.\ (40 - 4)/\binom{52}{5} = .000014.]$
    (c) Four of a kind (four cards of the same face value).
    $[Ans.\ 624/\binom{52}{5} = .00024.]$
    (d) Full house (one pair and one triple of the same face value).
    $[Ans.\ 3744/\binom{52}{5} = .0014.]$
    (e) Flush (five cards in a single suit but not a straight or royal flush).
    $[Ans.\ (5148 - 40)/\binom{52}{5} = .0020.]$
    (f) Straight (five cards in a row, not all of the same suit).
    $[Ans.\ (10{,}240 - 40)/\binom{52}{5} = .0039.]$
    (g) Straight or better. [*Ans.* .0076.]

4. Probability of a sample from a finite two-valued set

In Section 6 of Chapter III we discussed the problem of counting the number of ways of obtaining a partition with $\mathbf{n}(S) = n$ elements from a set $\mathfrak{U}$ containing $\mathbf{n}(\mathfrak{U}) = N$ elements, subject to the cell $A \cap S$ containing $\mathbf{n}(A \cap S) = r$ elements, where $\mathbf{n}(A) = R$. One interpretation which we gave to this problem was to let $\mathfrak{U}$ be a finite set, S be a subset of $\mathfrak{U}$ which was called a sample, and $[A, \tilde{A}]$ be a two-celled partition of $\mathfrak{U}$. Thus $\mathfrak{U}$

could be a shipment of a particular product, S a sample, and A the subset of $\mathfrak{U}$ which consists of defective pieces.

In this section, instead of *counting the number of ways* of obtaining a sample of given size with a specified number of defectives, we shall show how to *calculate the probability* of obtaining such a sample result. We do this by assigning to the set of $[S, \tilde{S}]$ partitions the equiprobable measure. Recall that there are $\binom{N}{n}$ ways of forming the partition $[S, \tilde{S}]$ so that $\mathbf{n}(S) = n$ and $\mathbf{n}(\tilde{S}) = N - n$. Then any particular partition has probability $1/\binom{N}{n}$. For example, let $N = 10$ and $n = 3$. Then, if

$$\mathfrak{U} = \{d_1, d_2, d_3, g_1, g_2, g_3, g_4, g_5, g_6, g_7\},$$

the probability of the partition

$$[S, \tilde{S}] = \{d_1, g_2, g_6 \mid d_2, d_3, g_1, g_3, g_4, g_5, g_7\}$$

is $1/\binom{10}{3} = \frac{1}{120}$.

We are interested, however, not in the probability of a specified partition, but in the probability of a partition with a specified number of defectives. From Section 6 of Chapter III we recall that there are $\binom{R}{r} \cdot \binom{N-R}{n-r}$ partitions in which there are exactly r defectives in the first cell. Accordingly, the probability of obtaining exactly r defectives in a sample containing n elements from a set containing N elements R of which are defective is given by

$$(1) \qquad \mathbf{h}(r; n, R, N) = \frac{\binom{R}{r} \binom{N-R}{n-r}}{\binom{N}{n}}.$$

Thus, in our example, the probability of obtaining exactly one defective in a sample of three from a lot of ten containing three defectives is

$$\mathbf{h}(1; 3, 3, 10) = \frac{\binom{3}{1} \binom{10-3}{3-1}}{\binom{10}{3}} = \frac{3 \cdot 21}{120} = \frac{21}{40}.$$

A probability that is given by the formula (1) is called a *hypergeometric* probability.

As in the discussion of Section 6 of Chapter III, the restrictions on the variables given by the inequalities (1) of that section apply.

Although hypergeometric probabilities often apply in sampling situations, it is frequently extremely laborious to calculate the probabilities —particularly when N is large, n and R are neither very large nor very small compared with N, and r is neither very large nor very small compared with n and R. The student may convince himself of this by trying to calculate, for example, $h(200; 500, 500, 1000)$. Under such circumstances approximations are useful, and we shall show later in this chapter how some approximations to hypergeometric probabilities can be found.

E X E R C I S E S

1. In Exercises 3 and 4 of Chapter III, Section 6, find the probability of having various numbers of union men in a subcommittee of five if the equiprobable measure is assigned to all subcommittees of five. Show that the sum of the probabilities is 1.

2. In Exercise 7 of Chapter III, Section 6, what is the probability of obtaining one good piece and one defective in a sample of two?   [*Ans.* .6.]

3. In Exercise 12 of Chapter III, Section 6, show that the ratios which you were asked to calculate are hypergeometric probabilities.

4. In Exercise 12 of Section 3, recalculate the probabilities by using formula (1).

5. Show that

$$\mathbf{h}(r+1; n, R, N) = \frac{(R-r)(n-r)}{(r+1)(N-R-n+r+1)}\, \mathbf{h}(r; n, R, N).$$

Show that if $n \leq N - R$,

$$\mathbf{h}(0; n, R, N) = \frac{(N-R)!(N-n)!}{(N-R-n)!N!}$$

and if $n \leq R$,

$$\mathbf{h}(n; n, R, N) = \frac{R!(N-n)!}{(R-n)!N!}.$$

Use these relationships to calculate the probability of each possible value of r in Exercises 1(b) and 1(d) of Chapter III, Section 6.

6. In a community in which a particular issue of a magazine was purchased by 25% of all households, what is the probability of finding, out of a random sample of ten households, exactly two in which the magazine was purchased if the community has 20 households?   [*Ans.* .348.]

7. Of ten intercontinental ballistic missiles, five will misfire. If a salvo of n missiles is aimed at a particular target, what is the probability of obtaining at least one hit if (a) $n = 1$? (b) $n = 2$? (c) $n = 3$? (d) $n = 4$? (e) $n = 5$? (f) $n > 5$? [*Hint:* Calculate the probability of obtaining no hits and subtract this from 1.]   [*Ans.* (c) .917.]

8. Referring to Figure 7 of Chapter III, Section 6, show that there are $\binom{N}{R}$

ways of forming the partition $[A, \tilde{A}]$ of $\mathfrak{U}$, $\binom{n}{r}$ ways of forming the partition of S, and $\binom{N-n}{R-r}$ ways of partitioning $\tilde{S}$. Assuming all the partitions of $\mathfrak{U}$ are equally likely, derive from these facts an alternative formula for hypergeometric probabilities. Express this formula and formula (1) in this section in terms of factorials, and show that they are algebraically equivalent.

*5. Two nonintuitive examples

There are occasions in probability theory when one finds a problem for which the answer, based on probability theory, is not at all in agreement with one's intuition. It is usually possible to arrange a few wagers that will bring one's intuition into line with the mathematical theory. A particularly good example of this is provided by the matching birthdays problem.

Assume that we have a room with r people in it and we propose the bet that there are at least two people in the room having the same birthday, i.e., the same month and day of the year. We ask for the value of r which will make this a fair bet. Few people would be willing to bet even money on this wager unless there were at least 100 people in the room. Most people would suggest 150 as a reasonable number. However, we shall see that with 150 people the odds are approximately 4,500,000,000,000,000 to 1 in favor of two people having the same birthday, and that one should be willing to bet even money with as few as 23 people in the room.

Let us first find the probability that in a room with r people, no two have the same birthday. There are 365 possibilities for each person's birthday (neglecting February 29). There are then 365^r possibilities for the birthdays of r people. We assume that all these possibilities are equally likely. To find the probability that no two have the same birthday we must find the number of possibilities for the birthdays which have *no* day represented twice. The first person can have any of 365 days for his birthday. For each of these, if the second person is to have a different birthday, there are only 364 possibilities for his birthday. For the third man, there are 363 possibilities if he is to have a different birthday than the first two, etc. Thus the probability that no two people have the same birthday in a group of r people is

$$q_r = \frac{365 \cdot 364 \cdot \ldots \cdot (365 - r + 1)}{365^r}.$$

The probability that at least two people have the same birthday is then $p_r = 1 - q_r$. In Figure 1 the values of p_r and the odds for a fair bet, $p_r : (1 - p_r)$, are given for several values of r.

Number of People in the Room	Probability of at Least Two with Same Birthday	Approximate Odds for a Fair Bet
5	.027	
10	.117	
15	.253	
20	.411	70:100
21	.444	80:100
22	.476	91:100
23	.507	103:100
24	.538	117:100
25	.569	132:100
30	.706	242:100
40	.891	819:100
50	.970	33:1
60	.994	169:1
70		1,200:1
80		12,000:1
90		160,000:1
100		3,300,000:1
125		31,000,000,000:1
150		4,500,000,000,000,000:1

Figure 1

We consider now a second problem in which intuition does not lead to the correct answer. We have seen that there are $n!$ permutations of the numbers from 1 to n. Let us consider a rearrangement of these numbers as the operation of placing each of the numbers in one of n boxes or *positions* (one number to a position). The positions are assumed to be numbered in serial order. We shall say that the ith number is unchanged by the permutation if, after the rearrangement, number i is still in the ith position. For example, if we consider the permutations of the numbers 1, 2, and 3, then the permutation 123 leaves *all* numbers fixed, the permutation 213 leaves *one* number fixed, and the permutations 312 and 231 leave *no* numbers fixed. It is obviously impossible, in this example, to leave exactly two numbers fixed. (Why?)

DEFINITION. A *complete permutation* is one that leaves no numbers fixed.

The problem that we now consider can be stated as follows. If a permutation of n numbers is chosen at random, what is the probability that the permutation chosen is a complete permutation? A more colorful but equivalent problem is the following. A hat-check girl has checked n hats, but they have become hopelessly scrambled. She hands back the hats at random. What is the probability that no man gets his own hat? For this problem some people's intuition would lead them to guess that for a large number of hats this probability should be small, while others guess that it should be large. Few people guess that the probability is neither large nor small and essentially independent of the number of hats involved.

To find the desired probability, we assume that all $n!$ permutations are equally likely, and hence we need only count the number of complete permutations which there are for n elements. Let w_n be the number of such permutations. Then the desired probability is $p_n = w_n/n!$. If this procedure is carried out (see Exercise 14), the answer is found to be

$$p_n = \frac{1}{2!} - \frac{1}{3!} + \frac{1}{4!} - \cdots \pm \frac{1}{n!}$$

where the $+$ sign is chosen if n is even and the $-$ sign if n is odd. In Figure 2, these numbers are given for the first few values of n.

Number of Hats	Probability p_n That No Man Gets His Hat
2	.500000
3	.333333
4	.375000
5	.366667
6	.368056
7	.367857
8	.367882

Figure 2

It can be shown that, as the number of hats increases, the probabilities approach a number $1/e = .367879 \ldots$, where the number $e = 2.718281 \ldots$ is a number that plays an important role in many branches of mathematics.

E X E R C I S E S

1. What odds should you be willing to give on a bet that at least two people in the United States Senate have the same birthday?
   [*Ans.* 3,300,000:1.]

2. What is the probability that in the House of Representatives at least two men have the same birthday?

3. What odds should you be willing to give on a bet that at least two of the Presidents of the United States have had the same birthday? Would you win the bet?
   [*Ans.* More than 3:1; Yes. Polk and Harding were born on Nov. 2.]

4. What odds should you be willing to give on the bet that at least two of the Presidents of the United States have died on the same day of the year? Would you win the bet?
   [*Ans.* More than 2.4:1; Yes. Jefferson, Adams, and Monroe all died on July 4.]

5. Statistical evidence indicates that not all dates are equally likely to produce birthdays; for example, there tend to be more births in the summer than in the winter. Qualitatively, how does this affect the probabilities of Figure 1 (i.e., does it tend to increase them or decrease them)?

6. What is the qualitative effect on the probabilities of Figure 1 of including the possibility of a person's having a birthday on February 29?

7. By assigning the equiprobable measure to births in each of the twelve months of the year, derive a table like Figure 1 showing the probability that at least two out of a group of r randomly selected people have birthdays in the same month for $r = 1, 2, 3, 4, 5$. What side would you take of an even-money bet that there were at least two people in the room who had birthdays in the same month if there were five people in the room? If there were four? What is the qualitative effect on the probabilities which you derived of the fact that the months have different numbers of days?

8. Four men check their hats. Assuming that the hats are returned at random, what is the probability that exactly four men get their own hats? Calculate the answer for exactly 3, 2, 1, 0 men.   [*Ans.* $\frac{1}{24}$; 0; $\frac{1}{4}$; $\frac{1}{3}$; $\frac{3}{8}$.]

9. A group of 50 men and their wives attend a dance. The partners for a dance are chosen by lot. What is the approximate probability that no man dances with his wife?

10. Show that the probability that, in a group of r people, *exactly* one pair has has the same birthday is

$$t_r = \binom{r}{2} \frac{365 \cdot 364 \ldots (365 - r + 2)}{365^r}.$$

11. Show that $t_r = \binom{r}{2} \dfrac{q_r}{366 - r}$, where t_r is defined in Exercise 10, and q_r is the probability that no pair has the same birthday.

12. Using the result of Exercise 11 and the results given in Figure 1, find the probability of exactly one pair of people with the same birthday in a group of r people, for $r = 15, 20, 25, 30, 40,$ and 50.
    [*Ans.* .22; .32; .38; .38; .26; .12.]

13. What is the approximate probability that there has been exactly one pair of Presidents with the same birthday?

14. Let w_n be the number of complete permutations of n numbers.
    (a) Show that
$$w_1 = 0, \qquad w_2 = 1, \ldots$$
$$w_n = (n - 1)w_{n-1} + (n - 1)w_{n-2}, \qquad n = 2, 3, \ldots.$$

[*Hint:* Any complete permutation of n numbers can be obtained from a complete permutation of $n - 1$ numbers or from a permutation of $n - 1$ numbers that leaves one number fixed. Describe how this can be done, and show that the two terms on the right side of the equation represent the number that can be obtained from each of these methods.]

(b) Let p_n be the probability that a permutation of n numbers chosen at random is a complete permutation. From part (a) show that

$$p_1 = 0, \qquad p_2 = \tfrac{1}{2}$$

$$p_n = \frac{n-1}{n}\, p_{n-1} + \frac{1}{n}\, p_{n-2} \qquad \text{for } n = 3, 4, \ldots.$$

(c) Let $v_n = p_n - p_{n-1}$ for $n = 2, 3, 4, \ldots$. From part (b), show that

$$n(p_n - p_{n-1}) = -(p_{n-1} - p_{n-2}), \qquad n = 3, \ldots$$

and hence that

$$nv_n = -v_{n-1}, \qquad n = 3, \ldots.$$

(d) Using the fact that $p_1 = 0$, and $p_2 = \tfrac{1}{2}$, find v_2. From the result of part (c) find $v_3, v_4, \ldots, v_n$.

(e) Using the result of part (d), show that

$$p_n = \frac{1}{2!} - \frac{1}{3!} + \ldots \pm \frac{1}{n!}.$$

6. *Conditional probability and Bayes' theorem*

Suppose that we have a given $\mathfrak{U}$ and that measures have been assigned to all subsets of $\mathfrak{U}$. A statement p will have probability $\mathbf{Pr}[p] = \mathbf{m}(P)$. Suppose we now receive some additional information, say that the statement q is true. How does this additional information alter the probability of p?

The probability of p after the receipt of the information q is called its *conditional probability*, and it is denoted by $\mathbf{Pr}[p \mid q]$, which is read "the probability of p given q." In this section we will construct a method of finding this conditional probability in terms of the measure $\mathbf{m}$.

If we know that q is true, then the original possibility set $\mathfrak{U}$ has been reduced to Q and therefore we must define our measure on the subsets of Q instead of on the subsets of $\mathfrak{U}$. Of course, every nonempty subset X of Q is a subset of $\mathfrak{U}$, and hence we know $\mathbf{m}(X)$, its measure before q was discovered. Since q cuts down on the number of possibilities, its new measure $\mathbf{m}'(X)$ should be larger.

The basic idea on which the definition of $\mathbf{m}'$ is based is that, while we know that the possibility set has been reduced to Q, we have no new information about subsets of Q. If X and Y are subsets of Q, and $\mathbf{m}(X) =$

$2 \cdot m(Y)$, then we will want $m'(X) = 2 \cdot m'(Y)$. This will be the case if the measures of subsets of Q are simply increased by a proportionality factor $m'(X) = k \cdot m(X)$, and all that remains is to determine k. Since we know that $1 = m'(Q) = k \cdot m(Q)$, we see that $k = 1/m(Q)$ and our new measure on subsets of $\mathfrak{U}$ is determined by the formula

$$(1) \qquad\qquad m'(X) = \frac{m(X)}{m(Q)}.$$

How does this affect the probability of p? First of all the truth set of p has been reduced. Because all elements of $\tilde{Q}$ have been eliminated, the new truth set of p is $P \cap Q$ and therefore

$$(2) \qquad \mathbf{Pr}[p \mid q] = m'(P \cap Q) = \frac{m(P \cap Q)}{m(Q)} = \frac{\mathbf{Pr}[p \wedge q]}{\mathbf{Pr}[q]}.$$

Note that if the original measure m is the equiprobable measure, then the new measure m' will also be the equiprobable measure on the set Q.

We must take care that the denominators in (1) and (2) be different from zero. Observe that $m(Q)$ will be zero if Q is the empty set, which happens only if q is self-contradictory. This is also the only case in which $\mathbf{Pr}[q] = 0$, and hence we make the obvious assumption that our information q is not self-contradictory.

Example 1. In Example 2 of Section 1, in which three computer manufacturers, A, B, and C, are trying to contract for the installation of a computer system with the X Company, the probability assigned to A, B, or C winning the contract was $\frac{2}{5}$, $\frac{2}{5}$, and $\frac{1}{5}$, respectively. Suppose it is learned that B has subsequently decided not to compete on this contract. What are the chances of A and C now? Let q be the statement that B will not win, i.e., that either A or C will win the contract. *Prior* to the receipt of the information that B has withdrawn from competition, $\mathbf{Pr}[q] = \frac{3}{5}$, while *subsequent* to receipt of this information, $\mathbf{Pr}[q] = 1$. Hence the other two probabilities are increased by a factor of $1/(\frac{3}{5}) = \frac{5}{3}$. Company A now has a $(\frac{2}{5})(\frac{5}{3}) = \frac{2}{3}$ chance of winning the contract while C has a $(\frac{1}{5})(\frac{5}{3}) = \frac{1}{3}$ chance.

Example 2. In Example 2 of Chapter I, Section 6, let us partition the set $\mathfrak{U}$ of holes drilled after a seismographic recording has been made into $[S, \tilde{S}]$ and into $[D, O]$, where S is the set of holes on which the test revealed subsurface structure, D is the set of dry holes, and O is the set of oil-producing holes. Letting s, d, and o stand for the statements of which S, D, and O are the truth sets, suppose

$$\mathbf{Pr}[s \wedge o] = .2, \qquad \mathbf{Pr}[s \wedge d] = .3,$$
$$\mathbf{Pr}[\sim s \wedge o] = .1, \qquad \mathbf{Pr}[\sim s \wedge d] = .4.$$

This data can be conveniently summarized in the table of Figure 3, in which the numbers in the body of the table are the probabilities of the basic conjunctions of the simple statements at the top and the side of the table, and the numbers in the margins are the probabilities of the simple statements themselves. For example,

$$\mathbf{Pr}[s \wedge o] + \mathbf{Pr}[\sim s \wedge o] = .2 + .1 = .3 = \mathbf{Pr}[o]$$

(see Section 2, Exercise 25).

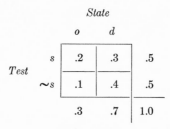

Figure 3

Thus the probability that a test will reveal structure is $\mathbf{Pr}[s] = .5$, and the probability of oil is $\mathbf{Pr}[o] = .3$, before the test has been taken or drilling has commenced. Now suppose that a seismographic recording has been made and that the test reveals structure. Then the set of logical possibilities is reduced to those in the upper row of the table of Figure 3. Thus,

$$\mathbf{Pr}[o \mid s] = .2/.5 = .4, \qquad \mathbf{Pr}[d \mid s] = .3/.5 = .6.$$

Observe that *after* the test which revealed structure, the probability of oil $\mathbf{Pr}[o \mid s] = .4$, whereas *before* the test the probability of oil $\mathbf{Pr}[o] = .3$. The test result revealing structure, therefore, provides imperfect information which, however, increases the probability of oil from .3 to .4.

A particularly interesting case of conditional probability is that in which $\mathbf{Pr}[p \mid q] = \mathbf{Pr}[p]$. Here the new information q has no effect on the probability of p, and we then say that p is *independent* of q. If in (2) we replace $\mathbf{Pr}[p \mid q]$ by $\mathbf{Pr}[p]$, and cross-multiply, we get

(3) $$\mathbf{Pr}[p \wedge q] = \mathbf{Pr}[p] \cdot \mathbf{Pr}[q].$$

On the other hand, if we express the condition that q is independent of p, we arrive at the same result. Hence the two statements are independent of each other. We can therefore say that p and q are independent if and only if (3) holds.

Example 3. Consider three throws of an ordinary coin, where we consider the eight possibilities to be equally likely. Let p be the statement, "A head turns up on the first throw," and q be the statement, "A tail turns up on the second throw." Then $\mathbf{Pr}[p] = \mathbf{Pr}[q] = \frac{1}{2}$ and $\mathbf{Pr}[p \wedge q] = \frac{1}{4}$ and therefore p and q are independent statements.

While we have an intuitive notion of independence, it can happen that two statements, which may not seem to be independent, are in fact independent. For example, let r be the statement "The same side turns up all three times."

Let s be the statement "At most one head occurs." Then r and s are independent statements (see Exercise 10).

Example 4. In a survey of consumer expectations, individuals are asked whether they expect to buy a new car in the next twelve months; after a year they are interviewed again to see whether they in fact bought a car. Let p be the statement "the individual plans to buy a car within a given year" and b the statement "the individual bought a car within the given year." Suppose the following probabilities are assigned to the four possible conjunctions of these two statements and their denials:

$$\mathbf{Pr}[p \wedge b] = .06, \qquad \mathbf{Pr}[p \wedge \sim b] = .24,$$
$$\mathbf{Pr}[\sim p \wedge b] = .14, \qquad \mathbf{Pr}[\sim p \wedge \sim b] = .56.$$

These data are summarized in the table of Figure 4, in which we also include in the margins the probabilities of the simple statements; for example,

$$\mathbf{Pr}[p \wedge b] + \mathbf{Pr}[\sim p \wedge b] = \mathbf{Pr}[b] = .06 + .14 = .20.$$

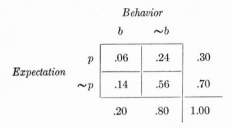

Figure 4

From this we observe that

$$\mathbf{Pr}[b]\cdot\mathbf{Pr}[p] = .30\cdot.20 = .06 = \mathbf{Pr}[p \wedge b]$$

from which we conclude that b is independent of p. Accordingly, with these hypothetical probabilities, an individual's expectations regarding the purchase of a new car provide no information as to whether he will in fact buy a new car.

Conditional probabilities play an important role in many business problems; we may start with a probability assigned to a prediction p, and then revise our probability on the basis of added information q. It is customary to refer to the original probability $\mathbf{Pr}[p]$ as the *prior* probability, and the resulting conditional probability $\mathbf{Pr}[p \mid q]$ as the *posterior* probability.

For instance, in Example 1 the prior probability that Company A will win the contract was $\frac{2}{5}$, while the posterior probability is $\frac{2}{3}$. In Example 2, the probability of oil prior to the seismological test was .3, but after structure was revealed we raised the probability to .4. These computations are so common that we shall derive a simple formula for the posterior probability.

From the definition of conditional probability we have

$$\Pr[p \mid q] = \frac{\Pr[p \wedge q]}{\Pr[q]} \quad \text{and} \quad \Pr[q \mid p] = \frac{\Pr[q \wedge p]}{\Pr[p]}.$$

Since $q \wedge p$ is equivalent to $p \wedge q$, we find that

(4) $$\Pr[p \mid q] = \frac{\Pr[q \mid p] \cdot \Pr[p]}{\Pr[q]}.$$

We also know that (see Exercise 12):

(5) $$\Pr[q] = \Pr[q \mid p] \cdot \Pr[p] + \Pr[q \mid \sim p] \cdot \Pr[\sim p].$$

Formulas (4) and (5) together give us a means of computing the posterior probability $\Pr[p \mid q]$ from $\Pr[p]$, $\Pr[q \mid p]$, and $\Pr[q \mid \sim p]$. This result is sometimes known as "Bayes' theorem," after the Reverend Thomas Bayes who first published it in 1763.

Example 5. Ten per cent of the employees of a certain company have been to business school. Of these, 70 per cent hold administrative positions. Of those that have not been to business school, 30 per cent hold administrative positions. An employee is selected at random from the administrative staff. What is the probability that he went to business school?

Let p be the statement "the employee selected went to business school." Let q be the statement "the employee selected was an administrator." From the information given $\Pr[p] = .10$, $\Pr[q \mid p] = .70$, and $\Pr[q \mid \sim p] = .30$. Hence, from (5),

$$\Pr[q] = (.70)(.10) + (.30)(.90) = .34,$$

and from (4),

$$\Pr[p \mid q] = \frac{\Pr[q \mid p]\Pr[p]}{\Pr[q]}$$

$$= \frac{(.70)(.10)}{.34} = .21.$$

EXERCISES

1. Daily demand for a certain product can vary between one and thirteen units. If the equiprobable measure is assigned to all possible demands, what is the probability that on a particular day the demand was for exactly five units, given that on that day demand was between two and seven units inclusive?

2. There are seven potential bidders for a certain contract. It is believed that every bidder has about the same chance of winning. Just before the closing date, three of the potential bidders decide not to submit bids. How

much is the chance of one of the remaining four bidders to win the contract increased?

3. Let d_i be the statement, "The demand for product X today was for i units." Suppose $\Pr[d_0] = .1$, $\Pr[d_1] = .2$, $\Pr[d_2] = .4$, $\Pr[d_3] = .3$, and $\Pr[d_i] = 0$ for $i > 3$. Assume that demands on successive days are independent. What is the probability that total demand on two successive days will be for more than three units, given that:
(a) On one of the days demand was for one unit? [*Ans.* $\frac{1}{3}$.]
(b) On the first day, demand was for one unit? [*Ans.* .3.]

4. Referring to Section 3, Exercise 9, what is the probability that a given piece selected at random has a burr if:
(a) It has a tensile-strength defect?
(b) It has tensile-strength and diameter defects? [*Ans.* $\frac{1}{2}$.]
(c) It has neither a tensile-strength nor a diameter defect?

5. In the market leadership example of Chapter II, Section 1, assuming that the equiprobable measure has been assigned, find the probability that A is the leader in at least two territories given that B discontinues marketing in the North.

6. If $\Pr[\sim p] = \frac{1}{4}$ and $\Pr[q \mid p] = \frac{1}{2}$, what is $\Pr[p \wedge q]$? [*Ans.* $\frac{3}{8}$.]

7. The American Experience Table of Mortality shows that of 100,000 people alive at the age of ten, 57,917 will survive until their sixtieth year, and 56,371 will survive until their sixty-first year. What is the probability that a person selected at random at the age of sixty will die during the next year?

8. A researcher examines the output of an automatic machine by looking at the pieces produced in sequence and determining whether they are good or defective. He then partitions a sequence into *runs*, where a run is a sequence of pieces which ends whenever a defective occurs. For example, in the sequence gggdgdggddggggd, the runs are (gggd), (gd), (ggd), (d), (ggggd). He finally looks at the length of various runs and assigns probabilities to the future occurrences of runs of various lengths. In the example above, there are runs of length 4, 2, 3, 1, and 5. Let r_i be the statement, "The length of a run is i or more," $i = 1, 2, 3, \ldots$. After considerable research, the following probabilities are assigned to r_i:

i	$\Pr[r_i]$
1	1.00
2	.90
3	.81
4	.73
5	.66
6	.59

(a) Let p_i be the statement, "The run is *precisely* of length i." Show that $\Pr[p_i] = \Pr[r_i] - \Pr[r_{i+1}]$. Calculate $\Pr[p_i]$ for $i = 1, 2, 3, 4, 5$.

(b) Show that $\mathbf{Pr}[p_i \wedge r_i] = \mathbf{Pr}[p_i]$.

(c) Calculate $\mathbf{Pr}[p_i \mid r_i]$ for $i = 1, 2, 3, 4, 5$. What can you say regarding independence or dependence about $\mathbf{Pr}[p_i \mid r_i]$?

[*Partial Ans.* All approximately .1.]

9. Let a deck of cards consist of the jacks and queens chosen from a bridge deck, and let two cards be drawn from the new deck. Find:

(a) The probability that the cards are both jacks, given that one is a jack.
[*Ans.* $\frac{3}{11} = .27.$]

(b) The probability that the cards are both jacks, given that one is a red jack.
[*Ans.* $\frac{5}{13} = .38.$]

(c) The probability that the cards are both jacks, given that one is the jack of hearts.
[*Ans.* $\frac{3}{7} = .43.$]

10. Prove that statements r and s in Example 3 are independent.

11. The following example shows that r may be independent of p and q without being independent of $p \wedge q$ and $p \vee q$. We throw a coin twice. Let p be "The first toss comes out heads," q be "The second toss comes out heads," and r be "The two tosses come out the same." Compute $\mathbf{Pr}[r]$, $\mathbf{Pr}[r \mid p]$, $\mathbf{Pr}[r \mid q]$, $\mathbf{Pr}[r \mid p \wedge q]$, $\mathbf{Pr}[r \mid p \vee q]$.
[*Ans.* $\frac{1}{2}, \frac{1}{2}, \frac{1}{2}, 1, \frac{1}{3}.$]

12. Prove that formula (5) holds for any statements p and q.

13. Urn A contains three white balls and seven black balls; urn B contains twelve white balls and eight black balls. One of the urns is chosen at random and a ball is drawn from it.

(a) What is the probability that the ball is white *given* that it was drawn from urn A? *Given* that it was drawn from urn B?

(b) What is the (unconditional) probability that the ball is white?

(c) *Given* that the ball is white, what is the probability that it was drawn from urn A?
[*Ans.* $\frac{1}{3}.$]

14. In Exercise 13, five balls are drawn from one of the urns chosen at random.

(a) What is the probability that two of the balls are white and three are black *given* that they were drawn from urn A? *Given* that they were drawn from urn B?

(b) What is the (unconditional) probability of obtaining two white and three black balls?

(c) *Given* that the sample of five consists of two white and three black balls, what is the probability that it was drawn from urn A? [*Ans.* .636.]

15. Three candidates, Adams, Brown, and Jones, are competing for the same position in a large company. Adams has a good friend in Personnel, who has promised to give him some inside information. While his friend cannot tell him whether he has been chosen (for fear of losing his job), he will give Adams the name of one of the other candidates who has been eliminated. Adams argues that if his friend names Jones, then the possibilities have been narrowed to {Adams, Brown}, hence his chances of winning the position have increased from $\frac{1}{3}$ to $\frac{1}{2}$—assuming that all candidates had the same prior probability. If his friend names Brown, on the other hand, then the

possible winners have been narrowed to {Adams, Jones}, and again Adams has a $\frac{1}{2}$ chance. So it does not matter what information he will receive. By the very promise of such information Adams' chances have been increased from $\frac{1}{3}$ to $\frac{1}{2}$. What is wrong with Adams' reasoning?

16. Three urns, A, B, and C, contain mixtures of white, red, and black balls in the following numbers:

Urn	White	Red	Black	Total
A	2	3	5	10
B	12	6	2	20
C	8	15	7	30

An urn is chosen by the following randomizing device: a six-faced die is thrown; urn A is chosen if the die comes up 1, urn B if it comes up 2 or 3, and urn C otherwise.

(a) Given that a single ball drawn from an urn selected in this manner is red, what is the probability that the urn is urn A? urn B? urn C?
[*Ans.* $\frac{1}{8}, \frac{2}{8}, \frac{5}{8}$.]

(b) Given that three balls drawn in sequence from the urn are (in order) white, white, and black, what is the probability that the urn is urn A? urn B? urn C?

17. Urn A contains 2 white balls and one black ball; urn B contains 1001 white balls and 1000 black balls. One of the urns is selected at random. What is the probability that it was urn A if:

(a) One ball is drawn from the urn and it is white? [*Ans.* $\frac{1334}{2335}$.]

(b) Two balls are drawn from the urn, the first of which is white and the second black?

(c) Two balls are drawn from the urn, both of which are white? What information does the second ball give about the contents of the urn if the first ball drawn was white? [*Ans.* None.]

18. In Exercise 17, suppose the first ball drawn had been black. What is the probability that it was drawn from urn A? What is the probability for the sequences black-black and black-white? Does the second drawing give any information about the contents of the urn given that the first ball drawn was black?

19. A lot of ten pieces contains R defectives. A sample of five is drawn and two defectives are found. Suppose that the following prior probabilities are assigned to the number of defectives R in the lot: $\mathbf{Pr}[R = 3] = .2$; $\mathbf{Pr}[R = 5] = .8$. What are the posterior probabilities of the number of defectives in the lot given the sample result? What are the posterior probabilities of the number of defectives among the five pieces not sampled given the sample result? [*Partial Ans.* $\mathbf{Pr}[R = 3] = \frac{21}{101}$.]

20. In Exercise 7 of Section 4, suppose the following prior probabilities are assigned to the number R of missiles which will misfire: $\mathbf{Pr}[R = 3] = .2$, $\mathbf{Pr}[R = 5] = .6$, $\mathbf{Pr}[R = 7] = .2$.

(a) What is the probability that a salvo of three missiles will hit the target at least once?

(b) Given that a target was hit *at least* once by a salvo of three missiles, what is the posterior probability that among the original ten there were exactly three which would misfire?

(c) Given that a target was hit *exactly* once by a salvo of three missiles, what is the posterior probability that among the seven remaining the number which misfire is 2? 4? 6? 7?

7. *Finite stochastic processes*

We consider here a very general situation which we will specialize in later sections. We deal with a sequence of experiments where the outcome on each particular experiment depends on some chance element. Any such sequence is called a *stochastic process*. (The Greek word "stochos" means "guess"). We shall assume a finite number of experiments and a finite number of possibilities for each experiment. We assume that, if all the outcomes of the experiments which precede a given experiment were known, then both the possibilities for this experiment and the probability that any particular possibility will occur would be known. We wish to make predictions about the process as a whole. For example, in the case of repeated throws of an ordinary coin we would assume that on any particular experiment we have two outcomes, and the probabilities for each of these outcomes is one-half regardless of any other outcomes. We might be interested, however, in the probabilities of statements of the form, "More than two-thirds of the throws result in heads," or "The number of heads and tails which occur is the same," etc. These are questions which can be answered only when a probability measure has been assigned to the process as a whole. In this section we show how a probability measure can be assigned, using the given information. In the case of coin tossing, the probabilities (hence also the possibilities) on any given experiment do not depend upon the previous results. We will not make any such restriction here since the assumption is not true in general.

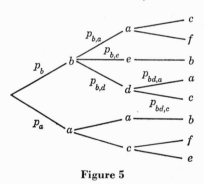

Figure 5

We shall show how the probability measure is constructed for a particular example, and the procedure in the general case is similar.

We assume that we have a sequence of three experiments, the possibilities for which are indicated in Figure 5. The set of all possible outcomes which might occur on any of the experiments is represented by the set $\{a, b, c, d, e, f\}$. Note that if we know that outcome b occurred on the first experiment, then we know that the possibilities on experiment two are $\{a, e, d\}$. Similarly if we know that b occurred on the first experiment and a on the second, then the only possibilities for the third are $\{c, f\}$. We denote by p_a the probability that the first experiment results in outcome a, and by p_b the probability that outcome b occurs in the first experiment. We denote by $p_{b,d}$ the probability that outcome d occurs on the second experiment, which is the probability computed on the assumption that outcome b occurred on the first experiment. Similarly for $p_{b,a}, p_{b,e}, p_{a,a}, p_{a,c}$. We denote by $p_{bd,c}$ the probability that outcome c occurs on the third experiment, the latter probability being computed on the assumption that outcome b occurred on the first experiment and d on the second. Similarly for $p_{ba,c}, p_{ba,f}$, etc. We have assumed that these numbers are given and the fact that they are probabilities assigned to possible outcomes would mean that they are positive and that

$$p_a + p_b = 1, \quad p_{b,a} + p_{b,e} + p_{b,d} = 1, \quad \text{and} \quad p_{bd,a} + p_{bd,c} = 1, \text{etc.}$$

It is convenient to associate each probability with a branch of the tree. We have done this in Figure 5 for several branches. The sum of the numbers assigned to branches from a particular branch point is one, e.g., $p_{b,a} + p_{b,e} + p_{b,d} = 1$.

A possibility for the sequence of three experiments is indicated by a path through the tree. We define now a probability measure on the set of all paths. We call this a *tree measure*. To the path corresponding to outcome b on the first experiment, d on the second, and c on the third, we assign the weight $p_b \cdot p_{b,d} \cdot p_{bd,c}$, that is, the *product* of the probabilities associated with each branch along the path being considered. We find the probability for each path through the tree.

Before showing the reason for this choice we must first show that it determines a probability measure, in other words, that the weights are positive and the sum of the weights is one. The weights are products of positive numbers and hence positive. To see that their sum is one we first find the sum of the weights of all paths corresponding to a particular outcome, say b, on the first experiment and a particular outcome, say d, on the second. We have

$$p_b \cdot p_{b,d} \cdot p_{bd,a} + p_b \cdot p_{b,d} \cdot p_{bd,c} = p_b \cdot p_{b,d}[p_{bd,a} + p_{bd,c}] = p_b \cdot p_{b,d}.$$

For any other first two outcomes we would obtain a similar result. For example, the sum of the weights assigned to paths corresponding to outcome a on the first experiment and c on the second is $p_a \cdot p_{a,c}$. Notice that when we have verified that we have a probability measure, this will be the probability that the first outcome results in a and the second experiment results in c.

Next we find the sum of the weights assigned to all the paths corresponding to the cases where the outcome of the first experiment is b. We find this by adding the sums corresponding to the different possibilities for the second experiment. But by our preceding calculation this is

$$p_b \cdot p_{b,a} + p_b \cdot p_{b,e} + p_b \cdot p_{b,d} = p_b[p_{b,a} + p_{b,e} + p_{b,d}] = p_b.$$

Similarly the sum of the weights assigned to paths corresponding to the outcome a on the first experiment is p_a. Thus the sum of all weights is $p_a + p_b = 1$. Therefore we do have a probability measure. Note that we have also shown that the probability that the outcome of the first experiment is a has been assigned probability p_a in agreement with our given probability.

To see the complete connection of our new measure with the given probabilities, let $X_j = z$ be the statement "The outcome of the jth experiment was z." Then the statement $[X_1 = b \wedge X_2 = d \wedge X_3 = c]$ is a compound statement that has been assigned probability $p_b \cdot p_{b,d} \cdot p_{bd,c}$. The statement $[X_1 = b \wedge X_2 = d]$ we have noted has been assigned probability $p_b \cdot p_{b,d}$ and the statement $[X_1 = b]$ has been assigned probability p_b. Thus

$$\mathbf{Pr}[X_3 = c \mid X_2 = d \wedge X_1 = b] = \frac{p_b \cdot p_{b,d} \cdot p_{bd,c}}{p_b \cdot p_{b,d}} = p_{bd,c}$$

$$\mathbf{Pr}[X_2 = d \mid X_1 = b] = \frac{p_b \cdot p_{b,d}}{p_b} = p_{b,d}.$$

Thus we see that our probabilities, computed under the assumption that previous results were known, become the corresponding conditional probabilities when computed with respect to the tree measure. It can be shown that the tree measure which we have assigned is the only one which will lead to this agreement. We can now find the probability of any statement concerning the stochastic process from our tree measure.

Example 1. Suppose that we have two urns. Urn 1 contains two black balls and three white balls. Urn 2 contains two black balls and one white ball. An urn is chosen at random and a ball chosen from this urn at random. What is the probability that a white ball is chosen? A hasty answer might be $\frac{1}{2}$, since there are an equal number of black and white balls involved and everything is done at random. However, it is hasty answers like this one (which is wrong) which show the need for a more careful analysis.

We are considering two experiments. The first consists in choosing the urn and the second in choosing the ball. There are two possibilities for the first experiment, and we assign $p_1 = p_2 = \frac{1}{2}$ for the probabilities of choosing the first and the second urn, respectively. We then assign $p_{1,W} = \frac{3}{5}$ for the probability that a white ball is chosen, under the assumption that urn 1 is chosen. Similarly we assign $p_{1,B} = \frac{2}{5}$, $p_{2,W} = \frac{1}{3}$, $p_{2,B} = \frac{2}{3}$. We indicate these probabilities on the possibility tree in Figure 6. The probability that a white ball is drawn is then found from the tree measure as the sum of the weights assigned to paths which lead to a choice of a white ball. This is $\frac{1}{2} \cdot \frac{3}{5} + \frac{1}{2} \cdot \frac{1}{3} = \frac{7}{15}$.

Observe that this same answer could have been obtained by using formula (5) of Section 6, where we let q be the statement "a white ball is chosen" and p be the statement "urn 1 was chosen."

Example 2. We may treat the process of sampling two-valued items from a finite set as a stochastic process. Suppose, for example, we draw a sample of three pieces from a lot of ten containing two defectives. In Figure 7 each of the three possible draws is shown as an experiment. The first piece drawn can be either good or defective, so that there are initially two branches.

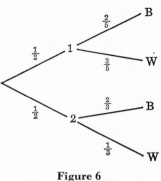

Figure 6

Given that the first is good, the second can be either good or defective, so that there are again two branches. This is the case at each experiment, except that which follows the initial drawing of two defectives. Since there are only two defectives in the lot, there is only one possible outcome on the third experiment.

On the first experiment we assign $p_g = \frac{8}{10}$ and $p_d = \frac{2}{10}$, since eight out of the ten pieces are good and each piece has the same probability of being drawn. We then assign $p_{g \cdot d} = \frac{2}{9}$ for the probability that the second piece chosen is

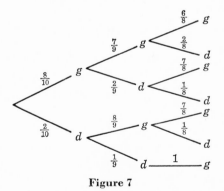

defective, given that the first piece was good, since in the second experiment there are only nine pieces remaining of which, under these conditions, two are defective. Similarly we find the other probabilities on the tree.

The probability that the sample will consist of three good pieces is the probability that the first, second, and third pieces will all be good. This is simply the path weight of the uppermost path of the tree, or $\frac{8}{10} \cdot \frac{7}{9} \cdot \frac{6}{8} = \frac{7}{15}$.

To obtain the probability that the sample contains exactly one defective,

Figure 7

we must obtain the sum of the path weights which result in two good pieces and one defective. There are three such paths—ggd, gdg, and dgg. The first has probability $\frac{8}{10} \cdot \frac{7}{9} \cdot \frac{2}{8} = \frac{7}{45}$, the second $\frac{8}{10} \cdot \frac{2}{9} \cdot \frac{7}{8} = \frac{7}{45}$, and the third $\frac{2}{10} \cdot \frac{8}{9} \cdot \frac{7}{8} = \frac{7}{45}$. (Why are the probabilities of the three paths the same?) Thus the probability of exactly one defective in the sample is $\frac{7}{45} + \frac{7}{45} + \frac{7}{45} = \frac{7}{15}$. The student should verify (see Exercise 8) that the probability of exactly two defectives in the sample is $\frac{1}{15}$, and (see Exercise 9) that the probability of r

defectives in the sample may be obtained as a hypergeometric probability $h(r; 3, 2, 10)$.

Example 3. In a tree diagram consisting of a sequence of acts and events, we obtain a stochastic process if we specify a sequence of acts, and we assign probabilities to the resulting events. In Example 3 of Chapter I, Section 6, for instance, we consider the sequence of acts (1) develop component, (2) develop A, (3) develop B, where the sequence will stop, of course, if any one of the developments turns out to be unsatisfactory. Figure 8 is a tree diagram showing the possible outcomes (s = satisfactory, u = unsatisfactory) at each stage. We assign probabilities to the outcome of each experiment, as shown on the branches. The higher probability of developing B satisfactorily is due primarily to the experience gained in developing A, and not to the fact that B is somewhat easier to develop.

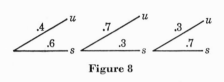

Figure 8

The probability of developing all three parts satisfactorily is the weight of the path sss, or

$$(.6)(.3)(.7) = .126.$$

The probability of not developing all three parts satisfactorily is the sum of the weights of the paths which end in u, that is, u, su, and ssu, giving

$$.4 + (.6)(.7) + (.6)(.3)(.3) = .874.$$

This same probability can, of course, be obtained by subtracting from 1 the probability .126 of developing all three parts satisfactorily.

We can use trees and tree measures to compute posterior probabilities for more complicated situations than those considered in Section 6. Assume that there are a number of alternatives $a_1, a_2, \ldots, a_r$, and that we know the probabilities of these alternatives. We also know the conditional probability of a certain statement p relative to each alternative. We learn that p is true, without learning which alternative is correct. We are then asked to find new probabilities for the alternatives. A convenient method of doing this is by means of tree diagrams. We illustrate this method by our next example.

Example 4. A car manufacturer makes three types of cars: sedans, station wagons, and convertibles. The same number of sedans and station wagons are manufactured, but only half as many convertibles as sedans. It is found that 50 per cent of the people who buy sedans buy a second car from the same manufacturer, while 75 per cent of those who buy station wagons and 25 per cent of those who buy convertibles buy a second car from the manufacturer. What is the probability that a customer returning for a second car will already have a specified type of car?

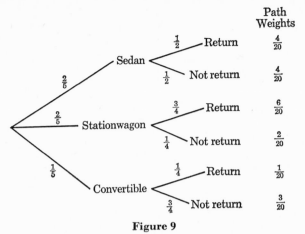

Path
Weights

Figure 9

We first construct a tree and tree measure for the type of the first car and for whether or not the customer returns for a second car. See Figure 9.

We next construct the tree in reverse order, putting first whether the customer returns, and then the type of his old car. We have the same six branches as in Figure 9, only the order of description has been changed. Hence the path weights may be obtained from Figure 9. Furthermore, we know that the probability of the customer's returning is

$$\tfrac{4}{20} + \tfrac{6}{20} + \tfrac{1}{20} = \tfrac{11}{20}$$

and hence we obtain the branch weights for the "first experiment" (see Figure 10a).

We may now fill in the missing branch weights by simple division. For example, let x be the probability that the customer has a sedan, given that he returns. Then $\tfrac{11}{20}x = \tfrac{4}{20}$ on the first path in Figure 10a. Hence

$$x = 4/20 \div 11/20 = 4/11.$$

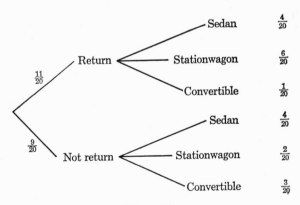

Figure 10a

The completed tree is shown in Figure 10b. From this we can find the posterior probabilities. For example, if the customer does not return, then the probabilities for his having the three types of cars have changed to $\frac{4}{9}$, $\frac{2}{9}$, and $\frac{3}{9}$, respectively.

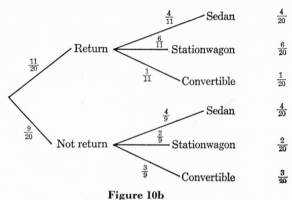

Figure 10b

EXERCISES

1. In a consumer panel in which records are kept of individuals' coffee purchases by brands, Consumer A purchases Brand X with probability .6 and other brands with probability .4, while Consumer B purchases X with probability .3 and other brands with probability .7. Assume that for both A and B each purchase is independent of all previous purchases.
   (a) Construct a tree diagram for three consecutive purchases by A; for three consecutive purchases by B.
   (b) Find the probability that A will buy Brand X exactly twice in three purchases; that B will buy X twice in three purchases.
   (c) Given that either A or B was chosen at random and that in three consecutive purchases Brand X was bought exactly twice, find the posterior probability that the consumer chosen was A. [*Ans.* .696.]

2. In Exercise 1, Consumer C has a pattern of purchasing coffee brands in which the probability of purchasing a particular brand depends on which brand was last purchased. If X was the last brand purchased, the probability of repurchasing X is .8 and the probability of purchasing some other brand is .2. If the last brand purchased was not X, the probability of buying X on the next purchase is .3, while the probability of buying some brand other than X is .7. Construct a tree diagram for the next three consecutive purchases of coffee and find the probability that Brand X is purchased exactly twice, given that Consumer C's last purchase was
   (a) Brand X.
   (b) Not Brand X.

3. In Exercise 2, assume that a prior probability of .6 has been assigned to Consumer C's last purchase being Brand X, and that we then observe that

of C's next three purchases, two were of Brand X. What is the posterior probability that the purchase preceding these last three was Brand X given that

(a) We do not know the order of the three purchases?

(b) The purchases were made in the order X, $\sim$X, X?   [Ans. .8.]

(c) The purchases were made in the order $\sim$X, X, X?

4. In blending whiskey, a panel of taste experts is often used to determine whether a given batch is distinguishable from previous batches. One well-known method of testing ability to distinguish is the "triad test," in which an expert is presented with two samples from the same batch and one from a different batch and asked to pick the odd sample. Suppose a given expert is given three such triad tests, and we are willing to concede that two batches are different if the expert picks the odd sample on at least two of the tests. Draw a tree to represent the possibilities (either right or wrong) for his answers. Construct the tree measure that will be applicable if the two batches are in fact indistinguishable and find the probability that two batches that are indistinguishable will be treated as if they were different.

5. In Example 3, consider the sequence of acts (1) develop component, (2) develop B, (3) develop A. Suppose, as in the example, that the probability of successfully developing the component is .6, but that the probabilities of successfully developing B next and A last are, respectively, .8 and .2. Draw a tree diagram and construct the tree measure.

6. A box contains three defective light bulbs and seven good ones. Construct a tree to show the possibilities if three consecutive bulbs are drawn at random from the box (they are not replaced after being drawn). Assign a tree measure and find the probability that at least one good bulb is drawn out. Find the probability that all three are good if the first bulb is good.
$$[Ans. \tfrac{119}{120}; \tfrac{5}{12}.]$$

7. In Exercise 7 of Section 4, suppose that the missiles are fired one at a time at the target until a hit is made. Construct a tree measure of the process and find the probability that more than two missiles will be used.

8. In Example 2, verify by means of the tree diagram that the probability of exactly two defectives in the sample is $\tfrac{1}{15}$.

9. In Example 2, obtain the probabilities for exactly 0, 1, and 2 defectives in the sample by using the hypergeometric formula.

10. In Example 4, use Bayes' theorem to find the probability that a customer already has a convertible given that he is returning for a second car.

11. In Example 2 of Chapter I, Section 6, consider the following sequence of acts: (1) take seismographic recordings; (2a) if the recordings indicate subsurface structure, drill; (2b) if the recordings do not indicate subsurface structure, do not drill. Draw a tree diagram and construct a tree measure from the data of Example 2 of Section 6. What is the probability of obtaining oil?

12. Demand for an item varies between zero and three units, inclusive. Let d_i be the statement, "Demand is for i units," and suppose $\Pr[d_0] = .1$, $\Pr[d_1] = .3, \Pr[d_2] = .4, \Pr[d_3] = .2$, and $\Pr[d_i] = 0$ for $i > 3$. Construct a tree measure to represent possible demands on each of two consecutive days and find the probability that
    (a) Demand will exceed four units on the two days.   [*Ans*. .2.]
    (b) Exactly three units will be demanded on the two days.   [*Ans*. .28.]
    (c) Sales will exceed three units on the two days, given that there are two units in stock at the beginning of the first day and two more units arrive at the beginning of the second day. (A *sale* is made only if a unit is *demanded* and it is in stock. Assume that inability to fulfill a demand on a particular day results in a lost sale.)   [*Ans*. .42.]

13. In Example 2, suppose there is a .5 probability that the lot contains two defectives and a .5 probability that it contains only one. Construct a tree measure to show the possibilities if three pieces are sampled, and find the probability
    (a) Of obtaining exactly one defective in the sample.
    (b) Of obtaining exactly two defectives in the sample.
    (c) That the lot originally contained two defectives given that the sample contains one.

14. There are two urns, A and B. Urn A contains one black and one red ball. Urn B contains two black and three red balls. A ball is chosen at random from urn A and put into urn B. A ball is then drawn at random from urn B.
    (a) What is the probability that both balls drawn are of the same color?
                                                                [*Ans*. $\frac{7}{12}$.]
    (b) What is the probability that the first ball drawn was red, given that the second ball drawn was black?   [*Ans*. $\frac{2}{3}$.]

15. Assume that in the World Series each team has probability one-half of winning each game, independently of the outcomes of any other game. Assign a tree measure. (See Chapter I, Section 5 for the tree.) Find the probability that the series ends in 4, 5, 6, and 7 games, respectively.

16. Assume that in the World Series one team is stronger than the other and has probability $\frac{2}{3}$ for winning each of the games. Assign a tree measure and find the following probabilities.
    (a) The probability that the stronger team wins in 4, 5, 6, and 7 games, respectively.
    (b) The probability that the weaker team wins in 4, 5, 6, and 7 games, respectively.
    (c) The probability that the series ends in 4, 5, 6, and 7 games, respectively.   [*Ans*. .21; .30; .27; .22.]
    (d) The probability that the strong team wins the series.   [*Ans*. .83.]

17. In the World Series from 1905 through 1961, excluding the nine-game series, there have been 10 four-game series, 14 five-game series, 13 six-game series, and 17 seven-game series. Add the results from 1962 to date to these and use these past records to estimate the probability that a series will last

4, 5, 6, or 7 games. Compare your answers with those obtained theoretically in Exercises 15 and 16(c). Which assumption about the World Series play seems to fit the data better?

18. During the month of May the probability of a rainy day is .2. The Dodgers win on a clear day with probability .7, but on a rainy day only with probability .4. If we know that they won a certain game in May, what is the probability that it rained on that day? [*Ans.* $\frac{1}{8}$.]

19. On a multiple-choice exam there are four possible answers for each question. Therefore, if a student knows the right answer, he has probability one of choosing correctly; if he is guessing, he has probability $\frac{1}{4}$ of choosing correctly. Let us further assume that a good student will know 90 per cent of the answers, a poor student only 50 per cent. If a good student has the right answer, what is the probability that he was only guessing? Answer the same question about a poor student, if the poor student has the right answer. [*Ans.* $\frac{1}{37}$, $\frac{1}{5}$.]

20. Three economic theories are proposed at a given time, which appear to be equally likely on the basis of existing evidence. The state of the American economy is observed the following year, and it turns out that its actual development had probability .6 of happening according to the first theory; and probabilities .4 and .2 according to the others. How does this modify the probabilities of correctness of the three theories?

21. In poker, Smith holds a very strong hand and bets a considerable amount. The probability that his opponent, Jones, has a better hand is .05. With a better hand Jones would raise the bet with probability .9, but with a poorer hand Jones would raise only with probability .2. Suppose that Jones raises, what is the new probability that he has a winning hand?
[*Ans.* $\frac{9}{47}$.]

8. Independent trials with two outcomes

In the preceding section we developed a way to determine a probability measure for any sequence of chance experiments where there are only a finite number of possibilities for each experiment. While this provides the framework for the general study of stochastic processes, it is too general to be studied in complete detail. Therefore, in probability theory we look for simplifying assumptions which will make our probability measure easier to work with. It is desired also that these assumptions be such as to apply to a variety of experiments which would occur in practice. We have already seen (see Example 2 of the preceding section) that sampling from a finite population may be treated as a stochastic process, and we have previously considered in detail (see Section 4) the probability theory associated with this process. In this book we shall limit ourselves to the study of two additional types of stochastic processes. The first of these, the independent trials process, will be considered in the present section. This process was the first one to be studied extensively in probability theory. The second, the Markov chain process, is a process that is finding increasing application, particularly in the behavioral sciences, and will be considered in Section 12.

A process of independent trials applies to the following situation. Assume that there is a sequence of chance experiments, each of which consists of a repetition of a single experiment, carried out in such a way that the results of any one experiment in no way affect the results in any other experiment. We label the possible outcome of a single experiment by $a_1, \ldots, a_r$. We assume that we are also given probabilities $p_1, \ldots, p_r$ for each of these outcomes occurring on any single experiment, the probabilities being independent of previous results. The tree representing the possibilities for the sequence of experiments will have the same outcomes from each branch point, and probability p_j will be assigned to any branch leading to outcome a_j. The tree measure determined in this way is the measure of an *independent trials process*. In this section we shall consider the important case of two outcomes for each experiment. The more general case is studied in Section 10.

In the case of two outcomes we arbitrarily label one outcome "success" and the other "failure." For example, in repeated throws of a coin we might call heads success, and tails failure. We assume there is given a probability p for success and a probability $q = 1 - p$ for failure. The tree measure for a sequence of three such experiments is shown in Figure 11. The weights assigned to each path are indicated at the end of the path.

The question which we now ask is the following. Given an independent trials process with two outcomes, what is the probability of *exactly r suc-*

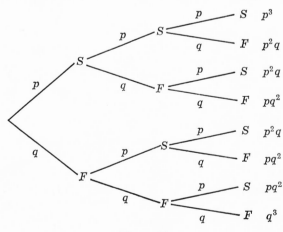

Figure 11

cesses in n experiments? We denote this probability by $\mathbf{b}(r; n, p)$ to indicate that it depends upon r, n, and p.

Assume that we had a tree for this general situation, similar to the tree in Figure 11 for three experiments, with the branch points labeled S for success and F for failure. Then the truth set of the statement, "Exactly r successes occur," consists of all paths which go through r branch points labeled S and $n - r$ labeled F. To find the probability of this statement we must add the weights for all such paths. We are helped first by the fact that our tree measure assigns the same weight to any such path, namely $p^r q^{n-r}$. The reason for this is that every branch leading to an S is assigned probability p, and every branch leading to F is assigned probability q, and in the product there will be r p's and $n - r$ q's. To find the desired probability we need only find the number of paths in the truth set of the statement, "Exactly r successes occur." Each such path is made to correspond to an ordered partition of the integers from 1 to n which has two cells, r elements in the first and $n - r$ in the second. We do this by putting the numbers of the experiments on which success occurred in the first cell and those for which failure occurred in the second cell. Since there are $\binom{n}{r}$ such partitions there are also this number of paths in the truth set of the statement considered. Thus we have proved:

In an independent trials process with two outcomes the probability of exactly r successes in n experiments is given by

(1) $$\mathbf{b}(r; n, p) = \binom{n}{r} p^r q^{n-r}.$$

A probability computed by the formula (1) is called a *binomial* probability. In Table I, p. 466, values of $\mathbf{b}(r, n, p)$ are given to three decimal places for $p = .01, .02, .05, .10, .15, .20, .25, .30, .40, .50$, for $n = 2, 3, 4, 5, 6, 7, 8, 9, 10, 15, 20$, and for r between 0 and n inclusive, except where $\mathbf{b}(r; n, p) < .0005$.

Example 1. Consider n throws of an ordinary coin. We label heads "success" and tails "failure," and we assume that the probability is $\frac{1}{2}$ for heads on any one throw independently of the outcome of any other throw. Then the probability that exactly r heads will turn up is

$$\mathbf{b}(r; n, \tfrac{1}{2}) = \binom{n}{r} \left(\frac{1}{2}\right)^n.$$

For instance, in 100 throws the probability that exactly 50 heads will turn up is $\mathbf{b}(50; 100, \frac{1}{2}) = \binom{100}{50} \left(\frac{1}{2}\right)^{100}$ which is approximately .08. Thus we see that it is quite unlikely that exactly one-half of the tosses will result in heads. On the other hand, suppose that we ask for the probability that *nearly* one-half of the tosses will be heads. To be more precise, let us ask for the probability that the number of heads which occur does not deviate by more than 10 from 50. To find this we must add $b(r; 100, \frac{1}{2})$ for $r = 40, 41, \ldots, 60$. If this is done, we obtain a probability of approximately .96. Thus, while it is unlikely that exactly 50 heads will occur, it is very likely that the number of heads which occur will not deviate from 50 by more than 10.

Example 2. An electronic component is mass-produced and then tested unit by unit on an automatic testing machine. According to the electrical characteristics of each component, the machine automatically classifies it as "good" or "defective." If the same unit is tested twice, the machine should, theoretically, classify it in the same way both times. We assume, however, that the machine has a certain probability q of misclassifying a part on any given trial, because of electrical or mechanical failure on the part of the testing machine. To improve the accuracy of our classification we may have the machine test the same unit not just once but r times, and finally classify a unit according to the classification which a majority of the tests give. To avoid ties we assume that r is odd. Let us see how this process decreases the probability of classification error.

Consider r experiments on each unit, where the jth experiment results in success if the jth test classifies the unit without error. The probability of success is then $p = 1 - q$. The majority decision will classify a unit correctly if we have more than $r/2$ successes. Suppose, for example, that we test each unit five times, and that the probability of misclassification on any single test is .1. Then the probability for success is .9, and the probability that the majority of the test results will correspond with the true state of the unit is

$$b(3; 5, .9) + b(4; 5, .9) + b(5; 5, .9)$$

which is found to be approximately .991 (see Exercise 3(d)).

Thus the above procedure decreases the probability of misclassification from .1 in the case of one test to .009 in the case of five.

In addition to serving as an exact description of certain real-world processes, the independent trials process may sometimes be used as an approximation to finite sampling processes. In Exercise 12 of Chapter III, Section 6, we found that as the number of elements N of the set $\mathfrak{U}$ increased, with the ratio R/N held constant, the ratios (which, as shown in Exercise 3 of Section 4, were hypergeometric probabilities) seemed to approach a limit; this limit is, in fact, the *binomial* probability $b(3; 5, .8) = .2048$.

In general, as N increases, with r, n, and $p = R/N$ held constant, $h(r; n, R, N)$ approaches $b(r; n, p)$. We shall prove this in several steps. First, for sufficiently large N, the branches of the tree diagram for the finite sampling process are identical with those of an independent trials process with two outcomes: at each stage there are exactly two possible outcomes of the next experiment. As long as N is large enough, we cannot run into the situation of Figure 7, in which all the elements of one of the cells of the partition are exhausted, so that there is only one possibility at some stage.

In the language of sampling lots for defectives, we can always find a lot size sufficiently large so that a sample of given size cannot exhaust all the good pieces, or all the defectives.

We next look at any path of length n through the tree resulting in r successes. The path weight must be

(2)

$$\frac{[R \cdot (R-1) \cdot \ldots \cdot (R-r+1)][(N-R) \cdot (N-R-1) \cdot \ldots \cdot (N-R-n+r+1)]}{[N \cdot (N-1) \cdot \ldots \cdot (N-r+1)][(N-r) \cdot (N-r-1) \cdot \ldots \cdot (N-n+1)]}$$

since, at the jth stage, there are $N - j + 1$ possibilities, the number of possibilities for a success must decrease one at a time from R to $R - r + 1$, and the number of possibilities for a failure must decrease one at a time from $N - R$ to $N - R - n + r + 1$.

By taking N sufficiently large, with $p = R/N$ constant, we can make the fraction above as close as we like to

(3)
$$\left(\frac{R}{N}\right)^r \left(\frac{N - R}{N}\right)^{n-r} = p^r q^{n-r}$$

where $q = 1 - p$. Finally, because the finite sampling tree has the same branches as the tree for the independent trials process, the number of paths resulting in r successes and $n - r$ failures is $\binom{n}{r}$, so that the probability of r successes in n trials can be made to approach

(4)
$$\binom{n}{r} p^r q^{n-r} = \mathbf{b}(r; n, p)$$

as was to be proved.

In quality control, lots received from vendors are often subjected to sampling inspection; depending on the information obtained from the sample, the lot from which it was drawn is either accepted or rejected. The purpose of sampling inspection is to obtain new information about the uninspected portion of the lot from the observations made on the inspected portion. We illustrate how this is done in the following example.

Example 3. Experience has shown that the lots received by a certain company can be classified roughly as good, fair, and poor. We assume that the defective items in a *good* lot can be described by an independent trials process with probability .2 for defective and .8 for nondefective. A lot that is *fair* is described by an independent trials process with probability .4 for defective, and a *poor* lot is described by such a process with probability .9 for a defective item. The company finds in the long run that 80 per cent of its lots are good, 10 per cent fair and 10 per cent poor.

A lot is received and a sample of two items from the lot inspected. The number of defectives in the sample is recorded. We wish to make use of the result of the inspection to assign posterior probabilities for the lot's being good, fair, or poor. Before inspection takes place all of the relevant probabilities are shown in the tree in Figure 12.

Now, constructing the tree in the reverse order and computing the branch probabilities as in Example 4 of Section 7, we have the tree in Figure 13. From this tree we obtain the posterior probabilities that the lot is good, fair, or poor for each possible sample outcome. If no defectives are found, we conclude that the lot is very likely to be good. However, if two defectives are found we feel that it is more likely poor than good or fair.

In general, sampling does give us information. However, there are cases where we do not obtain new information. For example, if we know the appropriate value of p before inspection, then by the nature of the

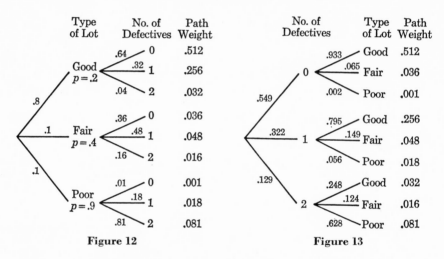

Figure 12   Figure 13

independent trials process any information we obtain about the first r experiments gives us no relevant information about future results. Hence, in that case, we cannot say anything more about the remaining elements in the lot than we could before inspection.

EXERCISES

1. Verify by direct computation the entries in Table I for $b(0; 2, .5)$, $b(4; 6, .1)$, $b(7; 8, .2)$, $b(10; 10, .3)$.

2. Use Table I to compute the probability of
   (a) Three or more successes in a sample of 6 when $p = .1$.
   (b) Less than two successes in a sample of 10 when $p = .2$.
   (c) Between three and five (inclusive) successes in a sample of 10 when $p = .3$.

3. Prove that $\mathbf{b}(r; n, p) = \mathbf{b}(n - r; n, 1 - p)$. Using this relationship and Table I, calculate the probability of

(a) Four successes in a sample of 6 when $p = .9$.

(b) More than eight successes in a sample of 10 when $p = .8$.

(c) Between six and eight (inclusive) successes in a sample of 10 when $p = .7$.

(d) More than two successes in a sample of 5 when $p = .9$.

In all the exercises that follow, use Table I wherever appropriate.

4. Compute for $n = 4$, $n = 8$, $n = 12$, and $n = 16$ the probability of obtaining exactly $\frac{1}{2}$ heads when an ordinary coin is thrown.

[*Ans.* .375; .273; .226; .196.]

5. Compute for $n = 4$, $n = 8$, $n = 12$, and $n = 16$ the probability that the fraction of heads deviates from $\frac{1}{2}$ by less than $\frac{1}{8}$.

[*Ans.* .375; .711; .854; .923.]

6. Assume that Peter and Paul match pennies four times. (In matching pennies, Peter wins a penny with probability $\frac{1}{2}$, and Paul wins a penny with probability $\frac{1}{2}$.) What is the probability that Peter wins more than Paul? Answer the same for five throws. For the case of 12,917 throws.

[*Ans.* $\frac{5}{16}$; $\frac{1}{2}$; $\frac{1}{2}$.]

7. If an ordinary die is thrown four times, what is the probability that exactly two 6's will occur?

8. In Example 2, if the probability for the machine's misclassifying a unit on a single trial is .2, how many times should a unit be tested on the machine to make the probability at least .90 that the answer obtained is correct?

9. A machine is set up to produce a lot of parts in sequence. Each piece has a certain fixed but unknown probability of being defective; this probability is independent of the quality of the preceding pieces produced. If the setup of the machine is bad, and therefore p is high, it is desired that the machine be set up again. If p is low, on the other hand, a small number of defectives in the lot can be tolerated better than the expense of setting up the machine again. To determine what to do, a sample of size n is taken from the process; if more than c defectives are found in the sample, the machine is set up again; otherwise, it is allowed to run as is. This is called an "(n, c) decision rule" (see Exercise 17 of Chapter I, Section 5). Find the probability of setting up the machine again using the following decision rules for $p = 0$, .05, .1, .2, .3, .4, .5:

(a) $(10, 0)$ (b) $(10, 1)$

(c) $(20, 0)$ (d) $(20, 1)$

(e) $(20, 2)$.

10. (a) Prove that in any process with two outcomes at each trial, the probability of r successes in n trials is the sum of the following two products:
(1) the probability of r successes in $n - 1$ trials times the probability

of a failure on the nth trial; (2) the probability of $r - 1$ successes in $n - 1$ trials times the probability of a success on the nth trial. From this derive a formula for the binomial probability of r successes in n trials given the probabilities of r and $r - 1$ successes in $n - 1$ trials.

(b) Verify the entry $b(3; 10, .2)$ from the entries $b(3; 9, .2)$ and $b(2; 9, .2)$ in Table I by using the formula which you have derived.

(c) Draw a flow diagram for a process that will compute the entries of Table I.

11. Prove that in any process with two outcomes at each trial, the probability of obtaining the rth success on the nth trial is the probability of achieving $r - 1$ successes in $n - 1$ trials times the probability of achieving a success on the nth trial. From this, given that the trials are independent, derive a formula for obtaining the rth success on the nth trial in terms of binomial probabilities.

12. Five missiles are fired at a target. If each missile has a probability .6 of hitting the target, what is the probability that the target will be hit at least once?

13. If missiles are fired sequentially at a target and the probability that a given missile hits the target is .6, use the results of Exercise 11 to find the probability that the first hit will occur on the fifth shot.   [*Ans*. .0154.]

14. In an independent trials process, the value of p is either .1 or .4; the prior probabilities of p are $\Pr[p = .1] = \frac{2}{3}$, $\Pr[p = .4] = \frac{1}{3}$. In a sample of ten from the process, four successes are observed. Calculate the posterior probability that $p = .4$.   [*Ans*. .919.]

15. In Exercise 14, suppose the four successes and six failures were observed in the order *sffsffsffs*. Calculate the posterior probability that $p = .4$. What is the effect on the posterior probability of knowing the order in which the successes occurred?

16. Defective pieces are produced by a machine according to an independent trials process and assembled into lots of 10. What is the probability that there are 0, 1, 2, 3 defectives in a given lot if the probability p of a defective

(a) Is .1?

(b) Is .4?

(c) Is .2?

(d) Is either .1 or .4, where $\Pr[p = .1] = \frac{2}{3}$, $\Pr[p = .4] = \frac{1}{3}$?

17. Calculate the following hypergeometric probabilities and their binomial approximations. If the approximation is not good, explain why.

(a) $h(3; 5, 20, 40)$.   (b) $h(2; 10, 200, 1000)$.

(c) $h(1; 10, 1, 20)$.   (d) $h(9; 10, 90, 100)$.

(e) $h(3; 8, 4, 10)$.   (f) $h(1; 8, 4, 10)$.

18. The independent trials process can be used as a model for sampling "with replacement" from a finite set, where the process of sampling with replacement consists of drawing an element at random from the set, ob-

serving it, replacing it in the set, and then drawing another item at random. Thus the same item may appear more than once in a sample. By contrast, the process which leads to hypergeometric probabilities may be thought of as a process of sampling *without* replacement, so that a given element of a set can appear at most once in a sample. If sampling is performed *with* replacement, calculate the required probabilities, and compare them with the probabilities calculated under the assumption that sampling took place *without* replacement, for the following problems:

(a) Exercise 6 of Section 4.
(b) Exercise 17 of Section 6.
(c) Exercise 18 of Section 6.

*9. The law of large numbers

In this section we shall study some further properties of the independent trials process with two outcomes. In Section 8 we saw that the probability for r successes in n trials is given by

$$\mathbf{b}(r; n, p) = \binom{n}{r} p^r q^{n-r}.$$

In Figure 14 we show these probabilities graphically for $n = 8$ and $p = \frac{3}{4}$.

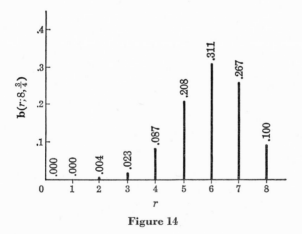

Figure 14

In Figure 15 we have done similarly for the case of $n = 7$ and $p = \frac{3}{4}$.

We see in the first case that the values increase up to a maximum value at $r = 6$ and then decrease. In the second case the values increase up to a maximum value at $r = 5$, have the same value for $r = 6$, and then decrease, and these two cases are typical of what can happen in general.

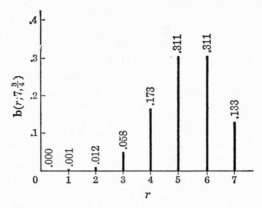

Figure 15

Consider the ratio of the probability of $r + 1$ successes in n trials to the probability of r successes in n trials, which is

$$\frac{\binom{n}{r+1}p^{r+1}q^{n-r-1}}{\binom{n}{r}p^r q^{n-r}} = \frac{n-r}{r+1} \cdot \frac{p}{q}.$$

This ratio will be greater than one as long as $(n - r)p > (r + 1)q$ or as long as $r < np - q$. If $np - q$ is not an integer, the values $\binom{n}{r}p^r q^{n-r}$ increase up to a maximum value, which occurs at the first integer greater than $np - q$, and then decrease. In case $np - q$ is an integer, the values $\binom{n}{r}p^r q^{n-r}$ increase up to $r = np - q$, are the same for $r = np - q$ and $r = np - q + 1$, and then decrease.

Thus we see that, in general, values near np will occur with the largest probability. It is not true that one particular value near np is highly likely to occur, but only that it is relatively more likely than a value further from np. For example, in 100 throws of a coin, $np = 100 \cdot \frac{1}{2} = 50$. The probability of exactly 50 heads is approximately .08. The probability of exactly 30 is approximately .00002.

More information is obtained by studying the probability of a given deviation of the proportion of successes r/n from the number p; that is, by studying, for ϵ greater than zero, the probability $\Pr[p - \epsilon < r/n < p + \epsilon]$.

For any fixed n, p, and ϵ, the latter probability could be found by adding all the values of $b(r; n, p)$ for values of r for which the inequality $p - \epsilon < r/n < p + \epsilon$ is satisfied. This would, for any particular choice of n, p, and ϵ, be a tedious task. However, it is proved in more advanced books that

$$\Pr\left[p - \epsilon < \frac{r}{n} < p + \epsilon \right] \geq 1 - \frac{pq}{n\epsilon^2}.$$

No matter how small ϵ is, if we choose n large enough, we can make $1 - (pq/n\epsilon^2)$ as near to 1 as we wish. Thus the probability for the proportion of successes deviating from p by less than ϵ can be made arbitrarily near to 1 by choosing n large enough. The fact that this can be done is a special case of a very general theorem in probability theory called the *law of large numbers*.

Let us put in the above inequality $\epsilon = k\sqrt{pq/n}$. Then we have

$$\Pr\left[p - k\sqrt{\frac{pq}{n}} < \frac{r}{n} < p + k\sqrt{\frac{pq}{n}} \right] \geq 1 - \frac{1}{k^2}$$

or

$$\Pr[np - k\sqrt{npq} < r < np + k\sqrt{npq}] \geq 1 - \frac{1}{k^2}$$

which in turn can be written

$$\Pr[-k\sqrt{npq} < r - np < k\sqrt{npq}] \geq 1 - \frac{1}{k^2}.$$

The quantity np is called the *expected value* for the number of successes, and the quantity $\sqrt{npq}$ is called the *standard deviation* for the number of successes. We note that the probability of a deviation of more than k standard deviations from the expected value is less than or equal to $1/k^2$. Thus for large k this probability will be small.

It is possible to show by more advanced theory that

$$\Pr[-k\sqrt{npq} < r - np < k\sqrt{npq}] \cong z_k$$

where z_k is a number which can be found for any k and does not depend on n or on p. The symbol $\cong$ means that the indicated probability is only approximately given by z_k. The approximation improves with increasing n.

We note that the approximation given above can also be interpreted as stating that the probability that $r - np$ is *either* greater than $k\sqrt{npq}$ or less than $-k\sqrt{npq}$ is approximately $1 - z_k$. In many applications one is interested only in the probability that $r - np$ is greater than $k\sqrt{npq}$. It follows from the more advanced theory that this is approximately $(1 - z_k)/2$. Hence also the probability that $r - np$ is less than $-k\sqrt{npq}$ is approximately $(1 - z_k)/2$.

It is convenient to think of the standard deviation as a unit of measurement. In this case z_k gives the approximate probability for a deviation of less than k units, or k standard deviations. The approximate values of z_k

for $k = 1, 2$, and 3 are $z_1 = .683$, $z_2 = .954$, $z_3 = .997$. Thus we see that it is very unlikely in a large number of trials to have a deviation from the expected value of more than three standard deviations. On the other hand $z_{.1} = .080$, which shows that it is quite unlikely that there will be a deviation of less than one-tenth of a standard deviation from the expected value.

Example 1. In throwing an ordinary coin 10,000 times, the expected number of heads is 5000, and the standard deviation for the number of heads is $\sqrt{10,000(\frac{1}{2})(\frac{1}{2})} = 50$. Thus the probability that the number of heads which turn up deviates from 5000 by less than one standard deviation, or 50, is approximately .683. The probability of a deviation of less than two standard deviations, or 100, is approximately .954. The probability of a deviation of less than three standard deviations, or 150, is approximately .997. On the other hand, the probability of a deviation of less than .1 standard deviation, or a deviation of less than five, is approximately .080. The statement that the number of heads deviates from 5000 by less than 150 is equivalent to the statement that the proportion of heads deviates from .5 by less than 150/10,000 = .015.

Example 2. Assume that in a certain large city 900 people are chosen at random and asked whether they watched a certain television program the previous night. Of the 900 asked, 150 say that they saw the program and 750 say that they did not. If, in fact, 10 per cent of the people in the city saw the program, would it be unlikely that as many as 150 would say they had seen it in a sample of 900? We assume that the 900 people asked would form approximately an independent trials process with probability .1 for a "yes" answer and .9 for a "no" answer. (The process is, strictly speaking, one of sampling *without* replacement, hence the trials are not actually independent. If the population of the city is large relative to the sample size of 900, however, the independent trials process is a good approximation. See Section 8.) Then the standard deviation for the number of "yes" answers in 900 trials is

$$\sqrt{(900)(.1)(.9)} = 9.$$

It would therefore be very unlikely that we would obtain a deviation of more than 27 from the expected number of 90. The fact that the deviation in the sample from the expected number was 60, then, is evidence that the hypothesis that 10 per cent of the people in the city saw the program is incorrect. The assumption that the true proportion is any value less than .1 would also lead to the fact that a number as large as 150 out of 900 saying they had seen the program is very unlikely. Thus we are led to suspect that the true proportion is greater than .1. On the other hand, if the number who reported seeing the program in the sample of 900 were 99, we would have only a deviation of one standard deviation, under the assumption that 10 per cent of all the residents of the city saw the show. Since such a deviation is not unlikely, we could not rule out this possibility on the evidence of the sample.

Suppose we let p be the fraction of people in the city who did, in fact, see the program. If we started with prior probabilities that p had certain values, then we could use the sample evidence to compute posterior probabilities of those values of p. We could then make somewhat more precise statements about p than simply saying that a certain sample result does or does not rule out the possibility that $p = .1$.

EXERCISES

1. If an ordinary die is thrown 20 times, what is the expected number of times that a 6 will turn up? What is the standard deviation for the number of 6's that turn up?   [$Ans.\ \frac{10}{3}; \frac{5}{3}.$]

2. Suppose that an ordinary die is thrown 450 times. What is the expected number of throws that result in either a 3 or a 4? What is the standard deviation for the number of such throws?

3. In 16 tosses of an ordinary coin, what is the expected number of heads that turn up? What is the standard deviation for the number of heads that occur?   [$Ans.\ 8; 2.$]

4. In 16 tosses of a coin, find the exact probability that the number of heads that turn up differs from the expected number by (a) less than one standard deviation, and (b) by not more than one standard deviation. Do the same for the case of two standard deviations, and for the case of three standard deviations. Show that the approximations given for large n lie between the values obtained, but are not very accurate for so small an n.
   [$Ans.\ .546, .790; .923, .979; .996, .999.$]

5. Consider n independent trials with probability p for success. Let s and t be numbers such that $p < s < t$. What does the law of large numbers say about

$$\Pr\left[s < \frac{r}{n} < t \right]$$

as we increase n indefinitely? Answer the same question in the case that $s < p < t$.

6. It is known that 20 per cent of frozen orange juice purchases are of a certain brand. Following an intensive advertising campaign, a random sample of 900 purchases revealed 250 purchases of this brand of frozen orange juice. What can be said about the effectiveness of the advertising campaign?

7. In a large number of independent trials with probability p for success, what is the approximate probability that the number of successes will deviate from the expected number by more than one standard deviation but less than two standard deviations?   [$Ans.\ .271.$]

8. A gasoline company has a large list of automobile owners to whom it intends to mail credit cards. It is undecided whether to offer as an incentive for supplying the necessary credit information (a) five free gallons

of gasoline, or (b) a free car wash. In a sample mailing, half the addressees, selected at random, are offered the first premium, and half are offered the second. If it really makes no difference which incentive is offered, what is the probability that in 10,000 returns, between 4850 and 5150 will consist of people who were offered five free gallons of gasoline?

9. Suppose that it is desired that in the situation of Example 2 the probability be approximately .95 that the fraction of people in a sample of size n who say they saw the program deviate by no more than .01 from the fraction p of city residents who saw the show, when $p = .20$. How large should n be? [*Ans.* Approximately 6400.]

10. Two railroads are competing for the passenger traffic of 1000 passengers by operating similar trains at the same hour. If a given passenger is as likely to choose one train as the other, how many seats should the railroad provide if it wants to be sure that its seating capacity is sufficient in 99 out of 100 cases? [*Ans.* 547.]

11. Assume that 20 per cent of the subscribers to a certain magazine can recall having seen a certain cigarette advertisement in that magazine. If 1600 of the subscribers are selected at random from the mailing list, what is the expected number who will recall having seen the advertisement? What is the standard deviation? What is the approximate probability that more than 352 of the 1600 chosen remember having seen the advertisement?
[*Ans.* 320; 16; .023.]

12. Suppose that in Exercise 11 the 1600 people are chosen at random from those subscribers to the magazine who smoke. Under the hypothesis that smoking has no effect on a person's recollection of the advertisement, what is the expected number in the 1600 who will recall having seen the advertisement? Suppose that more than 370 of the 1600 chosen recall having seen the advertisement. What might be said concerning the hypothesis that smoking has no effect on the ability of a person to remember having seen the advertisement?

13. In Example 2, we made the assumption in our calculations that, if the true proportion of people who saw the television program were p, then the 900 people chosen at random represented an independent trials process with probability p for a "yes" answer, and $1 - p$ for a "no" answer. Give a method for choosing the 900 people which would make this a reasonable assumption. Criticize the following methods:
(a) Choose the first 900 people in the list of registered Republicans.
(b) Choose 900 names at random from the telephone book.
(c) Choose 900 houses at random and ask one person from each house, the houses being visited in the mid-morning.
(d) Choose 30 representative blocks in the city and choose 30 representative houses in each block.

14. For n throws of an ordinary coin, let t_n be such that

$$\Pr\left[-t_n < \frac{r}{n} - \tfrac{1}{2} < t_n\right] = .997$$

where r is the number of heads that turn up. Find t_n for $n = 10^4$, $n = 10^6$, and $n = 10^{20}$.   [*Ans.* .015; .0015; .000,000,000,15.]

15. Assume that a calculating machine carries out a million operations to solve a certain problem. In each operation the machine gives the answer 10^{-5} too small, with probability $\frac{1}{2}$, and 10^{-5} too large, with probability $\frac{1}{2}$. Assume that the errors are independent of one another. What is a reasonable accuracy to attach to the answer? What if the machine carries out 10^{10} operations?   [*Ans.* ±.02; ±2]

*10. Independent trials with more than two outcomes

By extending the results of Section 8, we shall study the case of independent trials in which we allow more than two outcomes. We assume that we have an independent trials process where the possible outcomes are a_1, $a_2, \ldots, a_k$, occurring with probabilities $p_1, p_2, \ldots, p_k$, respectively. We denote by

$$\mathbf{m}(r_1, r_2, \ldots, r_k; p_1, p_2, \ldots, p_k)$$

the probability that, in $n = r_1 + r_2 + \ldots + r_k$ such trials, there will be r_1 occurrences of a_1, r_2 of a_2, etc. In the case of two outcomes this notation would be $\mathbf{m}(r_1, r_2; p_1, p_2)$. In Section 8 we wrote this as $\mathbf{b}(r_1; n, p_1)$ since r_2 and p_2 are determined from n, r_1, and p_1. We shall indicate how this probability is found in general, but carry out the details only for a special case. We choose $k = 3$, and $n = 5$ for purposes of illustration. We shall find $\mathbf{m}(1, 2, 2; p_1, p_2, p_3)$.

We show in Figure 16 enough of the tree for this process to indicate the branch probabilities for a path (heavy lined) corresponding to the outcomes a_2, a_3, a_1, a_2, a_3. The tree measure assigns weight $p_2 \cdot p_3 \cdot p_1 \cdot p_2 \cdot p_3 = p_1 \cdot p_2^2 \cdot p_3^2$ to this path.

There are, of course, other paths through the tree corresponding to one occurrence of a_1, two of a_2 and two of a_3. However, they would all be assigned the same weight, $p_1 \cdot p_2^2 \cdot p_3^2$, by the tree measure. Hence to find

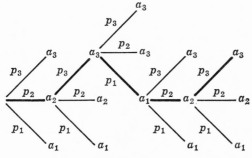

Figure 16

$\mathbf{m}(1, 2, 2; p_1, p_2, p_3)$, we must multiply this weight by the number of paths having the specified number of occurrences of each outcome.

We note that the path a_2, a_3, a_1, a_2, a_3 can be specified by the three-cell partition $[\{3\}, \{1, 4\}, \{2, 5\}]$ of the numbers from 1 to 5. Here the first cell shows the experiment which resulted in a_1, the second cell shows the two that resulted in a_2, and the third shows the two that resulted in a_3. Conversely, any such partition of the numbers from 1 to 5 with one element in the first cell, two in the second, and two in the third corresponds to a unique path of the desired kind. Hence the number of paths is the number of such partitions. But this is

$$\binom{5}{1, 2, 2} = \frac{5!}{1!2!2!}$$

(see Chapter III, Section 5), so that the probability of one occurrence of a_1, two of a_2, and two of a_3 is

$$\binom{5}{1, 2, 2} \cdot p_1 \cdot p_2^2 \cdot p_3^2.$$

The above argument carried out in general leads, for the case of independent trials with outcomes $a_1, a_2, \ldots, a_k$ occurring with probabilities $p_1, p_2, \ldots, p_k$, to the following.

The probability for r_1 occurrences of a_1, r_2 occurrences of a_2, etc., is given by

$$\mathbf{m}(r_1, r_2, \ldots, r_k; p_1, p_2, \ldots, p_k) = \binom{n}{r_1, r_2, \ldots, r_k} p_1^{r_1} \cdot p_2^{r_2} \ldots p_k^{r_k}.$$

Example 1. A die is thrown 12 times. What is the probability that each number will come up twice? Here there are six outcomes, 1, 2, 3, 4, 5, 6 corresponding to the six sides of the die. We assign each outcome probability $\frac{1}{6}$. We are then asked for

$$\mathbf{m}(2, 2, 2, 2, 2, 2; \tfrac{1}{6}, \tfrac{1}{6}, \tfrac{1}{6}, \tfrac{1}{6}, \tfrac{1}{6}, \tfrac{1}{6})$$

which is

$$\binom{12}{2, 2, 2, 2, 2, 2}\left(\frac{1}{6}\right)^2\left(\frac{1}{6}\right)^2\left(\frac{1}{6}\right)^2\left(\frac{1}{6}\right)^2\left(\frac{1}{6}\right)^2\left(\frac{1}{6}\right)^2 = .0034.$$

Example 2. Suppose that we have a repeated-trials process with four outcomes, a_1, a_2, a_3, a_4, occurring with probability p_1, p_2, p_3, p_4, respectively. It might be that we are interested only in the probability that r_1 occurrences of a_1 and r_2 occurrences of a_2 will take place with no specification about the number of each of the other possible outcomes. To answer this question we simply consider a new experiment where the outcomes are $a_1, a_2, \bar{a}_3$. Here $\bar{a}_3$ corresponds to an occurrence of either a_3 or a_4 in our original experiment. The corresponding probabilities would be p_1, p_2, and $\bar{p}_3$ with $\bar{p}_3 = p_3 + p_4$. Let $\bar{r}_3 = n - (r_1 + r_2)$. Then our question is answered by finding the probability in our new experiment for r_1 occurrences of a_1, r_2 of a_2, and $\bar{r}_3$ of $\bar{a}_3$, which is

$$\binom{n}{r_1, r_2, \bar{r}_3} p_1^{r_1} \cdot p_2^{r_2} \cdot p_3^{r_3}.$$

The same procedure can be carried out for experiments with any number of outcomes where we specify the number of occurrences of such particular outcomes. For example, if a die is thrown ten times, the probability that a one will occur exactly twice and a three exactly three times is given by

$$\binom{10}{2, 3, 5} \left(\frac{1}{6}\right)^2 \left(\frac{1}{6}\right)^3 \left(\frac{4}{6}\right)^5 = 043 \, .$$

EXERCISES

1. The diameter of a particular piece may be within tolerance limits, or too large, or too small. If a machine produces pieces 10 per cent of which have too large a diameter and 20 per cent of which have too small a diameter, what is the probability that if three pieces are chosen at random, one will be too big, one too small, and one will be within tolerance limits?

2. In Exercise 1, suppose pieces whose diameters are within tolerance limits are classified as good, and all others as defective. What is the probability of obtaining one good piece and two defectives in a sample of three?

3. The most recent purchases of coffee by members of a consumer panel were distributed among brands as follows:

Brand	Per Cent
A	20
B	30
C	40
All other	10

What is the probability that in a random sample of five drawn (with replacement) from the panel, the most recent purchase of two of the members will have been Brand C, two Brand B, and one Brand A?
[*Ans.* .0864.]

4. In Exercise 3, what is the probability that in the sample of five, exactly two most recent purchases were Brand C and exactly one Brand A?
[*Ans.* .154.]

5. In Exercise 3, what is the probability that in the sample of five, more than one of the most recent purchases was some brand other than A, B, or C?
[*Ans.* .082.]

6. Assume that the following percentages apply to the daily coffee-drinking habits of the population of the United States:
    25 per cent do not drink coffee,
    30 per cent drink 1–3 cups per day,
    30 per cent drink 4–6 cups per day,
    15 per cent drink more than 6 cups per day.

What is the probability that in a random sample of four people in the United States, two will not be coffee drinkers, one will drink one to three cups per day, and one will drink more than six cups per day?

7. An urn contains five white balls, three black balls, and two red balls. What is the probability that a sample of five will consist of one black, one red, and three white balls if the sample is drawn (a) with replacement? (b) without replacement?

8. In an independent trials process with three possible outcomes, a_1, a_2, and a_3, the following prior probabilities are assigned to p_1, p_2, p_3:

$$\text{Pr}[(p_1 = .1) \wedge (p_2 = .2) \wedge (p_3 = .7)] = .6$$
$$\text{Pr}[(p_1 = .4) \wedge (p_2 = .2) \wedge (p_3 = .4)] = .4.$$

In $n = 6$ experiments, a_1 was observed $r_1 = 1$ time, a_2 was observed $r_2 = 4$ times, and a_3 was observed $r_3 = 1$ time.
(a) What is the posterior probability

$$\text{Pr}[(p_1 = .1) \wedge (p_2 = .2) \wedge (p_3 = .7) \mid (r_1 = 1) \wedge (r_2 = 4) \wedge (r_3 = 1)]?$$
[Ans. .396.]

(b) What effect do the $r_2 = 4$ observations of a_2 have on the calculation of the posterior probability? Why?
(c) Suppose the six observations were in the order a_1, a_2, a_3, a_2, a_2, a_2. How does this information affect the posterior probability?

9. In Exercise 8, suppose that it is known only that a_1 was observed exactly $r_1 = 1$ time in $n = 6$ experiments, but that the values of r_2 and r_3 are not known. Now what is the posterior probability that

$$(p_1 = .1) \wedge (p_2 = .2) \wedge (p_3 = .7)?$$

10. In Exercise 8, what is the probability that in four trials we will observe $r_1 = 1$, $r_2 = 1$, $r_3 = 2$? [Ans. .132.]

11. An oil wildcatter estimates the following probabilities of hitting a hole containing oil, a hole containing gas, and a dry hole:

$$\text{Pr}[\text{Oil}] = .2, \qquad \text{Pr}[\text{Gas}] = .3, \qquad \text{Pr}[\text{Dry}] = .5.$$

If, on a series of holes, the probabilities are considered independent, what is the probability that of ten holes drilled, five will be dry, three will contain gas, and two will contain oil?

11. Expected value

In this section we shall discuss the concept of expected value. Although it originated in the study of gambling games, it enters into almost any detailed probabilistic discussion.

DEFINITION. If in an experiment the possible outcomes are numbers, $a_1, a_2, \ldots, a_k$, occurring with probability $p_1, p_2, \ldots, p_k$, then the *expected value* is defined to be

$$E = a_1 p_1 + a_2 p_2 + \ldots + a_k p_k.$$

We sometimes use "mean value" synonymously with "expected value."

The term "expected value" is not to be interpreted as the value that will necessarily occur on a single experiment. For example, if a person bets $1 that a head will turn up when a coin is thrown, he expects to win $1 or to lose $1. His expected value is $(1)(\frac{1}{2}) + (-1)(\frac{1}{2}) = 0$, which is not one of the possible outcomes. The term, expected value, had its origin in the following consideration. If we repeat an experiment with expected value E a large number of times, and if we expect a_1 a fraction p_1 of the time, a_2 a fraction p_2 of the time, etc., then the average that we expect per experiment is E. In particular, in a gambling game E is interpreted as the average winning expected in a large number of plays. Here the expected value is often taken as the value of the game to the player. If the game has a positive expected value, the game is said to be favorable, if the game has expected value zero it is said to be fair, and if it has negative expected value it is described as unfavorable. These terms are not to be taken too literally, since many people are quite happy to play games that, in terms of expected value, are unfavorable.

Example 1. For the first example of the application of expected value we consider the game of roulette as played at Monte Carlo. There are several types of bets which the gambler can make, and we consider two of these.

The wheel has the number 0 and the numbers from 1 to 36 marked on equally spaced slots. The wheel is spun and a ball comes to rest in one of these slots. If the player puts a stake, say of $1, on a given number, and the ball comes to rest in this slot, then he receives from the croupier 36 times his stake, or $36. Thus for a payment of $1 his expected winning is $\frac{36}{37} = .973$ dollars. This can be interpreted to mean that in the long run he can expect to lose about 2.7 per cent of his stakes.

A second way to play is the following. A player may bet on "red" or "black." The numbers from 1 to 36 are evenly divided between the two colors. If a player bets on "red," and a red number turns up, he receives twice his stake. If a black number turns up, he loses his stake. If 0 turns up, then the wheel is spun until it stops on a number different from 0. If this is black, the player loses; but if it is red, he receives only his original stake, not twice it. For this type of play, the gambler pays $1 for an expected winning of

$$2(\tfrac{18}{37}) + 1(\tfrac{1}{74}) = \tfrac{73}{74} = .9865 \text{ dollars.}$$

In this case the player can expect to lose about 1.35 per cent of his stakes in the long run. Thus the expected loss in this case is only half as great as in the previous case.

Example 2. A player rolls a die and receives a number of dollars corresponding to the number of dots on the face which turns up. What should the player pay for playing, to make this a fair game? To answer this question, we note that the player wins 1, 2, 3, 4, 5 or 6 dollars, each with probability $\frac{1}{6}$. Hence, his expected winning is

$$1(\tfrac{1}{6}) + 2(\tfrac{1}{6}) + 3(\tfrac{1}{6}) + 4(\tfrac{1}{6}) + 5(\tfrac{1}{6}) + 6(\tfrac{1}{6}) = 3\tfrac{1}{2}.$$

Thus if he pays \$3.50, his expected net profit will be zero.

Example 3. What is the expected number of successes in the case of four independent trials with probability $\frac{1}{3}$ for success? We know that the probability of r successes is $\binom{4}{r}\left(\frac{1}{3}\right)^r\left(\frac{2}{3}\right)^{4-r}$. Thus

$$E = 0 \cdot \binom{4}{0}\left(\frac{1}{3}\right)^0\left(\frac{2}{3}\right)^4 + 1 \cdot \binom{4}{1}\left(\frac{1}{3}\right)^1\left(\frac{2}{3}\right)^3 + 2 \cdot \binom{4}{2}\left(\frac{1}{3}\right)^2\left(\frac{2}{3}\right)^2$$

$$+ 3 \cdot \binom{4}{3}\left(\frac{1}{3}\right)^3\left(\frac{2}{3}\right)^1 + 4 \cdot \binom{4}{4}\left(\frac{1}{3}\right)^4\left(\frac{2}{3}\right)^0$$

$$= 0 + \frac{32}{81} + \frac{48}{81} + \frac{24}{81} + \frac{4}{81} = \frac{108}{81} = \frac{4}{3}.$$

In general, it can be shown that in n trials with probability p for success, the expected number of successes is np.

Example 4. In the game of craps a pair of dice is rolled by one of the players. If the sum of the spots shown is 7 or 11, he wins. If it is 2, 3, or 12, he loses. If it is another sum, he must continue rolling the dice until he either repeats the same sum or rolls a 7. In the former case he wins, in the latter he loses. Let us suppose that he wins or loses \$1. Then the two possible outcomes are $+1$ and -1. We will compute the expected value of the game. First we must find the probability that he will win.

We represent the possibilities by a two-stage tree shown in Figure 17. While it is theoretically possible for the game to go on indefinitely, we do not consider this possibility. This means that our analysis applies only to games which actually stop at some time.

The branch probabilities at the first stage are determined by thinking of the 36 possibilities for the throw of the two dice as being equally likely and taking in each case the fraction of the possibilities which correspond to the branch as the branch probability. The probabilities for the branches at the second level are obtained as follows. If, for example, the first outcome was a 4, then when the game ends, a 4 or 7 must have occurred. The possible outcomes for the dice were

$$\{(3, 1), (1, 3), (2, 2), (4, 3), (3, 4), (2, 5), (5, 2), (1, 6), (6, 1)\}.$$

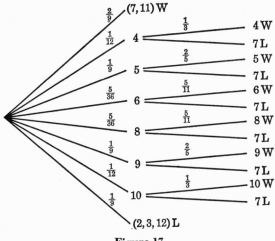

Figure 17

Again we consider these possibilities to be equally likely and assign to the branch considered the fraction of the outcomes which correspond to this branch. Thus to the 4 branch we assign a probability $\frac{3}{9} = \frac{1}{3}$. The other branch probabilities are determined in a similar way. Having the tree measure assigned, to find the probability of a win we must simply add the weights of all paths leading to a win. If this is done, we obtain $\frac{244}{495}$. Thus the player's expected value is $1 \cdot (\frac{244}{495}) + (-1) \cdot (\frac{251}{495}) = -\frac{7}{495}$, or approximately $-.0141$. Hence he can expect to lose about 1.41 per cent of his stakes in the long run. It is interesting to note that this is just slightly less favorable than his losses in betting on "red" in roulette.

Example 5. In business decision problems under uncertainty, businessmen often want to know the expected monetary value of one or several *strategies*, where we define a strategy as a sequence of acts which depend on the events that actually happen. If, for every sequence of events which can occur with a given strategy we have, or can calculate, (1) a monetary value and (2) a probability, then we can calculate the expected monetary value of the strategy.

In the case of the oil wildcatter in Example 2 of Section 6, for instance, we want to determine the expected monetary value of the following strategy: take seismographic recordings; if they indicate structure, drill; if not, sell rights. Suppose that it costs $10,000 to take the recordings, that $50,000 can be realized by selling the rights before a well is drilled, but nothing after the well is drilled, that it costs $80,000 to drill a well, and that an oil-producing well is worth $400,000. Then, the monetary values of the possible events which can occur with the given strategy are

$$
\begin{aligned}
\sim\!s \wedge d: &\quad -\$10{,}000 + \$50{,}000 = +\$40{,}000 \\
\sim\!s \wedge o: &\quad -\$10{,}000 + \$50{,}000 = +\$40{,}000 \\
s \wedge d: &\quad -\$10{,}000 - \$80{,}000 = -\$90{,}000 \\
s \wedge o: &\quad -\$10{,}000 - \$80{,}000 + \$400{,}000 = +\$310{,}000.
\end{aligned}
$$

Using the probabilities of Example 2 of Section 6,

$$\mathbf{Pr}[\sim\!s \wedge d] = .4, \qquad \mathbf{Pr}[\sim\!s \wedge o] = .1$$
$$\mathbf{Pr}[s \wedge d] = .3, \qquad \mathbf{Pr}[s \wedge o] = .2.$$

Then

$$E = (.4)(\$40,000) + (.1)(\$40,000) + (.3)(-\$90,000) + (.2)(\$310,000)$$
$$= +\$55,000.$$

Observe that we could also treat the sequence of possible events for the given strategy as a stochastic process. In Figure 18 we have drawn a tree

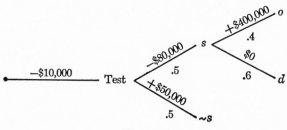

Figure 18

diagram for the strategy, and have labeled each branch with a dollar value above the branch and a probability below the branch. Of course the first stage (test) has probability 1, since under the given strategy a test will always be made. The probabilities at each stage are consistent with those of the example; for instance,

$$\mathbf{Pr}[s \wedge o] = (.5)(.4) = .2.$$

To obtain the expected value in this form, we may proceed in one of two ways. The first corresponds to the way in which the expected value was previously calculated: for each path we first calculate the path weight, and then find the value of the path by adding the value of each branch along the path. We form the product of path weight times path value, and add these products for all paths. Thus, for the path "test, structure, oil," the weight is $(.5)(.4) = .2$, the value is

$$-\$10,000 - \$80,000 + \$400,000 = +\$310,000$$

and the product is $(\$310,000)(.2) = \$62,000$. Similarly, the product for the path "test, structure, dry" is $-\$27,000$, and for "test, no structure," $+\$20,000$, so that the expected value is as before,

$$+\$62,000 - \$27,000 + \$20,000 = +\$55,000.$$

An alternative way of performing the computation is first to replace the consequences of the last stage by *their* expected value, to add this number to the value of the preceding stage, and to take the expected value of the values thus obtained. Thus if we had tested, found structure, had decided to drill and committed the required $80,000 to this operation, but had not yet determined whether the hole contained oil or was dry, the expected net cash proceeds from this point would be

$$(.4)(\$400,000) + (.6)(0) = \$160,000.$$

The net expected value of proceeding along the branch labeled "structure" would thus be the $160,000 expected value less the $80,000 cost of drilling, or $80,000. Since one will proceed along this branch with probability .5, and along the branch labeled "no structure," with a known cash consequence of +$50,000, with probability .5, the expected value of being at the junction of the two branches is

$$(.5)(\$80,000) + (.5)(\$50,000) = \$65,000.$$

But to get to the junction, one must pay $10,000 for the test. Hence, once again, the expected value of the entire strategy is $65,000 − $10,000 = $55,000. This method of analysis is called "backwards induction."

EXERCISES

1. Suppose that A tosses two coins and receives $2 if two heads appear, $1 if one head appears, and nothing if no heads appear. What is the expected value of the game to him?   [*Ans.* $1.]

2. Smith and Jones are matching coins. If the coins match, Smith gets $1, and if they do not, Jones gets $1.
   (a) If the game consists of matching twice, what is the expected value of the game for Smith?
   (b) Suppose that if Smith wins the first round he quits, and if he loses the first he plays the second. Jones is not allowed to quit. What is the expected value of the game for Smith?

3. If five coins are thrown, what is the expected number of heads that will turn up?   [*Ans.* $\frac{5}{2}$.]

4. A coin is thrown until the first time a head comes up or until three tails in a row occur. Find the expected number of times the coin is thrown.

5. In bets in which the probability of winning is .5, a popular betting "system" is to continue to bet each time one loses, doubling the stake at each stage, until a win occurs. Suppose the first bet is for $1, and that the bettor's capital is $3, so that if he loses twice in a row he must stop the procedure. What is the expected value of the game?   [*Ans.* 0.]

6. In Exercise 5, what is the expected value of the game if the bettor's capital is limited to (a) $7? (b) $15? (c) $31? (d) Suppose a bettor has enough capital to play 20 times, doubling his stake each time. What is the expected value of the game? How much capital is required?

7. Prove that if the expected value of a given experiment is E, and if a constant c is added to each of the outcomes, the expected value of the new experiment is $E + c$.

8. Prove that, if the expected value of a given experiment is E, and if each of the possible outcomes is multiplied by a constant k, the expected value of the new experiment is $k \cdot E$.

9. In the oil wildcatter example, obtain the expected value of the following strategies by drawing the appropriate portion of the tree diagram and (1) calculating path weights and path values; (2) using "backwards induction":
   (a) Drill.
   (b) Sell rights.
   (c) Take seismographic recordings; if they indicate no structure, drill; if they indicate structure, sell rights.
   Which is the best strategy?

10. In Exercise 9, two other possible strategies are
   (d) Take seismographic recordings; if they indicate structure, drill; if they indicate no structure, drill.
   (e) Take seismographic recordings; if they indicate structure, sell rights; if they indicate no structure, sell rights.
   What are the expected values of these strategies? Why is it unnecessary to consider them when trying to find the best strategy?

11. In Example 3 of Chapter I, Section 6, suppose the probability of successfully developing the component is .6; the probability of developing A successfully is .3 and the probability of then developing B successfully is .7. If, however, the order of development is B, then A, the probabilities of success are .5 and .4, respectively. Suppose that the cost of attempting to develop the component is $100,000; of then attempting to develop A, $100,000, then B, an additional $50,000. If, however, the order of development is B, then A, the costs would be $150,000 for B and $50,000 for A. Finally, the revenue that would result from successfully developing the component is $150,000, that for A is $120,000, and that for B is $300,000, regardless of the order of development.
   List the possible strategies and determine the expected value of each. What strategy produces the highest expected value?

12. Show that in an independent trials process with two outcomes, where $p = .2$ is the probability of success, the expected number of successes in $n = 8$ trials is $np = (.2)(8) = 1.6$.

13. In Exercise 7(c) of Section 4, what is the expected number of hits?
                                                         [$Ans. \frac{3}{2}.$]

14. In Exercise 3 of Section 6,
   (a) What is the expected demand on one day?
   (b) Show that the total expected demand on two successive days is twice the expected demand on one day.
   (c) What is the total expected demand on two successive days given that on one of the days demand was for one unit?
   (d) What is the total expected demand on two successive days given that on the first day demand was for one unit?

15. In Exercise 9 of Section 3, what is the expected number of defects of a piece selected at random?   [*Ans.* .260.]

16. In Exercise 13 of Section 7,
    (a) What is the expected number of defectives in a sample of three?
    [*Ans.* $\frac{9}{20}$.]
    (b) Before the sample is drawn, what is the expected number of defectives in the lot?   [*Ans.* $\frac{3}{2}$.]
    (c) After one defective has been found in a sample of three, what is the expected number of defectives originally in the lot? What is the expected number of defectives among the seven uninspected pieces?
    [*Ans.* 1.61, .61.]

17. In Exercise 7 of Section 4, suppose that the missiles are fired sequentially until the target is hit once. What is the expected number of missiles which must be fired?

18. In Example 2 of Section 8, suppose that there is a .9 probability that on a particular measurement a unit will be correctly classified. Consider the following "curtailed inspection procedure": each unit is measured until the unit is classified twice as good or twice as defective. What is the expected number of times that a piece which is really good will be measured? What is the probability that it will be classified as defective?
[*Ans.* 2.18, .028.]

19. In Exercise 13 of Section 8, what is the expected number of missiles that will be fired if they are fired one by one until either (1) the target is hit, or (2) ten missiles are fired? What is the probability that more than ten missiles will have to be fired to obtain one hit?

20. In an independent trials process with three outcomes, a_1, a_2, and a_3, with probabilities p_1, p_2, and p_3, show that in $n = 3$ trials the expected number of outcomes a_i is $np_i = 3p_i$, $i = 1, 2, 3$. Use this result to calculate the expected number of pieces that are too large, too small, or within tolerance limits, in Exercise 1 of Section 10.

12. Markov chains

In this section we shall study a more general kind of process than the ones considered in the last three sections.

We assume that we have a sequence of experiments with the following properties. The outcome of each experiment is one of a finite number of possible outcomes $a_1, a_2, \ldots, a_r$. It is assumed that the probability of outcome a_j on any given experiment is not necessarily independent of the outcomes of previous experiments but depends at most upon the outcome of the immediately preceding experiment. We assume that there are given numbers p_{ij} which represent the probability of outcome a_j on any given experiment, given that outcome a_i occurred on the preceding experiment.

The outcomes $a_1, a_2, \ldots, a_r$ are called *states*, and the numbers p_{ij} are called *transition probabilities*. If we assume that the process begins in some particular state, then we have enough information to determine the tree measure for the process and can calculate probabilities of statements relating to the over-all sequence of experiments. A process of the above kind is called a *Markov chain process*.

The transition probabilities can be exhibited in two different ways. The first way is that of a square array. For a Markov chain with states a_1, a_2, and a_3, this array is written as

$$P = \begin{pmatrix} p_{11} & p_{12} & p_{13} \\ p_{21} & p_{22} & p_{23} \\ p_{31} & p_{32} & p_{33} \end{pmatrix}.$$

Such an array is a special case of a *matrix*. Matrices are of fundamental importance to the study of Markov chains as well as being important in the study of other branches of mathematics. They will be studied in detail in the next chapter.

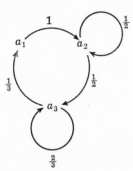

Figure 19

A second way to show the transition probabilities is by a *transition diagram*. Such a diagram is illustrated for a special case in Figure 19. The arrows from each state indicate the possible states to which a process can move from the given state.

The matrix of transition probabilities which corresponds to this diagram is the matrix

$$P = \begin{array}{c} \\ a_1 \\ a_2 \\ a_3 \end{array} \begin{array}{ccc} a_1 & a_2 & a_3 \end{array} \\ \begin{pmatrix} 0 & 1 & 0 \\ 0 & \frac{1}{2} & \frac{1}{2} \\ \frac{1}{3} & 0 & \frac{2}{3} \end{pmatrix}.$$

An entry of 0 indicates that the transition is impossible.

Notice that in the matrix P the sum of the elements of each row is 1. This must be true in any matrix of transition probabilities, since the elements of the ith row represent the probabilities for all possibilities when the process is in state a_i.

The kind of problem in which we are most interested in the study of Markov chains is the following. Suppose that the process starts in state i. What is the probability that after n steps it will be in state j? We denote this probability by $p_{ij}^{(n)}$. Notice that we do *not* mean by this the nth power of the number p_{ij}. We are actually interested in this probability for all possible starting positions i and all possible terminal positions j. We can represent these numbers conveniently again by a matrix. For example for

n steps in a three-state Markov chain we write these probabilities as the matrix

$$P^{(n)} = \begin{pmatrix} p_{11}^{(n)} & p_{12}^{(n)} & p_{13}^{(n)} \\ p_{21}^{(n)} & p_{22}^{(n)} & p_{23}^{(n)} \\ p_{31}^{(n)} & p_{32}^{(n)} & p_{33}^{(n)} \end{pmatrix}.$$

Example 1. Let us find for a Markov chain with transition probabilities indicated in Figure 19 the probability of being at the various possible states after three steps, assuming that the process starts at state a_1. We find these probabilities by constructing a tree and a tree measure as in Figure 20.

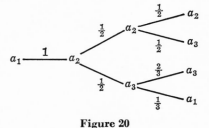

The probability $p_{13}^{(3)}$, for example, is the sum of the weights assigned by the tree measure to all paths through our tree which end at state a_3. That is,

Figure 20

$$1 \cdot \tfrac{1}{2} \cdot \tfrac{1}{2} + 1 \cdot \tfrac{1}{2} \cdot \tfrac{2}{3} = \tfrac{7}{12}.$$

Similarly

$$p_{12}^{(3)} = 1 \cdot \tfrac{1}{2} \cdot \tfrac{1}{2} = \tfrac{1}{4} \quad \text{and} \quad p_{11}^{(3)} = 1 \cdot \tfrac{1}{2} \cdot \tfrac{1}{3} = \tfrac{1}{6}.$$

By constructing a similar tree measure, assuming that we start at state a_2, we could find $p_{21}^{(3)}$, $p_{22}^{(3)}$, and $p_{23}^{(3)}$. The same is true for $p_{31}^{(3)}$, $p_{32}^{(3)}$, and $p_{33}^{(3)}$. If this is carried out (see Exercise 7) we can write the results in matrix form as follows:

$$P^{(3)} = \begin{array}{c} \\ a_1 \\ a_2 \\ a_3 \end{array} \overset{\begin{array}{ccc} a_1 & a_2 & a_3 \end{array}}{\begin{pmatrix} \tfrac{1}{6} & \tfrac{1}{4} & \tfrac{7}{12} \\ \tfrac{7}{36} & \tfrac{7}{24} & \tfrac{37}{72} \\ \tfrac{4}{27} & \tfrac{7}{18} & \tfrac{25}{54} \end{pmatrix}}.$$

Again the rows add up to 1, corresponding to the fact that if we start at a given state we must reach some state after three steps. Notice now that all the elements of this matrix are positive, showing that it is possible to reach any state from any state in three steps. In the next chapter we will develop a simple method of computing $P^{(n)}$.

Example 2. Suppose that we are interested in studying the process by which a given consumer purchases a certain product. We wish to make long-term predictions and so will not consider conditions peculiar to a particular purchase, such as an unusually intensive advertising campaign, or a special price reduction. We shall base our predictions only on past history of previous purchases, which would be available, for example, from consumer panels. We shall consider past purchases, and classify our data into purchases of Brand A (which we shall symbolize by A) and purchases of some other brand (which we shall symbolize by X). It is clear that a knowledge of past behavior would influence our predictions for the future. As a first approximation, we assume that the knowledge of the past beyond the last purchase would not cause us to change the probabilities for the outcomes on the next purchase. With this assumption we obtain a Markov chain with two states A and X and a matrix of transition probabilities

$$\begin{matrix} & A & X \\ A & \\ X \end{matrix} \begin{pmatrix} 1-a & a \\ b & 1-b \end{pmatrix}.$$

The numbers a and b could be estimated from past results as follows. We could take for a the fraction of the purchases of A which were followed by X, and similarly for b.

We can obtain a better approximation by taking into account the previous two purchases. In this case our states are AA, AX, XA, and XX, indicating the outcome of two successive purchases. Being in state AA means that the last two purchases were of Brand A. Being in state XX means that the last two purchases were of brands different from A; it does not necessarily mean that the last two purchases were of the same brand. If we are now in state XX and the next purchase is of Brand A, we will be in state XA. If a series of purchases can be represented by $XXXAXAA$, then our process has moved from state XX to XX to XA to AX to XA, and finally to AA. Notice that the first letter of the state to which we move must agree with the second letter of the state from which we came, since these refer to the same purchase. Our matrix of transition probabilities will then have the form

$$\begin{matrix} & AA & XA & AX & XX \\ AA & \\ XA & \\ AX & \\ XX \end{matrix} \begin{pmatrix} 1-a & 0 & a & 0 \\ b & 0 & 1-b & 0 \\ 0 & 1-c & 0 & c \\ 0 & d & 0 & 1-d \end{pmatrix}.$$

Again the numbers a, b, c, and d would have to be estimated. The study of this example is continued in Chapter V, Section 8.

Example 3. The following example of a Markov chain has been used in physics as a simple model for diffusion of gases.

We imagine n black balls and n white balls which are put into two urns so that there are n balls in each urn. A single experiment consists in choosing a ball from each urn at random and putting the ball obtained from the first urn into the second urn, and the ball obtained from the second urn into the first. We take as state the number of black balls in the first urn. If at any time we know this number, then we know the exact composition of each urn. That is, if there are j black balls in urn 1, there must be $n - j$ black balls in urn 2, $n - j$ white balls in urn 1, and j white balls in urn 2. If the process is in state j, then after the next exchange it will be in state $j - 1$ if a black ball is chosen from urn 1 and a white ball from urn 2. It will be in state j if a ball of the same color is drawn from each urn. It will be in state $j + 1$ if a white ball is drawn from urn 1 and a black ball from urn 2. The transition probabilities are then given by (see Exercise 14):

$$p_{jj-1} = \left(\frac{j}{n}\right)^2 \qquad j > 0$$

$$p_{jj} = \frac{2j(n-j)}{n^2}$$

$$p_{jj+1} = \left(\frac{n-j}{n}\right)^2 \qquad j < n$$

$$p_{jk} = 0 \qquad \text{otherwise.}$$

A physicist would be interested, for example, in predicting the composition of the urns after a certain number of exchanges have taken place. Certainly any predictions about the early stages of the process would depend upon the initial composition of the urns. For example, if we started with all black balls in urn 1, we would expect that for some time there would be more black balls in urn 1 than in urn 2. On the other hand, it might be expected that the effect of this initial distribution would wear off after a large number of exchanges. We shall see later, in Chapter V, Section 8, that this is indeed the case.

EXERCISES

1. Draw a transition diagram for the Markov chain with transition probabilities given by the following matrices.

$$\begin{pmatrix} \frac{1}{2} & \frac{1}{2} & 0 \\ 0 & 1 & 0 \\ \frac{1}{2} & 0 & \frac{1}{2} \end{pmatrix}, \quad \begin{pmatrix} \frac{1}{3} & \frac{1}{3} & \frac{1}{3} \\ \frac{1}{3} & \frac{1}{3} & \frac{1}{3} \\ \frac{1}{3} & \frac{1}{3} & \frac{1}{3} \end{pmatrix},$$

$$\begin{pmatrix} 0 & 1 \\ 1 & 0 \end{pmatrix}, \quad \begin{pmatrix} 0 & 1 & 0 & 0 \\ 1 & 0 & 0 & 0 \\ 0 & 0 & \frac{1}{2} & \frac{1}{2} \\ 0 & 0 & \frac{1}{2} & \frac{1}{2} \end{pmatrix}.$$

2. Give the matrices of transition probabilities corresponding to the following transition diagrams.

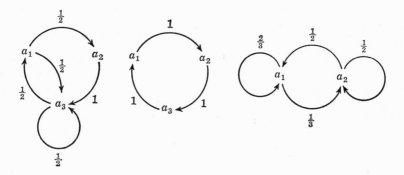

3. Find the matrix $P^{(2)}$ for the Markov chain determined by the matrix of transition probabilities

$$P = \begin{pmatrix} \frac{1}{2} & \frac{1}{2} \\ \frac{1}{3} & \frac{2}{3} \end{pmatrix}. \qquad \left[Ans. \ \begin{pmatrix} \frac{5}{12} & \frac{7}{12} \\ \frac{7}{18} & \frac{11}{18} \end{pmatrix}. \right]$$

4. What is the matrix of transition probabilities for the Markov chain in Example 3, for the case of two white balls and two black balls?

5. Find the matrices $P^{(2)}$, $P^{(3)}$, $P^{(4)}$ for the Markov chain determined by the transition probabilities

$$\begin{pmatrix} 1 & 0 \\ 0 & 1 \end{pmatrix}.$$

Find the same for the Markov chain determined by the matrix

$$\begin{pmatrix} 0 & 1 \\ 1 & 0 \end{pmatrix}.$$

6. Suppose that a Markov chain has two states, a_1 and a_2, and transition probabilities given by the matrix

$$\begin{pmatrix} \frac{1}{3} & \frac{2}{3} \\ \frac{1}{2} & \frac{1}{2} \end{pmatrix}.$$

By means of a separate chance device we choose a state in which to start the process. This device chooses a_1 with probability $\frac{1}{2}$ and a_2 with probability $\frac{1}{2}$. Find the probability that the process is in state a_1 after the first step. Answer the same question in the case that the device chooses a_1 with probability $\frac{1}{3}$ and a_2 with probability $\frac{2}{3}$. [$Ans.$ $\frac{5}{12}$; $\frac{4}{9}$.]

7. Referring to the Markov chain with transition probabilities indicated in Figure 19, construct the tree measures and determine the values of

$$p_{21}^{(3)}, p_{22}^{(3)}, p_{23}^{(3)} \quad \text{and} \quad p_{31}^{(3)}, p_{32}^{(3)}, p_{33}^{(3)}.$$

8. In Example 2, suppose that we wanted to predict brand purchasing behavior by taking into account the last three purchases. Construct the matrix of transition probabilities. How many numbers would have to be estimated from the data? How many if we wanted to take into account the last four purchases? The last n purchases? What does this suggest about obtaining more and more complex "models" of purchasing behavior? [$Partial\ Ans.$ For n purchases, 2^n.]

9. Suppose that in Example 2 we wanted to predict the purchasing behavior of a consumer with respect to three named brands, A, B, and C, and "all other" brands, symbolized by X. If we assume a Markov chain process and take into account only the last purchase, construct the matrix of transition probabilities. How many numbers must be estimated from the data? Construct the matrix of transition probabilities based on taking into account the last two purchases. How many numbers must be estimated from the data?

10. A certain calculating machine uses only the digits 0 and 1. It is supposed to transmit one of these digits through several stages. However, at every stage there is a probability p that the digit which enters this stage will be changed when it leaves. We form a Markov chain to represent the process of transmission by taking as states the digits 0 and 1. What is the matrix of transition probabilities?

11. For the Markov chain in Exercise 10, draw a tree and assign a tree measure, assuming that the process begins in state 0 and moves through three stages of transmission. What is the probability that the machine after three stages produces the digit 0, i.e., the correct digit? What is the probability that the machine never changed the digit from 0?

12. Assume that a man's profession can be classified as professional, skilled laborer, or unskilled laborer. Assume that of the sons of professional men 80 per cent are professional, 10 per cent are skilled laborers, and 10 per cent are unskilled laborers. In the case of sons of skilled laborers, 60 per cent are skilled laborers, 20 per cent are professional, and 20 per cent are unskilled laborers. Finally, in the case of unskilled laborers, 50 per cent of the sons are unskilled laborers, and 25 per cent each are in the other two categories. Assume that every man has a son, and form a Markov chain by following a given family through several generations. Set up the matrix of transition probabilities. Find the probability that the grandson of an unskilled laborer is a professional man.   [Ans. .375.]

13. In Exercise 12 we assumed that every man has a son. Assume instead that the probability a man has a son is .8. Form a Markov chain with four states. The first three states are as in Exercise 12, and the fourth state is such that the process enters it if a man has no son, and that the state cannot be left. This state represents families whose male line has died out. Find the matrix of transition probabilities and find the probability that an unskilled laborer has a grandson who is a professional man.   [Ans. .24.]

14. Explain why the transition probabilities given in Example 3 are correct.

*13. Monte Carlo simulation

So far we have studied only very simple stochastic processes—the independent trials process with two outcomes and with more than two outcomes, the finite sampling process, and the Markov chain process. There are other stochastic processes that are mathematically tractable, but we shall not study them here. However, there are others that are inherently so difficult that a purely mathematical treatment, no matter how advanced, is not practical. A method for analyzing stochastic processes of any degree of complication is the so-called *Monte Carlo simulation method.*

We have already seen that any stochastic process can be described by a tree diagram. The Monte Carlo method substitutes for a real-world stochastic process a simulated process with the same tree diagram. And in order to simulate the outcomes of real-world events that are probabilistic in nature, it uses random devices. In order to describe Monte Carlo simulations we will commonly use flow diagrams.

The random devices used in the simulation may be mechanical devices such as a roulette wheel, a pair of dice, a spinning pointer, etc. For instance, since the roulette wheel has 37 equally spaced slots, we assume that the 37 possible outcomes are equally likely. Accordingly, the roulette wheel can be used as a randomizing device for any stochastic process for which the probability of each outcome of each experiment is an integral multiple of $\frac{1}{37}$.

Example 1. Consider a machine that produces good pieces and defectives according to an independent trials process with two outcomes. Let the probability that a defective is produced be $\frac{2}{37} = .054$. Then we may simulate the production process by spinning the roulette wheel and saying that a defective is produced if the numbers 0 or 1 turn up, but a good piece is produced if any other number turns up. We could then simulate the process of examining a sample of three pieces produced by the process of spinning the roulette wheel three times. And we could approximate the binomial probabilities $b(r; 3, \frac{2}{37})$ by observing the relative frequency with $r = 0, 1, 2$, and 3 "defectives" in a large series of such trials. The fraction of cases in which 1 defective is found in 10,000 such tries will differ from the expected number $10,000\, b(1; 3, \frac{2}{37})$ in a way that is described in the law of large numbers.

Observe that we could have used the outcomes 16 and 23, say, to represent the drawing of a defective, instead of the numbers 0 and 1. Such changes do not alter the basic probability process.

Reliance on mechanical random devices would be very slow and clumsy, especially if a large number of trials is to be made. For this reason, random digit tables, such as Table II, p. 468, have been prepared, and by properly using them we can simulate any chance device. A random digit table is, in principle, created by recording the results of an independent trials process with ten outcomes—the digits $0, 1, \ldots, 9$. The probability assigned to each of the ten possible outcomes is $\frac{1}{10}$. Since the probability of each digit occurring is $\frac{1}{10}$, the probability of a two-digit number occurring is $\frac{1}{100}$ and the probability of a three-digit number is $\frac{1}{1000}$, etc.

Then to simulate an event whose occurrence has probability .173, all we do is to assign any 173 of the 1000 possible three-digit numbers as representing a success. For instance, we could say that the numbers 000 through 172 represent success. But we could equally well have chosen the sequence 827 through 999 to represent success. We then select from the random number table a number and record the experiment as success or failure depending upon whether the chosen number corresponds with one of the numbers we have labeled success.

In using the table of random numbers it is important not to use the same part of the table over and over again, since this will lead to a repetition of the same series of experiments. Instead, start at some arbitrary place in the table and move up or down a column, or right or left across a row, or take every other number group, and so on. It is a good idea to use a different rule each time the table is used. However, it is necessary to pick the rule in advance and, once it is chosen, to stick to it.

Example 2. Let us simulate the brand-purchasing behavior of a consumer who buys three brands of coffee, A, B, and C, according to the Markov chain process whose transition matrix P is given by

$$P = \begin{array}{c} \\ A \\ B \\ C \end{array} \begin{array}{ccc} A & B & C \\ \begin{pmatrix} .8 & .1 & .1 \\ .1 & .7 & .2 \\ .2 & .2 & .6 \end{pmatrix} \end{array}.$$

Assume that the last brand purchased was C. Then for the next purchase we assign the numbers 0 and 1 to choosing A, 2 and 3 to choosing B, and 4 through 9 to choosing C. In Figure 21 we show the calculations for 15 trials where we chose the random digits to be the first figure in each five-figure group starting in the first row and working from left to right. The first random number chosen was 6, so that according to our convention stated above we choose

Trial	Random Number	Brand Chosen
1	6	C
2	5	C
3	8	C
4	4	C
5	2	B
6	0	A
7	6	A
8	0	A
9	7	A
10	7	A
11	4	A
12	5	A
13	9	C
14	9	C
15	1	A

Figure 21

Brand C again. The next three numbers are 5, 8, and 4 so that we continue to choose Brand C. The fifth number is 2 so that we shift to Brand B and look at the second row of P. Here we let 0 represent choosing A, we let the numbers 1 through 7 represent choosing B and the numbers 8 and 9 represent choosing C. The next number 0 indicates that we choose Brand A, etc. The reader should check the rest of the entries in Figure 21.

Example 3. In a factory, machinists have to obtain tools at a tool crib which is serviced by a clerk, and hence a queue tends to form. The clerk takes three minutes to service a machinist. We are interested in the problem of how many new machinists arrive during three minutes. We assume that only one can arrive in any one-minute interval; and if there are s machinists, the probability of a machinist's joining the queue during a given minute when it is of length q is given by

$$p\left(\frac{s-q}{s}\right)$$

where p is a fixed number between 0 and 1. We get a new queue length of 0, 1, 2, or 3; the probability of getting each of these when $p = \frac{1}{2}$ and $s = 5$ is given in the table of Figure 22.

q	0	1	2	3
Probability	.125	.455	.360	.060

Figure 22

We now have the choice of simulating the formation of queues either by using the distribution of Figure 22 or by actually simulating the process of deciding when a machinist is to be added to the queue. Figure 23 shows a

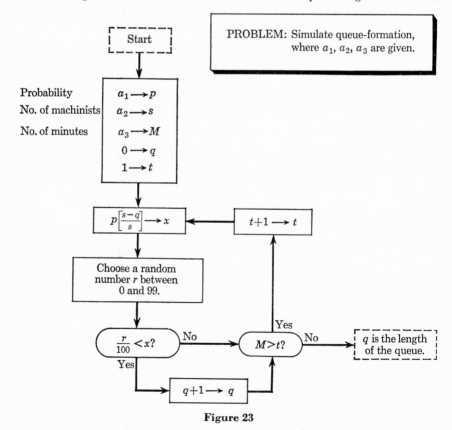

Figure 23

flow diagram for carrying out the latter simulation. This diagram will be used again as a subroutine in a simulation problem of the next section.

In Figure 23 we have set up a simulation for deciding whether a new person is to be added to the queue, given that there are q people already in the queue and s people in all who can be chosen in M minutes. The three initial pieces of data to be used are a_1, which is the value of p, a_2 which is s, the number of machinists, and a_3 which is the number of trials to be run. The reader should study the figure to see that it simulates the above process.

In Figure 24 we show 16 runs of the simulation diagrammed in Figure 23, for $p = \frac{1}{2}$, $s = 5$, $M = 3$. The random numbers were taken to be the first two digits of the third column in Table II. The observed frequencies for queues of length 0, 1, 2, and 3 were $\frac{3}{16} = .19$, $\frac{7}{16} = .44$, $\frac{6}{16} = .38$, and $\frac{0}{16} = 0$, respec-

Trial	Random Number	x	q	Trial	Random Number	x	q
1	80	.50	0	1	58	.50	0
2	07	.50	1	2	14	.50	1
3	95	.40	1	3	11	.40	2
1	40	.50	1	1	05	.50	1
2	54	.40	1	2	91	.40	1
3	64	.40	1	3	67	.40	1
1	60	.50	0	1	64	.50	0
2	08	.50	1	2	56	.50	0
3	26	.40	2	3	86	.50	0
1	59	.50	0	1	61	.50	0
2	88	.50	0	2	13	.50	1
3	54	.50	0	3	30	.40	2
1	57	.50	0	1	08	.50	1
2	88	.50	0	2	78	.40	1
3	28	.50	1	3	42	.40	1
1	83	.50	0	1	09	.50	1
2	05	.50	1	2	00	.40	2
3	56	.40	1	3	47	.30	2
1	83	.50	0	1	70	.50	0
2	74	.50	0	2	48	.50	1
3	96	.50	0	3	06	.40	2
1	40	.50	1	1	57	.50	0
2	61	.40	1	2	89	.50	0
3	05	.40	2	3	12	.50	1

Figure 24

tively. These are in surprisingly good agreement with Figure 22, better than
could normally be expected in so short a run. However, the law of large numbers guarantees with high probability excellent agreement in sufficiently long
runs. But queues of length 3 should turn up only with probability .06;
thus in 16 runs the expected number is only .96, or less than 1. Hence we would
expect to have to run a much larger number of trials than 16 to obtain a reasonable estimate for this probability.

It should be re-emphasized that simulation techniques are designed for
much more complex problems than here illustrated. They are useful when
explicit probabilistic calculations are too cumbersome to carry out. The
above examples illustrate the use of simulation, but the examples are simple
enough to have been treated by the methods discussed in earlier sections.

EXERCISES

1. Draw a tree diagram of the possibilities for the queueing situation of
   Example 3 when $p = \frac{1}{2}$, $s = 5$, and $M = 3$. Assign probabilities and show
   that the numbers in Figure 22 are correct.

2. Use the flow diagram of Figure 23 and the random number table (Table II)
   to carry out 16 more simulations of the queueing situation of Example 3
   when $p = \frac{1}{2}$, $s = 5$, and $M = 3$. Compute the observed frequencies of
   queue lengths and compare your numbers with those in Figure 22.

3. In Exercise 2, compute the relative frequencies of queue lengths observed
   in the simulations of all the students in the class and again compare with
   the table of Figure 22.

4. A machine produces good pieces and defectives according to an independent trials process, where the probability of a defective is $p = .4$.
   Use the random number table to simulate a sample of 20, and count the
   number of "defectives" in the simulated "sample." What is the binominal
   probability of obtaining this number of defectives? What is the probability
   that this number of defectives *or more* would be obtained?

5. A lot of 20 pieces contains six defectives. A sample of five is taken from
   the lot. Simulate the sampling operation and count the number of "defectives" in the sample. What is the hypergeometric probability of obtaining this number of defectives? What is the probability of obtaining this
   number of defectives *or less?*

6. A person buys Brand X of coffee according to a Markov chain process,
   with the following matrix of transition probabilities:

$$
\begin{array}{cc}
 & \text{X} \quad \text{Not X} \\
\begin{array}{c} \text{X} \\ \text{Not X} \end{array} &
\left(\begin{array}{cc} .6 & .4 \\ .2 & .8 \end{array} \right)
\end{array}
$$

Simulate ten consecutive purchases given that (a) the last purchase was X;

(b) the last purchase was not X; (c) the last purchase was X with probability $\frac{1}{3}$ and not X with probability $\frac{2}{3}$.

7. A model for the behavior of a stock traded on the New York Stock Exchange is that its price goes up, stays the same, or goes down from day to day according to a Markov chain process, with the following matrix of transition probabilities:

$$
\begin{array}{c}
 \\
\text{Up} \\
\text{Unchanged} \\
\text{Down}
\end{array}
\begin{array}{ccc}
\text{Up} & \text{Unchanged} & \text{Down} \\
\left(\begin{array}{c} .7 \\ .3 \\ .1 \end{array} \right. & \begin{array}{c} .2 \\ .4 \\ .3 \end{array} & \left. \begin{array}{c} .1 \\ .3 \\ .6 \end{array} \right)
\end{array}
$$

Suppose, in addition, that *if* the price goes up or down, the *amount* by which it changes is given by the following probabilities:

Amount of Change	Probability
$\frac{1}{2}$	.30
1	.40
$1\frac{1}{2}$	.20
2	.05
$2\frac{1}{2}$	.05

Simulate the next 20 days' trading on the assumption that the stock closed yesterday unchanged at 100.

8. A common model for predicting a company's sales volume by periods is to assume that sales are affected by four factors: trend, cycle, seasonal, and random fluctuations. Suppose that the trend of sales is increasing by 2000 units per quarter, that the business cycle is expected to affect sales in the next twelve quarters according to Table 1 below, that the deviation of sales from average in each of the four quarters is given by Table 2, and that the probabilities of various random fluctuations are given by Table 3. Simulate three years' sales by quarters if the next season's basic sales

	Table 1		Table 2		Table 3	
Qtr.	Cyclical deviations	Qtr.	Seasonal deviations	Random fluctuations	Prob- ability	
1	+ 3000	1	− 8000	−10,000	.02	
2	+ 5000	2	− 2000	−8,000	.04	
3	+ 6000	3	+ 1000	−6,000	.08	
4	+ 7000	4	+ 9000	−4,000	.11	
5	+ 7000			−2,000	.15	
6	+ 6000			0	.20	
7	+ 4000			+2,000	.15	
8	+ 2000			+4,000	.11	
9	− 1000			+6,000	.08	
10	− 3000			+8,000	.04	
11	− 4000			+10,000	.02	
12	− 4000					

level, including trend, but excluding cyclical, seasonal, and random factors, is 150,000 units.

9. The X company supplies Companies A, B, C, and D with a certain part. A orders 3 units every 5 days; B orders every 3 days, but the size of its order varies according to Table 1 below. C orders 5 units whenever it orders, but the interval between successive orders varies according to Table 2. D orders varying amounts at varying intervals, the amount ordered being independent of the time interval since the last order; Tables 3 and 4 show D's variation in amount and interval between orders. Simulate 20 days' demand for the part.

Table 1		Table 2		Table 3		Table 4	
Size of B's order	Prob- ability	Days btwn. C's orders	Prob- ability	Size of D's orders	Prob- ability	Days btwn. D's orders	Prob- ability
3	.2	2	.4	2	.2	1	.1
5	.3	3	.3	4	.2	2	.2
7	.4	4	.2	6	.3	3	.3
10	.1	5	.1	8	.3	4	.4

10. Suppose consumers buy Brand X of coffee according to a Markov chain process, with the matrix of transition probabilities given in Exercise 6. Assume that each consumer buys one pound a week, every week. At a certain time the X Company initiates a three-week advertising campaign. This may change a consumer's matrix of transition probabilities to

$$
\begin{array}{cc}
 & \begin{array}{cc} X & \text{Not X} \end{array} \\
\begin{array}{c} X \\ \text{Not X} \end{array} & \left(\begin{array}{cc} .7 & .3 \\ .4 & .6 \end{array} \right)
\end{array}
$$

but it is not certain when the change will occur or whether it will take place at all. There is a .7 probability that the change will occur but it may happen after the first, second, or third weeks of the campaign according to the following probabilities:

Number of Weeks After Start of Campaign	Probability
1	.2
2	.2
3	.3

Suppose each of five consumers last bought Brand X with probability $\frac{1}{3}$ and some brand other than X with probability $\frac{2}{3}$. Simulate ten weeks' purchases for the five consumers under the assumption that the advertising campaign begins after the third purchase.

11. Toss a coin 100 times, recording the results by writing 1 each time the coin comes up heads, and writing 0 each time it comes up tails. The resulting table may be considered a table of random bits. (See Chapter I, Section 11.) Use this table to simulate
    (a) A sample of five drawn from an independent trials process where the probability of success is .5.
    (b) A sample of ten drawn from an independent trials process where the probability of success is .125.

12. In Exercise 11 arrange the bits in the table you have created into groups of four. Interpret each such group as a binary coded decimal number (see Exercise 11, Chapter I, Section 12). Where a particular group has no interpretation as a binary coded decimal, disregard it. Show that the method produces random decimal digits. Can you think of a way of converting a table of random bits into a table of random decimal digits which makes more efficient use of the bits?

*14. Monte Carlo analysis of decision rules

Although the Monte Carlo technique is useful as a method of simulating a stochastic process for purely descriptive purposes, it is most important for the analysis of decision rules applied to complex systems. Although in recent years there has been considerable development of advanced mathematical techniques to handle systems such as inventory control, waiting lines, and so forth, these techniques can usually be applied only when the system in question obeys certain carefully defined probabilistic laws. And when these laws do not apply to a given situation, the best method of analysis available is often the Monte Carlo method.

We shall illustrate the application of this technique to decision problems in inventory control and waiting lines. The reader will quickly observe that the number of trials that can be simulated by hand calculation seldom will be sufficient to permit any firm conclusions about the adequacy of a particular decision rule. However, the ability to perform these calculations very rapidly on computers makes the Monte Carlo method a practical way to analyze decision rules. Here we shall simply illustrate the method by means of hand calculations, but the flow diagrams we draw can easily be translated into computer programs. And those readers who have a computer available can try them out.

Example 1. *Waiting Line.* Machinists in a factory have to obtain new tools as a result of tool wear or because of setup requirements for new jobs. They obtain these tools at a tool crib, which is serviced by clerks. Suppose that it takes exactly two minutes for a clerk to service a single machinist's request. Then one clerk can handle up to 30 requests an hour, two clerks can handle up to 60 requests, etc.

A clerk in the tool crib is paid $2 an hour. The cost of having a machinist wait in line while his machine is idle is assessed at $24 an hour. In Figure 25 a flow chart is shown for calculating the total cost of running a tool bin with r clerks for H hours, in a shop having s machinists. A subroutine in this program

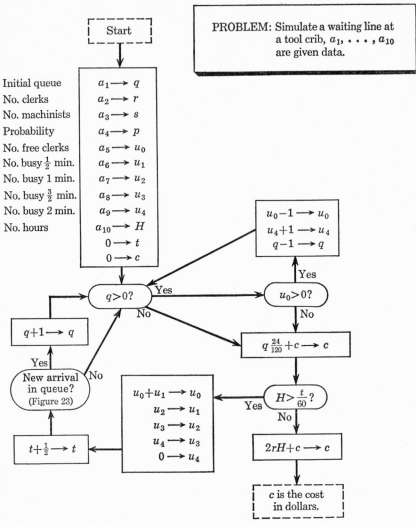

Figure 25

is the flow diagram of Figure 23 of the preceding section for $M = 1$, in which the new arrival in the queue is simulated. It is assumed that time is measured in intervals of $\frac{1}{2}$ minute. The quantity u_0 counts the number of idle clerks, u_1 the number who will be busy for $\frac{1}{2}$ minute more servicing a particular machinist,

u_2 the number who will be busy for 1 minute, u_3 the number who will be busy for $\frac{3}{2}$ minutes, and u_4 the number who will be busy for 2 minutes. The quantity q is the length of the queue at any time, p is the probability needed in the queue arrival subroutine, and t is the current time, measured in $\frac{1}{2}$-minute intervals. The reader should study the flow chart until he is convinced that it simulates the problem described in words above.

In Figures 26 and 27 a simulation is carried out for 10 minutes of the prob-

Time	q^*	"Arrival" 001 to	Random dom No.	No. Arriving	q	u_0	u_1	u_2	u_3	u_4	c
0				0	0	0	0	1	1	0	
1/2	2	450	430	1	1	0	1	1	0	0	.20
1	3	425	776	0	0	0	1	0	0	1	.20
3/2	2	450	990	0	0	1	0	0	1	0	.20
2	1	475	186	1	0	0	0	1	0	1	.20
5/2	2	450	612	0	0	0	1	0	1	0	.20
3	2	450	297	1	0	0	0	1	0	1	.20
7/2	2	450	467	0	0	0	1	0	1	0	.20
4	2	450	806	0	0	1	0	1	0	0	.20
9/2	1	475	783	0	0	1	1	0	0	0	.20
5	1	475	273	1	0	1	0	0	0	1	.20
11/2	1	475	128	1	0	0	0	0	1	1	.20
6	2	450	155	1	1	0	0	1	1	0	.40
13/2	3	425	111	1	2	0	1	1	0	0	.80
7	4	400	823	0	1	0	1	0	0	1	1.00
15/2	3	425	392	1	1	0	0	0	1	1	1.20
8	3	425	056	1	2	0	0	1	1	0	1.60
17/2	4	400	275	1	3	0	1	1	0	0	2.20
9	5	375	602	0	2	0	1	0	0	1	2.60
19/2	4	400	540	0	1	0	0	0	1	1	2.80
10	3	425	772	0	1	0	0	1	1	0	3.00

Cost of 2 clerks for 10 min.   .67

Total cost for 10 min.   \$3.67

Figure 26

lem, assuming that there are 2 and 3 clerks, respectively. It is also assumed that there are 20 machinists. It is initially assumed that two people are being served. The entry q^* in the tables counts the total number of people who were being served or were waiting to be served in the previous period. The probability of a machinist arriving is

$$\frac{1}{2}\left(\frac{20 - q^*}{20}\right).$$

The random numbers were chosen between 000 and 999 from Table II.

Note that the total cost with 2 clerks is \$3.67 for 10 minutes, which would mean that the hourly cost would be \$22.02. On the other hand, the total cost

Time	q^*	"Arrival" 001 to	Ran- dom No.	No. Arri- ving	q	u_0	u_1	u_2	u_3	u_4	c
0				0	0	1	0	1	1	0	0
1/2	2	450	430	1	0	0	1	1	0	1	0
1	3	425	776	0	0	1	1	0	1	0	0
3/2	2	450	990	0	0	2	0	1	0	0	0
2	1	475	186	1	0	1	1	0	0	1	0
5/2	2	450	612	0	0	2	0	0	1	0	0
3	1	475	297	1	0	1	0	1	0	1	0
7/2	2	450	467	0	0	1	1	0	1	0	0
4	2	450	806	0	0	2	0	1	0	0	0
9/2	1	475	783	0	0	2	1	0	0	0	0
5	1	475	273	1	0	2	0	0	0	1	0
11/2	1	475	128	1	0	1	0	0	1	1	0
6	2	450	155	1	0	0	0	1	1	1	0
13/2	3	425	111	1	1	0	1	1	1	0	.20
7	4	400	823	0	0	0	1	1	0	1	.20
15/2	3	425	392	1	0	0	1	0	1	1	.20
8	3	425	056	1	0	0	0	1	1	1	.20
17/2	3	425	275	1	1	0	1	1	1	0	.40
9	3	425	602	0	0	0	1	1	0	1	.40
19/2	3	425	540	0	0	1	1	0	1	0	.40
10	2	450	772	0	0	2	0	1	0	0	.40

Cost of 3 clerks for 10 min.   1.00

Total cost for 10 min. $1.40

Figure 27

with 3 clerks is $1.40 for 10 minutes, which would mean that the hourly cost would be $8.40. Clearly, it pays to have 3 rather than 2 clerks. It might just barely pay to add a fourth clerk since the cost for the clerks would be $8.00 per hour and it is unlikely that any machinist would ever have to wait with 4 clerks. However, the greatest possible savings are only $.40 per hour so that the decision as to whether or not to add the fourth clerk may depend upon other factors.

The results of one short simulation run are not, of course, sufficient to make certain that the conclusions drawn will always hold. However, with a fast computer it is possible to make very long simulation runs, and study the effects of a particular situation over days or even months or years of operation. From such large-scale simulations, the law of large numbers assures us that reliable conclusions can be drawn. The main problem for such studies is to be certain that the simulation accurately describes the situation under study.

Example 2. *Inventory Control.* A distributor observes that the daily demand for an item varies probabilistically. At the beginning of any day an order can be placed for any number of units of the item at a total cost of $2, regardless of the number of units ordered. But if no order is placed, the \$2 cost is not incurred. Units ordered are delivered and available for sale on the third day after the order is made. It costs the distributor \$.20 per day for each item held in inventory. If demand exceeds inventory on a given day, the excess demand constitutes a negative inventory or a "back order." If the inventory becomes negative in this manner, there is a cost of \$1 for each day per item. As soon as an order arrives, it is used first to reduce back orders. The remainder of an order, if any, is then used to fill current demand. Thus, when an order arrives, it is simply added to the (negative or positive) inventory.

The distributor observes that the probabilities of various sizes of demand are as shown in Figure 28. Given the table, it is easy, using the techniques of the preceding section, to simulate the demand.

Random numbers	1–8	9–21	22–37	38–57	58–74	75–85	86–94	95–00
Demand	0	1	2	3	4	5	6	7
Probability	.08	.13	.16	.20	.17	.11	.09	.06

Figure 28

The flow diagram for the simulation of the above situation is shown in Figure 29. The names of the variables are given on the diagram. I_t is the inventory at time t. Time $t = 4$ is chosen as the starting time. The box labeled "Find demand d_t" is simulated, using the data in Figure 28. We assign to the event "demand is 0" the two-digit random numbers 01 through 08, to the event "demand is 1" we assign the numbers 09 through 21, etc., and finally we assign the numbers 95 through 00 to the event "demand is 7." These numbers are marked in Figure 28.

The box labeled "Determine x_t" may be simulated in several ways. One way is to permit a person to make this decision on the basis of the previous orders and the back orders. When we do this we have what is commonly known as a *business game*, since part of the simulation involves the decisions of a person. Such games have recently come into the fore as useful tools for teaching as well as for simulation and research. It is likely that such games will be of increasing importance in the future. The above example is a business game involving only one person, but larger games involving several players have been devised.

The other way of simulating the box labeled "Determine x_t" is to replace it by a decision rule, which automatically determines x_t for each possible given set of values of the various variables. Examples of decision rules are the following:

1. Order 7 units every other day, starting today.
2. Order every fourth day so that the total number of units on order plus in inventory is equal to 16.
3. Order 5 units whenever previous orders plus present inventory falls below 10 units.

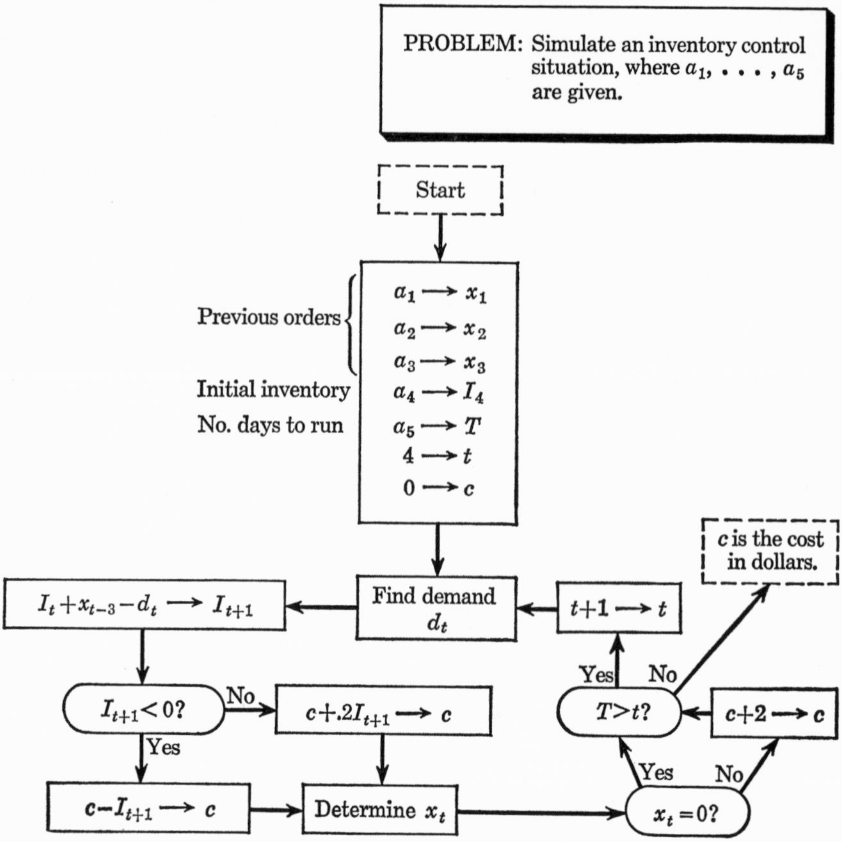

PROBLEM: Simulate an inventory control
situation, where $a_1, \ldots, a_5$
are given.

Start

Previous orders $\begin{cases} a_1 \longrightarrow x_1 \\ a_2 \longrightarrow x_2 \\ a_3 \longrightarrow x_3 \end{cases}$

Initial inventory $a_4 \longrightarrow I_4$

No. days to run $a_5 \longrightarrow T$

$4 \longrightarrow t$

$0 \longrightarrow c$

c is the cost
in dollars.

$I_t + x_{t-3} - d_t \longrightarrow I_{t+1}$

Find demand
d_t

$t+1 \longrightarrow t$

$I_{t+1} < 0?$ No $c + .2 I_{t+1} \longrightarrow c$ Yes | No $T > t?$ $c + 2 \longrightarrow c$

Yes

$c - I_{t+1} \longrightarrow c$ Determine x_t Yes   No $x_t = 0?$

Figure 29

4. Order 10 units whenever previous orders plus present inventory falls
below 15 units.

The first two of these rules are called "cyclical ordering" rules, since an order
is always placed at a predetermined time. Rules 3 and 4 are called "trigger
level" rules since no action is taken until the sum of previous orders plus
present inventory falls below a preset trigger level. In rule 3 the trigger level
is 10 while in rule 4 the trigger level is 15. In these rules the amount ordered—
5 or 10—is called the "reorder quantity."

We summarize the results of 20 days' simulation in Figure 30. This simulation was based on rule 3 to determine x_t. (See Exercises 8–10.) It was assumed
that the initial inventory is 10 and that 5 units were ordered 3 days ago. For
the determination of the demand d_t the last two digits of the numbers in column
two of Table II were used.

Of course, a run of 20 days is too short to make an accurate estimate. A
run of 500 days was carried out on a high-speed computer. This run indicates

Day	Random No.	Demand	I_t	x_{t-3}	x_{t-2}	x_{t-1}	I_{t+1}	x_t	c
1 ($t = 4$)	45	3	10	5	0	0	12	0	$ 2.40
2	32	2	12	0	0	0	10	0	4.40
3	07	0	10	0	0	0	10	0	6.40
4	52	3	10	0	0	0	7	5	9.80
5	59	4	7	0	0	5	3	5	12.40
6	33	2	3	0	5	5	1	0	12.60
7	23	2	1	5	5	0	4	5	15.40
8	92	6	4	5	0	5	3	5	18.00
9	70	4	3	0	5	5	-1	5	21.00
10	80	5	-1	5	5	5	-1	5	24.00
11	85	5	-1	5	5	5	-1	5	27.00
12	38	3	-1	5	5	5	1	0	27.20
13	63	4	1	5	5	0	2	5	29.60
14	59	4	2	5	0	5	3	5	32.20
15	06	0	3	0	5	5	3	0	32.80
16	29	2	3	5	5	0	6	0	34.00
17	07	0	6	5	0	0	11	0	36.20
18	01	0	11	0	0	0	11	0	38.40
19	62	4	11	0	0	0	7	5	41.80
20	80	5	7	0	0	5	2	5	44.20

Figure 30

that there is a tendency for back orders to pile up. The results can be improved by either increasing the reorder quantity or the trigger level. Figure 31 shows the result of eight different runs of 500 days each, in which these two quantities

Trigger Level	Reorder Quantity	Average Total Cost Per Day	Costs for 500 Days*			
			Total	Ordering	Back Orders	Inventory
10	5	$2.62	$1312	$656	$412	$244
10	8	2.11	1054	422	244	388
10	10	2.02	1011	330	175	506
10	11	1.93	965	284	99	582
10	12	2.00	998	272	132	594
10	14	2.11	1055	246	155	654
10	5	2.62	1312	656	412	244
12	5	2.38	1191	632	115	444
15	5	2.76	1381	646	26	709

* Totals to nearest dollar.

Figure 31

were varied. We note, for example, that by increasing the reorder quantity to 11, we can cut the average daily cost from \$2.62 to \$1.93, which is a saving of more than 25 per cent.

There is evidence in Figure 31 that even a run of 500 days is subject to considerable variance. For example, we would expect that back order costs would decrease in the first six lines of the table. (Why?) Back order costs were recomputed for trigger level 10 and reorder quantities 10, 11, 12 on a run of 12,000 days. The results were 152, 147, 127 per 500 days, as opposed to the figures 175, 99, 132 given in the table. On the other hand, the new estimates for the average daily total costs differed from Figure 31 by less than 5¢ in each case. Hence the runs of 500 days may be useful for many purposes.

EXERCISES

1. In Example 1, suppose that at the time of the first arrival there are five machinists waiting, including those who are being serviced, and that servicing has just begun on all who can be served. Recompute the waiting-line data.

2. In Example 1, suppose that the service time is not a constant two minutes, but can vary between one and four minutes with the following probabilities:

Service Time (Minutes)	Probability
1	.20
1½	.25
2	.25
2½	.15
3	.05
3½	.05
4	.05

Simulate the service time as well as the arrival time, and find the cost of using two or three clerks. What is the expected service time?

3. In Example 2, fill in the data in Figure 30 for the twenty-first day.
   [Ans. 42, 3, 2, 0, 5, 5, −1, 5, 47.20.]

4. In Example 2, modify the flow chart (Figure 29) to include decision rule 3.

5. In Example 2, suppose the lead time between the placement and delivery of an order can vary between two and four (inclusive) days, with probabilities as follows:

Lead Time (Days)	Probability
2	.3
3	.4
4	.3

Simulate the lead time and, using the data of Figure 30, find the cost of the third decision rule. What is the expected lead time?

6. In Example 2, suppose once again that the lead time is constant, but that demand which occurs during a stockout is not back-ordered but lost. Let the foregone profit on an item which is demanded but which cannot be supplied be $3. In Figure 30 revise the costs of using the third decision rule.

7. Suppose that in Example 2 a unit demanded during a stockout is sometimes back-ordered, but sometimes the sale is lost. Let the probability of back-ordering decrease as the number of units back-ordered (and hence the expected delay in filling the order) increases. Discuss how you would modify the flow chart of Figure 29 and how you would modify the simulation procedure to take this into account, but do not perform any calculations.

8. In Example 2 simulate decision rule 1 for 20 days.

9. In Example 2 simulate decision rule 2 for 20 days.

10. In Example 2 simulate decision rule 4 for 20 days.

11. Play Example 2 as a business game making the decisions yourself for the amounts to reorder. Simulate your decision for 20 days and compare your results with each of the four decision rules. Did you do better?

12. Use the results of Exercises 8–11 to formulate a decision rule that is superior to rules 1 through 4. Make your rule as simple as possible.

13. In Example 2 compute the expected total demand in 20 days and compare this with the result obtained in Figure 30. It can be shown that a "standard deviation" for the total demand in n days is $\sqrt{(3.72)n}$. By how many standard deviations did the obtained value differ from the expected value? [*Ans.* 64.8; less than one standard deviation.]

*15. Reliability of components

In modern technology it often happens that for a system to function correctly it is necessary that each of a large number of component parts function correctly. If we assume that each component has a probability less than one of functioning correctly, then finding the probability that the entire system functions correctly is a problem in elementary probability.

We shall assume first that the system functions correctly only if all components function correctly, and that whether a single component functions correctly or not when a signal is put into the system is independent of whether or not the other components function. If we have four components A, B, C, D with probabilities p_A, p_B, p_C, and p_D of functioning, then the probability that the system S_1 (shown in Figure 32) functions is

$$p_{S_1} = p_A \cdot p_B \cdot p_C \cdot p_D.$$

System S_1

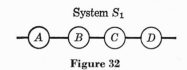

Figure 32

If we wished to improve on this probability we could imagine two systems of the type S_1 connected in parallel in such a way that the entire system S_2 would function if either of the two systems functioned (see Figure 33).

System S_2

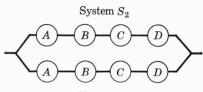

Figure 33

Another way of improving the reliability would be to form the system S_3 by putting two of each type of component in parallel (see Figure 34). This system will function if at least one component in each pair functions.

System S_3

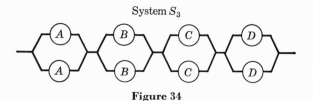

Figure 34

To see how much we have improved our reliability we must compute the probabilities of functioning for each of the new systems. Before doing this, however, observe that on purely logical grounds system S_2 is at least as good as system S_1. The reason is that every possibility for system S_1 that makes the system function is also favorable for S_2. Also, each possible way that S_2 functions correctly is favorable for S_3, and there are additional favorable possibilities. Hence S_3 is at least as good as S_2.

Let us now consider the probability that system S_2 works correctly. In order for this not to happen it must be true that both systems of type S_1 fail. This probability is $(1 - p_{S_1})^2$. Hence

$$p_{S_2} = 1 - (1 - p_{S_1})^2.$$

For system S_3 to be reliable it is necessary that all component pairs function correctly. Each pair functions incorrectly only if both components fail. Hence the probability that S_3 is reliable is

$$p_{S_3} = (1 - (1 - p_A)^2)(1 - (1 - p_B)^2)(1 - (1 - p_C)^2)(1 - (1 - p_D)^2).$$

We can further improve the system by putting three of each type of component in parallel (see Figure 35). Then the probability that system S_4

System S_4

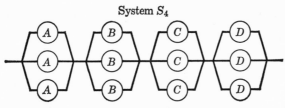

Figure 35

functions correctly is

$$p_{S_4} = (1 - (1 - p_A)^3)(1 - (1 - p_B)^3)(1 - (1 - p_C)^3)(1 - (1 - p_D)^3).$$

This probability is still larger than that of S_3 since each factor has increased. It is clear that by adding enough components in parallel for components of each type we can make the probability of correct functioning as large as we please.

There is, of course, an objection to adding components indiscriminately from the point of view of cost and space. However, there is still another objection. Assume that our system consists of a number of stations which are to signal the start of missile launching upon the detection of the approach of enemy missiles. By increasing the number of stations we increase the probability that at least one station will be able to get through the order. However, with each new station the chance of a signal sent by accident increases. Hence we would also want to take this into account.

To do this let us assume that for each component there is a probability that the component *will* function at a time that it should *not*. We shall, therefore, assume that every component functions when it should with probability p, and does not function without a signal with probability r. Of course $0 < p < 1$, and $0 < r < 1$ for any actual system.

Consider first the simple case of four components connected in parallel (see Figure 36). In order for the system to function correctly it is necessary that at least one of

System S_5

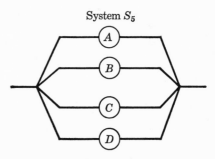

Figure 36

the components function when the signal is put in and that none of them function when the signal is not put in. This probability is

$$P_4 = r^4(1 - (1 - p)^4).$$

If there are m such components the probability is

$$P_m = r^m(1 - (1 - p)^m).$$

It is now no longer true that as we increase the number of components the probability that the system functions correctly increases indefinitely. In fact by choosing m large enough we can make the probability that the system functions correctly as *small* as we please (see Exercise 8). To investigate the dependence of this probability on m let us form the ratio

$$t_m = \frac{P_{m+1}}{P_m}.$$

We let $q = 1 - p$. Then

$$t_m = \frac{r^{m+1}(1 - q^{m+1})}{r^m(1 - q^m)}$$

$$= \frac{r(1 - q)(1 + q + q^2 + \ldots + q^m)}{(1 - q)(1 + q + q^2 + \ldots + q^{m-1})}$$

$$= r\left(1 + \frac{q^m}{1 + q + q^2 + \ldots + q^{m-1}}\right).$$

For $m = 1, 2, 3$ we have

$$t_1 = r(1 + q)$$

$$t_2 = r\left(1 + \frac{q^2}{1 + q}\right)$$

$$t_3 = r\left(1 + \frac{q^3}{1 + q + q^2}\right).$$

From the form of t_m we see clearly (see Exercise 7) that as we increase m we always decrease t_m. However, we increase P_m by increasing m as long as $t_m > 1$. Thus we are interested in finding the first time that $t_m < 1$. This will depend upon r and p.

In Figure 37 we have plotted the equations obtained by setting $t_1 = 1$, $t_2 = 1$, $t_3 = 1$, $t_4 = 1$, and $t_5 = 1$. For all pairs (p, r) that lie below the line $t_1 = 1$ we would use only one component. When (p, r) lies between the line $t_1 = 1$ and $t_2 = 1$ it is best to use two components, and so on. For instance, if $p = .8$ we would use one component if r is less than .83, and two components if it is between .83 and .97. We note, for instance, that for p values between .7 and 1 we would use one or two components unless r were quite near to 1. A critical region of Figure 37 is shown, enlarged, in Figure 38.

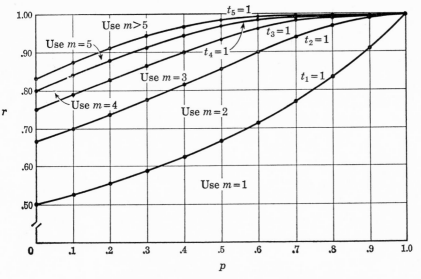

Figure 37

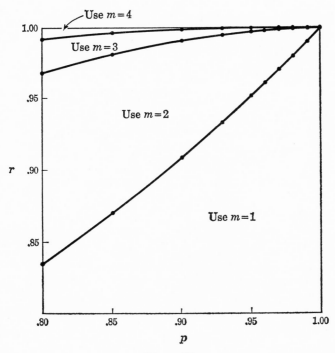

Figure 38

EXERCISES

In Exercises 1–3 consider systems with three types of components A, B, and C. A component of type A is reliable with probability .9, type B is reliable with probability .7, and type C with probability .8.

1. For systems of the type S_1, S_2, S_3, S_4 find the probability for correct functioning.

2. For the cases of Exercise 1, find the probability of correct functioning given that one component of type A is known to be faulty.

3. A system of type S_1 is used once a day for a week. What is the probability that the system functions every day?

4. Consider the two systems shown in Figure 39 having components of type A and B both of which are reliable with probability p. Show that system S' is always better than system S''.

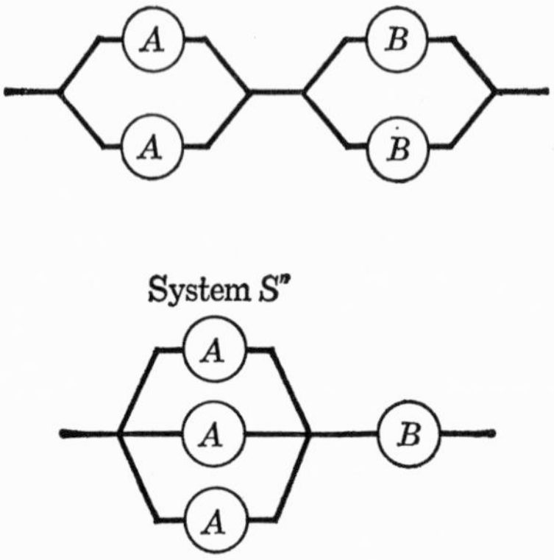

Exercises 5–9 relate to a system in which identical components are connected in parallel, each component having probability p for functioning correctly when a signal is put in and probability r for not functioning in the absence of a signal.

5. Assume that $p = .9$ and $r = .65$. How many components should be used to give the maximum probability of correct functioning?
[*Ans.* 1.]

6. Assume that $p = .9$ and r can be adjusted. It is desired to use no more than two components and necessary that the probability of reliable operation be at least .90. How large should r be? [*Ans.* $r > .95$.]

7. Prove that $t_{m+1} < t_m$.

8. Prove that the probability of correct functioning can be made as small as we please by making the number of components sufficiently large.

9. For many systems $.90 < p < .98$ and $.98 < r < .999$. Show that P_m is maximum for $m = 2$ or $m = 3$ for all such systems.

10. A satellite is to send a message to earth upon receiving a signal from the ground. A primitive switch is installed for this purpose, which will react to the signal with probability .7, and is assured not to react without a signal with probability .95. How many different switches should be installed to maximize the probability that the message is sent at the right time? What is the maximum probability? [*Ans.* 3; .83.]

System S'

System S''

Figure 39

11. A spy is sent on a dangerous mission. He has probability .3 of obtaining the desired information; and he has only a .9 chance of returning. If we assume that these probabilities are independent of each other, as are the probabilities for different spies, how many spies should we send to maximize the probability of getting the information without having any of the spies caught? What is the maximum probability?   [*Ans.* 4; .499.]

12. A bomb is to be set off by a time fuse. Each fuse will ignite the bomb at roughly the right time with probability .95. But there is a probability of .01 that the fuse may fire earlier owing to malfunction. How many fuses should be used to maximize the probability of an explosion at roughly the right time? What is the maximum probability?

*16. Decision theory

We have seen in Section 6 that the probabilities of a particular outcome calculated after test or sample information has been obtained may be different from the probabilities assigned to that outcome prior to the acquisition of the information. When this occurs, we say that the test or sample has yielded information.

In the oil wildcatter example which we have discussed repeatedly, we could either select a terminal act (drill or sell rights) at once, or decide to obtain information in the form of seismographic recordings. If information were obtained, we then had the problem of determining how to use it to help make the choice of a terminal act. We were not, however, faced with the problem of *how much* information should be obtained. If information were to be acquired, it would be in the form of a test which would cost $10,000.

In most sampling problems, we have, in addition to the question of whether or not further information should be acquired and of how it should be used if acquired, the question of *how much* information should be obtained. It is intuitively obvious that a very small sample provides, on the average, some, but not very much, information, while a very large sample may provide virtually perfect information about whatever is unknown. Why, then, are we ever content to settle for anything less than the largest possible sample? The answer, of course, is that sampling costs money. The larger the sample, the more it costs. We are, therefore, led to seek a way of measuring the value of information. Once this can be done, the question of how much information should be obtained can be answered by applying the principle that any quantity should be increased so long as the incremental value exceeds the incremental cost.

To illustrate the principles involved, while keeping the computations as simple as possible, we shall limit our discussion to one example. A machine produces good pieces and defectives according to an independent trials process with two outcomes, with probability p for a defective. If the machine is properly set up, the value of p is .1; if it is set up incorrectly, $p = .3$. When the machine is set up by an ordinary mechanic, the value of p is not known with certainty, but, before a run is made, a master mechanic can check the setup and adjust the machine if necessary, thereby guaranteeing that p will be .1. The cost of having the master mechanic check and adjust the machine is $25.

A run of 1000 pieces is to be made. Defective pieces in the production run can be rectified at a cost of $.25 per piece. Before a run is started, however, a sample run of predetermined size can first be made. On the basis of the sample outcome it can then be decided whether or not to use the services of the master mechanic. It costs $.40 to inspect each piece in the sample. For simplicity, we shall assume that the sample, if taken, does not constitute part of the production run.

There are, thus, two possible terminal acts: "proceed" and "readjust." There are two possible states of the machine characterized by the value of p: these are "$p = .1$" and "$p = .3$." For each act-state combination there is a cost. Thus, the act "proceed" will result in an expected $1000p$ defectives, each costing $.25, so that the expected cost of "proceed" is $250 \times p$. If $p = .1$, then the expected cost is $25; if $p = .3$, it is $75. Looking at the costs associated with the act "readjust," it is apparent that, no matter what the original state of the machine, this act will result in an immediate cost of $25 for the mechanic plus the expected cost of defectives produced when the machine is in state "$p = .1$." We have already seen that this latter amount is $25, so that the total expected cost of "readjust" is $50, regardless of whether the machine was originally in state "$p = .1$" or "$p = .3$." These costs are summarized in Figure 40.

		Act	
		Proceed	*Readjust*
State	$p = .1$	$25	$50
	$p = .3$	$75	$50

Figure 40

Now suppose that from long experience it has been found that the probability that the machine is initially in the state $p = .1$ is .6, while the prior probability that $p = .3$ is .4. We can then easily compute the expected costs of the two acts if one of them must be selected at once. In Figure 41, we show a decision tree, in which the four possible act-state combinations appear, along with the costs and probabilities associated with each. We can then compute:

Expected cost of proceed $= E_p = (.6)(25) + (.4)(75) = \$45$
Expected cost of readjust $= E_r = (.6)(50) + (.4)(50) = \$50.$

If a terminal act has to be chosen at once, the one with the lower expected cost is "proceed."

Our problem is to determine how much additional information it is worth paying for. Let us first consider the value of "perfect information." If someone told us what the value of p was, we could make our decision (perform the act "Proceed" or "Readjust") after knowing p. Hence the decision problem differs from Figure 41 in that the event precedes the act. This new problem is shown in Figure 42.

In this problem we can select the less expensive act in each case (circled in Figure 42). Hence the expected cost with perfect information is

$$(.6)(25) + (.4)(50) = \$35.$$

Since with existing information we can guarantee an expected cost of \$45 by always choosing the act "proceed," while with hypothetically perfect information we would reduce this only to \$35, the most that it would be

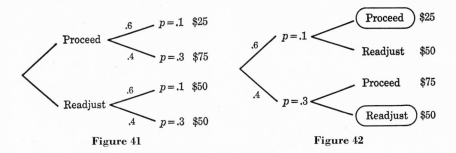

Figure 41   **Figure 42**

worth paying to obtain further information is \$45 − \$35 = \$10. In terms of sampling, this implies that a sample larger than \$10/\$.40 = 25 will never be economical.

Now suppose we take a sample of size n and observe r defectives. The probability of r is

(1) $\Pr[r] = \Pr[r \mid p = .1] \Pr[p = .1] + \Pr[r \mid p = .3] \Pr[p = .3]$

$$= \mathbf{b}(r; n, .1) \cdot (.6) + \mathbf{b}(r; n, .3) \cdot (.4)$$

since, given p, the process by which we obtain good pieces and defectives is an independent trials process. We may then use Bayes' Theorem to reassess the probabilities assigned to $p = .1$ and $p = .3$. For example,

$$\Pr[p = .1 \mid r] = \frac{\Pr[r \mid p = .1] \Pr[p = .1]}{\Pr[r]}$$

$$= \frac{\mathbf{b}(r; n, .1) \cdot (.6)}{\mathbf{b}(r; n, .1) \cdot (.6) + \mathbf{b}(r; n, .3) \cdot (.4)}$$

$$\Pr[p = .3 \mid r] = 1 - \Pr[p = .1 \mid r].$$

Although we are free to choose a terminal act after r has been observed, we shall find it convenient to note the following facts: (a) By the argument above, each value of r implies a unique posterior probability that $p = .1$ and that $p = .3$. (b) We can state, before any sample is taken, the values of $\mathbf{Pr}[p = .1]$ calculated posterior to the sample, for which "proceed" is the act with the lower expected cost, and the values for which "readjust" has the lower expected cost. We do this by writing the expected cost of the two acts as:

Expected cost of proceed $= E_p = \$25 \cdot \mathbf{Pr}[p = .1] + \$75(1 - \mathbf{Pr}[p = .1])$

$$= \$75 - \$50 \, \mathbf{Pr}[p = .1]$$

Expected cost of readjust $= E_r = \$50$.

Then $E_r < E_p$ if and only if $\mathbf{Pr}[p = .1] < .5$.

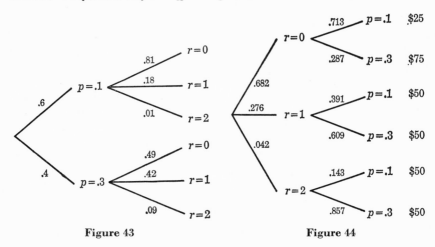

Figure 43   Figure 44

Let us now look at a numerical example. Suppose we take a sample of size $n = 2$. The conditional (binomial) probabilities of the various possible outcomes and the various possible values of p are shown in the tree diagram of Figure 43. By calculating the probabilities of p and r for all combinations and redrawing the tree as in Figure 44 (see Example 4 of Section 7), we can obtain the probabilities of r and the probabilities of p given r. For each path a cost is shown. These are the costs of terminal action, which are obtained by the following reasoning. When $r = 0$, $\mathbf{Pr}[p = .1] = .713 > .5$. Hence, given $r = 0$, "proceed" is the better act. If $p = .1$, the cost of proceeding is \$25; if $p = .3$, the cost of proceeding is \$75. For $r = 1$, $\mathbf{Pr}[p = .1] = .391 < .5$. Hence, the act with the lower expected cost is "readjust," and its cost of \$50 applies regardless of p. If $r = 2$, then surely the probability that $p = .1$ is less than when $r = 1$, and therefore "readjust" is again the better act.

To obtain the expected terminal cost, we multiply each path value by its weight and add. Because the same act is taken whenever r is greater than 0, and because its cost is independent of p, the tree diagram of Figure 44 can first be reduced to Figure 45. We now compute expected terminal cost (when n is 2):

$$.682[(.713)(25) + (.287)(75)] + (.318)(50) = \$42.75.$$

Observe that this is less than the \$45 expected cost of taking the better terminal act without sampling, but it is not nearly so good as the \$35 expected cost with a perfect forecast about p.

In order to achieve this reduction in expected cost, it is necessary to incur a sampling cost of $\$.40n = \$.80$. Therefore the expected cost of taking a sample of 2, proceeding if $r = 0$ and readjusting otherwise, is $\$42.75 + \$.80 = \$43.55$. Even when we include the cost of sampling, the expected cost using a sample of 2 and taking that act which is optimal in the light of the sample evidence is less than that of taking the better terminal act without sampling.

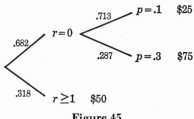

Figure 45

The following question now arises: can we do better with a sample of some other size? We know that n must be less than 25, so that we are restricted to a finite number of calculations of exactly the kind which we have just performed. This is a laborious procedure, and we shall simply supply the results here, except for a few blank spaces for which you will be asked to supply data in the exercises. In Figure 46 are listed, for values of n from 1 through 25, the values of r for which the terminal act with lower expected cost is "proceed." We also show the expected cost of terminal action, and the total expected cost, which includes the cost of sampling.

From this it should be clear that the optimal sample size is $n = 6$. Its expected total cost is \$43.31, or \$1.69 less than the cost of the better act without sampling. With a sample of size $n = 6$, the better decision is to proceed if $r = 0$ or 1 defective are found. If $r \geq 2$, the better act is to readjust.

EXERCISES

1. Fill in the entries in the table of Figure 46 for $n = 1$ and for $n = 3$.

2. An "error" occurs if we "proceed" when $p = .3$, or if we "readjust" when $p = .1$. When $n = 6$, using an optimal strategy,
   (a) What is the conditional probability of error given $p = .1$?   [*Ans.* .114.]
   (b) What is the conditional probability of error given $p = .3$?   [*Ans.* .420.]
   (c) What is the probability that an error will be made?   [*Ans.* .236.]

n	Values of r for which "Proceed" is Better	Expected Terminal Cost	Expected Total Cost
1	?	?	?
2	$r = 0$	$42.75	$43.55
3	?	?	?
4	$r \leq 1$	42.30	43.90
5	$r \leq 1$	41.51	43.51
6	$r \leq 1$	40.91	43.31
7	$r \leq 1$	40.54	43.34
8	$r \leq 1$	40.36	43.56
9	$r \leq 1$	40.34	43.94
10	$r \leq 2$	39.88	43.88
11	$r \leq 2$	39.47	43.87
12	$r \leq 2$	39.19	43.99
13	$r \leq 2$	39.03	44.23
14	$r \leq 2$	38.98	44.58
15	$r \leq 3$	38.80	44.80
16	$r \leq 3$	38.48	44.88
17	$r \leq 3$	38.26	45.06
18	$r \leq 3$	38.12	45.32
19	$r \leq 3$	38.06	45.66
20	$r \leq 4$	38.02	46.02
21	$r \leq 4$	37.77	46.17
22	$r \leq 4$	37.58	46.38
23	$r \leq 4$	37.45	46.65
24	$r \leq 4$	37.39	46.99
25	$r \leq 4$	37.37	47.37

Figure 46

3. It is frequently suggested that in situations like that of the example in this section, a sample size should be chosen so that the conditional probabilities of error given each of two values of p be less than some pre-assigned number. For example, an objective might be to limit the conditional probability of error given $p = .1$ to .05, and to limit the conditional probability of error given $p = .3$ to .1. Discuss this approach in the light of the results of Exercise 2.

4. The optimal sampling approach to the example of this section may be summarized by the *decision rule* $(n, c) = (6, 1)$ (see Exercise 17 of Chapter I, Section 5). The rule $(6, 1)$ means "take a sample of 6; if the number of defectives $r \leq 1$, proceed; if $r > 1$, readjust." An *operating characteristic* (see Exercise 9 of Section 8) shows the probabilities of choosing one of the acts—for example, "proceed"—using a decision rule. Draw a graph of the operating characteristic of the decision rule $(6, 1)$, by first computing the probability of "proceed" for each value of p in Table I, and then plotting p on the horizontal axis and the probability of "proceed" on the vertical axis.

5. Consider the example of this section. With identical costs, suppose p can take on the values .1, .15, and .3, and suppose

$$\Pr[p = .1] = .3$$
$$\Pr[p = .15] = .4$$
$$\Pr[p = .3] = .3.$$

(a) Prepare a table showing the expected cost for each act-state combination.

(b) Calculate the better act if immediate terminal action is taken. What is its expected cost?

(c) If free and perfect information about the value of p were supplied, what act should be taken if $p = .1$? If $p = .15$? If $p = .3$? What is the expected cost of acting optimally with free and perfect information? What is the expected value of perfect information? Derive an upper bound on sample size from this calculation.

6. In Exercise 5, suppose a sample of size $n = 6$ is taken.

(a) For which values of r is "proceed" the better act? For which values is "readjust" better?

(b) Before the sample is drawn, what is the probability of choosing the act "proceed" *after* the sample?

(c) Calculate the expected terminal cost of acting optimally after the sample has been taken.

(d) Calculate the total expected cost of sampling if $n = 6$. Compare it with that of the example. Why is it higher than the expected cost in the example?

7. In the example of this section, suppose that a sample of 2 was taken and no defectives were found in the sample. What is the expected cost of proceeding optimally from this point on? What is the expected cost if one defective was found? If two were found? [*Partial Ans.* If $r = 0$, $39.37.]

8. Urns I and II contain white balls and black balls. The contents of the urns are:

Urn I: 2 black, 8 white

Urn II: 7 black, 3 white.

One of the urns is chosen at random according to the outcome of a toss of a coin. A sample of n balls can be drawn from the chosen urn, on the basis of which an attempt is made to identify the urn. If it is correctly identified, you win $50. Sampling costs $10n$. What is the expected value of this "game" if the sample size must be fixed in advance?   [*Ans.* $27.50.]

SUGGESTED READING

Cramer, Harold, *The Elements of Probability Theory*, Wiley, New York, 1955, Part I.

Feller, W., *An Introduction to Probability Theory and its Applications*, Wiley, New York, 1950.

Schlaifer, R., *Probability and Statistics for Business Decisions*, McGraw-Hill, New York, 1959.

Whitworth, W. A., *Choice and Chance, with 1000 Exercises*, Stechert, New York, 1934.

Gordon, R., "Optimum Component Redundancy for Maximum System Reliability." *Operations Research*, **5** (1957), p. 229.

Vectors and Matrices

1. Column and row vectors

A *column vector* is an ordered collection of numbers written in a column. Examples of such vectors are

$$\begin{pmatrix} 1 \\ -2 \end{pmatrix}, \quad \begin{pmatrix} .6 \\ .4 \end{pmatrix}, \quad \begin{pmatrix} 0 \\ 0 \\ 0 \end{pmatrix}, \quad \begin{pmatrix} 3 \\ -4 \\ 0 \end{pmatrix}, \quad \begin{pmatrix} 1 \\ -1 \\ 2 \\ 4 \end{pmatrix}.$$

The individual numbers in these vectors are called *components*, and the number of components a vector has is one of its distinguishing characteristics. Thus the first two vectors above have two components; the next two have three components; and the last has four components. When talking more generally about n-component column vectors we shall write

$$u = \begin{pmatrix} u_1 \\ u_2 \\ \cdot \\ \cdot \\ \cdot \\ u_n \end{pmatrix}.$$

Analogously, a *row vector* is an ordered collection of numbers written in a row. Examples of row vectors are

$$(1, 0), \quad (-2, 1), \quad (2, -3, 4, 0), \quad (-1, 2, -3, 4, -5).$$

Each number appearing in the vector is again called a *component* of the vector, and the number of components a row vector has is again one of its important characteristics. Thus, the first two examples are two-component, the third a four-component, and the fourth a five-component vector. The vector $v = (v_1, v_2, \ldots, v_n)$ is an n-component row vector.

Two row vectors, or two column vectors, are said to be *equal* if and only if corresponding components of the vector are equal. Thus for the vectors

$$u = (1, 2), \quad v = \begin{pmatrix} 1 \\ 2 \end{pmatrix}, \quad w = (1, 2), \quad x = (2, 1)$$

we see that $u = w$ but $u \neq v$, and $u \neq x$.

If u and v are three-component column vectors, we shall define their sum $u + v$ by component-wise addition as follows:

$$u + v = \begin{pmatrix} u_1 \\ u_2 \\ u_3 \end{pmatrix} + \begin{pmatrix} v_1 \\ v_2 \\ v_3 \end{pmatrix} = \begin{pmatrix} u_1 + v_1 \\ u_2 + v_2 \\ u_3 + v_3 \end{pmatrix}.$$

Similarly, if u and v are three-component row vectors, their sum is defined to be

$$u + v = (u_1, u_2, u_3) + (v_1, v_2, v_3)$$
$$= (u_1 + v_1, u_2 + v_2, u_3 + v_3).$$

Note that the sum of two three-component vectors yields another three-component vector. For example,

$$\begin{pmatrix} 1 \\ -1 \\ 2 \end{pmatrix} + \begin{pmatrix} 2 \\ 3 \\ -1 \end{pmatrix} = \begin{pmatrix} 3 \\ 2 \\ 1 \end{pmatrix}$$

and

$$(4, -7, 12) + (3, 14, -14) = (7, 7, -2).$$

The sum of two n-component vectors (either row or column) is defined by component-wise addition in an analogous manner, and yields another n-component vector. Observe that we do not define the addition of vectors unless they are both row or both column vectors, having the same number of components.

Because the order in which two numbers are added is immaterial as far as the answer goes, it is also true that the order in which vectors are added does not matter; that is,

$$u + v = v + u$$

where u and v are both row or both column vectors. This is the so-called *commutative law of addition*. A numerical example is

$$\begin{pmatrix} 1 \\ -1 \\ 2 \end{pmatrix} + \begin{pmatrix} 2 \\ 3 \\ -1 \end{pmatrix} = \begin{pmatrix} 3 \\ 2 \\ 1 \end{pmatrix} = \begin{pmatrix} 2 \\ 3 \\ -1 \end{pmatrix} + \begin{pmatrix} 1 \\ -1 \\ 2 \end{pmatrix}.$$

Once we have the definition of the addition of two vectors we can easily see how to add three or more vectors by grouping them in pairs as in the addition of numbers. For example,

$$\begin{pmatrix} 1 \\ 0 \\ 0 \end{pmatrix} + \begin{pmatrix} 0 \\ 2 \\ 0 \end{pmatrix} + \begin{pmatrix} 0 \\ 0 \\ 3 \end{pmatrix} = \begin{pmatrix} 1 \\ 0 \\ 0 \end{pmatrix} + \begin{pmatrix} 0 \\ 2 \\ 3 \end{pmatrix} = \begin{pmatrix} 1 \\ 2 \\ 3 \end{pmatrix}$$

$$= \begin{pmatrix} 1 \\ 2 \\ 0 \end{pmatrix} + \begin{pmatrix} 0 \\ 0 \\ 3 \end{pmatrix} = \begin{pmatrix} 1 \\ 2 \\ 3 \end{pmatrix},$$

and

$$(1, 0, 0) + (0, 2, 0) + (0, 0, 3) = (1, 2, 0) + (0, 0, 3) = (1, 2, 3)$$

$$= (1, 0, 0) + (0, 2, 3) = (1, 2, 3).$$

In general, the sum of any number of vectors (row or column), each having the same number of components, is the vector whose first component is the sum of the first components of the vectors, whose second component is the sum of the second components, etc.

The multiplication of a number a times a vector v is defined by component-wise multiplication of a times the components of v. For the three-component case we have

$$au = a \begin{pmatrix} u_1 \\ u_2 \\ u_3 \end{pmatrix} = \begin{pmatrix} au_1 \\ au_2 \\ au_3 \end{pmatrix}$$

for column vectors and

$$av = a(v_1, v_2, v_3) = (av_1, av_2, av_3)$$

for row vectors. If u is an n-component vector (row or column), then au is defined similarly by component-wise multiplication.

If u is any vector we define its negative $-u$ to be the vector $-u = (-1)u$. Thus in the three-component case for row vectors we have

$$-u = (-1)(u_1, u_2, u_3) = (-u_1, -u_2, -u_3).$$

Once we have the negative of a vector it is easy to see how to subtract vectors, i.e., we simply add "algebraically." For the three-component column vector case we have

$$u - v = \begin{pmatrix} u_1 \\ u_2 \\ u_3 \end{pmatrix} - \begin{pmatrix} v_1 \\ v_2 \\ v_3 \end{pmatrix} = \begin{pmatrix} u_1 - v_1 \\ u_2 - v_2 \\ u_3 - v_3 \end{pmatrix}.$$

Specific examples of subtraction of vectors occur in the exercises at the end of this section.

An important vector is the zero vector, all of whose components are zero. For example, three-component zero vectors are

$$0 = \begin{pmatrix} 0 \\ 0 \\ 0 \end{pmatrix} \quad \text{and} \quad 0 = (0, 0, 0).$$

When there is no danger of confusion we shall use the symbol 0, as above, to denote the zero (row or column) vector. The meaning will be clear from the context. The zero vector has the important property that, if u is any vector, then $u + 0 = u$. A proof for the three-component column vector case is as follows:

$$u + 0 = \begin{pmatrix} u_1 \\ u_2 \\ u_3 \end{pmatrix} + \begin{pmatrix} 0 \\ 0 \\ 0 \end{pmatrix} = \begin{pmatrix} u_1 + 0 \\ u_2 + 0 \\ u_3 + 0 \end{pmatrix} = \begin{pmatrix} u_1 \\ u_2 \\ u_3 \end{pmatrix} = u.$$

One of the chief advantages of the vector notation is that one can denote a whole collection of numbers by a single letter such as $u, v, \ldots$, and treat such a collection as if it were a single quantity. By using the vector notation it is possible to state very complicated relationships in a simple manner. The student will see many examples of this in the remainder of the present chapter and the three succeeding chapters.

EXERCISES

1. Compute the quantities below for the vectors

$$u = \begin{pmatrix} 3 \\ 1 \\ 2 \end{pmatrix}, \quad v = \begin{pmatrix} -2 \\ 3 \\ 0 \end{pmatrix}, \quad w = \begin{pmatrix} -1 \\ -1 \\ 1 \end{pmatrix}.$$

(a) $2u$. $\left[Ans. \begin{pmatrix} 6 \\ 2 \\ 4 \end{pmatrix}. \right]$

(b) $-v$.

(c) $2u - v$.

(d) $v + w$. $\left[Ans. \begin{pmatrix} -3 \\ 2 \\ 1 \end{pmatrix}. \right]$

(e) $u + v - w$.

(f) $2u - 3v - w$.

(g) $3u - v + 2w$. $\left[Ans. \begin{pmatrix} 9 \\ -2 \\ 8 \end{pmatrix}. \right]$

2. Compute (a) through (g) of Exercise 1 if the vectors u, v, and w are

$$u = (7, 0, -3), \quad v = (2, 1, -5), \quad w = (1, -1, 0).$$

3. (a) Show that the zero vector is not changed when multiplied by any number.
   (b) If u is any vector, show that $0 + u = u$.

4. If u and v are two row or two column vectors having the same number of components, prove that $u + 0v = u$ and $0u + v = v$.

5. If $2u - v = 0$, what is the relationship between the components of u and those of v?   [$Ans.\ v_i = 2u_i.$]

6. Answer the question in Exercise 5 for the equation $-3u + 5v + u - 7v = 0$. Do the same for the equation $20v - 3u + 5v + 8u = 0$.

7. When possible compute the following sums; when not possible give reasons.

   (a) $\begin{pmatrix} -1 \\ 3 \end{pmatrix} + \begin{pmatrix} 6 \\ -2 \\ 5 \\ -4 \end{pmatrix} = ?$

   (b) $(2, -1, -1) + 0(4, 7, -2) = ?$

   (c) $(5, 6) + 7 - 21 + \begin{pmatrix} 0 \\ 1 \end{pmatrix} = ?$

   (d) $1\begin{pmatrix} 1 \\ 0 \\ 1 \end{pmatrix} + 2\begin{pmatrix} 1 \\ 1 \\ 0 \end{pmatrix} + 3\begin{pmatrix} 0 \\ 1 \\ 1 \end{pmatrix} = ?$

8. If $\begin{pmatrix} 1 \\ 1 \\ 2 \end{pmatrix} + \begin{pmatrix} u_1 \\ u_2 \\ u_3 \end{pmatrix} = \begin{pmatrix} 1 \\ -1 \\ 0 \end{pmatrix}$, find u_1, u_2, and u_3.   [$Ans.\ 0;\ -2;\ -2.$]

9. If $2\begin{pmatrix} v_1 \\ v_2 \\ v_3 \end{pmatrix} = \begin{pmatrix} 0 \\ 1 \\ 3 \end{pmatrix}$, find the components of v.

10. If $\begin{pmatrix} 0 \\ 0 \\ 0 \end{pmatrix} + \begin{pmatrix} u_1 \\ u_2 \\ u_3 \end{pmatrix} = \begin{pmatrix} 0 \\ 0 \\ 0 \end{pmatrix}$, what can be said concerning the components u_1, u_2, u_3?

11. If $0 \cdot \begin{pmatrix} u_1 \\ u_2 \\ u_3 \end{pmatrix} = \begin{pmatrix} 0 \\ 0 \\ 0 \end{pmatrix}$, what can be said concerning the components u_1, u_2, u_3?

12. Suppose that we associate with each person a three-component row vector having the following entries: age, height, and weight. Would it make sense to add together the vectors associated with two different persons? Would it make sense to multiply one of these vectors by a constant?

13. Suppose that we associate with each person leaving a supermarket a row vector whose components give the quantities of each available item that he has purchased. Answer the same questions as those in Exercise 12.

14. Let us associate with each supermarket a column vector whose entries give the prices of each item in the store. Would it make sense to add together the vectors associated with two different supermarkets? Would it make sense to multiply one of these vectors by a constant? Discuss the differences in the situations given in Exercises 12, 13, and 14.

2. The product of vectors; examples

The reader may have wondered why it was necessary to introduce both column and row vectors when their properties are so similar. This question can be answered in several different ways. In the first place, in many applications there are two kinds of quantities which are studied simultaneously, and it is convenient to represent one of them as a row vector and the other as a column vector. Second, there is a way of combining row and column vectors that is very useful for certain types of calculations. To bring out these points let us look at the following simple economic example.

Example 1. Suppose a man named Smith goes into a grocery store to buy a dozen each of eggs and oranges, a half dozen each of apples and pears, and three lemons. Let us represent his purchases by means of the following row vector:

$$x = [6 \text{ (apples)}, 12 \text{ (eggs)}, 3 \text{ (lemons)}, 12 \text{ (oranges)}, 6 \text{ (pears)}]$$
$$= (6, 12, 3, 12, 6).$$

Suppose that apples are 4 cents each, eggs are 6 cents each, lemons are 9 cents each, oranges are 5 cents each, and pears are 7 cents each. We can then represent the prices of these items as a column vector

$$y = \begin{pmatrix} 4 \\ 6 \\ 9 \\ 5 \\ 7 \end{pmatrix} \begin{matrix} \text{cents per apple} \\ \text{cents per egg} \\ \text{cents per lemon} \\ \text{cents per orange} \\ \text{cents per pear.} \end{matrix}$$

The obvious question to ask now is, what is the total amount that Smith must pay for his purchases? What we would like to do is to multiply the quantity vector x by the price vector y, and we would like the result to be Smith's bill. We see that our multiplication should have the following form:

$$x \cdot y = (6, 12, 3, 12, 6) \begin{pmatrix} 4 \\ 6 \\ 9 \\ 5 \\ 7 \end{pmatrix}$$

$$= 6 \cdot 4 + 12 \cdot 6 + 3 \cdot 9 + 12 \cdot 5 + 6 \cdot 7$$
$$= 24 + 72 + 27 + 60 + 42$$
$$= 225 \text{ cents or } \$2.25.$$

This is, of course, the computation that the cashier performs in figuring Smith's bill.

We shall adopt in general the above definition of multiplication of row times column vectors.

DEFINITION. Let u be a row vector and v a column vector each having the same number n of components; then we shall define the product $u \cdot v$ to be

$$u \cdot v = u_1 v_1 + u_2 v_2 + \ldots + u_n v_n.$$

Notice that we always write the row vector first and the column vector second, and this is the only kind of vector multiplication that we consider. Some examples of vector multiplication are given below:

$$(2, 1, -1) \cdot \begin{pmatrix} 3 \\ -1 \\ 4 \end{pmatrix} = 2 \cdot 3 + 1 \cdot (-1) + (-1) \cdot 4 = 1.$$

$$(1, 0) \cdot \begin{pmatrix} 0 \\ 1 \end{pmatrix} = 1 \cdot 0 + 0 \cdot 1 = 0 + 0 = 0.$$

Note that the result of vector multiplication is always a *number*.

Example 2. Consider an oversimplified economy which has three industries which we call coal, electricity, and steel, and three consumers 1, 2, and 3. Suppose that each consumer uses some of the output of each industry and also that each industry uses some of the output of each other industry. We assume that the amounts used are positive or zero, since using a negative quantity has no immediate interpretation. We can represent the needs of each consumer and industry by a three-component demand (row) vector, the first component measuring the amount of coal needed by the consumer or industry; the second component the amount of electricity needed; and the third component the amount of steel needed, in some convenient units. For example, the demand vectors of the three consumers might be

$$d_1 = (3, 2, 5), \qquad d_2 = (0, 17, 1), \qquad d_3 = (4, 6, 12)$$

and the demand vectors of each of the industries might be

$$d_C = (0, 1, 4), \qquad d_E = (20, 0, 8), \qquad d_S = (30, 5, 0)$$

where the subscript C stands for coal; the subscript E, for electricity; and the subscript S, for steel. Then the total demand for these goods by the consumers is given by the sum

$$d_1 + d_2 + d_3 = (3, 2, 5) + (0, 17, 1) + (4, 6, 12) = (7, 25, 18).$$

Also, the total industrial demand for these goods is given by the sum

$$d_C + d_E + d_S = (0, 1, 4) + (20, 0, 8) + (30, 5, 0) = (50, 6, 12).$$

Therefore the total over-all demand is given by the sum

$$(7, 25, 18) + (50, 6, 12) = (57, 31, 30).$$

Suppose now that the price of coal is \$1 per unit, the price of electricity is \$2 per unit, and the price of steel is \$4 per unit. Then these prices can be represented by the column vector

$$p = \begin{pmatrix} 1 \\ 2 \\ 4 \end{pmatrix}.$$

Consider the steel industry: it sells a total of 30 units of steel at \$4 per unit so that its total income is \$120. Its bill for the various goods is given by the vector product

$$d_S \cdot p = (30, 5, 0) \cdot \begin{pmatrix} 1 \\ 2 \\ 4 \end{pmatrix} = 30 + 10 + 0 = \$40.$$

Hence the profit of the steel industry is \$120 − \$40 = \$80. In the exercises below the profits of the other industries will be found.

This model of an economy is unrealistic in two senses. First, we have not chosen realistic numbers for the various quantities involved. Second, and more important, we have neglected the fact that the more an industry produces the more inputs it requires. The latter complication will be introduced in Chapter VIII.

Example 3. Consider the rectangular coordinate system in the plane shown in Figure 1. A two-component row vector $x = (a, b)$ can be regarded as a point

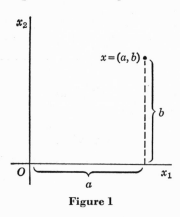

Figure 1

in the plane located by means of the coordinate axes as shown. The point x can be found by starting at the origin of coordinates O and moving a distance a along the x_1 axis; then moving a distance b along a line parallel to the x_2 axis. If we have two such points, say $x = (a, b)$ and $y = (c, d)$, then the points $x + y$, $-x$, $-y$, $x - y$, $y - x$, $-x - y$ have the geometric significance shown in Figure 2.

The idea of multiplying a row vector by a number can also be given a geometric meaning (see Figure 3). There we have plotted the point corresponding to the vector $x = (1, 2)$, and $2x$, $\frac{1}{2}x$, $-x$, and $-2x$. Observe that all these points lie on a line through the origin of coordinates. Another vector quantity which has geometrical significance is the

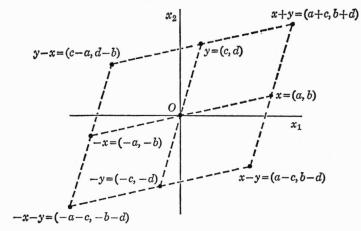

Figure 2

vector $z = ax + (1 - a)y$, where a is any number between 0 and 1. Observe in Figure 4 that the points z all lie on the line segment between the points x and y. If $a = \frac{1}{2}$ the corresponding point on the line segment is the mid-point of the segment. Thus, if $x = (a, b)$ and $y = (c, d)$ then the point

$$\tfrac{1}{2}x + \tfrac{1}{2}y = \tfrac{1}{2}(a, b) + \tfrac{1}{2}(c, d)$$

$$= \left(\frac{a + c}{2}, \frac{b + d}{2} \right)$$

is the mid-point of the line segment between x and y.

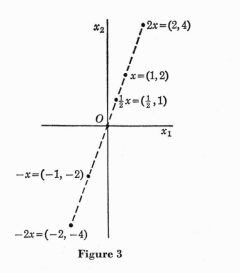

Figure 3

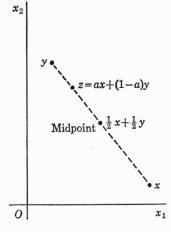

Figure 4

EXERCISES

1. Compute the quantities below for the following vectors:

$$u = (1, -1, 4), \qquad x = (0, 1, 2)$$

$$v = \begin{pmatrix} 5 \\ 0 \\ 1 \end{pmatrix}, \qquad y = \begin{pmatrix} -1 \\ -1 \\ 2 \end{pmatrix}.$$

(a) $u \cdot v + x \cdot y = ?$ [*Ans.* 12.]
(b) $(-u + 5x) \cdot (3v - 2y) = ?$
(c) $5u \cdot v + 10[x \cdot (2v - y)] = ?$ [*Ans.* 55.]
(d) $2[(u - x) \cdot (v + y)] = ?$

2. Plot the points corresponding to the row vectors $x = (3, 4)$ and $y = (-2, 7)$. Then compute and plot the following vectors.

(a) $\frac{1}{2}x + \frac{1}{2}y$.   (c) $x - 2y$.   (e) $3x - 2y$.
(b) $x + y$.   (d) $\frac{7}{8}x + \frac{1}{8}y$.   (f) $4y - 3x$.

3. If $x = (1, -1, 2)$ and $y = (0, 1, 3)$ are points in space, what is the midpoint of the line segment joining x to y?   [*Ans.* $(\frac{1}{2}, 0, \frac{5}{2})$.]

4. If u is a three-component row vector, v is a three-component column vector having the same number of components, and a is a number, prove that $a(u \cdot v) = (au) \cdot v = u \cdot (av)$.

5. Suppose that Brown, Jones, and Smith go to the grocery store and purchase the following items:

    Brown: two apples, six lemons, and five pears;
    Jones: two dozen eggs, two lemons, and two dozen oranges;
    Smith: ten apples, one dozen eggs, two dozen oranges, and a half
              dozen pears.

(a) How many different kinds of items did they purchase?   [*Ans.* 5.]
(b) Write each of their purchases as row vectors with as many components as the answer found in (a).
(c) Using the price vector given in Example 1, compute each man's grocery bill.   [*Ans.* \$0.97; \$2.82; \$2.74.]
(d) By means of vector addition find the total amount of their purchases as a row vector.
(e) Compute in two different ways the total amount spent by the three men at the grocery store.   [*Ans.* \$6.53.]

6. Prove that vector multiplication satisfies the following two properties:

    (i) $u \cdot (av) = a(u \cdot v)$
    (ii) $u \cdot (v + w) = u \cdot v + u \cdot w$

where u is a three-component row vector, v and w are three-component column vectors, and a is a number.

7. The production of a book involves several steps: first it must be set in type, then it must be printed, and finally it must be supplied with covers

and bound. Suppose that the typesetter charges $6 an hour, paper costs $\frac{1}{4}$ cent per sheet, that the printer charges 11 cents for each minute that his press runs, that the cover costs 28 cents, and that the binder charges 15 cents to bind each book. Suppose now that a publisher wishes to print a book that requires 300 hours of work by the typesetter, 220 sheets of paper per book, and 5 minutes of press time per book.

(a) Write a five-component row vector which gives the requirements for the first book. Write another row vector which gives the requirements for the second, third, . . . copies of the book. Write a five-component column vector whose components give the prices of the various requirements for each book, in the same order as they are listed in the requirement vectors above.

(b) Using vector multiplication, find the cost of publishing one copy of a book. [*Ans.* $1801.53.]

(c) Using vector addition and multiplication, find the cost of printing a first edition run of 5000 copies. [*Ans.* $9450.]

(d) Assuming that the type plates from the first edition are used again, find the cost of printing a second edition of 5000 copies.
[*Ans.* $7650.]

8. Perform the following calculations for Example 2.

(a) Compute the amount that each industry and each consumer has to pay for the goods it receives.

(b) Compute the profit made by each of the industries.

(c) Find the total amount of money that is paid out by all the industries and consumers.

(d) Find the proportion of the total amount of money found in (c) paid out by the industries. Find the proportion of the total money that is paid out by the consumers.

9. A building contractor has accepted orders for five ranch style houses, seven Cape Cod houses, and twelve Colonial style houses. Write a three-component row vector x whose components give the numbers of each type of house to be built. Suppose that he knows that a ranch style house requires 20 units of wood; a Cape Cod, 18 units; and a Colonial style, 25 units of wood. Write a column vector u whose components give the various quantities of wood needed for each type of house. Find the total amount of wood needed by computing the vector product xu. [*Ans.* 526.]

10. Let $x = (x_1 \quad x_2)$ and let a and b be the vectors

$$a = \begin{pmatrix} 3 \\ 4 \end{pmatrix}, \qquad b = \begin{pmatrix} 2 \\ 3 \end{pmatrix}.$$

If $x \cdot a = -1$ and $x \cdot b = 7$, determine x_1 and x_2.
[*Ans.* $x_1 = -31; x_2 = 23.$]

11. Let $x = (x_1 \quad x_2)$ and let a and b be the vectors

$$a = \begin{pmatrix} 4 \\ 8 \end{pmatrix}, \qquad b = \begin{pmatrix} 1 \\ 2 \end{pmatrix}.$$

If $x \cdot a = x_1$ and $x \cdot b = x_2$, determine x_1 and x_2.

3. Matrices and their combination with vectors

A matrix is a rectangular array of numbers written in the form

$$
A = \begin{pmatrix}
a_{11} & a_{12} & \ldots & a_{1n} \\
a_{21} & a_{22} & \ldots & a_{2n} \\
\cdot & \cdot & \ldots & \cdot \\
a_{m1} & a_{m2} & \ldots & a_{mn}
\end{pmatrix}.
$$

Here the letters a_{ij} stand for real numbers and m and n are integers. Observe that m is the number of rows and n is the number of columns of the matrix. For this reason we call it an $m \times n$ matrix. If $m = n$ the matrix is *square*. The following are examples of matrices.

$$
(1, 2, 3), \qquad \begin{pmatrix} 1 \\ 2 \\ 3 \end{pmatrix}, \qquad \begin{pmatrix} 1 & -1 \\ -2 & 2 \end{pmatrix},
$$

$$
\begin{pmatrix}
1 & 0 & 0 & 0 \\
0 & 1 & 0 & 0 \\
0 & 0 & 1 & 0 \\
0 & 0 & 0 & 1
\end{pmatrix}, \qquad
\begin{pmatrix}
1 & 7 & -8 & 9 & 10 \\
3 & -1 & 14 & 2 & -6 \\
0 & 3 & -5 & 7 & 0
\end{pmatrix}.
$$

The first example is a row vector which is a 1×3 matrix; the second is a column vector which is a 3×1 matrix; the third example is a 2×2 square matrix; the fourth is a 4×4 square matrix; and the last is a 3×5 matrix.

Two matrices having the same shape (i.e., having the same number of rows and columns) are said to be *equal* if and only if the corresponding entries are equal.

Recall that in Chapter IV, Section 12, we found that a matrix arose naturally in the consideration of a Markov chain process. To give another example of how matrices occur in practice and are used in connection with vectors we consider the following example.

Example 1. Suppose that a building contractor has accepted orders for five ranch style houses, seven Cape Cod houses, and twelve Colonial style houses. We can represent his orders by means of a row vector $x = (5, 7, 12)$. The contractor is familiar, of course, with the kinds of "raw materials" that go into each type of house. Let us suppose that these raw materials are steel, wood, glass, paint, and labor. The numbers in the matrix below give the amounts of each raw material going into each type of house, expressed in convenient units. (The numbers are put in arbitrarily, and are not meant to be realistic.)

	Steel	Wood	Glass	Paint	Labor	
Ranch:	5	20	16	7	17	
Cape Cod:	7	18	12	9	21	$= R$
Colonial:	6	25	8	5	13	

Observe that each row of the matrix is a five-component row vector which gives the amounts of each raw material needed for a given kind of house. Similarly, each column of the matrix is a three-component column vector which gives the amounts of a given raw material needed for each kind of house. Clearly, a matrix is a succinct way of summarizing this information.

Suppose now that the contractor wishes to compute how much of each raw material to obtain in order to fulfill his contracts. Let us denote the matrix above by R; then he would like to obtain something like the product xR, and he would like the product to tell him what orders to make out. The product should have the following form:

$$xR = (5, 7, 12) \begin{pmatrix} 5 & 20 & 16 & 7 & 17 \\ 7 & 18 & 12 & 9 & 21 \\ 6 & 25 & 8 & 5 & 13 \end{pmatrix}$$

$$= (5 \cdot 5 + 7 \cdot 7 + 12 \cdot 6, 5 \cdot 20 + 7 \cdot 18 + 12 \cdot 25,$$

$$5 \cdot 16 + 7 \cdot 12 + 12 \cdot 8, 5 \cdot 7 + 7 \cdot 9 + 12 \cdot 5,$$

$$5 \cdot 17 + 7 \cdot 21 + 12 \cdot 13)$$

$$= (146, 526, 260, 158, 388).$$

Thus we see that the contractor should order 146 units of steel, 526 units of wood, 260 units of glass, 158 units of paint, and 388 units of labor. Observe that the answer we get is a five-component row vector and that each entry in this vector is obtained by taking the vector product of x times the corresponding column of the matrix R.

The contractor is also interested in the prices that he will have to pay for these materials. Suppose that steel costs $15 per unit, wood costs $8 per unit, glass costs $5 per unit, paint costs $1 per unit, and labor costs $10 per unit. Then we can write the cost as a column vector as follows:

$$y = \begin{pmatrix} 15 \\ 8 \\ 5 \\ 1 \\ 10 \end{pmatrix}.$$

Here the product Ry should give the costs of each type of house, so that the multiplication should have the form

$$Ry = \begin{pmatrix} 5 & 20 & 16 & 7 & 17 \\ 7 & 18 & 12 & 9 & 21 \\ 6 & 25 & 8 & 5 & 13 \end{pmatrix} \begin{pmatrix} 15 \\ 8 \\ 5 \\ 1 \\ 10 \end{pmatrix}$$

$$= \begin{pmatrix} 5 \cdot 15 + 20 \cdot 8 + 16 \cdot 5 + 7 \cdot 1 + 17 \cdot 10 \\ 7 \cdot 15 + 18 \cdot 8 + 12 \cdot 5 + 9 \cdot 1 + 21 \cdot 10 \\ 6 \cdot 15 + 25 \cdot 8 + 8 \cdot 5 + 5 \cdot 1 + 13 \cdot 10 \end{pmatrix}$$

$$= \begin{pmatrix} 492 \\ 528 \\ 465 \end{pmatrix}.$$

Thus the cost of materials for the ranch style house is \$492, for the Cape Cod house is \$528, and for the Colonial house \$465.

The final question which the contractor might ask is what is the total cost of raw materials for all the houses he will build. It is easy to see that this is given by the vector xRy. We can find it in two ways as shown below.

$$xRy = (xR)y = (146, 526, 260, 158, 388) \cdot \begin{pmatrix} 15 \\ 8 \\ 5 \\ 1 \\ 10 \end{pmatrix} = 11{,}736$$

$$xRy = x(Ry) = (5, 7, 12) \cdot \begin{pmatrix} 492 \\ 528 \\ 465 \end{pmatrix} = 11{,}736.$$

The total cost is then \$11,736.

We shall adopt, in general, the following definitions for the multiplication of a matrix times a row or a column vector.

DEFINITION. Let A be an $m \times n$ matrix, let x be an m-component row vector, and let u be an n-component column vector; then we define the products xA and Au as follows:

$$xA = (x_1, x_2, \ldots, x_m) \begin{pmatrix} a_{11} & a_{12} & \cdots & a_{1n} \\ a_{21} & a_{22} & \cdots & a_{2n} \\ \cdot & \cdot & \cdots & \cdot \\ a_{m1} & a_{m2} & \cdots & a_{mn} \end{pmatrix}$$

$$= (x_1 a_{11} + x_2 a_{21} + \ldots + x_m a_{m1}, \ x_1 a_{12} + x_2 a_{22} + \ldots + x_m a_{m2}, \ldots,$$

$$x_1 a_{1n} + x_2 a_{2n} + \ldots + x_m a_{mn})$$

$$Au = \begin{pmatrix} a_{11} & a_{12} & \cdots & a_{1n} \\ a_{21} & a_{22} & \cdots & a_{2n} \\ \cdot & \cdot & \cdots & \cdot \\ a_{m1} & a_{m2} & \cdots & a_{mn} \end{pmatrix} \begin{pmatrix} u_1 \\ u_2 \\ \cdot \\ \cdot \\ u_n \end{pmatrix} = \begin{pmatrix} a_{11} u_1 + a_{12} u_2 + \ldots + a_{1n} u_n \\ a_{21} u_1 + a_{22} u_2 + \ldots + a_{2n} u_n \\ \cdot \qquad \cdot \qquad \cdots \qquad \cdot \\ a_{m1} u_1 + a_{m2} u_2 + \ldots + a_{mn} u_n \end{pmatrix}.$$

The reader will find these formulas easy to work with if he observes that each entry in the products xA or Au is obtained by vector multiplication of x or u by a column or row of the matrix A. Notice that in order to multiply a row vector times a matrix, the number of rows of the matrix must equal the number of components of the vector, and the result is another row vector; similarly, to multiply a matrix times a column vector, the number of columns of the matrix must equal the number of components of the vector, and the result of such a multiplication is another column vector.

Some numerical examples of the multiplication of vectors and matrices are:

$$(1, 0, -1)\begin{pmatrix} 3 & 1 \\ 2 & 3 \\ 2 & 8 \end{pmatrix} = (1\cdot3 + 0\cdot2 - 1\cdot2, 1\cdot1 + 0\cdot3 - 1\cdot8)$$

$$= (1, -7);$$

$$\begin{pmatrix} 3 & 1 & 2 \\ 2 & 3 & 8 \end{pmatrix}\begin{pmatrix} 1 \\ -1 \\ 2 \end{pmatrix} = \begin{pmatrix} 3 - 1 + 4 \\ 2 - 3 + 16 \end{pmatrix} = \begin{pmatrix} 6 \\ 15 \end{pmatrix};$$

$$\begin{pmatrix} 3 & 2 & -1 \\ 1 & 0 & 2 \\ 0 & 3 & 1 \\ 5 & -4 & 7 \\ -3 & 2 & -1 \end{pmatrix}\begin{pmatrix} 1 \\ 0 \\ -2 \end{pmatrix} = \begin{pmatrix} 5 \\ -3 \\ -2 \\ -9 \\ -1 \end{pmatrix}.$$

Observe that if x is an m-component row vector and A is $m \times n$, then xA is an n-component row vector; similarly, if u is an n-component column vector, then Au is an m-component column vector. These facts can be observed in the examples above.

Example 2. In Example 1 of Section 2 assume that Smith has two stores at which he can make his purchases, and let us say that the prices charged at these two stores are slightly different. Let the price vector at the second store be

$$y = \begin{pmatrix} 5 \\ 5 \\ 10 \\ 4 \\ 6 \end{pmatrix} \begin{array}{l} \text{cents per apple} \\ \text{cents per egg} \\ \text{cents per lemon} \\ \text{cents per orange} \\ \text{cents per pear.} \end{array}$$

Smith now has the option of buying all his purchases at Store 1, all at Store 2, or buying just the lower-priced items at the store charging the lower price. To help him decide, we form a price matrix, as follows:

	Prices Store 1	Prices Store 2	Minimum Price
	4	5	4
	6	5	5
$P =$	9	10	9
	5	4	4
	7	6	6

The first column lists the prices of Store 1, the second column lists the prices of Store 2, and the third column lists the lesser of these two prices. To compute Smith's bill under the three possible ways he can make his purchases, we compute the product xP, as follows:

$$xP = (6, 12, 3, 12, 6) \begin{pmatrix} 4 & 5 & 4 \\ 6 & 5 & 5 \\ 9 & 10 & 9 \\ 5 & 4 & 4 \\ 7 & 6 & 6 \end{pmatrix} = (225, 204, 195).$$

We thus see that if Smith buys only in Store 1 his bill will be $2.25, if he buys only in Store 2 his bill will be $2.04, but if he buys each item in the cheaper of the two stores (apples and lemons in Store 1, the rest in Store 2) his bill will be $1.95.

Exactly what Smith will, or should, do depends on circumstances. If both stores are equally close to him, he will probably split his purchases and obtain the smallest bill. If Store 1 is close and Store 2 is very far away, he may buy everything at Store 1. If Store 2 is closer and Store 1 is far enough away so that the 9 cents he would save by splitting his purchases is not worth the effort, he may buy everything at Store 2.

The example just cited is an example of a *decision problem*. In such problems it is necessary to choose one of several courses of action, or *strategies*. For each such course of action or strategy, it is possible to compute the cost or *worth* of such a strategy. The decision maker will choose a strategy with maximum worth.

Sometimes the worth of an outcome must be measured in psychological units and we then say that we measure the *utility* of an outcome. For the purposes of this book we shall always assume that the utility of an outcome is measured in monetary units, so that we can compare the worths of two different outcomes to the decision maker.

Many of the applications of mathematics to business and industrial problems consist in formulating such problems as decision problems and then choosing a strategy that has maximum worth. We shall discuss such decision problems in greater detail in the next example, in Section 13 of the present chapter, and in parts of the last three chapters of the book.

Example 3. As a second example of a decision problem consider the following. An urn contains 5 red, 3 green, and 1 white ball. One ball will be drawn at random, and then payments will be made to holders of lottery tickets according to the following schedule:

$$M = \begin{array}{ccc} \text{Red} & \text{Green} & \text{White} \\ \begin{pmatrix} 1 & 4 & 0 \\ 3 & 1 & 0 \\ 0 & 0 & 16 \end{pmatrix} & & \begin{array}{l} \text{Ticket 1} \\ \text{Ticket 2} \\ \text{Ticket 3} \end{array} \end{array}$$

Thus, if a red ball is selected, holders of Ticket 1 will get $1, holders of Ticket 2 will get $3, and holders of Ticket 3 will get nothing. If green is chosen, the payments are 4, 1, and 0, respectively. And if white is chosen, holders of Ticket 3 get $16, and the others nothing. Which ticket would we prefer to have?

Our decision will depend upon the concept of expected value discussed in the preceding chapter. The statements, "draw a red ball," "draw a green ball," "draw a white ball," have probabilities $\frac{5}{9}$, $\frac{3}{9}$, and $\frac{1}{9}$, respectively. From these probabilities we can calculate the expected value of holding each of the lottery tickets as described in the last chapter. However, a compact way of performing all these calculations is to compute the product Mp, where p is the probability vector

$$p = \begin{pmatrix} \frac{5}{9} \\ \frac{3}{9} \\ \frac{1}{9} \end{pmatrix}.$$

From this we have

$$Mp = \begin{pmatrix} 1 & 4 & 0 \\ 3 & 1 & 0 \\ 0 & 0 & 16 \end{pmatrix} \begin{pmatrix} \frac{5}{9} \\ \frac{3}{9} \\ \frac{1}{9} \end{pmatrix}$$

$$= \begin{pmatrix} 1 \cdot \frac{5}{9} + 4 \cdot \frac{3}{9} + 0 \cdot \frac{1}{9} \\ 3 \cdot \frac{5}{9} + 1 \cdot \frac{3}{9} + 0 \cdot \frac{1}{9} \\ 0 \cdot \frac{5}{9} + 0 \cdot \frac{3}{9} + 16 \cdot \frac{1}{9} \end{pmatrix} = \begin{pmatrix} \frac{17}{9} \\ \frac{18}{9} \\ \frac{16}{9} \end{pmatrix}.$$

It is easy to see that the three components of Mp give the expected values of holding lottery tickets 1, 2, and 3, respectively. From these numbers we can see that Ticket 2 is the best one, 1 is the next best, and 3 is third best.

If we have to buy the tickets, then the cost of the tickets will determine which is the best buy. If each ticket cost $3 we would be better off by not buying any ticket at all, since we would then expect to lose money. If each ticket cost $1 then we should buy Ticket 2, since it would give us a net expected gain of $2 − $1 = $1. If the first two tickets cost $2.10, and the third $1.50, we should buy the third ticket since it is the only one for which we would have a positive net expectation.

EXERCISES

1. Perform the following multiplications:

(a) $\begin{pmatrix} 1 & -1 \\ -2 & 2 \end{pmatrix} \begin{pmatrix} 7 \\ 2 \end{pmatrix} = ?$

(b) $(3, -4) \begin{pmatrix} 1 & -1 \\ -2 & 2 \end{pmatrix} = ?$ [*Ans.* (11, −11).]

(c) $\begin{pmatrix} 1 & 3 & 0 \\ 7 & -1 & 3 \\ -8 & 14 & -5 \\ 9 & 2 & 7 \\ 10 & -6 & 0 \end{pmatrix} \cdot \begin{pmatrix} 3 \\ -1 \\ 1 \end{pmatrix} = ?$

(d) $(2, 2) \begin{pmatrix} 1 & -1 \\ -1 & 1 \end{pmatrix} = ?$ [*Ans.* (0, 0).]

(e) $\begin{pmatrix} 1 & -1 \\ -1 & 1 \end{pmatrix} \begin{pmatrix} 5 \\ 5 \end{pmatrix} = ?$

(f) $(0, 2, -3)\begin{pmatrix} 1 & 7 & -8 & 9 & 10 \\ 3 & -1 & 14 & 2 & -6 \\ 0 & 3 & -5 & 7 & 0 \end{pmatrix} = ?$

(g) $(x_1, x_2)\begin{pmatrix} a & b \\ c & d \end{pmatrix} = ?$ [$Ans.$ $(ax_1 + cx_2, bx_1 + dx_2)$.]

(h) $\begin{pmatrix} a & b \\ c & d \end{pmatrix}\begin{pmatrix} u_1 \\ u_2 \end{pmatrix} = ?$

(i) $\begin{pmatrix} 1 & 0 & 0 \\ 0 & 1 & 0 \\ 0 & 0 & 1 \end{pmatrix}\begin{pmatrix} u_1 \\ u_2 \\ u_3 \end{pmatrix} = ?$

(j) $(x_1, x_2, x_3)\begin{pmatrix} 1 & 0 & 0 \\ 0 & 1 & 0 \\ 0 & 0 & 1 \end{pmatrix} = ?$

2. What number does the matrix in parts (i) and (j) above resemble?

3. Notice that in Exercise 1(d) above the product of a row vector, none of whose components is zero, times a matrix, none of whose components is zero, yields the zero row vector. Find another example which is similar to this one. Answer the analogous question for Exercise 1(e).

4. When possible, solve for the indicated quantities.

   (a) $(x_1, x_2)\begin{pmatrix} 0 & -1 \\ 7 & 3 \end{pmatrix} = (7, 0)$. Find the vector x.   [$Ans.$ (3, 1).]

   (b) $(2, -1)\begin{pmatrix} a & b \\ c & d \end{pmatrix} = (6, 3)$. Find the matrix $\begin{pmatrix} a & b \\ c & d \end{pmatrix}$. In this case can you find more than one solution?

   (c) $\begin{pmatrix} 1 & -1 \\ -1 & 1 \end{pmatrix}\begin{pmatrix} u_1 \\ u_2 \end{pmatrix} = \begin{pmatrix} 3 \\ 4 \end{pmatrix}$. Find the vector u.

   (d) $\begin{pmatrix} -1 & 4 \\ 2 & -8 \end{pmatrix}\begin{pmatrix} u_1 \\ u_2 \end{pmatrix} = \begin{pmatrix} 3 \\ -6 \end{pmatrix}$. Find u.

   How many solutions can you find?

   $$[Ans.\ u = \begin{pmatrix} 4k - 3 \\ k \end{pmatrix}, \text{ for any number } k.]$$

5. Solve for the indicated quantities below and give an interpretation for each.

   (a) $(1, -1)\begin{pmatrix} 0 & 2 \\ -2 & 4 \end{pmatrix} = a(1, -1)$; find a.   [$Ans.$ $a = 2$.]

   (b) $\begin{pmatrix} 1 & 2 \\ 2 & 4 \end{pmatrix}\begin{pmatrix} u_1 \\ u_2 \end{pmatrix} = 5\begin{pmatrix} u_1 \\ u_2 \end{pmatrix}$; find u. How many answers can you find?

   $$[Ans.\ u = \begin{pmatrix} k \\ 2k \end{pmatrix} \text{ for any number } k.]$$

   (c) $\begin{pmatrix} \frac{5}{8} & \frac{1}{8} \\ \frac{3}{8} & \frac{7}{8} \end{pmatrix}\begin{pmatrix} u_1 \\ u_2 \end{pmatrix} = \begin{pmatrix} u_1 \\ u_2 \end{pmatrix}$; find u. How many answers are there?

6. In Exercise 5 of the preceding section construct the 3 × 5 matrix whose rows give the various purchases of Brown, Jones, and Smith. Multiply on the right by the five-component price (column) vector to find the three-component column vector whose entries give each person's grocery bill. Multiply on the left by the row vector $x = (1, 1, 1)$ and on the right by the price vector to find the total amount that they spent in the store.

7. In Example 1 of this section, assume that the contractor is to build seven ranch style, three Cape Cod, and five Colonial type houses. Recompute, using matrix multiplication, the total cost of raw materials, in two different ways, as in the example.

8. The following matrix gives the vitamin contents of three food items, in conveniently chosen units:

$$
\begin{array}{cccccc}
\text{Vitamin:} & A & B & C & D \\
\text{Food I:} & .5 & .5 & 0 & 0 \\
\text{Food II:} & .3 & 0 & .2 & .1 \\
\text{Food III:} & .1 & .1 & .2 & .5
\end{array}
$$

If we eat 5 units of food I, 10 units of food II, and 8 units of food III, how much of each type of vitamin have we consumed? If we pay only for the vitamin content of each food, paying 10 cents, 20 cents, 25 cents, and 50 cents, respectively, for units of the four vitamins, how much does a unit of each type of food cost? Compute in two ways the total cost of the food we ate.

$$
[Ans.\ (6.3, 3.3, 3.6, 5.0);\ \begin{pmatrix} 15 \\ 13 \\ 33 \end{pmatrix};\ \$4.69.]
$$

9. In Example 2, by how much would Store 1 have to reduce the price of apples to make Smith's purchases less expensive at Store 1 than at Store 2?

10. In Example 2, find the store at which the total cost to Smith is the least when he wishes to purchase
    (a) $x = (4, 1, 2, 0, 1)$.
    (b) $x = (2, 1, 3, 1, 0)$.
    (c) $x = (2, 1, 1, 2, 0)$.

11. In Example 3, let us assume that an individual chooses Ticket 1 with probability r_1, Ticket 2 with probability r_2, and Ticket 3 with probability r_3. Let $r = (r_1, r_2, r_3)$. Give an interpretation for rMp. Compute this for the case that $r_1 = r_2 = r_3 = \frac{1}{3}$.

12. A company is considering which of three methods of production it should use in producing three goods, A, B, and C. The amount of each good produced by each method is shown in the matrix

$$
\begin{array}{cccc}
 & A & B & C \\
R = & \begin{pmatrix} 2 & 3 & 1 \\ 1 & 2 & 3 \\ 2 & 4 & 1 \end{pmatrix} & & \begin{array}{l} \text{Method 1} \\ \text{Method 2} \\ \text{Method 3} \end{array}
\end{array}
$$

Let p be a vector whose components represent the profit per unit for each of the goods. What does the vector Rp represent? Find three different vectors p such that under each of these profit vectors a different method would be the most profitable.

4. The addition and multiplication of matrices

Two matrices of the same shape, that is, having the same number of rows and columns, can be added together by adding corresponding components. For example, if A and B are two 2×3 matrices, we have

$$A + B = \begin{pmatrix} a_{11} & a_{12} & a_{13} \\ a_{21} & a_{22} & a_{23} \end{pmatrix} + \begin{pmatrix} b_{11} & b_{12} & b_{13} \\ b_{21} & b_{22} & b_{23} \end{pmatrix}$$

$$= \begin{pmatrix} a_{11} + b_{11} & a_{12} + b_{12} & a_{13} + b_{13} \\ a_{21} + b_{21} & a_{22} + b_{22} & a_{23} + b_{23} \end{pmatrix}.$$

Observe that the addition of vectors (row or column) is simply a special case of the addition of matrices. Numerical examples of the addition of matrices are the following:

$$(1, 0, -2) + (0, 5, 0) = (1, 5, -2)$$

$$\begin{pmatrix} 1 & 0 \\ 0 & 1 \end{pmatrix} + \begin{pmatrix} -1 & 0 \\ 0 & -1 \end{pmatrix} = \begin{pmatrix} 0 & 0 \\ 0 & 0 \end{pmatrix}$$

$$\begin{pmatrix} 7 & 0 & 0 \\ -3 & 1 & -6 \\ 4 & 0 & 7 \\ 0 & -2 & -2 \\ 1 & 1 & 1 \end{pmatrix} + \begin{pmatrix} -8 & 0 & 1 \\ 4 & 5 & -1 \\ 0 & 3 & 0 \\ -1 & 1 & -1 \\ 0 & -4 & 2 \end{pmatrix} = \begin{pmatrix} -1 & 0 & 1 \\ 1 & 6 & -7 \\ 4 & 3 & 7 \\ -1 & -1 & -3 \\ 1 & -3 & 3 \end{pmatrix}.$$

Other examples occur in the exercises. The reader should observe that we do *not* add matrices of different shapes.

If A is a matrix and k is any number, we define the matrix kA as

$$kA = k \begin{pmatrix} a_{11} & a_{12} & \cdots & a_{1n} \\ a_{21} & a_{22} & \cdots & a_{2n} \\ \cdot & \cdot & \cdots & \cdot \\ a_{m1} & a_{m2} & \cdots & a_{mn} \end{pmatrix} = \begin{pmatrix} ka_{11} & ka_{12} & \cdots & ka_{1n} \\ ka_{21} & ka_{22} & \cdots & ka_{2n} \\ \cdot & \cdot & \cdots & \cdot \\ ka_{m1} & ka_{m2} & \cdots & ka_{mn} \end{pmatrix}.$$

Observe that this is merely component-wise multiplication as was the analogous concept for vectors. Some examples of multiplication of matrices by constants are

$$-2 \begin{pmatrix} 7 & -2 & 8 \\ 0 & 5 & -1 \end{pmatrix} = \begin{pmatrix} -14 & 4 & -16 \\ 0 & -10 & 2 \end{pmatrix}$$

$$6\begin{pmatrix} 1 & 0 \\ 0 & 1 \\ 3 & -4 \end{pmatrix} = \begin{pmatrix} 6 & 0 \\ 0 & 6 \\ 18 & -24 \end{pmatrix}.$$

The multiplication of a vector by a number is, of course, a special case of the multiplication of a matrix by a number.

Under certain conditions two matrices can be multiplied together to give a new matrix. As an example, let A be a 2×3 matrix and B be a 3×2 matrix. Then the product AB is found as

$$AB = \begin{pmatrix} a_{11} & a_{12} & a_{13} \\ a_{21} & a_{22} & a_{23} \end{pmatrix} \begin{pmatrix} b_{11} & b_{12} \\ b_{21} & b_{22} \\ b_{31} & b_{32} \end{pmatrix}$$

$$= \begin{pmatrix} a_{11}b_{11} + a_{12}b_{21} + a_{13}b_{31} & a_{11}b_{12} + a_{12}b_{22} + a_{13}b_{32} \\ a_{21}b_{11} + a_{22}b_{21} + a_{23}b_{31} & a_{21}b_{12} + a_{22}b_{22} + a_{23}b_{32} \end{pmatrix}.$$

Observe that the product is a 2×2 matrix. Also notice that each entry in the new matrix is the product of one of the rows of A times one of the columns of B; for example, the entry in the second row and first column is found as the product

$$(a_{21} \quad a_{22} \quad a_{23})\begin{pmatrix} b_{11} \\ b_{21} \\ b_{31} \end{pmatrix} = a_{21}b_{11} + a_{22}b_{21} + a_{23}b_{31}.$$

The following definition holds for the general case of matrix multiplication:

DEFINITION. Let A be an $m \times k$ matrix and B be a $k \times n$ matrix; then the product matrix $C = AB$ is an $m \times n$ matrix whose components are

$$c_{ij} = (a_{i1} \quad a_{i2} \quad \ldots \quad a_{ik})\begin{pmatrix} b_{1j} \\ b_{2j} \\ \cdot \\ \cdot \\ \cdot \\ b_{kj} \end{pmatrix}$$

$$= a_{i1}b_{1j} + a_{i2}b_{2j} + \ldots + a_{ik}b_{kj}.$$

The important things to remember about this definition are: first, in order to be able to multiply matrix A times matrix B, the number of columns of A must be equal to the number of rows of B; second, the product matrix $C = AB$ has the same number of rows as A and the same number of columns as B; finally, to get the entry in the ith row and jth column of AB we multiply the ith row of A times the jth column of B. Notice that the product of a vector times a matrix is a special case of matrix multiplication.

Below are several examples of matrix multiplication:

$$\begin{pmatrix} 2 & -1 \\ 0 & 3 \end{pmatrix} \begin{pmatrix} 7 & 0 \\ -2 & -3 \end{pmatrix} = \begin{pmatrix} 16 & 3 \\ -6 & -9 \end{pmatrix}$$

$$\begin{pmatrix} 3 & 0 & 1 \\ -1 & 2 & 0 \\ 0 & 0 & 2 \end{pmatrix} \begin{pmatrix} 1 & 0 & 0 \\ 0 & -1 & 0 \\ 1 & 1 & 1 \end{pmatrix} = \begin{pmatrix} 4 & 1 & 1 \\ -1 & -2 & 0 \\ 2 & 2 & 2 \end{pmatrix}$$

$$\begin{pmatrix} 3 & 1 & 4 \\ 2 & 0 & 5 \end{pmatrix} \begin{pmatrix} 1 & 3 & 0 & 0 \\ 1 & 1 & 0 & 0 \\ 0 & 0 & 1 & 1 \end{pmatrix} = \begin{pmatrix} 4 & 10 & 4 & 4 \\ 2 & 6 & 5 & 5 \end{pmatrix}.$$

One obvious question that now arises is that of multiplying more than two matrices together. Let A be an $m \times h$ matrix, let B be an $h \times k$ matrix, and let C be a $k \times n$ matrix. Then we can certainly define the products $(AB)C$ and $A(BC)$. It turns out that these two products are equal, and we define the product ABC to be their common value, i.e.,

$$ABC = A(BC) = (AB)C.$$

The rule expressed in the above equation is called the *associative law* for multiplication. We shall not prove the associative law here although the student will be asked to check an example of it in Exercise 5.

If A and B are square matrices of the same size, then they can be multiplied in either order. It is not true, however, that the product AB is necessarily equal to the product BA. For example, if

$$A = \begin{pmatrix} 1 & 1 \\ 0 & 0 \end{pmatrix} \quad \text{and} \quad B = \begin{pmatrix} 1 & 0 \\ 1 & 0 \end{pmatrix},$$

then we have

$$AB = \begin{pmatrix} 1 & 1 \\ 0 & 0 \end{pmatrix} \begin{pmatrix} 1 & 0 \\ 1 & 0 \end{pmatrix} = \begin{pmatrix} 2 & 0 \\ 0 & 0 \end{pmatrix},$$

whereas

$$BA = \begin{pmatrix} 1 & 0 \\ 1 & 0 \end{pmatrix} \begin{pmatrix} 1 & 1 \\ 0 & 0 \end{pmatrix} = \begin{pmatrix} 1 & 1 \\ 1 & 1 \end{pmatrix},$$

and it is clear that $AB \neq BA$.

EXERCISES

1. Perform the following operations.

(a) $2 \begin{pmatrix} 6 & 1 \\ 0 & -3 \\ -1 & 2 \end{pmatrix} - 3 \begin{pmatrix} 4 & 2 \\ 0 & 1 \\ -5 & -1 \end{pmatrix} = ?$ [*Ans.* $\begin{pmatrix} 0 & -4 \\ 0 & -9 \\ 13 & 7 \end{pmatrix}$.]

(b) $\begin{pmatrix} 6 & 1 & -1 \\ 1 & -3 & 2 \end{pmatrix} - 5 \begin{pmatrix} 4 & 0 & -5 \\ 2 & 1 & -1 \end{pmatrix} = ?$

(c) $\begin{pmatrix} 6 & 1 \\ 0 & -3 \end{pmatrix} \begin{pmatrix} 4 & 0 & -4 \\ 2 & 1 & -1 \end{pmatrix} = ?$

(d) $\begin{pmatrix} 6 & 0 & -1 \\ 1 & -3 & 2 \end{pmatrix} \begin{pmatrix} 4 & 2 \\ 0 & 1 \\ -5 & -1 \end{pmatrix} = ?$ $\left[Ans. \begin{pmatrix} 29 & 13 \\ -6 & -3 \end{pmatrix} \right.]$

(e) $\begin{pmatrix} 1 & -1 \\ -1 & 1 \end{pmatrix} \begin{pmatrix} 1 & -1 \\ -1 & 1 \end{pmatrix} = ?$

(f) $\begin{pmatrix} 4 & 1 & 4 \\ -1 & -2 & -1 \\ 2 & -1 & -2 \end{pmatrix} \begin{pmatrix} 3 & 0 & 1 \\ -1 & 2 & 0 \\ 0 & 0 & 2 \end{pmatrix} = ?$ $\left[Ans. \begin{pmatrix} 11 & 2 & 12 \\ -1 & -4 & -3 \\ 7 & -2 & -2 \end{pmatrix} \right.]$

(g) $\begin{pmatrix} 1 & -2 \\ 0 & 0 \\ 7 & 5 \\ -4 & 8 \\ 0 & -2 \end{pmatrix} \begin{pmatrix} -7 & 9 & -5 & 6 & 0 \\ -1 & 0 & 3 & -4 & 1 \end{pmatrix} = ?$

2. Let A be any 3×3 matrix and let I be the matrix

$$I = \begin{pmatrix} 1 & 0 & 0 \\ 0 & 1 & 0 \\ 0 & 0 & 1 \end{pmatrix}.$$

Show that $AI = IA = A$. The matrix I acts for the products of matrices in the same way that the number 1 acts for products of numbers. For this reason it is called the identity matrix.

3. Let A be any 3×3 matrix and let 0 be the matrix

$$0 = \begin{pmatrix} 0 & 0 & 0 \\ 0 & 0 & 0 \\ 0 & 0 & 0 \end{pmatrix}.$$

Show that $A0 = 0A = 0$ for any A. Also show that $A + 0 = 0 + A = A$ for any A. The matrix 0 acts for matrices in the same way that the number 0 acts for numbers. For this reason it is called the zero matrix.

4. If $A = \begin{pmatrix} 0 & 0 \\ 0 & 1 \end{pmatrix}$ and $B = \begin{pmatrix} 1 & 0 \\ 0 & 0 \end{pmatrix}$ show that $AB = \begin{pmatrix} 0 & 0 \\ 0 & 0 \end{pmatrix}$. Thus the

product of two matrices can be the zero matrix even though neither of the matrices is itself zero. Find another example that illustrates this point.

5. Verify the associative law for the special case when

$$A = \begin{pmatrix} -1 & 0 & 5 \\ 7 & -2 & 0 \end{pmatrix}, \quad B = \begin{pmatrix} 1 & 7 & 0 \\ -3 & -1 & 0 \\ 1 & 0 & 5 \end{pmatrix}, \quad C = \begin{pmatrix} -1 & -1 \\ 2 & 0 \\ 0 & 4 \end{pmatrix}.$$

6. Consider the matrices

$$A = \begin{pmatrix} 1 & 0 & 1 \\ -1 & 17 & 57 \end{pmatrix}, \qquad B = \begin{pmatrix} 1 & 1 & 1 \\ 2 & 2 & 2 \\ 3 & 3 & 3 \\ 0 & 0 & 0 \end{pmatrix}$$

$$C = \begin{pmatrix} 1 & 0 & -1 \\ 0 & -1 & 1 \\ -1 & 1 & 0 \end{pmatrix}, \qquad D = \begin{pmatrix} -1 & -1 \\ 2 & 2 \\ 1 & 1 \end{pmatrix}.$$

The shapes of these are 2×3, 4×3, 3×3, and 3×2, respectively. What is the shape of

(a) AC.   (c) AD.   (e) CB.   (g) $BCDA$.

(b) DA.   (d) BC.   (f) DAC.   [*Ans.* 4×3.]

7. In Exercise 6 find:

(a) The component in the second row and second column of AC.

[*Ans.* 40.]

(b) The component in the fourth row and first column of BC.

(c) The component in the last row and last column of DA.   [*Ans.* 58.]

(d) The component in the first row and first column of CB.

8. If A is a square matrix, it can be multiplied by itself; hence we can define (using the associative law)

$$A^2 = A \cdot A$$
$$A^3 = A^2 \cdot A = A \cdot A \cdot A$$
$$\cdots$$
$$A^n = A^{n-1} \cdot A = A \cdot A \cdot \ldots A \qquad (n \text{ factors}).$$

These are naturally called "powers" of a matrix—the first one being called the square; the second, the cube; etc. Compute the indicated powers of the following matrices.

(a) If $A = \begin{pmatrix} 1 & 0 \\ 3 & 4 \end{pmatrix}$, find A^2, A^3, and A^4.

$$[Ans. \begin{pmatrix} 1 & 0 \\ 15 & 16 \end{pmatrix}; \begin{pmatrix} 1 & 0 \\ 63 & 64 \end{pmatrix}; \begin{pmatrix} 1 & 0 \\ 255 & 256 \end{pmatrix}.]$$

(b) If I and 0 are the matrices defined in Exercises 2 and 3, find I^2, I^3, I^n, 0^2, 0^3, and 0^n.

(c) If $A = \begin{pmatrix} 0 & 0 & 0 \\ 1 & 0 & 0 \\ 2 & -1 & 0 \end{pmatrix}$, find A^2, A^3, and A^n.

(d) If $A = \begin{pmatrix} 1 & 1 \\ 1 & 1 \end{pmatrix}$, find A^n.

9. Cube the matrix

$$\begin{pmatrix} 0 & 1 & 0 \\ 0 & \frac{1}{2} & \frac{1}{2} \\ \frac{1}{3} & 0 & \frac{2}{3} \end{pmatrix}.$$

Compare your answer with the matrix $P^{(3)}$ in Example 1, Chapter IV, Section 12, and comment on the result.

10. Consider a two-stage Markov process whose transition matrix is

$$P = \begin{pmatrix} p_{11} & p_{12} \\ p_{21} & p_{22} \end{pmatrix}.$$

(a) Assuming that the process starts in state 1, draw the tree and set up tree measures for three stages of the process. Do the same, assuming that the process starts in state 2.

(b) Using the trees drawn in (a), compute the quantities $p_{11}^{(3)}, p_{12}^{(3)}, p_{21}^{(3)}, p_{22}^{(3)}$. Write the matrix $P^{(3)}$.

(c) Compute the cube P^3 of the matrix P.

(d) Compare the answers you found in parts (b) and (c) and show that $P^{(3)} = P^3$.

11. Show that the fifth and all higher powers of the matrix

$$\begin{pmatrix} 0 & 1 & 0 \\ 0 & 0 & 1 \\ 1 & 1 & 0 \end{pmatrix}$$

have all entries positive. Show that no smaller power has this property.

12. In Example 1 of Section 3 assume that the contractor wishes to take into account the cost of transporting raw materials to the building site as well as the purchasing cost. Suppose the costs are as given in the matrix below:

	Purchase	Transport	
	15	4.5	Steel
	8	2	Wood
$Q =$	5	3	Glass
	1	0.5	Paint
	10	0	Labor

Referring to the example:

(a) By computing the product RQ find a 3×2 matrix whose entries give the purchase and transportation costs of the materials for each kind of house.

(b) Find the product xRQ, which is a two-component row vector whose first component gives the total purchase price and second component gives the total transportation cost.

(c) Let $z = \begin{pmatrix} 1 \\ 1 \end{pmatrix}$ and then compute $xRQz$, which is a number giving the total cost of materials and transportation for all the houses being built.
[$Ans.$ \$14,304.]

13. A college survey at an all-male school shows that dates of students are distributed as follows: a freshman dates one blonde and one brunette during the year; each sophomore dates one blonde, three brunettes, and one redhead; each junior dates three blondes, two brunettes, and two redheads; each senior dates three redheads. It is further known that each blonde

brings three dresses with her, two skirts, two blouses, and one sweater; each brunette brings five dresses, four skirts, one blouse, and three sweaters; each redhead brings one dress, four skirts, and four sweaters. If each dress costs $50, each skirt $15, each blouse $10, and each sweater $5; and if there are 500 freshmen, 400 sophomores, 300 juniors, and 200 seniors,

(a) What is the total number of blondes, brunettes, and redheads dated?
(b) What is the total number of each type of clothing item in the dates' wardrobes?
(c) What is the cost of the wardrobe of a blonde? a brunette? a redhead?
(d) What is the total cost of all the wardrobes of all the dates? Calculate two ways. [*Ans.* $1,347,500.]

5. The solution of linear equations

There are many occasions when the simultaneous solution of linear equations is important. In this section we shall develop methods for finding out whether a set of linear equations has solutions, and for finding all such solutions.

Example 1. Consider the following example of three linear equations in three unknowns:

(1) $$x_1 + 4x_2 + 3x_3 = 1$$
(2) $$2x_1 + 5x_2 + 4x_3 = 4$$
(3) $$x_1 - 3x_2 - 2x_3 = 5.$$

Before we discuss the solution of these equations we note that they can be written as a single equation in matrix form as follows:

$$\begin{pmatrix} 1 & 4 & 3 \\ 2 & 5 & 4 \\ 1 & -3 & -2 \end{pmatrix} \begin{pmatrix} x_1 \\ x_2 \\ x_3 \end{pmatrix} = \begin{pmatrix} 1 \\ 4 \\ 5 \end{pmatrix}.$$

One of the uses of vector and matrix notation is in writing a large number of linear equations in a single simple matrix equation such as the one above. It also leads to the detached coefficient form of solving simultaneous equations that we shall discuss at the end of the present section and in the next section.

The method of solving the linear equations above is the following. First we use equation (1) to eliminate the variable x_1 from equations (2) and (3); i.e., we subtract 2 times (1) from (2) and then subtract (1) from (3), giving

(1') $$x_1 + 4x_2 + 3x_3 = 1$$
(2') $$-3x_2 - 2x_3 = 2$$
(3') $$-7x_2 - 5x_3 = 4.$$

Next we divide equation (2') through by the coefficient of x_2, namely, -3, obtaining $x_2 + \frac{2}{3}x_3 = -\frac{2}{3}$. We use this equation to eliminate x_2 from each of the other two equations. In order to do this we subtract 4 times this equation from (1') and add 7 times this equation to (3'), obtaining

(1'') $$x_1 + 0 + \tfrac{1}{3}x_3 = \tfrac{11}{3}$$
(2'') $$x_2 + \tfrac{2}{3}x_3 = -\tfrac{2}{3}$$
(3'') $$-\tfrac{1}{3}x_3 = -\tfrac{2}{3}.$$

The last step is to divide through (3'') by $-\tfrac{1}{3}$, which is the coefficient of x_3, obtaining the equation $x_3 = 2$; we use this equation to eliminate x_3 from the first two equations as follows:

(1''') $$x_1 + 0 + 0 = 3$$
(2''') $$x_2 + 0 = -2$$
(3''') $$x_3 = 2.$$

The solution can now be read from these equations as $x_1 = 3$, $x_2 = -2$, and $x_3 = 2$. The reader should substitute these values into the original equations (1), (2), and (3) above to see that the solution has actually been obtained.

In the example just discussed we saw that there was only one solution to the set of three simultaneous equations in three variables. Example 2 will be one in which there is *more* than one solution, and Example 3 will be one in which there are *no* solutions to a set of three simultaneous equations in three variables.

Example 2. Consider the following linear equations.

(4) $$x_1 - 2x_2 - 3x_3 = 2$$
(5) $$x_1 - 4x_2 - 13x_3 = 14$$
(6) $$-3x_1 + 5x_2 + 4x_3 = 0.$$

Let us proceed as before and use equation (4) to eliminate the variable x_1 from the other two equations. We have

(4') $$x_1 - 2x_2 - 3x_3 = 2$$
(5') $$-2x_2 - 10x_3 = 12$$
(6') $$-x_2 - 5x_3 = 6.$$

Proceeding as before, we divide equation (5') by -2, obtaining the equation $x_2 + 5x_3 = -6$. We use this equation to eliminate the variable x_2 from each of the other equations—namely, we add twice this equation to (4') and then add the equation to (6').

(4'') $$x_1 + 0 + 7x_3 = -10$$
(5'') $$x_2 + 5x_3 = -6$$
(6'') $$0 = 0.$$

Observe that we have eliminated the last equation completely! We also see that the variable x_3 can be chosen completely arbitrarily in these equations. To emphasize this, we move the terms involving x_3 to the right-hand side, giving

(4''') $$x_1 = -10 - 7x_3$$
(5''') $$x_2 = -6 - 5x_3.$$

The reader should check, by substituting these values of x_1 and x_2 into equations (4), (5), and (6), that they are solutions regardless of the value of x_3. Let us also substitute particular values for x_3 to obtain numerical solutions. Thus, if we let $x_3 = 1, 0, -2$, respectively, and compute the resulting numbers, using (4''') and (5'''), we obtain the following numerical solutions:

$$\begin{aligned} x_1 &= -17, & x_2 &= -11, & x_3 &= 1 \\ x_1 &= -10, & x_2 &= -6, & x_3 &= 0 \\ x_1 &= 4, & x_2 &= 4, & x_3 &= -2. \end{aligned}$$

The reader should also substitute these numbers into (4), (5), and (6) to show that they are solutions. To summarize, our second example has an infinite number of solutions, one for each numerical value of x_3 which is substituted into equations (4''') and (5''').

Example 3. Suppose that we modify equation (6) by changing the number on the right-hand side to 2. Then we have

(7) $$x_1 - 2x_2 - 3x_3 = 2$$
(8) $$x_1 - 4x_2 - 13x_3 = 14$$
(9) $$-3x_1 + 5x_2 + 4x_3 = 2.$$

If we carry out the same procedure as before and use (7) to eliminate x_1 from (8) and (9), we obtain

(7') $$x_1 - 2x_2 - 3x_3 = 2$$
(8') $$-2x_2 - 10x_3 = 12$$
(9') $$-x_2 - 5x_3 = 8.$$

We divide (8') by -2, the coefficient of x_2, obtaining, as before, $x_2 + 5x_3 = -6$. Using this equation to eliminate x_2 from the other two equations, we have

(7'') $$x_1 + 0 + 7x_3 = -10$$
(8'') $$x_2 + 5x_3 = -6$$
(9'') $$0 = 2.$$

Observe that the last equation is *false*. Because our elimination procedure has led to a false result we conclude that the equations (7), (8), and (9) have *no* solution. The student should always keep in mind that this possibility exists when considering simultaneous equations.

In the examples above the equations we considered had the same number of variables as equations. The next example has more variables than equations and the last has more equations than variables.

Example 4. Consider the following two equations in three variables:

(10) $$-4x_1 + 3x_2 + 2x_3 = -2$$
(11) $$5x_1 - 4x_2 + x_3 = 3.$$

Using the elimination method outlined above, we divide (10) by -4, and then subtract 5 times the result from (11), obtaining

(10') $\quad\quad\quad\quad\quad\quad\quad x_1 - \frac{3}{4}x_2 - \frac{1}{2}x_3 = \frac{1}{2}$

(11') $\quad\quad\quad\quad\quad\quad\quad\quad -\frac{1}{4}x_2 + \frac{7}{2}x_3 = \frac{1}{2}.$

Multiplying (11') by -4 and using it to eliminate x_2 from (10'), we have

(10'') $\quad\quad\quad\quad\quad\quad\quad x_1 + 0 - 11x_3 = -1$

(11'') $\quad\quad\quad\quad\quad\quad\quad\quad x_2 - 14x_3 = -2.$

We can now let x_3 take on any value whatsoever and solve these equations for x_1 and x_2. We emphasize this fact by rewriting them as in Example 2 as

(10''') $\quad\quad\quad\quad\quad\quad\quad x_1 = 11x_3 - 1$

(11''') $\quad\quad\quad\quad\quad\quad\quad x_2 = 14x_3 - 2.$

The reader should check that these are solutions and also, by choosing specific values for x_3, find numerical solutions to these equations.

Example 5. Let us consider the other possibility suggested by Example 4, namely, the case in which we have more equations than variables. Consider the following equations:

(12) $\quad\quad\quad\quad\quad\quad\quad -4x_1 + 3x_2 = 2$

(13) $\quad\quad\quad\quad\quad\quad\quad\quad 5x_1 - 4x_2 = 0$

(14) $\quad\quad\quad\quad\quad\quad\quad\quad 2x_1 - x_2 = a$

where a is an arbitrary number. Using equation (12) to eliminate x_1 from the other two we obtain

(12') $\quad\quad\quad\quad\quad\quad\quad x_1 - \frac{3}{4}x_2 = -\frac{1}{2}$

(13') $\quad\quad\quad\quad\quad\quad\quad\quad -\frac{1}{4}x_2 = \frac{5}{2}$

(14') $\quad\quad\quad\quad\quad\quad\quad\quad \frac{1}{2}x_2 = a + 1.$

Next we use (13') to eliminate x_2 from the other equations, obtaining

(12'') $\quad\quad\quad\quad\quad\quad\quad x_1 + 0 = -8$

(13'') $\quad\quad\quad\quad\quad\quad\quad\quad x_2 = -10$

(14'') $\quad\quad\quad\quad\quad\quad\quad\quad 0 = a + 6.$

These equations remind us of the situation in Example 3, since we will be led to a false result unless $a = -6$. We see that equations (12), (13), and (14) have the solution $x_1 = -8$ and $x_2 = -10$ only if $a = -6$. If $a \neq -6$, then there is *no* solution to these equations.

The examples above illustrate all the possibilities that can occur in the general case. There may be no solutions, exactly one solution, or an infinite number of solutions to a set of simultaneous equations.

The procedure that we have illustrated above is one that turns any set of linear equations into an equivalent set of equations from which the existence of solutions and the solutions can be easily read. A student who learned other ways of solving linear equations may wonder why we use the above procedure—one which is not always the quickest way of solving equations. The answer is that we use it because it always works, that is, it is a *canonical* procedure to apply to *any* set of linear equations. The faster methods usually work only for equations that have solutions, and even then they may not find all solutions. The value of a standard infallible method, especially for machine computation, should not be underestimated.

Let us return again to the equations of Example 1. Note that the variables, coefficients, and equals signs are in columns at the beginning of the solution and are always kept in the same column. It is obvious that the *location* of the coefficient is sufficient identification for it and that it is unnecessary to keep writing the variable. We can start with the format or *tableau*:

$$(15) \qquad \begin{pmatrix} 1 & 4 & 3 & | & 1 \\ 2 & 5 & 4 & | & 4 \\ 1 & -3 & -2 & | & 5 \end{pmatrix}.$$

Note that the coefficients of x_1 are found in the first column, the coefficients of x_2 in the second column, of x_3 in the third column, and the constants on the right-hand side of the equation all occur in the fourth column. The vertical line represents the equals signs in the equations.

The tableau of (15) will be called the *detached coefficient tableau* for simultaneous linear equations. We now show how to solve simultaneous equations using the detached coefficient tableau.

Example 6. Starting with the tableau of (15) we carry out exactly the same calculations as in Example 1, which lead to the following series of tableaus:

$$(16) \qquad \begin{pmatrix} 1 & 4 & 3 & | & 1 \\ 0 & -3 & -2 & | & 2 \\ 0 & -7 & -5 & | & 4 \end{pmatrix}$$

$$(17) \qquad \begin{pmatrix} 1 & 0 & \frac{1}{3} & | & \frac{11}{3} \\ 0 & 1 & \frac{2}{3} & | & -\frac{2}{3} \\ 0 & 0 & -\frac{1}{3} & | & -\frac{2}{3} \end{pmatrix}$$

$$(18) \qquad \begin{pmatrix} 1 & 0 & 0 & | & 3 \\ 0 & 1 & 0 & | & -2 \\ 0 & 0 & 1 & | & 2 \end{pmatrix}$$

From the tableau of (18) we can easily read the answer $x_1 = 3$, $x_2 = -2$, and $x_3 = 2$, which is the same as before.

The correspondence between the calculations of Example 1 and of the present example is as follows:

$$\begin{array}{ll} (1), (2), \text{ and } (3) & \text{correspond to } (15) \\ (1'), (2'), \text{ and } (3') & \text{correspond to } (16) \\ (1''), (2''), \text{ and } (3'') & \text{correspond to } (17) \\ (1'''), (2'''), \text{ and } (3''') & \text{correspond to } (18). \end{array}$$

Note that in the tableau form we are always careful to keep zero coefficients in each column when necessary.

Example 7. Suppose that we have two sets of simultaneous equations to solve and that they differ only in their right-hand sides. For instance, suppose we want to solve

$$\begin{pmatrix} 1 & 4 & 3 \\ 2 & 5 & 4 \\ 1 & -3 & -2 \end{pmatrix} \begin{pmatrix} x_1 \\ x_2 \\ x_3 \end{pmatrix} = \begin{pmatrix} 1 \\ 4 \\ 5 \end{pmatrix} \quad \text{and} \quad = \begin{pmatrix} -1 \\ 0 \\ 2 \end{pmatrix}.$$

It is obvious that the calculations on the left-hand side will be the same regardless of the numbers appearing on the right-hand side. Therefore, it is possible to solve both sets of simultaneous equations at once. We shall illustrate this in the following series of tableaus:

$$(20) \qquad \begin{pmatrix} 1 & 4 & 3 & 1 & -1 \\ 2 & 5 & 4 & 4 & 0 \\ 1 & -3 & -2 & 5 & 2 \end{pmatrix}$$

$$(21) \qquad \begin{pmatrix} 1 & 4 & 3 & 1 & -1 \\ 0 & -3 & -2 & 2 & 2 \\ 0 & -7 & -5 & 4 & 3 \end{pmatrix}$$

$$(22) \qquad \begin{pmatrix} 1 & 0 & \frac{1}{3} & \frac{11}{3} & \frac{5}{3} \\ 0 & 1 & \frac{2}{3} & -\frac{2}{3} & -\frac{2}{3} \\ 0 & 0 & -\frac{1}{3} & -\frac{2}{3} & -\frac{5}{3} \end{pmatrix}$$

$$(23) \qquad \begin{pmatrix} 1 & 0 & 0 & 3 & 0 \\ 0 & 1 & 0 & -2 & -4 \\ 0 & 0 & 1 & 2 & 5 \end{pmatrix}.$$

We find the answers

$$x_1 = 3, \qquad x_2 = -2, \qquad x_3 = 2$$

to the first set of equations and the answers

$$x_1 = 0, \qquad x_2 = -4, \qquad x_3 = 5$$

to the second set of equations. The reader should check these answers by substituting into the original equations.

EXERCISES

1. Work again Examples 2–4 using the detached coefficient tableau.

2. Find all the solutions of the following simultaneous equations.

(a) $4x_1 + 5x_3 = 6$
$x_2 - 6x_3 = -2$
$3x_1 + 4x_3 = 3.$ [*Ans.* $x_1 = 9$, $x_2 = -38$, $x_3 = -6$.]

(b) $3x_1 - x_2 - 2x_3 = 2$
$2x_2 - x_3 = -1$
$3x_1 - 5x_2 = 3.$ [*Ans.* No solution.]

(c) $-x_1 + 2x_2 + 3x_3 = 0$
$x_1 - 4x_2 - 13x_3 = 0$
$-3x_1 + 5x_2 + 4x_3 = 0.$ [*Ans.* $x_1 = -7x_3$, $x_2 = -5x_3$.]

3. Find all the solutions of the following simultaneous equations.

(a) $x_1 + x_2 + x_3 = 0$
    $2x_1 + 4x_2 + 3x_3 = 0$
       $4x_2 + 4x_3 = 0.$

(b) $x_1 + x_2 + x_3 = -2$
    $2x_1 + 4x_2 + 3x_3 = 3$
       $4x_2 + 2x_3 = 2.$

(c) $4x_1 \quad\quad + 4x_3 = 8$
        $x_2 - 6x_3 = -3$
    $3x_1 + x_2 - 3x_3 = 3.$

4. Find all solutions of the following equations using the detached coefficient tableau.

(a) $5x_1 - 3x_2 = -7$
   $-2x_1 + 9x_2 = 4$
    $2x_1 + 4x_2 = -2.$ [$Ans.$ $x_1 = -\frac{17}{13}$; $x_2 = \frac{2}{13}$.]

(b) $x_1 + 2x_2 = 1$
  $-3x_1 + 2x_2 = -2$
   $2x_1 + 3x_2 = 1.$ [$Ans.$ No solution.]

(c) $5x_1 - 3x_2 - 7x_3 + x_4 = 10$
  $-x_1 + 2x_2 + 6x_3 - 3x_4 = -3$
   $x_1 + x_2 + 4x_3 - 5x_4 = 0.$

5. Find all solutions of:

$$x_1 + 2x_2 + 3x_3 + 4x_4 = 10$$
$$2x_1 - x_2 + x_3 - x_4 = 1$$
$$3x_1 + x_2 + 4x_3 + 3x_4 = 11$$
$$-2x_1 + 6x_2 + 4x_3 + 10x_4 = 18.$$

[$Ans.$ $x_1 = \frac{12}{5} - x_3 - \frac{2}{5}x_4$; $x_2 = \frac{19}{5} - x_3 - \frac{9}{5}x_4$, x_3 and x_4 arbitrary.]

6. We consider buying three kinds of food. Food I has one unit of vitamin A, three units of vitamin B, and four units of vitamin C. Food II has two, three, and five units, respectively. Food III has three units each of vitamin A and vitamin C, none of vitamin B. We need to have 11 units of vitamin A, 9 of vitamin B, and 20 of vitamin C.

(a) Find all possible amounts of the three foods that will provide precisely these amounts of the vitamins.

(b) If Food I costs 60 cents and the others cost 10 cents each per unit, is there a solution costing exactly $1?   [$Ans.$ (b) Yes; 1, 2, 2.]

7. Solve the following four simultaneous sets whose right-hand sides are listed under (a), (b), (c), and (d) below. Use the detached coefficient tableau.

	(a)	(b)	(c)	(d)
$4x_1 \quad + 5x_3 =$	1	1	0	0
$x_2 - 6x_3 =$	2	0	0	1
$3x_1 \quad + 4x_3 =$	3	0	1	0.

[$Ans.$ (a) $x_1 = -11$, $x_2 = 56$, $x_3 = 9$.]

8. Solve the following four sets of simultaneous equations, which differ only in their right-hand sides.

$$
\begin{array}{ccccc}
 & \text{(a)} & \text{(b)} & \text{(c)} & \text{(d)} \\
x_1 + x_2 + \ x_3 = & 3 & 0 & 12 & 0 \\
x_1 - x_2 + 2x_3 = & 2 & -1 & 7 & 0 \\
2x_1 + x_2 - \ x_3 = & 2 & 3 & 11 & 0.
\end{array}
$$

9. Solve the following three sets of simultaneous equations.

$$
\begin{array}{cccc}
 & \text{(a)} & \text{(b)} & \text{(c)} \\
x_1 + x_2 + \ x_3 = & 1 & 2 & 0 \\
x_1 - x_2 + 2x_3 = & -2 & 2 & 0 \\
3x_1 - x_2 + 5x_3 = & -3 & 2 & 0.
\end{array}
$$

10. Show that the equations

$$-4x_1 + 3x_2 + ax_3 = c$$
$$5x_1 - 4x_2 + bx_3 = d$$

always have a solution for all values of a, b, c, and d.

11. Find conditions on a, b, and c in order that the equations

$$-4x_1 + 3x_2 = a$$
$$5x_1 - 4x_2 = b$$
$$-3x_1 + 2x_2 = c$$

have a solution.   [*Ans.* $2a + b = c$.]

12. (a) Let $x = (x_1, x_2)$ and let A be the matrix

$$A = \begin{pmatrix} 3 & -4 \\ 2 & -6 \end{pmatrix}.$$

Find all solutions of the equation $xA = x$.   [*Ans.* $x = (0, 0)$.]

(b) Let $x = (x_1, x_2)$ and let A be the matrix

$$A = \begin{pmatrix} 3 & 6 \\ -2 & -5 \end{pmatrix}.$$

Find all solutions of the equation $xA = x$.

[*Ans.* $x = (k, k)$ for any number k.]

13. Let $x = (x_1, x_2)$ and let P be the matrix

$$P = \begin{pmatrix} \frac{1}{3} & \frac{2}{3} \\ \frac{4}{5} & \frac{1}{5} \end{pmatrix}.$$

(a) Find all solutions of the equation $xP = x$.

(b) Choose the solution for which $x_1 + x_2 = 1$.

14. If $x = (x_1, x_2, x_3)$ and A is the matrix

$$A = \begin{pmatrix} 1 & -2 & 0 \\ 0 & 5 & 4 \\ 0 & -6 & -4 \end{pmatrix},$$

find all solutions of the equation $xA = x$.

[*Ans.* $x = (-k/2, 5k/4, k)$ for any number k.]

15. If $x = (x_1, x_2, x_3)$ and P is the matrix

$$P = \begin{pmatrix} 0 & \frac{1}{2} & \frac{1}{2} \\ \frac{1}{3} & \frac{1}{3} & \frac{1}{3} \\ \frac{1}{5} & 0 & \frac{4}{5} \end{pmatrix},$$

find all solutions of the equation $xP = x$. Select the unique solution for which $x_1 + x_2 + x_3 = 1$.

16. (a) Show that the simultaneous linear equations

$$\begin{aligned} x_1 + x_2 + x_3 &= 1 \\ x_1 + 2x_2 + 3x_3 &= 0 \end{aligned}$$

can be interpreted as a single matrix-times-column-vector equation of the form

$$\begin{pmatrix} 1 & 1 & 1 \\ 1 & 2 & 3 \end{pmatrix} \begin{pmatrix} x_1 \\ x_2 \\ x_3 \end{pmatrix} = \begin{pmatrix} 1 \\ 0 \end{pmatrix}.$$

(b) Show that *any* set of simultaneous linear equations may be interpreted as a matrix equation of the form $Ax = b$, where A is an $m \times n$ matrix, x is an n-component column vector, and b is an m-component column vector.

17. (a) Show that the equations of Exercise 16(a) can be interpreted as a row-vector-times-matrix equation of the form

$$(x_1 \quad x_2 \quad x_3)\begin{pmatrix} 1 & 1 \\ 1 & 2 \\ 1 & 3 \end{pmatrix} = (1 \quad 0).$$

(b) Show that *any* set of simultaneous linear equations may be interpreted as a matrix equation of the form $xA = b$, where A is an $m \times n$ matrix, x is an m-component row vector, and b is an n-component row vector.

18. (a) Show that the simultaneous linear equations of Exercise 16(a) can be interpreted as asking for all possible ways of expressing the column vector $\begin{pmatrix} 1 \\ 0 \end{pmatrix}$ in terms of the column vectors $\begin{pmatrix} 1 \\ 1 \end{pmatrix}$, $\begin{pmatrix} 1 \\ 2 \end{pmatrix}$, and $\begin{pmatrix} 1 \\ 3 \end{pmatrix}$.

(b) Show that *any* set of linear equations may be interpreted as asking for all possible ways of expressing a column vector in terms of given column vectors.

6. The inverse of a square matrix

If A is a square matrix and B is another square matrix of the same size having the property that $BA = I$ (where I is the identity matrix), then we say that B is the *inverse* of A. When it exists we shall denote the inverse of A by the symbol A^{-1}. To give a numerical example, let A and A^{-1} be the following:

$$(1) \qquad A = \begin{pmatrix} 4 & 0 & 5 \\ 0 & 1 & -6 \\ 3 & 0 & 4 \end{pmatrix}$$

$$(2) \qquad A^{-1} = \begin{pmatrix} 4 & 0 & -5 \\ -18 & 1 & 24 \\ -3 & 0 & 4 \end{pmatrix}.$$

Then we have

$$A^{-1}A = \begin{pmatrix} 4 & 0 & -5 \\ -18 & 1 & 24 \\ -3 & 0 & 4 \end{pmatrix} \cdot \begin{pmatrix} 4 & 0 & 5 \\ 0 & 1 & -6 \\ 3 & 0 & 4 \end{pmatrix} = \begin{pmatrix} 1 & 0 & 0 \\ 0 & 1 & 0 \\ 0 & 0 & 1 \end{pmatrix} = I.$$

If we multiply these matrices in the other order we also get the identity matrix; thus

$$AA^{-1} = \begin{pmatrix} 4 & 0 & 5 \\ 0 & 1 & -6 \\ 3 & 0 & 4 \end{pmatrix} \cdot \begin{pmatrix} 4 & 0 & -5 \\ -18 & 1 & 24 \\ -3 & 0 & 4 \end{pmatrix} = \begin{pmatrix} 1 & 0 & 0 \\ 0 & 1 & 0 \\ 0 & 0 & 1 \end{pmatrix} = I.$$

In general it can be shown that if A is a square matrix with inverse A^{-1}, then the inverse satisfies the equation

$$A^{-1}A = AA^{-1} = I.$$

It is easy to see that a square matrix can have only one inverse. Suppose that in addition to A^{-1} we also have a B such that

$$BA = I.$$

Then we see that

$$B = BI = B(AA^{-1}) = (BA)A^{-1} = IA^{-1} = A^{-1}.$$

Finding the inverse of a matrix is analogous to finding the reciprocal of an ordinary number, but the analogy is not complete. Every nonzero number has a reciprocal, but there are matrices, not the zero matrix, which have no inverse. For example, if

$$A = \begin{pmatrix} 1 & -1 \\ -1 & 1 \end{pmatrix} \quad \text{and} \quad B = \begin{pmatrix} 1 & 1 \\ 1 & 1 \end{pmatrix}$$

then

$$AB = \begin{pmatrix} 1 & -1 \\ -1 & 1 \end{pmatrix} \cdot \begin{pmatrix} 1 & 1 \\ 1 & 1 \end{pmatrix} = \begin{pmatrix} 0 & 0 \\ 0 & 0 \end{pmatrix} = 0.$$

From this it follows that neither A nor B can have an inverse. To show that A does not have an inverse, let us assume that A had an inverse A^{-1}. Then

$$B = (A^{-1}A)B = A^{-1}(AB) = A^{-1}0 = 0$$

contradicting the fact that $B \neq 0$. The proof that B cannot have an inverse is similar.

Let us now try to calculate the inverse of the matrix A in (1). Specifically, let's try to calculate the first column of A^{-1}. Let

$$x = \begin{pmatrix} x_1 \\ x_2 \\ x_3 \end{pmatrix}$$

be the desired entries of the first column. Then from the equation $AA^{-1} = I$ we see that we must solve

$$\begin{pmatrix} 4 & 0 & 5 \\ 0 & 1 & -6 \\ 3 & 0 & 4 \end{pmatrix} \begin{pmatrix} x_1 \\ x_2 \\ x_3 \end{pmatrix} = \begin{pmatrix} 1 \\ 0 \\ 0 \end{pmatrix}.$$

Similarly, to find the second and third columns of A^{-1} we want to solve the additional sets of equations,

$$\begin{pmatrix} 4 & 0 & 5 \\ 0 & 1 & -6 \\ 3 & 0 & 4 \end{pmatrix} \begin{pmatrix} x_1 \\ x_2 \\ x_3 \end{pmatrix} = \begin{pmatrix} 0 \\ 1 \\ 0 \end{pmatrix} \quad \text{and} \quad = \begin{pmatrix} 0 \\ 0 \\ 1 \end{pmatrix}$$

respectively. We thus have three sets of simultaneous equations that differ only in their right-hand sides. This is exactly the situation described in Example 7 of the previous section.

To solve them, we start with the tableau

(3)
$$\left(\begin{array}{ccc|ccc} 4 & 0 & 5 & 1 & 0 & 0 \\ 0 & 1 & -6 & 0 & 1 & 0 \\ 3 & 0 & 4 & 0 & 0 & 1 \end{array} \right)$$

and carry out the calculations as described in the last section. This gives rise to the following series of tableaus. In (3) divide the first row by 4, copy the second row, and subtract 3 times the new first row from the old third row, which yields the tableau:

(4)
$$\left(\begin{array}{ccc|ccc} 1 & 0 & \frac{5}{4} & \frac{1}{4} & 0 & 0 \\ 0 & 1 & -6 & 0 & 1 & 0 \\ 0 & 0 & \frac{1}{4} & -\frac{3}{4} & 0 & 1 \end{array} \right).$$

Next we multiply the third row of (4) by 4, multiply the new third row by 6 and add to the old second row, and multiply the new third row by $\frac{5}{4}$ and subtract from the old first row. We have the final tableau:

(5)
$$\left(\begin{array}{ccc|ccc} 1 & 0 & 0 & 4 & 0 & -5 \\ 0 & 1 & 0 & -18 & 1 & 24 \\ 0 & 0 & 1 & -3 & 0 & 4 \end{array} \right)$$

We see that the inverse A^{-1} which is given in (2) appears to the right of the vertical line in the tableau of (5).

The procedure just illustrated will find the inverse of any square matrix A, *providing* A *has* an inverse. We summarize it as follows:

RULE FOR INVERTING A MATRIX. Let A be a matrix that has an inverse. To find the inverse of A start with the tableau

$$(A \mid I)$$

and change it by row transformations (as described in Section 5) into the tableau

$$(I \mid B).$$

The resulting matrix B is the inverse A^{-1} of A.

Even if A has no inverse, the procedure just outlined can be started. At some point in the procedure a tableau will be found that is not of the desired final form and from which it is impossible to change by row transformations of the kind described.

Example 1. Show that the matrix

$$A = \begin{pmatrix} 4 & 0 & 8 \\ 0 & 1 & -6 \\ 2 & 0 & 4 \end{pmatrix}$$

has no inverse.

We set up the initial tableau as follows:

$$(6) \qquad \begin{pmatrix} 4 & 0 & 8 & | & 1 & 0 & 0 \\ 0 & 1 & -6 & | & 0 & 1 & 0 \\ 2 & 0 & 4 & | & 0 & 0 & 1 \end{pmatrix}.$$

Carrying out one set of row transformations, we obtain the second tableau as follows:

$$(7) \qquad \begin{pmatrix} 1 & 0 & 2 & | & \frac{1}{4} & 0 & 0 \\ 0 & 1 & -6 & | & 0 & 1 & 0 \\ 0 & 0 & 0 & | & -\frac{1}{2} & 0 & 1 \end{pmatrix}.$$

It is clear that we cannot proceed further since there is a row of zeros to the left of the equals sign on the third set of equations. Hence we conclude that A has no inverse.

Because of the form of the final tableau in (7) we see that it is impossible to solve the equations

$$\begin{pmatrix} 4 & 0 & 8 \\ 0 & 1 & -6 \\ 2 & 0 & 4 \end{pmatrix} \begin{pmatrix} x_1 \\ x_2 \\ x_3 \end{pmatrix} = \begin{pmatrix} 0 \\ 0 \\ 1 \end{pmatrix}$$

since these equations are inconsistent as is shown by the tests developed in Section 5. In other words, it is not possible to solve for the third column of the inverse matrix.

It is clear that an $n \times n$ matrix A has an inverse if and only if the following sets of simultaneous equations:

$$Ax = \begin{pmatrix} 1 \\ 0 \\ \cdot \\ \cdot \\ \cdot \\ 0 \end{pmatrix}, \quad Ax = \begin{pmatrix} 0 \\ 1 \\ \cdot \\ \cdot \\ \cdot \\ 0 \end{pmatrix}, \quad \ldots, \quad Ax = \begin{pmatrix} 0 \\ 0 \\ \cdot \\ \cdot \\ \cdot \\ 1 \end{pmatrix}$$

can all be uniquely solved. And these sets of simultaneous equations, since they all share the same left-hand sides, can be solved uniquely if and only if the transformation of the rule for inverting a matrix can be carried out. Hence we have proved the following theorem:

THEOREM. A square matrix A has an inverse if and only if the tableau

$$(A \mid I)$$

can be transformed by row transformations into the tableau

$$(I \mid A^{-1}).$$

Example 2. Let us find the inverse of the matrix

$$A = \begin{pmatrix} 1 & 4 & 3 \\ 2 & 5 & 4 \\ 1 & -3 & -2 \end{pmatrix}.$$

The initial tableau is:

$$\begin{pmatrix} 1 & 4 & 3 & 1 & 0 & 0 \\ 2 & 5 & 4 & 0 & 1 & 0 \\ 1 & -3 & -2 & 0 & 0 & 1 \end{pmatrix}.$$

Transforming it by row transformations we obtain the following series of tableaus:

$$\begin{pmatrix} 1 & 4 & 3 & 1 & 0 & 0 \\ 0 & -3 & -2 & -2 & 1 & 0 \\ 0 & -7 & -5 & -1 & 0 & 1 \end{pmatrix}$$

$$\begin{pmatrix} 1 & 0 & \frac{1}{3} & -\frac{5}{3} & \frac{4}{3} & 0 \\ 0 & 1 & \frac{2}{3} & \frac{2}{3} & -\frac{1}{3} & 0 \\ 0 & 0 & -\frac{1}{3} & \frac{11}{3} & -\frac{7}{3} & 1 \end{pmatrix}$$

$$\begin{pmatrix} 1 & 0 & 0 & 2 & -1 & 1 \\ 0 & 1 & 0 & 8 & -5 & 2 \\ 0 & 0 & 1 & -11 & 7 & -3 \end{pmatrix}.$$

The inverse of A is then

$$A^{-1} = \begin{pmatrix} 2 & -1 & 1 \\ 8 & -5 & 2 \\ -11 & 7 & -3 \end{pmatrix}.$$

The reader should check that $A^{-1}A = AA^{-1} = I$.

EXERCISES

1. Compute the inverse of each of the following matrices:

$$A = \begin{pmatrix} 1 & 0 & 0 \\ 3 & 1 & 5 \\ -2 & 0 & 1 \end{pmatrix}, \qquad B = \begin{pmatrix} 4 & 3 & 2 \\ 0 & 1 & -1 \\ 0 & 0 & 7 \end{pmatrix},$$

$$C = \begin{pmatrix} 9 & -1 & 0 & 0 \\ 0 & 8 & -2 & 0 \\ 0 & 0 & 7 & -3 \\ 0 & 0 & 0 & 6 \end{pmatrix}, \qquad D = \begin{pmatrix} 1 & 0 & 0 \\ \frac{1}{3} & 4 & 0 \\ \frac{1}{2} & 3 & 2 \end{pmatrix}.$$

$$\left[Partial\ Ans.\ A^{-1} = \begin{pmatrix} 1 & 0 & 0 \\ -13 & 1 & -5 \\ 2 & 0 & 1 \end{pmatrix}; \quad D^{-1} = \begin{pmatrix} 1 & 0 & 0 \\ -\frac{1}{12} & \frac{1}{4} & 0 \\ -\frac{1}{8} & -\frac{3}{8} & \frac{1}{2} \end{pmatrix}. \right]$$

2. Show that each of the following matrices fails to have an inverse.

$$A = \begin{pmatrix} 1 & 2 & 3 \\ -1 & 1 & 0 \\ 0 & 3 & 3 \end{pmatrix}, \qquad B = \begin{pmatrix} 1 & 1 & 0 \\ 2 & 0 & 5 \\ -1 & 1 & -5 \end{pmatrix},$$

$$C = \begin{pmatrix} 1 & 1 & 2 & 3 \\ 0 & 5 & 4 & 2 \\ -1 & -3 & 1 & 0 \\ 0 & 3 & 7 & 5 \end{pmatrix}, \qquad D = \begin{pmatrix} 1 & 1 & 1 \\ 1 & 1 & 1 \\ 1 & 1 & 1 \end{pmatrix}.$$

3. Let A, B, and D be the matrices of Exercise 1; let

$$x = \begin{pmatrix} x_1 \\ x_2 \\ x_3 \end{pmatrix} \quad \text{and} \quad w = (w_1, w_2, w_3);$$

let b, c, d, e, and f be the following vectors:

$$b = \begin{pmatrix} 3 \\ -1 \\ 0 \end{pmatrix}, \quad c = \begin{pmatrix} -1 \\ 2 \\ -3 \end{pmatrix}, \quad d = (3, 7, -2), \quad e = (1, 1, 1), \quad f = \begin{pmatrix} 1 \\ 1 \\ 1 \end{pmatrix}.$$

Use the inverses you computed in Exercise 1 to solve the following equations.

(a) $Ax = b$.   (b) $Bx = c$.   (c) $wD = e$.
(d) $wB = d$.   (e) $wA = e$.   (f) $Dx = f$.

$$\left[Partial\ Ans.\ \text{(a)}\ x = \begin{pmatrix} 3 \\ -40 \\ 6 \end{pmatrix}; \quad \text{(e)}\ w = (-10, 1, -4); \quad \text{(f)}\ x = \begin{pmatrix} 1 \\ \frac{1}{6} \\ 0 \end{pmatrix}. \right]$$

4. Rework Exercise 7 of Section 5 by first writing the equations in the form $Ax = b$, and finding the inverse of A.

5. Solve the following problem by first inverting the matrix. (Assume $ad \neq bc$.) If a grinding machine is supplied with x pounds of meat and y

pounds of scraps (meat scraps and fat) per day, then it will produce
$ax + by$ pounds of ground meat and $cx + dy$ pounds of hamburger per
day. In other words its production vector is

$$\begin{pmatrix} a & b \\ c & d \end{pmatrix} \begin{pmatrix} x \\ y \end{pmatrix}.$$

What inputs are necessary in order to get 25 pounds of ground meat and
70 pounds of hamburger? In order to get 20 pounds of ground meat and
100 pounds of hamburger?

6. For each of the matrices A and D in Exercise 2 find a nonzero vector
whose product with the given matrix is O.

7. Show that if A has no inverse, then neither does any of its positive powers
A^k.

8. The formula $(A^{-1})^{-1} = A$ really states that if A has an inverse A^{-1}, then
A^{-1} itself has an inverse, and this inverse is A. Prove both parts of this
statement.

9. Expand the formula $(AB)^{-1} = B^{-1}A^{-1}$ into a two-part statement analogous to the one in the exercise above. Then prove both parts of your
statement.

10. (a) Show that $(AB)^{-1} \neq A^{-1}B^{-1}$ for the matrices $A = \begin{pmatrix} 1 & 1 \\ 0 & 1 \end{pmatrix}$ and
$B = \begin{pmatrix} 1 & 0 \\ 2 & 1 \end{pmatrix}.$

   (b) Find $(AB)^{-1}$ in two different ways. [*Hint*: Use Exercise 9.]

11. Give a criterion for deciding whether the 2×2 matrix $\begin{pmatrix} a & b \\ c & d \end{pmatrix}$ has an
inverse.   [*Ans*. $ad \neq bc$.]

12. Give a formula for $\begin{pmatrix} a & b \\ c & d \end{pmatrix}^{-1}$, when it exists.

13. If $\begin{pmatrix} a & b \\ c & d \end{pmatrix}$ is invertible and has integer components, what condition must
it fulfill in order that $\begin{pmatrix} a & b \\ c & d \end{pmatrix}^{-1}$ have integer components?

*7. The parts requirements listing problem

Consider a factory that produces parts, subassemblies and assemblies
made from these parts, and subassemblies and assemblies made from parts
and subassemblies. The assemblies are finished goods that are shipped to
other factories, while the parts and subassemblies are constructed to go
into assemblies. Suppose that the factory has received an order for a certain number of each of the assemblies; how many of each kind of part must

be made to construct all the parts and subassemblies needed to fulfill the order?

For simple assemblies involving only a few parts this is a simple task. But for orders involving thousands of assemblies each involving thousands of parts and subassemblies the task becomes formidable. We shall develop matrix methods for solving this problem completely.

Let us assume that there are n different parts, subassemblies, and assemblies manufactured by the company. Denote these items by a_1, a_2, ..., a_n. It will be convenient to list these items in a certain order.

DEFINITION. We say that the manufactured items a_1, a_2, ..., a_n are listed in *technological order* if it is true that an item a_i does not appear on the list until all of the parts and subassemblies that must go into it have already appeared on the list.

For instance, a gasoline engine cannot appear on the list until all of its parts (such as pistons, rings, valves, connecting rods, block, head) have already appeared on the list.

It is also true that for any list of items that can actually be manufactured it must be possible to list them in technological order. For otherwise there would be a group of parts, no one of which could be listed until all others were listed, or in other words, no one of which could be produced until all the others were finished. And this would lead to an impossible manufacturing situation.

DEFINITION. Let q_{ij} be the number of units of items a_j directly needed to assemble one item a_i. Let Q be the matrix with components q_{ij}. We call Q the *quantity matrix*.

When we say that items are directly needed in the assembly of another item we mean that if we had on hand q_{i1} units of item a_1, q_{i2} units of item a_2, etc., and q_{in} units of a_n then we could immediately assemble one unit of a_i and have no parts left over. From this it is obvious that $q_{ii} = 0$, since an item cannot be required in the assembly of the same item without its being impossible to list the parts in technological order. Hence all entries *on* the main diagonal of Q are 0. Also, all entries *above* the main diagonal of Q are 0 since the technological order of listing the parts means that if a_j is needed to assemble a_i then a_j is listed before a_i and hence $j < i$.

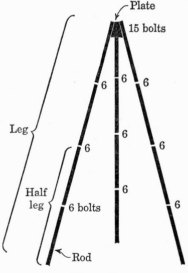

Figure 5

Example 1. A tripod mast of the type shown in Figure 5 is to be constructed. Each leg is assembled by bolting together (using 6 bolts) two rods to form a half leg, and then bolting together two half legs (again using 6 bolts) to form a leg. The three legs are bolted together at the top (using 15 bolts) to a plate to form the completed mast. Of course we can easily count the various parts requirements. But let us first set up the quantity matrix. From the foregoing description we see that Q is as given in Figure 6. For ease of reading, zero

$$Q = \begin{array}{r} \\ a_1 \text{ rods} \\ a_2 \text{ bolts} \\ a_3 \text{ half legs} \\ a_4 \text{ legs} \\ a_5 \text{ plate} \\ a_6 \text{ mast} \end{array} \begin{pmatrix} a_1 & a_2 & a_3 & a_4 & a_5 & a_6 \\ 0 & & & & & \\ 0 & 0 & & & & \\ 2 & 6 & 0 & & & \\ 0 & 6 & 2 & 0 & & \\ 0 & 0 & 0 & 0 & 0 & \\ 0 & 15 & 0 & 3 & 1 & 0 \end{pmatrix}$$

Figure 6

entries above the main diagonal are omitted from the matrix. We note that all the nonzero entries appear below the main diagonal.

Because of the lower triangular structure of the Q matrix it enjoys a special property asserted in the following theorem.

THEOREM 1. *If Q is a lower triangular $n \times n$ matrix, then $Q^k = 0$ for $k \geq n$.*

Proof. From the definition of matrix multiplication we note that Q^2 has a 0 diagonal below the main diagonal, Q^3 has two such diagonals, etc. Hence $Q^n = 0$, and thus if $k \geq n$, $Q^k = Q^{k-n}Q^n = 0$.

The powers of the matrix Q have interesting interpretations. To see what these are let $q_{ij}^{(2)}$ be the i, jth entry of Q^2. Then, using the rule for matrix multiplication, we see that

(1) $$q_{ij}^{(2)} = q_{i1}q_{1j} + q_{i2}q_{2j} + \ldots + q_{i,i-1}q_{i-1,j}$$

where the sum in (1) is terminated at $i - 1$ since $q_{ij} = 0$ when $j \geq i$. If we remember that all the entries q_{ij} are nonnegative integers we see from (1) that the only way $q_{ij}^{(2)}$ can be nonzero is for one or more products of the form $q_{ik}q_{kj}$ to be nonzero. But such a product is nonzero only if both terms are. And if $q_{ik} > 0$ and $q_{kj} > 0$, then a positive number of units of a_j are needed to produce one unit of a_k, and in turn a positive number of units of a_k are needed to produce one unit of a_i. We say in this case that a_i has *two-stage* requirements for a_j. We conclude that the entries of Q^2 give the number of two-stage requirements for items.

In the same way one can show that the entries of Q^3 give the three-stage requirements for items, and that Q^4 gives the number of four-stage requirements, etc.

From these interpretations we can get another intuitive proof of Theorem 1. For if Q^k is never zero no matter how large k is, then the production process has nonzero k-stage demands for items for every k. Hence, in order to produce one unit of output, an arbitrarily large number of parts must be on hand, which is clearly an impossible manufacturing situation. Hence $Q^k = 0$ for some k, and since only $n - 1$ items precede the final one, Q^n must be 0. Of course, Q^k may be 0 already for a smaller k.

Now suppose that we decide to produce x_1 units of a_1, x_2 units of a_2, etc., and x_n units of a_n. Let us call $x = (x_1, x_2, \ldots, x_n)$ the *production vector*. How many units of each item must we plan to produce? To be more specific, let us ask the question, how many units of a_j must we produce? The answer can be obtained from the quantity matrix Q and the production vector x. Thus, in order to produce x_1 units of a_1, we will need to produce $x_1 q_{1j}$ units of a_j; to produce x_2 units of a_2, we need to produce $x_2 q_{2j}$ units of a_j; etc., and to produce x_n units of a_n, we need to produce $x_n q_{nj}$ units of a_j. Adding these together we get

$$(2) \qquad x_1 q_{1j} + x_2 q_{2j} + \ldots + x_n q_{nj}$$

as the total number of units of a_j that must be produced to manufacture the production vector x. It is easy to see that (2) is just the jth component of the vector xQ. Hence the vector xQ gives the internal production requirements for the factory when it produces the amounts given in the production vector x. We shall call the vector xQ the *internal demand vector* since it measures the quantities of parts that must be manufactured and used internally by the factory in order to maintain production x.

Suppose now that the factory wants to ship d_1 units of a_1, d_2 units of a_2, etc., and d_n units of a_n. We call $d = (d_1, d_2, \ldots, d_n)$ the *outside demand vector*, since it measures the quantities of each part that are produced by the factory and shipped away, instead of being used internally by the factory for further production.

The question now is, what should the production vector x be in order to supply both the inside demand xQ and the outside demand d? It is easy to see that x must satisfy the following equation:

$$(3) \qquad x = xQ + d.$$

We now have the purely mathematical question of solving equation (3) for x. If we take the xQ term to the left-hand side and factor out x we get

$$(4) \qquad x(I - Q) = d.$$

If the matrix $I - Q$ has an inverse it is easy to solve (4) by multiplying on the right by $(I - Q)^{-1}$. We get

$$(5) \qquad x = d(I - Q)^{-1}$$

as the desired solution. We now show that the inverse does exist.

THEOREM 2. Let Q be any matrix that satisfies the statement of Theorem 1. Then $I - Q$ has an inverse given by the equation

(6) $$(I - Q)^{-1} = I + Q + Q^2 + \ldots + Q^{k-1}$$

where k is the smallest number such that $Q^k = 0$.

Proof. For any r the following identity can be established by multiplying out the left-hand side:

(7) $$(I - Q)(I + Q + Q^2 + \ldots + Q^{r-1}) = I - Q^r.$$

If we now let k be the smallest number such that $Q^k = 0$, we see that

(8) $$(I - Q)(I + Q + Q^2 + \ldots + Q^{k-1}) = I$$

which proves that the inverse exists and is given as stated in equation (6).

It can be shown from (6) that if the entries of Q are nonnegative integers, then so are the entries of $(I - Q)^{-1}$ (see Exercise 6).

The computation of the inverse of $I - Q$ can be carried out using the technique of Section 6, and the lower triangular structure of Q makes it particularly easy to do this.

Example 1 (continued). For the Q matrix given above, the matrices $I - Q$ and $(I - Q)^{-1}$ are given in Figures 7 and 8. The computation of $(I - Q)^{-1}$, by the algorithm of Section 6, is very easy and is left to the reader as an exercise.

$$I - Q = \begin{pmatrix} 1 & & & & & \\ 0 & 1 & & & & \\ -2 & -6 & 1 & & & \\ 0 & -6 & -2 & 1 & & \\ 0 & 0 & 0 & 0 & 1 & \\ 0 & -15 & 0 & -3 & -1 & 1 \end{pmatrix}$$

Figure 7

$$(I - Q)^{-1} = \begin{pmatrix} 1 & & & & & \\ 0 & 1 & & & & \\ 2 & 6 & 1 & & & \\ 4 & 18 & 2 & 1 & & \\ 0 & 0 & 0 & 0 & 1 & \\ 12 & 69 & 6 & 3 & 1 & 1 \end{pmatrix}$$

Figure 8

Suppose now that a telephone company orders 10 of the tripod masts for use in setting up temporary transmission lines, and also orders 1000 bolts, 6 half legs, and 2 plates as spare parts in case of damage to the original masts. What are the production requirements on the factory to fulfill this order? We see that

$$d = (0, 1000, 6, 0, 2, 10);$$

hence the required production is given by

$$x = d(I - Q)^{-1} = (132, 1726, 66, 30, 12, 10),$$

as the reader can easily verify by carrying out the matrix multiplication. Thus the factory must produce 132 rods, 1726 bolts, 66 half legs, 30 legs, 12 plates, and 10 masts. It then has exactly the items needed to fulfill the order.

It may be argued that the above problem can be solved directly by having a clerk simply count the parts requirements, and indeed this is so. (This suggests that $(I - Q)^{-1}$ can be calculated by counting total parts requirements, see Exercise 9.) However, he would have to do the same kind of arithmetic for each different order that came in and thus he would be doing over and over the same arithmetical calculations. Hence, even though the work of finding $(I - Q)^{-1}$ may be rather extensive, once it is done it can be used repeatedly in calculating the parts requirements for new orders. Then the single matrix multiplication $d(I - Q)^{-1}$ is all the calculation that is needed for each new demand d.

It should also be remarked that high-speed computers can be programmed to carry out these computations very quickly.

EXERCISES

1. The Ajax Electric Company makes a common household convenience called a Shock Unit. A Shock Unit contains two basic components A and B. These components are connected by a resistor and two electric coils. Component A has in it two resistors and one electric coil. Component B has in it three electric coils and one resistor. To make an electric coil requires 20 units of wire. For every coil or resistor two units of wire are needed for connections. Set up the technological matrix for producing a Shock Unit.

$$\text{Ans. } Q = \begin{bmatrix} W \\ C \\ R \\ A \\ B \\ S \end{bmatrix} \begin{pmatrix} 0 \\ 22 & 0 \\ 2 & 0 & 0 \\ 0 & 1 & 2 & 0 \\ 0 & 3 & 1 & 0 & 0 \\ 0 & 2 & 1 & 1 & 1 & 0 \end{pmatrix}.$$

2. Find $(I - Q)^{-1}$ for Exercise 1.

3. Compute the production vector x in Exercise 1 for each of the following demands:
   (a) Three Shock Units.   [Ans. $x = (420, 18, 12, 3, 3, 3)$.]
   (b) Two Shock Units, three spare resistors, two spare coils, and ten units of wire.
   (c) Two Shock Units, two spare units A, and two spare units B.

   [Ans. $x = (468, 20, 14, 4, 4, 2)$.]

4. Let Q be each of the lower triangular matrices listed below. Find $(I - Q)^{-1}$.

(a) $\begin{pmatrix} 0 & & & & \\ 2 & 0 & & & \\ 5 & 3 & 0 & & \\ 0 & 1 & 8 & 0 & \\ 10 & 4 & 0 & 3 & 0 \end{pmatrix}.$ (b) $\begin{pmatrix} 0 & & & \\ 7 & 0 & & \\ 2 & 0 & 0 & \\ 3 & 4 & 5 & 0 \end{pmatrix}.$

5. Find the production vectors needed to satisfy the outside demand vectors given below, if the quantity matrices are as given in the corresponding parts of Exercise 4.
(a) $d = (2, 0, 3, 10, 15)$.   (b) $d = (0, 1, 5, 8)$.

6. Use Theorem 2 to show that if the entries of a quantity matrix Q are nonnegative integers then so are the entries of $(I - Q)^{-1}$.

7. If Q is a quantity matrix, show that the entries of Q^3 give the three-stage requirements for items.

8. Write the solution x as a sum of terms dQ^i, using (5) and (6). Interpret the individual terms and verify that the sum does represent the required x.

9. Let Q be any lower triangular matrix with integer entries such as those in Exercise 4. Devise a method for computing $(I - Q)^{-1}$ by interpreting the entries of Q as parts requirements, and merely counting the total parts requirements. Check your method by using it on the matrices in Exercise 4 and comparing with your previous answers.

10. Compute the production vector, for each of the demands given below, for the production process of Example 1.
(a) $d = (10, 500, 50, 0, 20, 300)$.
(b) $d = (0, 2000, 0, 15, 5, 125)$.

8. Applications of matrix theory to Markov chains

In this section we shall show applications of matrix theory to Markov chains. For simplicity we shall confine our discussion to three-state Markov chains, but a similar procedure will work for any other Markov chain.

In Section 12 of Chapter IV, we noted that to each Markov chain there was a matrix of transition probabilities. For example, if there are three states, a_1, a_2, and a_3, then

$$P = \begin{array}{c} \\ a_1 \\ a_2 \\ a_3 \end{array} \begin{array}{ccc} a_1 & a_2 & a_3 \\ \begin{pmatrix} p_{11} & p_{12} & p_{13} \\ p_{21} & p_{22} & p_{23} \\ p_{31} & p_{32} & p_{33} \end{pmatrix} \end{array}$$

is the transition matrix for the chain. Recall that the *row sums* of P are all equal to 1. Such a matrix is called a transition matrix.

DEFINITION. A *transition matrix* is a square matrix with nonnegative entries such that the sum of the entries in each row is 1.

In order to obtain a Markov chain we must specify how the process starts. Suppose that the initial state is chosen by a chance device that selects state a_j with probability $p_j^{(0)}$. We can represent these initial probabilities by means of the vector $p^{(0)} = (p_1^{(0)}, p_2^{(0)}, p_3^{(0)})$. As in Exercise 10 of Section 4, we can construct a tree measure for as many steps of the process as we wish to consider. Let $p_j^{(n)}$ be the probability that the process will be in state a_j after n steps. Let the vector of these probabilities be $p^{(n)} = (p_1^{(n)}, p_2^{(n)}, p_3^{(n)})$.

DEFINITION. A row vector p is called a *probability vector* if it has nonnegative components whose sum is 1.

Obviously the vectors $p^{(0)}$ and $p^{(n)}$ are probability vectors. Also each row of a transition matrix is a probability vector.

By means of the tree measure it can be shown that these probabilities satisfy the following equations:

$$p_1^{(n)} = p_1^{(n-1)}p_{11} + p_2^{(n-1)}p_{21} + p_3^{(n-1)}p_{31}$$
$$p_2^{(n)} = p_1^{(n-1)}p_{12} + p_2^{(n-1)}p_{22} + p_3^{(n-1)}p_{32}$$
$$p_3^{(n)} = p_1^{(n-1)}p_{13} + p_2^{(n-1)}p_{23} + p_3^{(n-1)}p_{33}.$$

It is not hard to give intuitive meanings to these equations. The first one, for example, expresses the fact that the probability of being in state a_1 after n steps is the sum of the probabilities of being at each of the three possible states after $n - 1$ steps and then moving to state a_1 on the nth step. The interpretation of the other equations is similar.

If we recall the definition of the product of a vector times a matrix we can write the above equations as

$$p^{(n)} = p^{(n-1)}P.$$

If we substitute values of n we get the equations: $p^{(1)} = p^{(0)}P$; $p^{(2)} = p^{(1)}P = p^{(0)}P^2$; $p^{(3)} = p^{(2)}P = p^{(0)}P^3$; etc. In general, it can be seen that

$$p^{(n)} = p^{(0)}P^n.$$

Thus we see that, if we multiply the vector $p^{(0)}$ of initial probabilities by the nth power of the transition matrix P, we obtain the vector $p^{(n)}$, whose components give the probabilities of being in each of the states after n steps.

In particular, let us choose $p^{(0)} = (1, 0, 0)$ which is equivalent to letting the process start in state a_1. From the equation above we see that then $p^{(n)}$ is the first row of the matrix P^n. Thus the elements of the first row of the matrix P^n give us the probabilities that after n steps the process will be in a given one of the states, under the assumption that it started in state a_1.

In the same way, if we choose $p^{(0)} = (0, 1, 0)$, we see that the second row of P^n gives the probabilities that the process will be in one of the various states after n steps, given that it started in state a_2. Similarly the third row gives these probabilities, assuming that the process started in state a_3.

In Section 12 of Chapter IV, we considered special Markov chains that started in given fixed states. There we arrived at a matrix $P^{(n)}$ whose ith row gave the probabilities of the process ending in the various states, given that it started at state a_i. By comparing the work that we did there with what we have just done, we see that the matrix $P^{(n)}$ is merely the nth power of P, that is, $P^{(n)} = P^n$. (Compare Exercise 10 of Section 4.) Matrix multiplication thus gives a convenient way of computing the desired probabilities.

DEFINITION. The probability vector w is a *fixed point* of the matrix P, if $w = wP$.

Example 1. Consider the transition matrix

$$P = \begin{pmatrix} \frac{2}{3} & \frac{1}{3} \\ \frac{1}{2} & \frac{1}{2} \end{pmatrix} = \begin{pmatrix} .667 & .333 \\ .500 & .500 \end{pmatrix}.$$

If $w = (.6, .4)$, then we see that

$$wP = (.6, .4)\begin{pmatrix} \frac{2}{3} & \frac{1}{3} \\ \frac{1}{2} & \frac{1}{2} \end{pmatrix} = (.6, .4) = w$$

so that w is the fixed point of the matrix P.

If we had happened to choose the vector w as our initial probability vector $p^{(0)}$, we would have had $p^{(n)} = p^{(0)}P^n = wP^n = w = p^{(0)}$. In this case the probability of being at any particular state is the same at all steps of the process. Such a process is in *equilibrium*.

As seen above, in the study of Markov chains we are interested in the powers of the matrix P. To see what happens to these powers, let us further consider the example.

Example 1 (continued). Suppose that we compute powers of the matrix P in the example above. We have

$$P^2 = \begin{pmatrix} .611 & .389 \\ .583 & .417 \end{pmatrix}, \qquad P^3 = \begin{pmatrix} .602 & .398 \\ .597 & .403 \end{pmatrix}, \qquad \text{etc.}$$

It looks as if the matrix P^n is approaching the matrix

$$W = \begin{pmatrix} .6 & .4 \\ .6 & .4 \end{pmatrix}$$

and, in fact, it can be shown that this is the case. (When we say that P^n approaches W we mean that each entry in the matrix P^n gets close to the corresponding entry in W.) Note that each row of W is the fixed point w of the matrix P.

DEFINITION. A transition matrix is said to be *regular* if some power of the matrix has only positive components.

Thus the matrix in the example is regular, since every entry in it is positive, so that the first power of the matrix has all positive entries. Other examples occur in the exercises.

THEOREM. If P is a regular transition matrix, then
  (i)   The powers P^n approach a matrix W.
  (ii) Each row of W is the same probability vector w.
  (iii) The components of w are positive.

We omit the proof of this theorem*; however, we can prove the next theorem.

THEOREM. If P is a regular transition matrix, and W and w are given by the previous theorem, then
  (a) If p is any probability vector, pP^n approaches w.
  (b) The vector w is the unique fixed point probability vector of P.

Proof. First let us consider the vector pW. The first column of W has a w_1 in each row. Hence in the first component of pW each component of p is multiplied by w_1, and therefore we have w_1 times the sum of the components of p, which is w_1. Doing the same for the other components, we note that pW is simply w. But pP^n approaches pW; hence it approaches w. Thus if any probability vector is multiplied repeatedly by P, it approaches the fixed point w. This proves part (a).

Since the powers of P approach W, $P^{n+1} = P^n P$ approaches W, but it also approaches WP; hence $WP = W$. Any one row of this matrix equation states that $wP = w$; hence w is a fixed point (and by the previous theorem a probability vector). We must still show that it is unique. Let u be any probability vector fixed point of P. By part (a) we know that uP^n approaches w. But since u is a fixed point, $uP^n = u$. Hence u remains fixed but "approaches" w. This is possible only if $u = w$. Hence w is the only probability vector fixed point. This completes the proof of part (b).

The following is an important consequence of this theorem. If we take as p the vector $p^{(0)}$ of initial probabilities, then the vector $pP^n = p^{(n)}$ gives the probabilities after n steps, and this vector approaches w. Therefore, no matter what the initial probabilities are, if P is regular, then after a large number of steps the probability that the process is in state a_j will be very nearly w_j.

We noted for an independent trials process that if p is the probability of a given outcome a, then this may be given an alternate interpretation by means of the law of large numbers: in a long series of experiments the frac-

* For an elementary proof see Kemeny, Mirkil, Snell, and Thompson, *Finite Mathematical Structures* (Englewood Cliffs, N.J.: Prentice-Hall, Inc., 1959) Chapter 6, Section 3.

tion of outcomes in which a occurs is approximately p, and the approximation gets better and better as the number of experiments increases. For a
regular Markov chain it is the components of the vector w that play the
analogous role. That is, the fraction of times that the chain is in state a_i
approaches w_i, no matter how one starts.

Example 1 (continued). Let us take $p^{(0)} = (.1, .9)$ and see how $p^{(n)}$ changes.
Using P as in the example above, we have that $p^{(1)} = (.5167, .4833)$, $p^{(2)}$
$= (.5861, .4139)$, and $p^{(3)} = (.5977, .4023)$. Recalling that $w = (.6, .4)$, we see
that these vectors do approach w.

Example 2. As an example let us derive the formulas for the fixed point of a
2×2 transition matrix with positive components. Such a matrix is of the
form

$$S = \begin{pmatrix} 1 - a & a \\ b & 1 - b \end{pmatrix}$$

where $0 < a < 1$ and $0 < b < 1$. Since S is regular, it has a unique probability
vector fixed point $w = (w_1, w_2)$. Its components must satisfy the equations

$$w_1(1 - a) + w_2 b = w_1$$
$$w_1 a + w_2(1 - b) = w_2.$$

Each of these equations reduces to the single equation $w_1 a = w_2 b$. This single
equation has an infinite number of solutions. However, since w is a probability
vector, we must also have $w_1 + w_2 = 1$, and the new equation gives the point
$[b/(a + b), a/(a + b)]$ as the unique fixed-point probability vector of S.

Example 3. Suppose that the President of the United States tells person A
his intention either to run or not to run in the next election. Then A relays the
news to B, who in turn relays the message to C, etc., always to some new
person. Assume that there is a probability $p > 0$ that any one person, when
he gets the message, will reverse it before passing it on to the next person.
What is the probability that the nth man to hear the message will be told that
the President will run? We can consider this as a two-state Markov chain, with
states indicated by "yes" and "no." The process is in state "yes" at time
n if the nth person to receive the message was told that the President would
run. It is in state "no" if he was told that the President would not run. The
matrix P of transition probabilities is then

$$\begin{array}{cc} & \text{yes} \quad\ \text{no} \end{array}$$
$$\begin{array}{c} \text{yes} \\ \text{no} \end{array} \begin{pmatrix} 1 - p & p \\ p & 1 - p \end{pmatrix}.$$

Then the matrix P^n gives the probabilities that the nth man is given a certain
answer, assuming that the President said "yes" (first row) or assuming that
the President said "no" (second row). We know that these rows approach w.
From the formulas of the last section, we find that $w = (\frac{1}{2}, \frac{1}{2})$. Hence the probabilities for the nth man being told "yes" or "no" approach $\frac{1}{2}$ independently

of the initial decision of the President. For a large number of people, we can expect that approximately one-half will be told that the President will run and the other half that he will not, independently of the actual decision of the President.

Suppose now that the probability a that a person will change the news from "yes" to "no" when transmitting it to the next person is different from the probability b that he will change it from "no" to "yes." Then the matrix of transition probabilities becomes

$$\begin{array}{c} \\ \text{yes} \\ \text{no} \end{array} \begin{array}{cc} \text{yes} & \text{no} \\ \begin{pmatrix} 1 - a & a \\ b & 1 - b \end{pmatrix}. \end{array}$$

In this case $w = [b/(a + b), a/(a + b)]$. Thus there is a probability of approximately $b/(a + b)$ that the nth person will be told that the President will run. Assuming that n is large, this probability is independent of the actual decision of the President. For n large we can expect, in this case, that a proportion approximately equal to $b/(a + b)$ will have been told that the President will run, and a proportion $a/(a + b)$ will have been told that he will not run. The important thing to note is that, from the assumptions we have made, it follows that it is not the President but the people themselves who determine the probability that a person will be told "yes" or "no," and the proportion of people in the long run that are given one of these predictions.

Example 4. For this example, we continue the study of Example 2 in Chapter IV, Section 12. The first approximation treated in that example leads to a two-state Markov chain, and the results are similar to those obtained in Example 1 above. The second approximation led to a four-state Markov chain with transition probabilities given by the matrix

$$\begin{array}{c} \\ \text{AA} \\ \text{XA} \\ \text{AX} \\ \text{XX} \end{array} \begin{array}{cccc} \text{AA} & \text{XA} & \text{AX} & \text{XX} \\ \begin{pmatrix} 1 - a & 0 & a & 0 \\ b & 0 & 1 - b & 0 \\ 0 & 1 - c & 0 & c \\ 0 & d & 0 & 1 - d \end{pmatrix}. \end{array}$$

If a, b, c, and d are all different from 0 or 1, then the square of the matrix has no zeros, and hence the matrix is regular. The fixed probability vector is found in the usual way (see Exercise 18) and is

$$\left(\frac{bd}{bd + 2ad + ca}, \frac{ad}{bd + 2ad + ca}, \frac{ad}{bd + 2ad + ca}, \frac{ca}{bd + 2ad + ca} \right).$$

Note that the probability of being in state AX after a large number of steps is equal to the probability of being in state XA. This shows that in equilibrium a change from A to X must have the same probability as a change from X to A.

From the fixed vector we can find the probability of purchasing A in the far future. This is found by adding the probability of being in state AA and XA, giving

$$\frac{bd + ad}{bd + 2ad + ca}.$$

Notice that, to find the probability of purchasing A on the purchase preceding some purchase far in the future, we should add the probabilities of being in states AA and AX. That we get the same result corresponds to the fact that predictions far in the future are essentially independent of the particular period being predicted. In other words, the process is acting as if it were in equilibrium.

EXERCISES

1. Which of the following matrices are regular?

(a) $\begin{pmatrix} \frac{1}{2} & \frac{1}{2} \\ \frac{1}{2} & \frac{1}{2} \end{pmatrix}$.   (b) $\begin{pmatrix} 0 & 1 \\ \frac{1}{4} & \frac{3}{4} \end{pmatrix}$.   [Regular]

(c) $\begin{pmatrix} 1 & 0 \\ \frac{1}{3} & \frac{2}{3} \end{pmatrix}$.   (d) $\begin{pmatrix} \frac{1}{5} & \frac{4}{5} \\ 1 & 0 \end{pmatrix}$.   [Regular]

(e) $\begin{pmatrix} \frac{1}{2} & \frac{1}{2} \\ 0 & 1 \end{pmatrix}$.   (f) $\begin{pmatrix} 0 & 1 \\ 1 & 0 \end{pmatrix}$.   [Not regular]

(g) $\begin{pmatrix} \frac{1}{2} & \frac{1}{2} & 0 \\ 0 & \frac{1}{2} & \frac{1}{2} \\ \frac{1}{3} & \frac{1}{3} & \frac{1}{3} \end{pmatrix}$.   (h) $\begin{pmatrix} \frac{1}{3} & 0 & \frac{2}{3} \\ 0 & 1 & 0 \\ 0 & \frac{1}{5} & \frac{4}{5} \end{pmatrix}$.   [Not regular]

2. Show that the 2×2 matrix

$$S = \begin{pmatrix} 1 - a & a \\ b & 1 - b \end{pmatrix}$$

is a regular transition matrix if and only if either

   (i) $0 < a \le 1$ and $0 < b < 1$; or
   (ii) $0 < a < 1$ and $0 < b \le 1$.

3. Find the fixed point for the matrix in Exercise 2 for each of the cases listed there. [*Hint:* Most of the cases were covered in the text above.]

4. Find the fixed point w for each of the following regular matrices.

(a) $\begin{pmatrix} \frac{3}{4} & \frac{1}{4} \\ \frac{1}{2} & \frac{1}{2} \end{pmatrix}$.   [*Ans.* $w = (\frac{2}{3}, \frac{1}{3})$.]

(b) $\begin{pmatrix} .9 & .1 \\ .1 & .9 \end{pmatrix}$.

(c) $\begin{pmatrix} \frac{3}{4} & \frac{1}{4} & 0 \\ 0 & \frac{2}{3} & \frac{1}{3} \\ \frac{1}{4} & \frac{1}{4} & \frac{1}{2} \end{pmatrix}$.   [*Ans.* $w = (\frac{2}{7}, \frac{3}{7}, \frac{2}{7})$.]

5. Let $p^0 = (\frac{1}{2}, \frac{1}{2})$ and compute $p^{(1)}$, $p^{(2)}$, and $p^{(3)}$ for the matrices in Exercises 4(a) and 4(b). Do they approach the fixed points of these matrices?

6. Give a probability theory interpretation to the condition of regularity.

7. Consider the two-state Markov chain with transition matrix

$$P = \begin{matrix} & a_1 & a_2 \\ a_1 \\ a_2 \end{matrix} \begin{pmatrix} 0 & 1 \\ 1 & 0 \end{pmatrix}.$$

What is the probability that after n steps the process is in state a_1 if it started in state a_2? Does this probability become independent of the initial position for large n? If not, the theorem of this section must not apply. Why? Does the matrix have a unique fixed point probability vector?

8. Prove that, if a regular 3×3 transition matrix has the property that its column sums are 1, its fixed point probability vector is $(\frac{1}{3}, \frac{1}{3}, \frac{1}{3})$. State a similar result for $n \times n$ transition matrices having column sums equal to 1.

9. Compute the first five powers of the matrix

$$P = \begin{pmatrix} .8 & .2 \\ .2 & .8 \end{pmatrix}.$$

From these, guess the fixed point vector w. Check by computing what w is.

10. Show that all transition matrices of the form

$$\begin{pmatrix} 1 - a & a \\ a & 1 - a \end{pmatrix}$$

where $0 < a < 1$ have the same unique fixed point.   [Ans. $w = (\frac{1}{2}, \frac{1}{2})$.]

11. A professor has three pet questions, one of which occurs on every test he gives. The students know his habits well. He never uses the same question twice in a row. If he used question one last time, he tosses a coin, and uses question two if a head comes up. If he used question two, he tosses two coins and switches to question three if both come up heads. If he used question three, he tosses three coins and switches to question one if all three come up heads. In the long run, which question does he use most often, and how frequently is it used?
[Ans. Question two, 40 per cent of the time.]

12. A professor tries not to be late for class too often. If he is late one day, he is 90 per cent sure to be on time next time. If he is on time, then the next day there is a 30 per cent chance of his being late. In the long run, how often is he late for class?

13. The Land of Oz is blessed by many things, but not good weather. They *never* have two nice days in a row. If they have a nice day they are just as likely to have snow as rain the next day. If they have snow (or rain), they have an even chance of having the same the next day. If there is a change from snow or rain, only half of the time is this a change to a nice day. Set up a three-state Markov chain to describe this situation. Find the long-range probability for rain, for snow, and for a nice day. What fraction of the days does it rain in the land of Oz?
[Ans. The probabilities are: nice, $\frac{1}{5}$; rain, $\frac{2}{5}$; snow, $\frac{2}{5}$.]

14. Let S be the matrix

$$S = \begin{pmatrix} 1 & 0 \\ \frac{1}{2} & \frac{1}{2} \end{pmatrix}.$$

Compute the unique probability vector fixed point of S, and use your result to prove that S is not regular.

15. Show that the matrix

$$S = \begin{pmatrix} 1 & 0 & 0 \\ \frac{1}{2} & 0 & \frac{1}{2} \\ 0 & 0 & 1 \end{pmatrix}$$

has more than one probability vector fixed point. Find the matrix that S^n approaches, and show that it is not a matrix all of whose rows are the same.

16. Let P be a transition matrix in which all the entries that are not zero have been replaced by x's. Devise a method of raising such a matrix to powers in order to check for regularity. Illustrate your method by showing that

$$P = \begin{pmatrix} 0 & 1 & 0 \\ 0 & 0 & 1 \\ \frac{1}{2} & \frac{1}{2} & 0 \end{pmatrix}$$

is regular.

17. Consider a Markov chain such that it is possible to go from any state a_i to any state a_j and such that p_{kk} is not 0 for at least one state a_k. Prove that the chain is regular. [*Hint:* Consider the times that it is possible to go from a_i to a_j via a_k.]

18. Show that the vector given in Example 4 is the fixed vector of the transition matrix.

9. Absorbing Markov chains

In this section we shall consider a kind of Markov chain quite different from regular chains.

DEFINITION. A state in a Markov chain is an *absorbing state* if it is impossible to leave it. A Markov chain is *absorbing* if (1) it has at least one absorbing state, and (2) from every state it is possible to go to an absorbing state (not necessarily in one step).

Example 1. A particle moves on a line; each time it moves one unit to the right with probability $\frac{1}{2}$, or one unit to the left. We introduce barriers so that if it ever reaches one of these barriers it stays there. As a simple example, let the states be 0, 1, 2, 3, 4. States 0 and 4 are absorbing states. The transition matrix is then

$$P = \begin{array}{c} \\ 0 \\ 1 \\ 2 \\ 3 \\ 4 \end{array} \begin{array}{ccccc} 0 & 1 & 2 & 3 & 4 \\ \begin{pmatrix} 1 & 0 & 0 & 0 & 0 \\ \frac{1}{2} & 0 & \frac{1}{2} & 0 & 0 \\ 0 & \frac{1}{2} & 0 & \frac{1}{2} & 0 \\ 0 & 0 & \frac{1}{2} & 0 & \frac{1}{2} \\ 0 & 0 & 0 & 0 & 1 \end{pmatrix} \end{array}.$$

The states 1, 2, 3 are all nonabsorbing states, and from any of these it is possible to reach the absorbing states 0 and 4. Hence the chain is an absorbing chain. Such a process is usually called a *random walk*.

When a process reaches an absorbing state we shall say that it is *absorbed*.

THEOREM. In an absorbing Markov chain the probability that the process will be absorbed is 1.

We shall indicate only the basic idea of the proof of the theorem. From each nonabsorbing state, a_j, it is possible to reach an absorbing state. Let n_j be the minimum number of steps required to reach an absorbing state, starting from state a_j. Let p_j be the probability that, starting from state a_j, the process will *not* reach an absorbing state in n_j steps. Then $p_j < 1$. Let n be the largest of the n_j and let p be the largest of the p_j. The probability of not being absorbed in n steps is less than p, in $2n$ steps is less than p^2, etc. Since $p < 1$, these probabilities tend to zero.

For an absorbing Markov chain we consider three interesting questions: (a) What is the probability that the process will end up in a given absorbing state? (b) On the average, how long will it take for the process to be absorbed? (c) On the average, how many times will the process be in each nonabsorbing state? The answer to all these questions depends, in general, on the state from which the process starts.

Consider then an arbitrary absorbing Markov chain. Let us renumber the states so that the absorbing states come first. If there are r absorbing states and s nonabsorbing states, the transition matrix will have the following *canonical* (or standard) *form*.

(1)
$$P = \begin{array}{c} \\ r \\ s \end{array} \left(\begin{array}{c|c} I & O \\ \hline R & Q \end{array} \right).$$

$$\begin{array}{cc} r \text{ states} & s \text{ states} \end{array}$$

Here I is an r-by-r identity matrix, O is an r-by-s zero matrix, R is an s-by-r matrix, and Q is an s-by-s matrix. The first r states are absorbing and the last s states are nonabsorbing.

In Section 8 we saw that the entries of the matrix P^n gave the probabilities of being in the various states starting from the various states. It is easy to show that P^n is of the form

$$(2) \qquad\qquad P^n = \begin{pmatrix} I & O \\ * & Q^n \end{pmatrix}$$

where the asterisk * stands for the s-by-r matrix in the lower left-hand corner of P^n, which we do not compute here. The form of P^n shows that the entries of Q^n give the probabilities for being in each of the nonabsorbing states after n steps for each possible nonabsorbing starting state. (After zero steps the process must be in the same nonabsorbing state in which it started. Hence $Q^0 = I$.) By our first theorem, the probability of being in the nonabsorbing states after n steps approaches zero. Thus every entry of Q^n must approach zero as n approaches infinity, i.e., $Q^n \to 0$.

Consider then the infinite series

$$I + Q + Q^2 + Q^3 + \ldots.$$

Suppose that Q were a nonnegative number x instead of a nonnegative matrix. To correspond to the fact that $Q^n \to O$ we take x to be less than 1. Then

$$1 + x + x^2 + \ldots = (1 - x)^{-1}.$$

By an argument similar to that of Theorem 2, Section 7, it can be proved that the matrix series behaves in exactly the same way. That is,

$$I + Q + Q^2 + \ldots = (I - Q)^{-1}.$$

The matrix $(I - Q)^{-1}$ will be called the *fundamental matrix* for the given absorbing chain. It has the following important interpretation:

Let n_{ij} be the mean number of times that the chain is in state a_j if it starts in state a_i, for nonabsorbing states a_i and a_j. Let N be the matrix whose components are n_{ij}. We will show that $N = (I - Q)^{-1}$. If we take into account the contribution of the original (which is 1 if $i = j$ and 0 otherwise), we may write the equation

$$n_{ij} = d_{ij} + \sum_k p_{ik} n_{kj}$$

where d_{ij} is 1 if $i = j$ and 0 otherwise, and $\sum_k$ indicates that the quantities $p_{ik} n_{kj}$ should be computed for all nonabsorbing states and added. This equation may be written in matrix form:

$$N = I + QN.$$

Then $(I - Q)N = I$, and hence $N = (I - Q)^{-1}$, as was to be shown. Thus we have found a probabilistic interpretation for our fundamental matrix; its i, j entry is the mean number of times that the chain is in state a_j if it starts at a_i. The fact that $N = I + Q + Q^2 + \ldots$ also has a probabilistic interpretation. Since the i, j entry of Q^n is the probability of being in a_j on the nth step if we start at a_i, we have shown that the mean of the number of times in state a_j may be written as the sum of the probabilities of being there on particular steps. Thus we have answered question (c) as follows.

THEOREM. Let $N = (I - Q)^{-1}$ be the fundamental matrix for an absorbing chain. Then the entries of N give the mean number of times in each nonabsorbing state for each possible nonabsorbing starting state.

Example 1 (continued). In Example 1 the transition matrix in canonical form is

$$
\begin{array}{c c}
 & \begin{array}{c c c c c} 0 & 4 & 1 & 2 & 3 \end{array} \\
\begin{array}{c} 0 \\ 4 \\ \\ 1 \\ 2 \\ 3 \end{array} &
\left(\begin{array}{c c | c c c}
1 & 0 & 0 & 0 & 0 \\
0 & 1 & 0 & 0 & 0 \\
\hline
\frac{1}{2} & 0 & 0 & \frac{1}{2} & 0 \\
0 & 0 & \frac{1}{2} & 0 & \frac{1}{2} \\
0 & \frac{1}{2} & 0 & \frac{1}{2} & 0
\end{array} \right).
\end{array}
$$

From this we see that the matrix Q is

$$
Q = \begin{pmatrix} 0 & \frac{1}{2} & 0 \\ \frac{1}{2} & 0 & \frac{1}{2} \\ 0 & \frac{1}{2} & 0 \end{pmatrix}
$$

and

$$
I - Q = \begin{pmatrix} 1 & -\frac{1}{2} & 0 \\ -\frac{1}{2} & 1 & -\frac{1}{2} \\ 0 & -\frac{1}{2} & 1 \end{pmatrix}.
$$

Computing $(I - Q)^{-1}$, we find

$$
N = (I - Q)^{-1} = \begin{array}{c} 1 \\ 2 \\ 3 \end{array} \begin{pmatrix} \frac{3}{2} & 1 & \frac{1}{2} \\ 1 & 2 & 1 \\ \frac{1}{2} & 1 & \frac{3}{2} \end{pmatrix}.
$$

Thus, starting at state 2, the mean number of times in state 1 before absorption is 1, in state 2 it is 2, and in state 3 it is 1.

We next answer question (b). If we add all the entries in a row we will have the mean number of times in any of the nonabsorbing states for a given starting state, that is, the mean time required before being absorbed. This may be described as follows:

THEOREM. Consider an absorbing Markov chain with s nonabsorbing states. Let c be an s-component column vector with all entries 1. Then the vector $t = Nc$ has as components the mean number of steps before being absorbed for each possible nonabsorbing starting state.

Example 1 (continued). For Example 1 we have

$$t = Nc = \begin{array}{c} 1 \\ 2 \\ 3 \end{array} \begin{pmatrix} \frac{3}{2} & 1 & \frac{1}{2} \\ 1 & 2 & 1 \\ \frac{1}{2} & 1 & \frac{3}{2} \end{pmatrix} \begin{pmatrix} 1 \\ 1 \\ 1 \end{pmatrix}$$

$$= \begin{array}{c} 1 \\ 2 \\ 3 \end{array} \begin{pmatrix} 3 \\ 4 \\ 3 \end{pmatrix}.$$

Thus the mean number of steps to absorption starting at state 1 is 3, starting at state 2 it is 4, and starting at state 3 it is again 3. Since the process necessarily moves to 1 or 3 from 2 it is clear that it requires one more step starting from 2 than from 1 or 3.

We now consider question (a). That is, what is the probability that an absorbing chain will end up in a particular absorbing state? It is clear that this probability will depend upon the starting state and be interesting only for the case of a nonabsorbing starting state. We write as usual our matrix in the canonical form

$$P = \left(\begin{array}{c|c} I & O \\ \hline R & Q \end{array} \right).$$

THEOREM. Let b_{ij} be the probability that an absorbing chain will be absorbed in state a_j if it starts in the nonabsorbing state a_i. Let B be the matrix with entries b_{ij}. Then

$$B = NR$$

where N is the fundamental matrix and R is as in the canonical form.

Proof. Let a_i be a nonabsorbing state and a_j be an absorbing state. If we compute b_{ij} in terms of the possibilities on the outcome of the first step we have the equation

$$b_{ij} = p_{ij} + \sum_k p_{ik} b_{kj}$$

where the summation is carried out over all nonabsorbing states a_k. Writing this in matrix form gives

$$B = R + QB$$

$$(I - Q)B = R$$

and hence $B = (I - Q)^{-1} R = NR.$

Example 1 (continued). In the random walk example we found that

$$N = \begin{pmatrix} \frac{3}{2} & 1 & \frac{1}{2} \\ 1 & 2 & 1 \\ \frac{1}{2} & 1 & \frac{3}{2} \end{pmatrix}.$$

From the canonical form we find that

$$R = \begin{pmatrix} \frac{1}{2} & 0 \\ 0 & 0 \\ 0 & \frac{1}{2} \end{pmatrix}.$$

Hence

$$B = NR = \begin{pmatrix} \frac{3}{2} & 1 & \frac{1}{2} \\ 1 & 2 & 1 \\ \frac{1}{2} & 1 & \frac{3}{2} \end{pmatrix} \begin{pmatrix} \frac{1}{2} & 0 \\ 0 & 0 \\ 0 & \frac{1}{2} \end{pmatrix}$$

$$= \begin{matrix} 1 \\ 2 \\ 3 \end{matrix} \begin{pmatrix} \frac{3}{4} & \frac{1}{4} \\ \frac{1}{2} & \frac{1}{2} \\ \frac{1}{4} & \frac{3}{4} \end{pmatrix}.$$

Thus, for instance, starting from a_1, there is probability $\frac{3}{4}$ of absorption in a_0 and $\frac{1}{4}$ for absorption in a_4.

Let us summarize our results. We have shown that the answers to questions (a), (b), and (c) can all be given in terms of the fundamental matrix $N = (I - Q)^{-1}$. The matrix N itself gives us the mean number of times in each state before absorption depending upon the starting state. The column vector $t = Nc$ gives us the mean number of steps before absorption, depending upon the starting state. The matrix $B = NR$ gives us the probability of absorption in each of the absorbing states, depending upon the starting state.

EXERCISES

1. Which of the following transition matrices are from absorbing chains?

(a) $P = \begin{pmatrix} 1 & 0 \\ \frac{1}{2} & \frac{1}{2} \end{pmatrix}.$

(b) $P = \begin{pmatrix} 1 & 0 & 0 \\ 0 & \frac{1}{2} & \frac{1}{2} \\ 0 & \frac{1}{3} & \frac{2}{3} \end{pmatrix}.$

(c) $P = \begin{pmatrix} 1 & 0 & 0 & 0 & 0 \\ 0 & \frac{1}{2} & 0 & \frac{1}{2} & 0 \\ \frac{1}{5} & \frac{1}{5} & \frac{1}{5} & \frac{1}{5} & \frac{1}{5} \\ 0 & \frac{1}{3} & 0 & \frac{2}{3} & 0 \\ 0 & 0 & 0 & 0 & 1 \end{pmatrix}.$

(d) $P = \begin{pmatrix} 1 & 0 & 0 & 0 \\ \frac{1}{2} & 0 & 0 & \frac{1}{2} \\ \frac{1}{4} & \frac{1}{4} & \frac{1}{4} & \frac{1}{4} \\ 0 & 0 & 0 & 1 \end{pmatrix}.$

[*Ans.* (a) and (d).]

2. Consider the two-state transition matrix

$$P = \begin{pmatrix} 1 - a & a \\ b & 1 - b \end{pmatrix}.$$

For what choices of a and b do we obtain an absorbing chain?

3. In the random walk example (Example 1) of the present section, assume that the probability of a step to the right is $\frac{2}{3}$ and a step to the left is $\frac{1}{3}$. Find N, t, and B. Compare these with the results for probability $\frac{1}{2}$ for a step to the right and $\frac{1}{2}$ to the left.

4. In the Land of Oz example (see Exercise 13, Section 8) let us change the transition matrix by making R an absorbing state. This gives

$$\begin{array}{c} \\ R \\ N \\ S \end{array} \begin{array}{c} R \quad N \quad S \\ \begin{pmatrix} 1 & 0 & 0 \\ \frac{1}{2} & 0 & \frac{1}{2} \\ \frac{1}{4} & \frac{1}{4} & \frac{1}{2} \end{pmatrix}. \end{array}$$

Find the fundamental matrix N, and also t and B. What is the interpretation of these quantities?

5. An analysis of a recent hockey game between Dartmouth and Princeton showed the following facts: If the puck was in the center (C) the probabilities that it next entered Princeton territory (P) or Dartmouth territory (D) were .4 and .6, respectively. From D it went back to C with probability .95 or into the Dartmouth goal $(\overline{D})$ with probability .05 (Princeton scores one point). From P it next went to C with probability .9 and to Princeton's goal $\overline{P}$ with probability .1 (Dartmouth scores one point). Assuming that the puck begins in C after each point, find the transition matrix of this five-state Markov chain. Calculate the probability that Dartmouth will score.   [Ans. $\frac{4}{7}$.]

6. A number is chosen at random from the integers 1, 2, 3, 4, 5. If x is chosen, then another number is chosen from the set of integers less than or equal to x. This process is continued until the number 1 is chosen. Form a Markov chain by taking as states the largest number that can be chosen. Show that

$$\begin{array}{c} \\ 2 \\ N = \begin{array}{c} 3 \\ 4 \\ 5 \end{array} \end{array} \begin{array}{c} 2 \quad 3 \quad 4 \quad 5 \\ \begin{pmatrix} 1 & 0 & 0 & 0 \\ 1 & \frac{1}{2} & 0 & 0 \\ 1 & \frac{1}{2} & \frac{1}{3} & 0 \\ 1 & \frac{1}{2} & \frac{1}{3} & \frac{1}{4} \end{pmatrix} + I, \end{array}$$

where I is the 4×4 identity matrix. What is the mean number of draws?
[Ans. $\frac{25}{12}$.]

7. Using the result of Exercise 6, make a conjecture for the form of the fundamental matrix if we start with integers from 1 to n. What would the mean number of draws be if we started with numbers from 1 to 10?

8. Three tanks fight a three-way duel. Tank A has probability $\frac{1}{2}$ of destroying the tank it fires at. Tank B has probability $\frac{1}{3}$ of destroying, and Tank C has probability $\frac{1}{6}$ of destroying. The tanks fire together and each tank fires at the strongest opponent not yet destroyed. Form a Markov chain by taking as state the tanks which survive any one round. Find N, t, B, and interpret your results.

9. The following is an alternative method of finding the probability of absorption in a particular absorbing state, say a_j. Find the column vector d such that the jth component of d is 1, all other components corresponding to absorbing states are 0, and $Pd = d$. There is only one such vector. Component d_i is the probability of absorption in a_j if the process starts in a_i. Use this method to find the probability of absorption in state 0 in the random walk example given in this section.

10. The following is an alternative method for finding the mean number of steps to absorption. Let t_i be the mean number of steps to absorption starting at state a_i. This must be the same as taking one more step and then adding $p_{ij}t_j$ for every nonabsorbing state a_j.
   (a) Give reasons for the above claim that

$$t_i = 1 + \sum_j p_{ij}t_j,$$

   where the summation is over the nonabsorbing states.
   (b) Solve for t for the random walk example.
   (c) Verify that the solution agrees with that found in the text.

*10. An example from waiting line theory

In this section we are going to treat the following problem. Customers arrive at a service station, which has a single server. If the server is not busy the customer is given service. But if the server is busy the customer joins a line.

Examples of such a problem are people arriving at a post office window, airplanes arriving at an airport waiting in a "stack" to obtain a runway, people lining up at a theater window for tickets, people waiting at checkout counters in a supermarket, and mechanics waiting for service at a tool crib.

To make the problem more precise we must specify how the customers arrive and how much time is required for their service. There are a great variety of assumptions that might be made; we shall consider only one simple set of assumptions. We shall choose some convenient, small interval of time and assume that in a single interval of time at most one customer can arrive. The probability that a customer does arrive is p, independent of whether a customer arrived in any other time interval. We shall assume further that when a customer is being served there is a fixed probability

r that he finishes his service in any one interval, independent of the number of previous time units of service. Let $\bar{p} = 1 - p$ and $\bar{r} = 1 - r$.

We shall treat this problem by Markov chain theory. We shall form a Markov chain by taking as the state the number of individuals in line at the beginning of a time interval (including the customer being served). Naturally, the line cannot be greater than some preassigned number. This number could be taken to be the number of people in the world. But usually people are turned away when the line gets longer than a certain size. This is certainly the case for theater tickets. In the case of airplanes, when the traffic gets too heavy the planes must be sent to another airport, and so on. We suppose that n is the maximum possible length of a line.

We shall see that much of the behavior of our system can be described in terms of a quantity called the traffic intensity, denoted by u. This is the product of p and the mean service time of a customer. To find the mean service time we note first that the probability that a customer ends his service on the jth time period is $\bar{r}^{j-1}r$. Hence the mean service time is

$$1 \cdot r + 2 \cdot \bar{r}r + 3 \cdot \bar{r}^2 r + \ldots = r(1 + 2\bar{r} + 3\bar{r}^2 + 4\bar{r}^3 + \ldots)$$

$$= r[(1 + \bar{r} + \bar{r}^2 + \ldots) + (\bar{r} + \bar{r}^2 + \bar{r}^3 + \ldots)$$

$$+ (\bar{r}^2 + \bar{r}^3 + \bar{r}^4 + \ldots) + \ldots]$$

$$= r\left(\frac{1}{1 - \bar{r}} + \frac{\bar{r}}{1 - \bar{r}} + \frac{\bar{r}^2}{1 - \bar{r}} + \ldots\right)$$

$$= r\frac{1}{(1 - \bar{r})^2} = \frac{1}{r}.$$

Thus the traffic intensity is $u = p/r$. We will assume that $p \neq r$, i.e., that $u \neq 1$. (See Exercises 6–9.)

A convention is needed to cover the case of an empty line. We assume that a customer does *not* get served during the period in which he arrives, even if the line is empty. We now have all the necessary information to obtain the transition probabilities. We consider three cases depending upon the number of people waiting in line. The number waiting may be 0, or more than 0 but less than n, or n.

If there is no one in line, then during the next time unit there will be one person in line with probability p and no one in line with probability $\bar{p}$.

If the line is neither empty nor full, then the number can increase by one, stay the same, or decrease by one. It will increase by one if the customer being served is not finished and if a new customer arrives. The probability that this happens is $p\bar{r}$. In order that the line decrease by one it is necessary that the customer being served finish his service and no new customer arrive. The probability that this happens is $\bar{p}r$. Finally, the probability that the line stays the same is the probability that neither of these happens or $1 - p\bar{r} - \bar{p}r$.

When there are n customers in line the line decreases by one if the customer being served finishes and it remains the same if he does not finish; these have probabilities r and $\bar{r}$, respectively. Any new customer arriving in this period would be turned away.

For the case $n = 4$, we have then the transition matrix

$$
P = \begin{array}{c} \\ 0 \\ 1 \\ 2 \\ 3 \\ 4 \end{array}
\begin{array}{ccccc}
0 & 1 & 2 & 3 & 4 \\
\left(\begin{array}{ccccc}
\bar{p} & p & 0 & 0 & 0 \\
\bar{p}r & 1 - \bar{p}r - p\bar{r} & p\bar{r} & 0 & 0 \\
0 & \bar{p}r & 1 - \bar{p}r - p\bar{r} & p\bar{r} & 0 \\
0 & 0 & \bar{p}r & 1 - \bar{p}r - p\bar{r} & p\bar{r} \\
0 & 0 & 0 & r & \bar{r}
\end{array}\right)
\end{array}.
$$

To find the fixed vector we shall make use of an important property of the special nature of our chain. We have a chain that has integer states and can move at most one unit in each step. We know further that our chain is regular. (See Exercise 17, Section 8.) Hence for any state a_i it returns over and over again to this state. The fraction of the time in a large number of periods that it is in a_i is given by w_i. The fraction of the time that it moves from i to $i + 1$ is $w_i p_{i,i+1}$. The fraction of times it moves from $i + 1$ to i is $w_{i+1} p_{i+1,i}$. However, these fractions must be the same since every time it moves from i to $i + 1$ it must later move from $i + 1$ to i, since there is no other way of returning to i. Hence

$$
w_i p_{i,i+1} = w_{i+1} p_{i+1,i} \quad \text{or} \quad \frac{w_i}{w_{i+1}} = \frac{p_{i+1,i}}{p_{i,i+1}}.
$$

Using this fact we can find the fixed vector of our five-state chain to be

(1) $$ w = \frac{r - p}{r\bar{r} - p\bar{p}s^4} \left(\bar{r}, s, s^2, s^3, \bar{p}s^4\right) $$

where $s = p\bar{r}/r\bar{p}$.

Example 1. Let $p = .25$ and $r = .50$. Then the transition matrix is

$$
P = \begin{array}{c} \\ 0 \\ 1 \\ 2 \\ 3 \\ 4 \end{array}
\begin{array}{ccccc}
0 & 1 & 2 & 3 & 4 \\
\left(\begin{array}{ccccc}
.75 & .25 & 0 & 0 & 0 \\
.375 & .500 & .125 & 0 & 0 \\
0 & .375 & .500 & .125 & 0 \\
0 & 0 & .375 & .500 & .125 \\
0 & 0 & 0 & .5 & .5
\end{array}\right)
\end{array}
$$

and

$$ w = \tfrac{1}{107}(54, 36, 12, 4, 1) $$

$$ \approx (.505, .336, .112, .037, .009). $$

Example 2. Let $p = .8$ and $r = .4$. Then the transition matrix is

$$
P = \begin{matrix}
 & 0 & 1 & 2 & 3 & 4 \\
0 & .2 & .8 & 0 & 0 & 0 \\
1 & .08 & .44 & .48 & 0 & 0 \\
2 & 0 & .08 & .44 & .48 & 0 \\
3 & 0 & 0 & .08 & .44 & .48 \\
4 & 0 & 0 & 0 & .4 & .6
\end{matrix}
$$

and
$$
w = \tfrac{1}{5178}(6, 60, 360, 2160, 2592)
$$
$$
\approx (.001, .012, .070, .417, .501).
$$

We note in these two examples quite a different long-range prediction. In the first example, we see that a person would be turned away very infrequently. Also, approximately half the time the server would not be occupied. In the second example, over half of the time a person is turned away and the server is almost always busy. We see from the form of the fixed vector that these two different types of behavior correspond to the case $s < 1$ and $s > 1$. Let us see what these conditions mean in terms of u. If

$$
\frac{p\bar{r}}{r\bar{p}} < 1
$$

then $p\bar{r} < r\bar{p}$ or $p - pr < r - pr$. That is, $p < r$, or $u < 1$. Similarly, $s > 1$ corresponds to the case $r < p$ or $u > 1$. That is, our two types of behavior correspond to whether the traffic intensity is greater than one or less than one.

We consider now the general case where we allow a line of length n. The fixed vector for this case is

$$
(2) \qquad w = \frac{r - p}{r\bar{r} - p\bar{p}s^n} (\bar{r}, s, s^2, s^3, \ldots, s^{n-1}, \bar{p}s^n).
$$

There are two components of the fixed vector that are particularly interesting. These are w_0 and w_n. The component w_0 tells the fraction of the time in the long run that the server will be unoccupied. One would not want this to be too large in practice. The component w_n tells us how frequently the line is full and customers will have to be turned away in the long run. This should also be small. Let us examine these quantities when n is very large. If the traffic intensity is less than one and n is sufficiently large then s^n is very small. Hence w_n is small, and w_0 is approximately

$$
\frac{r - p}{r\bar{r}} \cdot \bar{r} = 1 - u.
$$

Thus the traffic intensity tells us how much time on the average the server will be busy. When u is near one this time is small, and when u is small it is large.

Similarly, when the traffic intensity is greater than one and n is large, s^n will be large. Thus w_0 will be very small, and w_n may be approximated by neglecting $r\bar{r}$ in comparison to $p\bar{p}s^n$. If we do this we obtain

$$w_n \approx \frac{p - r}{p} = 1 - \frac{1}{u}.$$

Again, the traffic intensity tells us how often in the long run customers will be turned away. When it is near one this will be rare, and when it is large this will happen often. We may therefore conclude that if n is large and the objective is (1) to keep the server busy and (2) to turn away few people, then u should be near one. Observe that this will almost surely mean that the average waiting time (see Equation (3) below) for a customer will be large. If we also have the objective of keeping customer waiting time low (see, for instance, Example 1 of Chapter IV, Section 14), it is not so easy to state the requirements of a well-designed system.

Another quantity of interest in the study of queues is the average length of the queue after the system has reached its equilibrium. From w we obtain the mean line length:

$$m = w_0 \cdot 0 + w_1 \cdot 1 + w_2 \cdot 2 + \ldots + w_n \cdot n$$

$$= \frac{r - p}{r\bar{r} - p\bar{p}s^n} (s + 2s^2 + 3s^3 + \ldots + (n - 1)s^{n-1} + n\bar{p}s^n).$$

If we assume that the traffic intensity is less than one, and not too near one, and n is large, this sum may be approximated by

$$m \approx \frac{r - p}{r\bar{r}} (s + 2s^2 + 3s^3 + \ldots).$$

Using the same method as for the mean service time, we find that

(3)
$$m \approx \frac{r - p}{r\bar{r}} \frac{s}{(1 - s)^2} = \bar{p} \frac{u}{1 - u}.$$

EXERCISES

In Exercises 1–3 consider the case $n = 4$, $p = .2$, and $r = .6$.

1. Find the transition matrix P and the fixed vector w. Check w against Equation (1).

2. Find the fraction of times in the long run that the server is free and the fraction of times that a customer is turned away.

3. Find the mean length of the line in equilibrium, and compare it to Equation (3).

4. Compute the mean length of the line in equilibrium for the case $p = .25$, $r = .50$, and compare the result to Equation (3).

5. Give an intuitive argument to show that if u is significantly greater than one, then the mean length of the line is near n. Check this in the case $p = .8, r = .4$.

Exercises 6–9 refer to the case $u = 1, n = 4$.

6. Set up P, making use of the fact that $p = r$.

7. Find the fixed vector w. What form will w take for general n if $u = 1$?

$$\left[Ans.\ w = \frac{1}{n - 1 + 2\overline{p}}\ (\overline{p}, 1, \ldots, 1, \overline{p}). \right]$$

8. Find the fraction of times in the long run that the server is free, and the fraction of times the line is full.

9. Find the mean length of the line in equilibrium. $[Ans.\ m = \frac{1}{2}n]$

10. Compare results for the cases (a) $p = .25, r = .50$, (b) $p = .8, r = .4$, (c) $p = r = .50$. Which seems most satisfactory?

When the probability that a customer finishes his service in a given time interval depends upon the number of previous time units of service he has had, the length of the line at each time is no longer a Markov chain. However, if the line is observed only when a customer finishes service, a Markov chain is obtained. The remaining exercises relate to this chain when the service time is a constant time of two units for each customer. The probability of an arrival is p for each time interval as before.

11. If the maximum line length is 4, show that the transition matrix is

$$P = \begin{array}{c} \\ 0 \\ 1 \\ 2 \\ 3 \\ 4 \end{array} \begin{array}{ccccc} 0 & 1 & 2 & 3 & 4 \\ \left(\begin{array}{ccccc} \overline{p}^2 & 2p\overline{p} & p^2 & 0 & 0 \\ \overline{p}^2 & 2p\overline{p} & p^2 & 0 & 0 \\ 0 & \overline{p}^2 & 2p\overline{p} & p^2 & 0 \\ 0 & 0 & \overline{p}^2 & 2p\overline{p} & p^2 \\ 0 & 0 & 0 & 1 & 0 \end{array} \right) \end{array}$$

12. Verify that the fixed vector is

$$w = \frac{1 - s}{1 - 2ps^3}\ (\overline{p}^2, 1 - \overline{p}^2, s, s^2, \overline{p}^2 s^3)$$

where $s = (p/\overline{p})^2$.

13. Give the form of the transition matrix for the general case where the maximum line allowed is n, and show that the fixed vector is

$$w = \frac{1 - s}{1 - 2ps^{n-1}}\ (\overline{p}^2, 1 - \overline{p}^2, s, s^2, \ldots, s^{n-2}, \overline{p}^2 s^{n-1})$$

where $s = (p/\overline{p})^2$.

14. Find the traffic intensity. For what value of r do we obtain the same intensity in the model discussed in this section?

15. Show that if $u < 1$, and n is sufficiently large, the fraction of time that the server is busy in the long run is again approximately u.

*11. Charge accounts

The purpose of this section is to analyze some actual data of the history of charge accounts in a certain department store.

A given customer may charge items over a period of months, and his payments often lag several months behind the charges. Our store classifies accounts according to the "oldest unpaid dollar." This is most simply explained in terms of an example. Suppose that a customer has three unpaid bills, $30 from two months ago, $50 from 3 months ago, and $16 left from a charge 5 months ago. This account is then classified as "5 months old." If he pays $10 on his account, this is credited against his oldest purchase, but this still leaves him with a 5-months-old account, since he owes $6 more on his 5-months-old debt. However, if he pays at least $16, the account is reclassified as "3 months old," if he pays at least $66 it is classified as "2 months old," and upon payment of $96 the account is labeled as "paid up." Any account that has 6-months-old items on it is labeled as a "bad debt" in our store.

We may analyze the change of status of any one account as a stochastic process. Until the account is settled, it is in one of six states, being labeled 0, 1, 2, 3, 4, or 5 months old. (A 0-months-old account has only current charges on it.) It can move up no more than one step, since debts age only one month during a month, but it may stay where it is or move down any number of steps. The account may be settled in one of two ways, either by being paid up, or by being written off as a bad debt. The former may occur at any time, but the latter only happens to an account that was 5 months old the step before.

Let us assume that it is reasonable to analyze this stochastic process as a Markov chain. Then we have an absorbing chain with the six nonabsorbing states 0, 1, 2, 3, 4, and 5, and the two absorbing states I (paid up) and II (bad debt). The transition probabilities for our store, as observed over a period of time, were as follows:

$$
P = \begin{array}{c} \\ I \\ II \\ \\ 0 \\ 1 \\ 2 \\ 3 \\ 4 \\ 5 \end{array}
\begin{array}{c} I \\ \hline 1 \\ 0 \\ \hline .21 \\ .14 \\ .13 \\ .11 \\ .15 \\ .08 \end{array}
\begin{array}{c} II \\ \hline 0 \\ 1 \\ \hline 0 \\ 0 \\ 0 \\ 0 \\ 0 \\ .21 \end{array}
\begin{array}{c} 0 \\ \hline 0 \\ 0 \\ \hline .67 \\ .19 \\ .08 \\ .01 \\ .02 \\ .01 \end{array}
\begin{array}{c} 1 \\ \hline 0 \\ 0 \\ \hline .12 \\ .44 \\ .20 \\ .04 \\ 0 \\ .02 \end{array}
\begin{array}{c} 2 \\ \hline 0 \\ 0 \\ \hline 0 \\ .23 \\ .36 \\ .17 \\ .09 \\ .01 \end{array}
\begin{array}{c} 3 \\ \hline 0 \\ 0 \\ \hline 0 \\ 0 \\ .23 \\ .29 \\ .20 \\ .10 \end{array}
\begin{array}{c} 4 \\ \hline 0 \\ 0 \\ \hline 0 \\ 0 \\ 0 \\ .38 \\ .42 \\ .11 \end{array}
\begin{array}{c} 5 \\ \hline 0 \\ 0 \\ \hline 0 \\ 0 \\ 0 \\ 0 \\ .12 \\ .46 \end{array}.
$$

By means of a computing machine we can compute the following approximate quantities:

$$
N = \begin{array}{c} 0 \\ 1 \\ 2 \\ 3 \\ 4 \\ 5 \end{array}
\begin{pmatrix}
3.68 & .94 & .40 & .16 & .11 & .03 \\
1.80 & 2.60 & 1.10 & .45 & .31 & .07 \\
1.33 & 1.20 & 2.34 & .97 & .66 & .15 \\
.86 & .74 & 1.08 & 2.24 & 1.53 & .34 \\
.73 & .55 & .85 & 1.07 & 2.53 & .56 \\
.47 & .39 & .46 & .67 & .82 & 2.04
\end{pmatrix}
\begin{array}{cccccc} 0 & 1 & 2 & 3 & 4 & 5 \end{array}
$$

$$
t = \begin{array}{c} 0 \\ 1 \\ 2 \\ 3 \\ 4 \\ 5 \end{array}
\begin{pmatrix}
5.33 \\ 6.32 \\ 6.65 \\ 6.80 \\ 6.29 \\ 4.85
\end{pmatrix},
\qquad
B = \begin{array}{c} 0 \\ 1 \\ 2 \\ 3 \\ 4 \\ 5 \end{array}
\begin{pmatrix}
.995 & .005 \\
.99 & .01 \\
.97 & .03 \\
.93 & .07 \\
.88 & .12 \\
.57 & .43
\end{pmatrix}
\begin{array}{cc} \text{I} & \text{II} \end{array}
$$

The interpretation of t is perfectly straightforward. It is the mean number of months until the account is settled one way or another. It is interesting to note that all of these times are around 5 or 6 months, and that there is surprisingly little variation.

Equally interesting is the interpretation of B. Let us look at the probabilities of absorption in II, i.e., the probability that the debt will turn out to be bad. It is not surprising that the older the debt is the higher the chance that it will turn bad. But it is interesting to see how rapidly the probability increases with age.

We will use this example to illustrate a new application of the N matrix. It is based on the following result.

Suppose that a number of individuals are started out in a Markov chain, at various states. We then introduce new individuals after one step, etc. At each stage we have all the previous individuals (unless they have been absorbed) and a number of new ones. We are interested in the number of individuals in a given state in the long run.

THEOREM. Suppose that P is an absorbing chain, and Q its nonabsorbing part. Suppose that at time 0 there are z_i individuals in state i. On all future steps x_i individuals are added at state i. Then introducing the vectors x, y, and z, with components x_i, y_i, and z_i, respectively,

(1)   the mean number of individuals in state i approaches y_i, where $y = xN$. This is independent of z.

(2) $z = y$ is the unique starting distribution under which the system is in equilibrium.

Proof. Let $z^{(n)}$ be the distribution after n steps. Then $z^{(n+1)} = z^{(n)}Q + x$. Thus, $z^{(1)} = zQ + x$, $z^{(2)} = zQ^2 + x(I + Q)$, etc. Thus we find that

$$z^{(n)} = zQ^n + x(I + Q + \ldots + Q^{n-1}).$$

Since Q^n tends to 0, so does zQ^n. And the series $I + Q + \ldots + Q^{n-1}$ converges to N, hence $z^{(n)}$ tends to xN, proving the first part of the theorem.

A system is said to be in equilibrium if $z^{(1)} = z$ (and hence all $z^{(n)}$ are the same). This means that

$$z = zQ + x \quad \text{or} \quad z(I - Q) = x.$$

But we can multiply this equation by $N = (I - Q)^{-1}$ to find that it is equivalent to $z = xN$. This proves the second part of the theorem.

Let us suppose that in our store m new accounts are opened each month. More precisely, m is the number of the customers who make a charge who do not have active balances, since once an account is paid up, a new charge is just like a new account in our model. Then $x = (m, 0, 0, 0, 0, 0)$. The theorem tells us that no matter what the present distribution of accounts is, this distribution will, in the long run, approach $xN = mN_1$, where N_1 is the first row of the N-matrix. Thus if 1000 new accounts are added to the list each month, then the long-run distribution will roughly be that of Figure 9. The total number of accounts on the books in the long run will be

Months old	0	1	2	3	4	5
Number of accounts	3680	940	400	160	110	30

Figure 9

the sum of these, or approximately 5320. Since a new account is expected to stay on the books for an average of 5.33 months (see t), we would expect 1000×5.330 accounts. This checks, except for a rounding error. Similarly, from B we find that approximately 995 accounts will be paid up each month, and that 5 will be declared bad.

Furthermore, the distribution of Figure 9 is an (approximate) equilibrium distribution for the model. That is, if the present distribution should happen to be exactly $y = xN$, and 1000 new accounts are added monthly, then the number of accounts of a given age will be the same in the future as it is now.

Let us now consider what we can say about the amounts of money tied up in charge accounts. The store finds over a long period that 0 or 1 month accounts average \$40, 2 or 3 months accounts average \$60, and older accounts average \$80. Weighting y by these amounts, we find that the amounts of money in the long run in accounts of various lengths are

$$(147.2, 37.6, 24, 9.6, 8.8, 2.4) \text{ thousands of dollars.}$$

Thus in the long run the store will have about \$229,600 tied up in charge accounts. This vector times R is (41864, 504). The first number gives the value of the accounts each month that are completely paid up, while the second gives the monthly average for debts newly declared bad.

EXERCISES

Exercises 1–6 refer to the following model. A retail store extends short-range credit to its customers. It classifies accounts according to the oldest unpaid dollar, but if there is any sum unpaid for three months, then the account is turned over to a collection agency. For simplicity we assume that if a customer pays an account, he pays all of it. Experience shows that there is probability $\frac{1}{2}$ that a current account is paid off, $\frac{1}{3}$ for a month-old account, and $\frac{1}{4}$ for a two-months-old account.

1. Set up the transition matrix. [*Hint:* There are 3 nonabsorbing and 2 absorbing states.]

2. Compute N, t, and B, and interpret the last two.

3. Suppose that each month 210 new accounts are added to the books. What will the long-range distribution of accounts be? How many will be paid off each month, and how many turned over to the collection agency in the long run?
   [*Partial Ans.* An average of 157.5 will be paid and 52.5 will be bad debts.]

4. Suppose that we modify the basic assumption that a customer always pays his entire account. Instead let us assume that he incurs a charge every month and is equally likely in any one month to pay off all of it or just the oldest charge (in which case the "age" of the account will be the same next month). Set up the new transition matrix.

5. Compute N, t, and B for the transition matrix of Exercise 4. Interpret t and B.

6. In Exercise 4 suppose again that 210 new accounts come in each month. Find the long-range distribution of accounts, the number paid off each month, and the number turned over to the collection agency.
   [*Partial Ans.* An average of 114 will be paid off and 96 will be bad debts.]

7. Suppose that P is an absorbing Markov chain. We move from state to state according to the transition probabilities, and receive a reward f_i when in state i. If we receive such a reward on all steps (including the original position), then show that using the column vectors f and g with components f_i and g_i respectively, the expected amount gained before reaching an absorbing state is g_i if we start in state i, where $g = Nf$.

Exercises 8–12 refer to the following model. A man buys a store. The profits of the store vary from month to month. For simplicity we suppose that he earns either \$5000 or \$2000 a month ("high" or "low"). The man may sell his store at any time, and there is a 10% chance of his selling during a high-profit month, and a 40% chance during a low-profit month. If he does not sell, with probability $\frac{2}{3}$ the profits will be the same next month, with $\frac{1}{3}$ they will change.

8. Set up the transition matrix. [*Hint:* There are two nonabsorbing and one absorbing states.]

9. Compute N, t, and B. Interpret t and B.

10. Set up the vector f (see Exercise 7) and compute g. Interpret the two components.

11. Suppose that the man switches his strategy, and sells the store during a high month with 40% probability, and in a low month with 10% probability. How are the answers in Exercises 8–10 changed?

12. In Exercise 11, how must the $5000 profit item change so that his expected total gain is the same whether he starts with a high or low month?

The remaining exercises refer to the following problem. A small college has a thesis requirement for graduation besides four years of course work that must be completed. Some of the students are able to finish their thesis by the end of the fourth year, but others require an additional year. Each year some of the students drop out, and if any student does not finish his thesis by the end of the fifth year he is dropped from the rolls. From his records the dean of the college estimates the probabilities of a given student's returning each year or dropping out to be as indicated below:

	1	2	3	4	5	D	G
1	0	.8				.2	0
2		0	.7			.3	0
3			0	.9		.1	0
4				0	.1	.1	.8
5					0	.2	.8

13. Set up the problem as an absorbing Markov chain with two absorbing states. Find Q and R.

14. Find directly Q^2, Q^3, and Q^4. Show that $Q^5 = 0$. Prove that $N = I + Q + Q^2 + Q^3 + Q^4$. Calculate N.

15. Compute t and B. Interpret each of these.

16. What is the probability that an entering student will graduate? What is the mean time that he is in college?   [*Ans.* .444; 2.91 years.]

*12. Further applications of Markov chains

Example 1. The techniques of the last section may be applied to the analysis of the work load in a given company. We will illustrate this in terms of a small company with four employees, consisting of a president, a vice-president, and a secretary for each. We suppose that some piece of business comes in, and we observe the way it passes through the company. It comes to a specific employee, who may carry out the task himself, or pass it on to another employee. We also allow for the possibility that the task may be laid aside and never carried out.

Adopting a Markov chain model, we will have four nonabsorbing states, corresponding to the four employees, P, V, PS, VS, and two absorbing states, I (done) and II (laid aside). The nature of the work is such that the president is equally likely to pass an item to his secretary or to the vice-president. The vice-president is in the habit of passing $\frac{3}{4}$ of his work on to his secretary. The remainder is equally likely to be done by him or laid aside. Each secretary does $\frac{3}{8}$ of her tasks personally, lays aside $\frac{1}{8}$, and the rest of the items are split evenly between items sent to the other secretary or returned to her boss for further instructions. The resulting R and Q matrices are:

$$
R = \begin{array}{c} \\ P \\ V \\ PS \\ VS \end{array} \begin{array}{cc} I & II \\ \begin{pmatrix} 0 & 0 \\ \frac{1}{8} & \frac{1}{8} \\ \frac{3}{8} & \frac{1}{8} \\ \frac{3}{8} & \frac{1}{8} \end{pmatrix} \end{array}, \qquad
Q = \begin{array}{c} \\ P \\ V \\ PS \\ VS \end{array} \begin{array}{cccc} P & V & PS & VS \\ \begin{pmatrix} 0 & \frac{1}{2} & \frac{1}{2} & 0 \\ 0 & 0 & 0 & \frac{3}{4} \\ \frac{1}{4} & 0 & 0 & \frac{1}{4} \\ 0 & \frac{1}{4} & \frac{1}{4} & 0 \end{pmatrix} \end{array}.
$$

From this we find:

$$
N = \begin{array}{c} \\ P \\ V \\ PS \\ VS \end{array} \begin{array}{cccc} P & V & PS & VS \\ \begin{pmatrix} 1.2 & .8 & .8 & .8 \\ .075 & 1.3 & .3 & 1.05 \\ .325 & .3 & 1.3 & .55 \\ .1 & .4 & .4 & 1.4 \end{pmatrix} \end{array}
$$

$$
t = \begin{array}{c} \\ P \\ V \\ PS \\ VS \end{array} \begin{pmatrix} 3.6 \\ 2.725 \\ 2.475 \\ 2.3 \end{pmatrix}, \qquad
B = \begin{array}{c} \\ P \\ V \\ PS \\ VS \end{array} \begin{array}{cc} I & II \\ \begin{pmatrix} .7 & .3 \\ .67 & .33 \\ .73 & .27 \\ .725 & .275 \end{pmatrix} \end{array}.
$$

Again, the interpretation of t and B is direct and enlightening. If we want to take some business to the company, it is safest to hand it to the president's secretary, and it is least likely to get done if it is handed to the vice-president. As far as time is concerned, it is fastest to hand it to one of the secretaries, and slowest to take it directly to the president.

Let us suppose that 60 items of business come in daily, and $\frac{2}{3}$ go to the president's secretary and the rest to the vice-president's secretary. Thus $x = (0, 0, 40, 20)$. We find

$$y = xN = (15, 20, 60, 50).$$

This is a fairly realistic distribution of labor in a small company. We should note in particular that although the president's secretary may complain that twice as much work comes to her each morning as to the other secretary, by the end of the day the vice-president's secretary has nearly as much work to do.

The total work load, measured in terms of number of items times people handling each item, is the sum of the components of y, or 145. We obtain the same answer by computing xt. And the components of $xB = (43.7, 16.3)$ show us that about 44 of the tasks get done and 16 are laid aside on an average day.

Suppose that the company wishes to redistribute its work load, by controlling where the 60 items of business are received. That is, the company wishes to specify y and to determine x suitably (subject to the condition that $xc = 60$). Since $y = xN$, we must have $x = y(I - Q)$. The restriction yields

$$xc = y(I - Q)c = 60.$$

Let $h = (I - Q)c$; then the company may specify any distribution of labor subject to the condition that $yh = 60$. In our example

$$h = (I - Q)c = \begin{pmatrix} 0 \\ \frac{1}{4} \\ \frac{1}{2} \\ \frac{1}{2} \end{pmatrix}.$$

Suppose that our company decides on a completely democratic work load, so that y should be of the form $y = (a, a, a, a)$. The restriction yields $(\frac{5}{4})a = 60$, or $a = 48$. That is, each employee will have a load of 48. Then

$$x = y(I - Q) = (36, 12, 12, 0).$$

Thus 60% of the work should come to the president, and 20% each to his secretary and to the vice-president.

Example 2. Let us study the changes in personnel need in a given department in a large industry. For simplicity we will consider only whether these needs increase, decrease, or stay the same in a given year. This will lead to a three-state regular Markov chain, with the three possibilities represented by $+$, $-$, and 0, respectively.

In our particular industry there is a fixed probability p that last year's trend will continue. Furthermore, the president of the company disapproves of a department's making a change in one year and making the opposite change in the next year. Thus our transition matrix has the form

$$P = \begin{array}{c} \\ + \\ 0 \\ - \end{array} \begin{array}{c} +\quad 0\quad - \\ \begin{pmatrix} p & q & 0 \\ r & p & s \\ 0 & q & p \end{pmatrix} \end{array}, \quad p + q = 1, \quad p + r + s = 1.$$

In particular, therefore, $q = r + s$. It is a simple computation to find the fixed vector $w = (r/2q, \frac{1}{2}, s/2q)$.

The components of the fixed vector give the long-run average for the number of years in which a certain trend holds. It is very interesting to note that although the numbers p, q, r, and s have not been specified, we can predict that in half the years the personnel need will be unchanged.

We can also compute the long-run rise or fall in employment, if we know the average size of an increase or decrease in staff. Suppose that in an increasing year an average of a people are hired, while in a decreasing year an average of b employees are let go. Then the average change in employment per year is

$$\left(\frac{r}{2q}\right) a + \left(\frac{1}{2}\right) 0 - \left(\frac{s}{2q}\right) b$$

or

$$(1) \qquad \frac{ra - sb}{2(r + s)}.$$

In particular, there will be a long-range expansion if $ra > sb$, a decline if $ra < sb$, and a rough equilibrium if $ra = sb$.

Example 3. A man is interested in investing in one of two companies. Of a potential of 12,000 customers, company A now attracts 10,000 while company B attracts only 2000. On the other hand, from a sample survey he notes that 20% of A's customers switch to B in the next month, while only 10% of B's customers switch to A. Assuming that this trend continues, what advice can we give him for his investment?

If we formulate the problem as a two-state Markov chain, we obtain the transition matrix

$$P = \begin{matrix} & A & B \\ A & \\ B \end{matrix} \begin{pmatrix} .8 & .2 \\ .1 & .9 \end{pmatrix}$$

and the fixed vector $w = (\frac{1}{3}, \frac{2}{3})$. This means that in the long run the customers will split $\frac{1}{3}$ to $\frac{2}{3}$, or 4000 for A and 8000 for B. But how long is this long run? Which is more important, the present highly favorable position of company A, or the long-run advantage of B? If we let $x = (10000, 2000)$, and if $x^{(n)}$ is the distribution of customers after n months, then $x^{(n)} = xP^n$. Or for computational purposes we let $x^{(0)} = x$, and $x^{(n+1)} = x^{(n)}P$, and we can compute the distributions step by step. The results for two years are shown in Figure 10. We

No. of Months	Number of Customers for	
	A	B
0	10,000	2,000
3	6,058	5,942
6	4,706	7,294
9	4,242	7,758
12	4,083	7,913
18	4,010	7,990
24	4,001	7,999

Figure 10

see that the "long-run" effect shows up very quickly. If the present trend continues, company B will catch up with A in about three months, far exceed it in six months, and then make small gains towards the 8000 figure. By the end of two years the long-range estimate is for all practical purposes exact. Hence the man should certainly invest in B. Of course in a more complex problem, with a larger number of states, the convergence to the long-range distribution will be slower, but the very same type of computation will show us the relative advantages of possible investments.

EXERCISES

Exercises 1–6 refer to the following problem. A car rental agency operates in three cities. The following table shows the transition of cars during a typical month:

	Go to A	Go to B	Go to C	Lost
From A:	.5	.2	.2	.1
From B:	.2	.5	.2	.1
From C:	.1	.3	.4	.2

For example, a car in city A stays there with probability .5, ends up at B or C with probability .2, and is lost (sold or destroyed) with probability .1.

1. Set up a Markov chain model.

2. Compute N, t, and B, and interpret your results.

3. Suppose that the agency supplies 70 new cars to each city each month. What is the long-run distribution of cars? How many are lost per month in the long run?   [*Ans.* A has 490, B 630, C 490; 210 are lost.]

4. How many cars should the agency supply to the various cities each month so that in the long run each city has 500 cars?
                                   [*Ans.* 100 to A and C, none to B.]

5. How many cars should the agency supply to the various cities each month so that in the long run there will be 600 cars in each of cities A and C, and 400 in B?   [*Ans.* Impossible.]

6. Prove that a long-run distribution vector y with components y_i is achievable if and only if $y \geq yQ$. Give a simple condition on Q for the possibility of achieving a uniform distribution (all y_i the same) in this type of model.

Exercises 7–10 refer to the following problem. Two manufacturers have competing products, A and B. If the present trend continues, customers will shift from product to product according to the following matrix:

$$
\begin{array}{c}
\begin{array}{cc} A & B \end{array} \\
\begin{array}{c} A \\ B \end{array}
\begin{pmatrix} .9 & .1 \\ .2 & .8 \end{pmatrix}.
\end{array}
$$

To improve his share of the market, manufacturer A considers the introduction of an additional product, which may be either X or Y. Pretesting indicates that the trends would then be as follows:

$$
\begin{array}{c}
\begin{array}{ccc} A & B & X \end{array} \\
\begin{array}{c} A \\ B \\ X \end{array}
\begin{pmatrix} .8 & .1 & .1 \\ .1 & .7 & .2 \\ .1 & .4 & .5 \end{pmatrix}
\end{array}
\quad \text{or} \quad
\begin{array}{c}
\begin{array}{ccc} A & B & Y \end{array} \\
\begin{array}{c} A \\ B \\ Y \end{array}
\begin{pmatrix} .8 & .1 & .1 \\ .1 & .6 & .3 \\ .2 & .2 & .6 \end{pmatrix}.
\end{array}
$$

7. Under the present arrangement, what fraction of the market would buy product A in the long run?

8. What fraction of the market could the manufacturer count on in the long run if he produced both A and X?

9. What fraction of the market could the manufacturer count on if he produced both A and Y?

10. Use the results of Exercises 7–9 to advise the manufacturer.

*13. Max and min operations; decision making

In Section 6 of Chapter I the problem of decision making was discussed. There a decision maker was confronted with the necessity of making choices among several alternatives, called *acts*. These alternatives are the ones that he can actually control. A complete set of acts is called a *strategy*.

Other alternatives, called *events*, are not under his control, but may be very important to him in making his decision. Examples of such events are: actual demand for a product that will be realized, the actual existence or nonexistence of oil below the surface where drilling is contemplated, the actual feasibility or nonfeasibility of the development of a certain component, and so on.

In business problems, decision makers want the results of their decisions to be optimal in some sense. For example, they want to *maximize profits*, or *minimize costs*, or *maximize efficiency*, or *minimize wastage*. In order to change such desires from mere vague wishes into methods for insuring the desired outcome, it is necessary to break down the problem into its component parts (perhaps by using a tree diagram as in Chapter I), and then assign numbers to the various parts of the analysis that measure the desired quantity. At the end of such an analysis, the decision maker is confronted with a vector of numerical outcomes, one for each of his strategies, and he will choose that strategy whose numerical outcome is optimum for his purposes.

Ordinarily, he will choose either the smallest or largest entry in the vector of outcomes. For this reason we recall the definition of two operations on vectors, the max and the min operations. (See Chapter III, Section 10.)

DEFINITION. Let $x = (x_1, \ldots, x_n)$ be a (row or column) vector. Then max $x = M$, where M is the *largest* component of x; and min $x = m$, where m is the *smallest* component of x.

Equivalent definitions for the max and min operators are given in Exercises 1 and 2.

Some examples of these operations are:

$$\max (4, 0, 3, -1, 4) = 4$$
$$\min (4, 0, 3, -1, 4) = -1$$
$$\max (-5, -2, -5, -3, -1) = -1$$
$$\min (-5, -2, -5, -3, -1) = -5.$$

When applied to sums, differences, and products of vectors these operations can be shown to satisfy various relations. We shall discuss three of these here and leave the rest for exercises. (See Exercises 11–20.)

The vector $-x$ has entries $(-x_1, \ldots, -x_n)$. If $x_i \leq M$ for all i, then $-x_i \geq -M$ for all i. Hence, it is clear that

(1) $$\max -x = -\min x.$$

It is similarly obvious that

(2) $$\min -x = -\max x.$$

If x and y are n-component row vectors, then

(3) $$\max (x + y) \leq \max x + \max y$$
(4) $$\min (x + y) \geq \min x + \min y.$$

We shall prove (3) and leave (4) for Exercise 11. To prove (3) let $x = (x_1, \ldots, x_n)$ and $y = (y_1, \ldots, y_n)$ and let $M = \max x$ and $N = \max y$. Then we know that

$$x_i \leq M \quad \text{for } i = 1, \ldots, n$$
and $$y_i \leq N \quad \text{for } i = 1, \ldots, n.$$

These imply that the ith component of $x + y$, which is $x_i + y_i$, satisfies

$$x_i + y_i \leq M + N \quad \text{for } i = 1, \ldots, n$$

which implies (3). It is interesting to find the conditions under which equality holds in (3); this question is discussed in Exercise 15.

Let us now apply these operations to some examples of decision problems.

Example 1. A building contractor plans to send a truck to one of three lumberyards to buy 5 units of wood, 3 units of glass, and 2 units of paint. The prices charged for these items at the three yards is given by the following table:

$$P = \begin{array}{c} \\ \text{Wood} \\ \text{Glass} \\ \text{Paint} \end{array} \begin{array}{ccc} L_1 & L_2 & L_3 \\ \begin{pmatrix} 10 & 11 & 9 \\ 8 & 7 & 9 \\ 15 & 13 & 12 \end{pmatrix} \end{array}.$$

To which yard shall he send the truck? If we let $x = (5, 3, 2)$ be the demand vector, then the components of xP will be the costs of buying at each of the lumberyards. It is easy to show that

$$xP = (104, 102, 96).$$

Since we want to minimize, we see that

$$\min xP = \min (104, 102, 96) = 96$$

is the minimum bill and is achieved by sending the truck to the third lumber-yard.

Example 1 is an example of *decision making under certainty*, which is the case when the outcome of each action is known in advance. If, instead, for some or all of the actions there is a whole set of possible events, and if the probability of occurrence of each such event is known, then we say that the problem is one of *decision making under uncertainty*. The remaining examples illustrate the latter kind of problem.

Example 2. Baker is a hot dog salesman who owns a stand near a baseball stadium. Each game he buys Q hot dogs. He makes a profit of 10 cents on each hot dog sold. The unsold hot dogs, if any, are returned to the manufacturer at a loss of 2 cents each to Baker. From his past records, Baker estimates the following probabilities for selling hot dogs:

d = number of hot dogs demanded   10   20   30   40   50
p = probability of that demand   .1   .2   .4   .2   .1

(For simplicity we assume his sales are always a multiple of 10.) How many hot dogs should Baker buy to maximize his net profit?

It is clear that Baker's net profit is

$$10Q \quad \text{if } Q \leq d$$

i.e., if the demand is sufficient to sell all hot dogs; and it is

$$10d - 2(Q - d) = 12d - 2Q, \quad \text{if } Q > d$$

i.e., if supply exceeds demand, since he makes 10 cents on those he sells and loses 2 cents on those he does not sell. If we compute his profit in cents for each of the ways he can order from 10 to 50 hot dogs and sell from 10 to 50 hot dogs we obtain the matrix M of Figure 11.

number of hot dogs demanded

		10	20	30	40	50
	10	100	100	100	100	100
number of	20	80	200	200	200	200
$M =$ hot dogs	30	60	180	300	300	300
ordered	40	40	160	280	400	400
	50	20	140	260	380	500

Figure 11

If we let p be the vector

$$p = \begin{pmatrix} .1 \\ .2 \\ .4 \\ .2 \\ .1 \end{pmatrix}$$

then we see that Mp is a column vector whose entries are Baker's expected profits for each number of hot dogs that he can order. We have

$$Mp = \begin{pmatrix} 100 \\ 188 \\ 252 \\ 268 \\ 260 \end{pmatrix}.$$

The action that we then expect Baker to take is to order 40 hot dogs to obtain the maximum profit of

$$\max Mp = 268.$$

If the number Baker expects to sell depends on the weather, then he may base his decision on the weather forecast. This problem is discussed in Exercise 6.

Example 3. In Example 2 of Section 6 of Chapter I we considered the case of an oil wildcatter who must decide whether to drill a well or to sell his rights in a given location. Suppose that he estimates on the basis of his past experience that the probabilities of the possible events following each of his actions are as indicated in Figure 12. Also indicated at the ends of the branches of

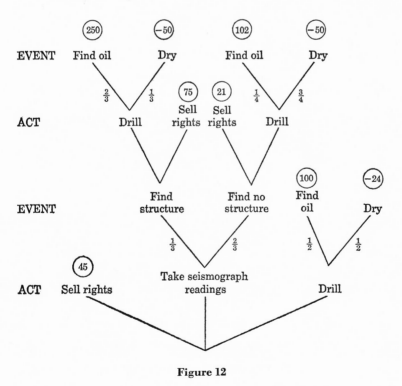

Figure 12

the tree are the payoffs in thousands of dollars expected for each terminal action. What shall the wildcatter do?

Here we have an example of a *multistage* decision problem under uncertainty. It is easy to solve the problem by working from the last decisions back to the first decisions. The solution is shown in Figure 13 where the optimal

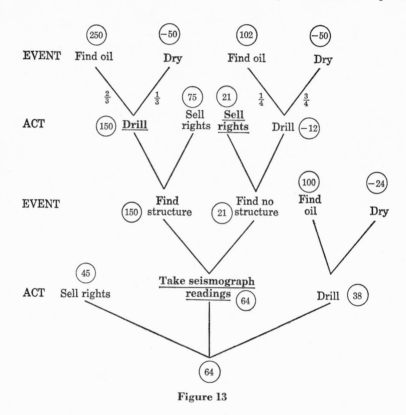

Figure 13

acts are indicated in boldface. Also in that figure the number next to each act or event represents the expected outcome of all later outcomes *assuming* that the optimal acts are always chosen. From Figure 13 we see that a description of the *optimal strategy*, which is the set of optimal acts, is as follows: "Take seismograph readings; if no structure is found, sell the rights; but if structure is found, drill." The expected outcome of this strategy is $64,000, as is indicated at the root of the tree.

In common parlance, decisions made under uncertainty are said to be calculated risks. The examples we discuss here show how to calculate risk (something that is not always done by people who speak of calculated risk).

EXERCISES

1. Let $x = (x_1, \ldots, x_n)$ be a row vector. Show that $M = \max x$ if and only if M satisfies the following two conditions:
   (a) $x_i \leq M$ for *all* i satisfying $i = 1, \ldots, n$
   (b) $x_i = M$ for *some* i.

2. Let x be as in Exercise 1. Show that $m = \min x$ if and only if m satisfies the following two conditions:
   (a) $x_i \geq m$ for *all* i satisfying $i = 1, \ldots, n$
   (b) $x_i = m$ for *some* i.

3. Apply the max and min operators to the following vectors:
   (a) $(-1, 0, 15, -7)$.
   (b) $(-\frac{1}{2}, -\frac{1}{3}, \frac{1}{3}, \frac{1}{5})$.
   (c) $(0, 0, 1.2, \frac{15}{7}, 3, .01)$.
   (d) $(-.1, -.03, -1.2, -.75, -1.37)$.
   [*Partial Ans.* (a) $m = -7$, $M = 15$, (b) $m = -\frac{1}{2}$, $M = \frac{1}{3}$].

4. In Example 1, suppose lumberyard 3 raises its prices on wood and glass to $10. Which lumberyard should the truck now go to?
   [*Ans.* Lumberyard 2.]

5. Rework Example 2 assuming that Baker loses 4 cents on each unsold hot dog instead of 2 cents.

6. In Example 2 suppose that Baker's records show the following probabilities of selling various numbers of hot dogs for fair, cloudy, and rainy days:

Number of hot dogs demanded	10	20	30	40	50
Probability of that demand on a fair day	.1	.1	.2	.3	.3
Probability of that demand on a cloudy day	.1	.2	.4	.2	.1
Probability of that demand on a rainy day	.4	.3	.2	.1	0

How many hot dogs should he order for each of the forecasts of fair, cloudy, and rain?
   [*Ans.* Fair: order 50; cloudy: order 40; rainy: order 30.]

7. Rework Exercise 6 if Baker's loss is 4 cents on each unsold hot dog.

8. Green is the owner of a small grocery. His estimates of the probabilities of selling various numbers of loaves of bread are as follows:

Number of loaves demanded	2	3	4	5	6	7
Probability of that demand	.1	.1	.2	.3	.2	.1

If he makes a profit of 8 cents on the loaves he sells and loses 3 cents on the loaves he returns, how many should he order?

9. In Example 3 suppose that if after taking seismograph readings, drilling, and finding oil the expected payoffs are $150 instead of $250. What should the company do?   ⌈*Ans.* Sell rights immediately.⌉

10. Deduce (2) from (1).

11. Show that (4) holds, namely

$$\min (x + y) \geq \min x + \min y.$$

12. Show that

$$\max (x - y) \leq \max x - \min y.$$

13. If $x \geq y$ means $x_i \geq y_i$ for each i, show that if $x \geq y$ then

$$\max x \geq \max y \quad \text{and} \quad \min x \geq \min y.$$

*14. If $\max x \geq \max y$ can we conclude that $x \geq y$?

*15. Show that

$$\max (x + y) = \max x + \max y$$

if and only if there is an i so that both $x_i = \max x$ and $y_i = \max y$.

*16. Under what circumstances does equality hold in the inequality of Exercise 11?

*17. If $x = (x_1, \ldots , x_n)$ is a vector, define

$$|x| = (|x_1|, \ldots , |x_n|)$$

i.e., we obtain $|x|$ from x by changing the signs of all components of x to plus. Now prove that
(a) $\max |x| \geq \max x$.
(b) $\min - |x| \leq \min -x$.

*18. For any vector x define

$$x^+ = \frac{x + |x|}{2}.$$

(a) Show that

$$x_i^+ = \begin{cases} x_i & \text{if } x_i \geq 0. \\ 0 & \text{if } x_i \leq 0. \end{cases}$$

(b) Prove that if $\max x \geq 0$, then $\max x = \max x^+$.
(c) Show that $\min x^+ \geq 0$.
(d) Show that $\min x^+ \geq \min x$. When does equality hold?

*19. Let x be an n-component row vector, y an n-component column vector with $x \geq 0$ and $y \geq 0$. Show that

$$(\min x)(\min y) \leq \frac{xy}{n} \leq (\max x)(\max y).$$

*20. When do equalities hold in the inequation of Exercise 19?

SUGGESTED READING

Birkhoff, G., and S. MacLane, *A Survey of Modern Algebra*, Macmillan, New York, 1941; revised edition, 1953, Chapters VII, VIII.

Johnson, R. E., *First Course in Abstract Algebra*, Prentice-Hall, New York, 1953.

Beaumont, R. A., and R. W. Ball, *Introduction to Modern Algebra and Matrix Theory*, Rinehart, New York, 1954, Chapters I, II, III, IV.

Hohn, Franz E., *Elementary Matrix Algebra*, Macmillan, New York, 1958.

Thrall, Robert M., and Leonard Tornheim, *Vector Spaces and Matrices*, Wiley, New York, 1957.

Kemeny, John G., and Snell, J. Laurie, *Finite Markov Chains*, Van Nostrand, Princeton, N.J., 1960.

Cyert, R. M., H. J. Davidson, and G. L. Thompson, "Estimation of the Allowance for Doubtful Accounts by Markov Chains," *Management Science*, **8** (1962), p. 287.

Vaszonyi, Andrew, *Scientific Programming in Business and Industry*, Wiley, New York, 1958, Chapter 13.

VI

Mathematics of Finance and Accounting

In this chapter we shall illustrate applications of finite mathematics to finance and accounting. The first six sections show how the mathematics of finite difference equations can be used as a method of evaluating investment alternatives when the consequences of the alternatives extend over a relatively long period of time. In Sections 7 through 9 matrices and flow diagrams are used to develop a system of bookkeeping which is different from, but analogous to, the traditional double entry system. The last three sections may be read independently of the first six.

1. A finite difference equation

We will consider a class of problems from the mathematics of finance, all of which may be treated by the same mathematical tool.

Example 1. A person has $5000 in a savings account. He adds $300 to this each year. The account earns 4% interest, compounded annually. How much money will he have at the end of 10 years?

The direct way of computing the answer to this problem is to find, step-by-

312

step, the balance after each year. Let x_j be the balance after j years. Suppose that we have already found this, how would we find the next year's balance? First of all, the balance x_j earns 4% interest during the year, which increases the balance by $.04x_j$. Second, $300 is added during the year. Hence

$$x_{j+1} = x_j + .04x_j + 300 = (1.04)x_j + 300.$$

We also know that $x_0 = 5000$ is the original balance, and from these two equations we may compute the balance x_{10} in ten steps.

Let us state the problem of Example 1 in more general form. Consider a fund with starting balance P, where $P \geq 0$. At the end of each period a "payment" p is made to the fund. (If the "payment" has the effect of increasing the balance, $p > 0$; if it decreases the balance, $p < 0$; if no payment is made, $p = 0$.) The balance bears interest in each period at a rate r. Then, as in Example 1, the next balance

$$x_{j+1} = x_j + rx_j + p.$$

Or, more simply,

(1) $$x_{j+1} = (1 + r)x_j + p, \qquad r > 0,$$

and

(2) $$x_0 = P.$$

Our problem is to find the final balance S after n periods. If we discover a formula for x_j, then $S = x_n$. As we shall see in the next section, this formulation has a wide variety of applications. It can be used, for example, to determine the accumulation of an annuity, or the accumulation of a deposit subject to compound interest, or the repayment of a loan or mortgage. In accumulating an annuity, for instance, we start with an initial balance $P = 0$, and make payments of amount $p > 0$ to the fund for n periods; we ask for the balance at the end of the nth period. If an amount $P > 0$ is deposited and earns compound interest, then $p = 0$ and we ask for the balance at the end of the nth period. In repaying a mortgage, P is the amount of the mortgage and the payments p reduce this amount, hence $p < 0$. The number of periods n is so selected that the mortgage is repaid at the end of it, hence $S = 0$.

We may also choose the periods to suit the problem. They may be monthly, quarterly, or annual computations. We simply let n be the number of months, or the number of quarters, or the number of years; r is the interest rate per period. So far we have assumed that the period of compounding and the period of payment are the same. For instance, we assumed in Example 1 that interest was compounded annually and that payments were made once a year. In Section 4 we shall show how to deal with situations where the period of compounding is different from the period of payment, but we shall assume in the remainder of this section and in Sections 2 and 3 that the two periods are the same.

Our immediate task is to find a general formula which will tell us the balance x_j after j periods. For this we must solve the *finite difference equation* (1), subject to the *initial condition* (2). It will be convenient to introduce new variables by the definition

(3)
$$y_j = \frac{x_j + \dfrac{p}{r}}{(1 + r)^j}.$$

The economic interpretation of the variables y_j is asked for in Exercise 9 of the next section. Let us now reformulate (1) in an equivalent form in terms of the variables y_j. For this we solve (3) for x_j as follows:

(4)
$$x_j = (1 + r)^j y_j - \frac{p}{r}$$

and substitute into (1).

$$(1 + r)^{j+1} y_{j+1} - \frac{p}{r} = (1 + r)\left[(1 + r)^j y_j - \frac{p}{r}\right] + p$$

$$= (1 + r)^{j+1} y_j - p\,\frac{1 + r}{r} + p$$

$$= (1 + r)^{j+1} y_j - \frac{p}{r}.$$

We now add p/r to both sides of the equation, and divide through by $(1 + r)^{j+1}$. This leads to the very simple equivalent form for (1),

(5)
$$y_{j+1} = y_j.$$

We must also reformulate (2) in terms of the y's. From (3) we find

$$y_0 = \frac{x_0 + \dfrac{p}{r}}{(1 + r)^0} = x_0 + \frac{p}{r},$$

remembering that any number to the 0th power is 1. Thus (2) becomes

$$y_0 = P + \frac{p}{r}.$$

However equation (5) states that each y is equal to the previous one; hence they must all be equal, so each has the same value as y_0. Thus our solution in terms of the y's is

(6)
$$y_j = P + \frac{p}{r}.$$

We can now obtain the desired formula by substituting this into (4). The solution of our general problem is

(7)
$$x_j = \left(P + \frac{p}{r}\right)(1 + r)^j - \frac{p}{r}.$$

Hence

(8) $$S = \left(P + \frac{p}{r}\right)(1 + r)^n - \frac{p}{r}.$$

For convenience in using this formula, Table III shows the values of $(1 + r)^n$ for several possible combinations of r and n.

Example 1 (continued) In our problem, $P = 5000$, $p = 300$, $n = 10$, and $r = .04$. Hence from (8),

$$S = \left(5000 + \frac{300}{.04}\right)(1.04)^{10} - \frac{300}{.04}.$$

From Table III we find that $(1.04)^{10} = 1.4802$; hence

$$S = (12,500)(1.4802) - 7500 = 11,002.50,$$

and our balance at the end of 10 years will be $11,002.50.

Example 2. We place $100 in a savings account. The bank pays 4% interest compounded quarterly, i.e., 1% interest is paid each quarter. What will our balance be after 5 years?

Here $P = 100$, $r = 1\% = .01$, and $n = 20$, since our basic period is $\frac{1}{4}$ of a year. Since there are no additional payments, $p = 0$. From (8) we find

$$S = (100 + 0)(1 + r)^{20} - 0 = 100(1 + r)^{20}.$$

From Table III we find that $(1 + r)^{20} = 1.2202$; hence $S = 122.02$. Our balance will be $122.02.

Example 3. Mr. Jones would like an income of $6000 per year, paid in equal annual installments for 20 years. How much must he invest in order to obtain this income if the invested balance earns 5% per year?

In this case P is the unknown amount to be invested. The yearly payments decrease the balance, hence $p = -6000$. Also, $n = 20$, $r = .05$, hence $p/r = -120,000$ according to the information given. If the capital invested is just barely enough to provide the desired installments, then S will be 0. Hence from (8) we obtain

$$0 = (P - 120,000)(1.05)^{20} + 120,000.$$

From Table III we find that $(1.05)^{20} = 2.6533$; hence

$$0 = 2.6533P - 198,396; \qquad P = \frac{198,396}{2.6533} = 74,773.$$

Thus $74,773 must be invested by Mr. Jones.

Example 4. A company can construct a factory building for $800,000, or it can lease an equivalent building for $75,000 a year for 25 years with the option of purchasing the building for $100,000 at the end of the 25-year period. The company can earn 14% per year before taxes on its invested capital. What should it do?

Here we want to make a comparison between a lump sum payment now and a series of equal payments over 25 years. We can proceed by either (a) finding the lump sum equivalent of the 25 lease payments, or (b) finding the equal annual installment equivalent of the $800,000 lump sum payment. We shall do the former, leaving the latter procedure as an exercise (see Exercise 10).

Let L be the lump sum equivalent of the rent-buy option. Then $p = -75,000$, $S = 100,000$, $n = 25$, and $r = .14$. However, there is a slight additional complication in that lease payments must be made at the beginning of each year rather than at the end. Hence we must take $P = L - 75,000$ and correct (8) by recalling that no payment is made at the end of the last period. Thus,

$$100,000 = \left(L - 75,000 - \frac{75,000}{.14}\right)(1.14)^{25} + \frac{75,000}{.14} + 75,000.$$

From Table III we find that $(1.14)^{25} = 26.462$. Solving for L we obtain $L = \$591,414$.

Thus $591,414 invested in a fund which earned interest at the rate of the company's own operations would produce earnings sufficient to meet the lease payments and purchase the building after 25 years. For $591,414, the company would have exactly the same facilities which would cost $800,000 if the company were to build. Clearly, leasing is preferable.

EXERCISES

1. If $20,000 is invested in a company that earns 6% per year on invested capital, and if the earnings are reinvested, how much is the investment worth at the end of 10 years?

2. If Mr. Jones lends Mr. Smith $2000 at 6% interest compounded quarterly, (i.e., 1.5% interest is paid each quarter) how much must Mr. Smith pay at the end of 6 years?   [*Ans.* $2859.]

3. An annuity is set up into which $100 per year is paid for 16 years. If the money paid in bears interest at 5% per year, what will be the value of the annuity at the end of the sixteenth year?

4. A company can invest in a project which will raise its revenues by $10,000 per year. The project costs $30,000 initially and has an anticipated life of 4 years. If the company can earn 20% on capital invested in other projects, should it invest in the proposed project?

5. In Exercise 4 what is the present value of a fund that earns 20% on its balance each year, from which $10,000 a year must be paid for 4 years, after which the balance of the fund will be 0?   [*Ans.* $25,887.]

6. In Exercise 5 prepare a schedule showing the balance of the fund, the amount it earns each year, and the amount it pays out each year. Prepare a flow diagram showing how to compute the balance at the end of each year.

7. In Exercises 4–5, find the present value of the fund by working backwards from the facts that (a) the balance of the fund at the end of year 4 is 0; (b) the fund pays out $10,000 per year; (c) neglecting the $10,000 paid out each year, the balance at the beginning of a year is $1/1.2$ times the

balance at the end. Prepare a flow diagram to compute the present value of the fund.

8. A sum of money deposited at compound interest earns interest on the previous period's balance. A sum deposited at *simple* interest, however, earns interest only on the original deposit, and not on any additions to the original deposit which result from interest payments. Write the difference equation for the balance in the jth period of a sum P deposited at simple interest at the rate r. Solve the difference equation and write a flow diagram for computing its values.

[*Partial Ans.* $x_j = x_{j-1} + r\,x_0$, where $x_0 = P$.]

9. Recompute Example 1 assuming that the $5000 original deposit as well as the $300 annual deposits earn 4% simple interest rather than compound interest. Over the 10-year period, how much extra interest did the compounding yield?

10. In Example 4 suppose the $800,000 were to be invested in a fund from which 25 equal annual installments would be made starting at the *beginning* of year 1. If the fund earns 14% per year on its current balance, and if we want $100,000 left at the *end* of the twenty-fifth year, what size payments will be made? Compare these with the lease payments. To what decision does this method of analysis lead?

11. Show that the following flow diagram describes the computational process needed to compute the entries of Table III.

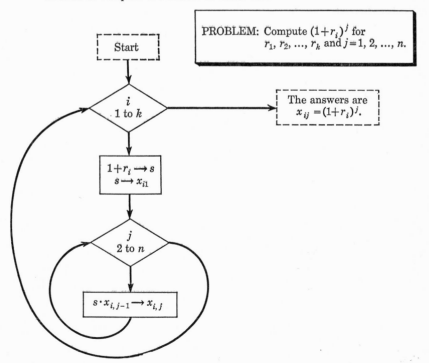

12. Draw a flow diagram for computing $x_1, x_2, \ldots, x_n$ if $x_0 = P$ and $x_{j+1} = (1 + r)x_j + p$, where r, n, p, and P are given numbers.

13. Consider the sequence $1, \frac{2}{3}, \frac{4}{9}, \frac{8}{27}, \frac{16}{81}, \ldots$. Let x_j be the sum of the first j terms of the sequence. Show that

$$x_{j+1} = x_j + \left(\tfrac{2}{3}\right)^j$$

subject to $x_1 = 1$. Show that the solution is

$$x_j = 3[1 - \left(\tfrac{2}{3}\right)^j]$$

by showing that it satisfies both the difference equation and the initial condition $x_1 = 1$. Calculate x_5 (a) by summing the terms in the sequence and (b) by using the formula.

14. Generalize the result of Exercise 13 by letting x_j be the sum of the first j terms of any geometric sequence $a, ar, ar^2, ar^3, \ldots$, where $r \neq 1$. Show that

$$x_{j+1} = x_j + ar^j$$

subject to $x_1 = a$. Show that the solution is

$$x_j = a \frac{1 - r^j}{1 - r}.$$

Derive the formula for x_j by first writing out the sum which it represents, then writing out the sum for rx_j, and finally performing the subtraction $x_j - rx_j$ term by term.

15. Consider the sequence $1, 2, 3, 4, \ldots$. Let x_j be the sum of the first j terms of the sequence. Show that x_j satisfies the difference equation

$$x_{j+1} = x_j + j + 1$$

subject to $x_1 = 1$. Show that the solution is

$$x_j = \tfrac{1}{2}j(j + 1).$$

Derive the formula for x_j by first writing the sum which it represents term by term in ascending order, then writing the sum term by term in descending order, and adding term by term.

16. Let x_j be the sum of the first j terms of the sequence $r, 2r^2, 3r^3, \ldots, r \neq 1$ (see Chapter V, Section 10). Show that the resulting difference equation

$$x_{j+1} = x_j + (j + 1)r^{j+1}$$

with initial condition $x_1 = r$ has as its solution

$$x_j = \frac{r}{(1 - r)^2} [1 - r^j(1 + j - rj)].$$

Derive the formula for x_j by writing the sum it represents and also by writing the sum for rx_j, performing the subtraction $x_j - rx_j$ term by term, and finally applying the results of Exercise 14.

17. Let x_j equal

$$a^{i-1} + a^{i-2}c + a^{i-3}c^2 + \ldots + a^2c^{i-3} + ac^{i-2} + c^{i-1}.$$

Show that x_j satisfies the difference equation

$$x_{j+1} = ax_j + c^j$$

with initial condition $x_1 = 1$. Show that the solution is

$$x_j = \frac{a^j - c^j}{a - c}.$$

Derive the formula for x_j by writing out the sum which it represents and also by writing out the sum for cx_j/a and performing the subtraction $x_j - cx_j/a$ term by term.

2. Some important special cases

In Section 1 we solved the following problem: If P dollars are invested, interest is paid on the current balance at a rate of r per period for n periods, and a sum p is added to the fund each period, then the final balance S is given by (8). Also, we could rewrite the result as

$$(9) \qquad S = (1 + r)^n P + \left[\frac{(1 + r)^n - 1}{r}\right]p.$$

In Section 1 we assumed that r, n, P, and p were known, and that S was to be found. We will again assume that the interest rate r and the number of periods n are known, but we will consider various assumptions concerning S, P, and p. Particularly interesting and useful formulas are obtained if one variable is known to be 0, another is also known—but not 0—and the third is to be found. The solutions of (9) for the six such possible combinations are shown in Figure 1. Each of these is a frequently used formula in the mathematics of finance. However it is important to recall that each is but a special case of (9), and the solutions of our problems could be obtained directly from (9) without the use of Figure 1.

The expressions in brackets in the formulas of Figure 1 are called investment formula "factors." Thus $(1 + r)^n$ is the single payment compound amount factor, $[(1 + r)^n - 1]/[r(1 + r)^n]$ is the uniform payment present value factor, etc. In books which deal with this subject, these six factors are sometimes tabulated in terms of r and n (see, for example, Grant and Ireson, *Principles of Engineering Economy*). A table of $(1 + r)^n$, however, is actually sufficient to permit the computation of each of the factors with ease.

Nevertheless, for reasons that will be made apparent in the next section, the present value factor has been tabulated separately as Table IV. This makes the computation of the various factors easier still. If we represent the numbers tabulated in Tables III and IV for given r and n by [III] and [IV], respectively, then the investment formula factors are related to these tabulated values according to Figure 2.

Name of Formula	Zero Variable	Given Variable	Unknown Variable	Formula
Single payment compound amount:	p	P	S	$S = [(1 + r)^n]P$
Single payment present value:	p	S	P	$P = \left[\dfrac{1}{(1 + r)^n}\right]S$
Uniform payment compound amount:	P	p	S	$S = \left[\dfrac{(1 + r)^n - 1}{r}\right]p$
Uniform payment sinking fund:	P	S	p	$p = \left[\dfrac{r}{(1 + r)^n - 1}\right]S$
Uniform payment capital recovery:	S	P	p	$p = -\left[\dfrac{r(1 + r)^n}{(1 + r)^n - 1}\right]P$
Uniform payment present value:	S	p	P	$P = -\left[\dfrac{(1 + r)^n - 1}{r(1 + r)^n}\right]p$

Figure 1

Factor	Relation to Tabulated Factors
Single payment compound amount	[III]
Single payment present value	1/[III]
Uniform payment compound amount	[III]·[IV]
Uniform payment sinking fund	1/([III]·[IV])
Uniform payment capital recovery	1/[IV]
Uniform payment present value	[IV]

Figure 2

Example 1. In Example 3 of Section 1, p was given and we wanted to find the value of P that made $S = 0$ after $n = 20$ years. This is, therefore, a uniform payment present value problem. Using Table III in conjunction with the formula of Figure 1, with $p = -6000$, $r = .05$, $n = 20$, we obtain

$$P = \left[\frac{(1.05)^{20} - 1}{.05(1.05)^{20}}\right]6000 = \left[\frac{2.6533 - 1}{(.05)(2.6533)}\right]6000 = 74,773$$

as before. Using Table IV, we look up the uniform payment present value factor for $r = .05$, $n = 20$, obtaining 12.46, and compute

$$P = (12.462)(6000) = 74,772,$$

which agrees with the previous result except for rounding.

Example 2. In Example 2 of the previous section we were given $P = 100$ and wanted to find S after $n = 20$ quarter years, when no further payments were made ($p = 0$). From Figure 1 this is a single payment compound amount problem, the solution to which is given by

$$S = (1 + r)^n P$$
$$= (1 + .01)^{20}(100)$$
$$= 122.02$$

as before.

Example 3. It is desired to repay a loan of $100,000 in 12 equal annual installments, where the loan earns interest at the rate of 6% per year. How much should be paid each year? In this problem $S = 0$, $P = $100,000, and p is unknown. It is, therefore, a capital recovery problem. From Table III we find $(1.06)^{12} = 2.0122$, and apply the formula of Figure 1 to obtain

$$p = \left[\frac{(.06)(2.0122)}{2.0122 - 1} \right](-100,000)$$

$$(.11928)(-100,000) = -11,928.$$

Thus payments of $11,928 per year for 12 years will liquidate a fund of $100,000 that earns 6% per year. Hence $11,928 per year will repay a $100,000 loan in 12 years at 6% interest per year.

Using Table IV, we find the uniform payment present value factor for $n = 12, r = .06$ is 8.3838. From Figure 2 we conclude that

$$p = \frac{1}{8.3838}(-100,000) = -11,928,$$

as before.

It should be observed that the single payment compound amount and present value formulas can be applied to each of a series of nonuniform payments.

Example 4. A machine can be purchased for $10,000. It will permit a company to manufacture a new product which is expected to increase the company's profits by the following amounts over the next 5 years:

Year	Profit Increase
1	$1000
2	3000
3	4000
4	4000
5	5000

After 5 years the machine will be scrapped. The company can earn 10% per year on alternative investments. Should the machine be purchased?

We may think of this as a series of single payment present value problems. Let S_j be the balance in a fund at the end of the jth year, and let us find the value of P_j which, if invested now, will accumulate to S_j in j years at 10% interest. Clearly,

$$P_j = \frac{S_j}{(1 + .10)^j}.$$

If we consider 5 such funds, then the present value of the sum of them will be $P = P_1 + P_2 + P_3 + P_4 + P_5$. If the present value P exceeds the present cost of the machine ($10,000), the machine should be acquired; otherwise it should not. We summarize the necessary calculations in Figure 3.

j	S_j	P_j
1	1000	909
2	3000	2,479
3	4000	3,005
4	4000	2,732
5	5000	3,105
		12,230 = P

Figure 3

Since $P = \$12,230 > \$10,000$, the machine should be purchased.

EXERCISES

1. How much must be paid back on a loan of $1000 for 2 years if 6% interest a year is charged and (a) if the loan is repaid at the end of the 2-year period? (b) if the loan is repaid in two equal annual installments?

2. A man has a son who will enter college in 15 years. He wants to set up an annuity that will yield $5000 towards the expenses of the college education at that time. If an insurance company will pay him 4%, compounded quarterly (i.e., 1% per quarter on his balance), what must his quarterly payments be?   [*Ans.* $61.22.]

3. Find the uniform payment which has to be made each year to accumulate to $1,000,000 in 30 years if one can earn 30% per year on the balance.

4. An investment of $100,000 will yield savings for a company of $20,000 per year for 10 years. If the company can earn 10% per year on investment of its capital elsewhere, find the net present value of this investment; i.e., the present value of the savings less the cost of the investment. Should the investment be made?   [*Ans.* $22,890; yes.]

5. What sum of money invested today will yield $10,000 thirty years from now if interest is paid at 6% per year and is compounded quarterly (i.e., $1\frac{1}{2}$% interest is paid each quarter)?

6. Compute the present value of $10,000 to be received in 30 years, if interest of 6% per year is compounded (a) annually, (b) quarterly, or (c) monthly.

7. An investment of $100,000 will yield savings of $25,000 a year for 5 years, and $10,000 per year for an additional 5 years. If a company can earn 14% per year on alternative investments, calculate the net present value of the investment (a) by adding the present value of each year's savings and subtracting the initial investment cost; (b) by taking the uniform payment

present value for the first five years and for the second five years, discounting the latter value to the present, adding the results, and subtracting the initial investment cost; (c) by taking the present value of a series of uniform $10,000 payments for 10 years, adding to this the present value of a series of uniform payments of $15,000 for 5 years, and subtracting the initial investment cost. Justify these three methods, and show that they all yield the same answer. Should the investment be made?

8. An initial deposit P which earns interest at a rate r per year will yield a stream of payments $p = Pr$ forever. Thus, if one can obtain earnings at a rate r on capital invested elsewhere, the present value of a stream of earnings of p per year forever (a *perpetuity* of p per year) is $P = p/r$. Verify this by showing that as n approaches infinity the present value formula approaches $P = -p/r$.

9. Using the results of Exercise 8, give an economic interpretation to the variable

$$y_j = \frac{x_j + \dfrac{p}{r}}{(1 + r)^j}$$

defined in equation (3) of Section 1. Use this economic interpretation to show why $y_{j+1} = y_j$.

10. Machine A can be purchased for $6000. It will produce earnings of $1000 per year for 10 years, after which it will be sold. Salvage value will be $2000 at that time. Should the machine be purchased if 10% can be obtained on alternative investments? What is the net present value of purchasing?   [*Ans.* Yes; $916.]

11. Consider Machine B. It can be purchased to perform the same task as Machine A described in the preceding exercise. It costs $10,000, will last 14 years, will produce earnings of $1500 per year, and will have no salvage value at the end of its life.

    (a) If the choice were only between purchasing Machine B and doing nothing, would it pay to purchase Machine B? What is its net present value?   [*Ans.* Yes; $1050.]

    (b) Between Machines A and B, what is the better investment? Why?

12. A machine is purchased for $20,000. After 5 years its salvage value will be $8000 at which time a new $20,000 machine will have to be purchased. If 10% can be earned on capital invested elsewhere, what uniform series of payments must be made into a sinking fund to accumulate the $12,000 needed in addition to the salvage value of the old machine in order to purchase the new machine at the end of the fifth year?

13. An oil well is currently producing earnings at the rate of $100,000 per year. The well is believed to have reserves which will last an additional 10 years at the present rate of recovery. For a cost of $160,000, a pump can be installed that will double the rate of recovery (and thereby halve the anticipated life of the well).

(a) Find the incremental effect on earnings over the next 10 years of installing the new pump now.

(b) Find the net present value of the pump if capital can be invested in alternative projects that will return 10% per year. Should the investment be made? [*Ans.* −$16,300; no.]

(c) Same as (b) if alternative investments return 20% per year.
[*Ans.* +$18,870; yes.]

(d) Same as (b) if alternative investments return 50%.
[*Ans.* −$9,210; no.]

14. A trucking company purchases trucks for $10,000 each. The annual operating cost and the salvage value for a truck j years old is given in the table below for $j = 1, 2, 3, 4$, and 5.

j	Annual Operating Cost	Salvage Value
1	$1500	$6000
2	2000	5000
3	2500	4000
4	3000	2000
5	4000	1000

The annual operating cost may be treated as occurring at the *end* of the year. Consider a policy of replacing the trucks every 3 years. If the company can earn 20% on invested capital, show that a fund of $17,940 will (a) provide the annual operating costs at the end of years 1, 2, and 3; (b) provide the $6000 capital needed in addition to the salvage value of the old truck to buy a new truck for $10,000 at the end of year 3; (c) have a balance of $17,940 at the end of year 3.

15. Generalize the result of Exercise 14 as follows: An asset has a cost of C. Its salvage value at the end of j years is S_j, where $0 \leq S_j \leq C$ and $S_{j+1} \leq S_j$. Operating expenses incurred at the end of the jth year are given by p_j, where $p_{j+1} \geq p_j > 0$. Invested capital earns interest at a rate r per year. How large a sum P must be invested at the beginning to meet all the operating expenses, to allow replacement of the asset at the end of n years, and still have P left over at the end of n years? Show that the solution of this problem is characterized by the following equations for the balance x_j after j years.

(i) $$x_0 = P$$
(ii) $$x_{j+1} = (1 + r)x_j - p_{j+1}$$
(iii) $$x_n = C - S_n + P.$$

16. In Exercise 15, let $q_j = p_j/(1 + r)^j$ be the present value of the operating expense in year j. Prove that the solution of (i) and (ii) is given by

(iv) $$x_j = (1 + r)^j[P - (q_1 + q_2 + \ldots + q_j)].$$

17. From (iii) and (iv) in Exercises 15 and 16, show that the sum to be invested is

(v) $P = \dfrac{1}{(1 + r)^n - 1} [C - S_n + (1 + r)^n(q_1 + q_2 + \ldots + q_n)]$.

Obtain the result of Exercise 14 by use of this formula.

18. Use formula (v) to find the necessary investment P in Exercise 14 if $n = 1, 2, 4$, and 5. What is the optimal replacement policy?
[*Partial Ans.* For $n = 2$, $P = \$20,000$; for $n = 4$, $P = \$18,138$.]

19. Given that the present value of a payment $-p$ to be made j years hence is $-p/(1 + r)^j$, derive the uniform payment present value formula for a series of n such payments that start in one time period from now, by summing the appropriate series using the results of Exercise 14, Section 1.

20. Given that the compound amount of a payment p is $p(1 + r)^i$ j years after the date of payment, derive equation (8) by summing the appropriate series, using the results of Exercise 14, Section 1.

3. Solving for interest rate and number of payments

In equation (9) there are five variables: P, S, p, n, and r. In Section 2 we have shown, given r and n and two of the three other variables, how to find the fifth variable. In this section we shall assume that P, S, p, and either r or n are given and shall discuss methods of finding the other. We shall also give interpretations of these solutions to equation (9).

We start first with the problem of finding n given P, S, p, and r. To do this we solve (9) for $(1 + r)^n$, thereby obtaining

$$(10) \qquad (1 + r)^n = \frac{Sr + p}{Pr + p}, \qquad r > 0.$$

We can readily find the conditions under which (10) has a solution. For fixed r, the left-hand side of (10) increases as n increases. Since $(1 + r)^0 = 1$, as n increases $(1 + r)^n$ takes on all values greater than 1. Hence (10) will have a solution $n > 0$ provided the right-hand side is greater than 1, i.e.,

$$(11a) \qquad \frac{Sr + p}{Pr + p} > 1.$$

Recalling the rules for working with inequalities, it is easy to show that this condition will be satisfied under the following circumstances: either

$$(11b) \qquad P + \frac{p}{r} > 0 \quad \text{and} \quad S > P$$

or

$$(11c) \qquad P + \frac{p}{r} < 0 \quad \text{and} \quad S < P.$$

Either of these conditions will guarantee a solution $n > 0$, but the solution will usually not be an integer.

That these conditions make economic sense can be seen by observing that p/r is (see Exercise 8, Section 2) the present value of a perpetuity of p per year at interest r per year. Thus, if $P + (p/r) < 0$, the balance of the fund can never increase, and therefore we can never obtain a final balance S greater than the initial balance P. Accordingly, we must have $S < P$, as given by (11c). A similar argument applies to the condition (11b)·

Example 1. A mortgage of $30,000 is to be paid off in annual installments of $2000. If interest of 5% per year is charged on the unpaid balance, how many years will it take until the unpaid balance is $10,000? We are given that $P = 30{,}000$, $S = 10{,}000$, $r = .05$, and $p = -2000$. We must find n.

The problem has a solution since

$$P + \frac{p}{r} = \$30{,}000 - \frac{\$2000}{.05} = -\$10{,}000 < 0$$

and

$$S = \$10{,}000 < P = \$30{,}000$$

so that (11c) is satisfied. We compute

$$\frac{Sr + p}{Pr + p} = \frac{(10{,}000)(.05) + (-2000)}{(30{,}000)(.05) + (-2000)} = 3$$

and find in Table III that

$$(1 + .05)^{20} = 2.6533 \quad \text{and} \quad (1 + .05)^{25} = 3.3864.$$

Interpolating roughly, we find n is about 22 years.

Example 2. A machine can be purchased that will produce earnings of $1000 per year. The machine costs $6000 and will have a salvage value at the end of its useful life of $2000 regardless of the number of years that it is used. If 12% can be earned on alternative investments, how many years must the machine last to make it equally attractive with alternative investments? We can phrase the problem as follows: $P = 6000$, $p = -1000$, $r = .12$ per year; in how many years will the balance become $S = 2000$?

There is a solution since

$$P + \frac{p}{r} = \$6000 + \frac{-\$1000}{.12} = -\$2333 < 0$$

and $S = 2000 < P = 6000$, so that (11c) is satisfied. We compute

$$\frac{Sr + p}{Pr + p} = \frac{(2000)(.12) - 1000}{(6000)(.12) - 1000} = 2.71$$

and find in Table III that

$$(1 + .12)^{8} = 2.4760 \quad \text{and} \quad (1 + .12)^{9} = 2.7731.$$

Hence n is just less than 9 years. If the machine lasts more than 9 years, it is more attractive than alternative investments; if it lasts less than 9 years, it is less attractive than alternative investments.

In decision problems in which a choice is made whether or not to invest in an asset and in which P, S, p, and r are given, the n which satisfies (10) is called the *payback period*. It is a kind of "break-even value." If the anticipated life of the asset exceeds the payback period, the asset is preferable to alternative investments and should be purchased; if it is less, the asset should not be purchased.

We now return to (10), and assume that r is the unknown quantity. This is a harder problem than those previously considered, and first we will solve the important special case in which $S = 0$. Here we have an original principal P which is reduced to 0 (as in the case of a loan), and hence p is always negative. Let $Z = -P/p$ be the number of payments needed if no interest were charged. We then deduce from (10) that

$$(12) \qquad Z = -\frac{P}{p} = \frac{(1+r)^n - 1}{r(1+r)^n}.$$

However, the right-hand side of (12) is the present value factor, which is given in Table IV. Hence the problem may be solved by means of that table. We know Z and n. We look in the row corresponding to n until we find Z, which gives us the desired r; or, if Z does not occur exactly in this row, we perform a rough interpolation. Since the present value decreases with r, the answer will be unique.

Example 3. A bank offers to make an "auto-loan" of $2000 for 2 years, and it sets the monthly payments at $92.62. What interest is the bank charging? Here $Z = 2000/92.62 = 21.6$, and $n = 24$ months. In the line $n = 24$ of Table IV we find that $r = .0075$ yields 21.89 while $r = .01$ yields 21.24. Roughly interpolating we obtain $r = .0086$, or an interest rate of .86% a month (compounded monthly), or more than 10% annually. For the effective annually compounded annual interest rate, see Exercise 1 of Section 4.

If S is not 0, then we must adopt a trial-and-error method. We must substitute a sequence of values for r in (10), compute the ratio of the two sides for each r, and find the $r > 0$ for which the ratio is 1.

Example 4. In Example 2, suppose the machine will last 7 years and it is desired to find the rate of interest that will permit the fund, starting with a balance of $6000, to pay out $1000 for 7 years and end with a balance of $2000. In Figure 4 are listed values of $(1+r)^7$ and

$$\frac{Sr+p}{Pr+p} = \frac{2000r - 1000}{6000r - 1000}$$

for various values of $r \geqslant 0$.

r	$(1+r)^n$	$\dfrac{Sr+p}{Pr+p}$	$\dfrac{Sr+p}{Pr+p} \div (1+r)^n$
0	1.000	1.000	1.00
.02	1.149	1.091	.95
.04	1.316	1.211	.92
.06	1.504	1.375	.91
.08	1.714	1.615	.94
.09	1.828	1.783	.98
.10	1.949	2.000	1.03
.12	2.211	2.714	1.23

Figure 4

Hence the required interest rate is between 9% and 10%.

When P is the price paid for a bond, S is the maturity value of the bond, p is the periodic coupon payment, and n is the number of periods to maturity, the interest rate r calculated above is called the *yield* per period to maturity. We shall give an example of a bond yield calculation after having discussed nominal and equivalent interest rates (see Example 4, Section 4).

In investment decision problems, where P is the price paid for an asset, S is its salvage value n years hence, and p is the annual earnings of the asset (see Example 4), the interest rate r which satisfies (10) or (11) is called the *internal rate of return*. Like the payback period, it is a kind of break-even value. If the internal rate of return on an asset is greater than the rate which can be earned on other investments, then the asset should be acquired. Otherwise it should not be acquired.

Even when payments are not uniform, or when an investment is made in some way other than a lump sum at the beginning, we may *define* the internal rate of return as that interest rate r which makes the net present value of all the cash flows (investment, annual returns, and salvage) equal to zero. Under some circumstances there will be *two* rates of return which satisfy this condition (see Exercise 2). To find the internal rate of return under these conditions we must almost always proceed by trial-and-error.

Example 5. By investing $3400 now and $2000 two years from now, earnings of $1000 + 200j$ dollars a year can be obtained in the jth year, where $j = 1, 2, \ldots, 6$, after which the investment will earn no more and have no salvage value. What is the internal rate of return?

In Figure 5 we show the net cash flows in years 0 through 6.

Year	Net Cash Flow
0	$-3400
1	+1200
2	-600
3	+1600
4	+1800
5	+2000
6	+2200

Figure 5

r	Present Value of Net Cash Flow
.001	$4800
.05	3271
.10	2111
.20	518
.25	-36
.30	-479
.35	-839
.40	-1133

Figure 6

In Figure 6 we show the present value of these cash flows for various values of $r \geqslant 0$. The internal rate of return is just below 25%.

EXERCISES

1. In Exercise 4 of Section 2, find the payback period and the internal rate of return.

2. In Exercise 13 of Section 2, find the internal rates of return. Show that there are two such rates. Interpret your results.

3. In Exercise 13 of Section 2, is there a "payback period?" Discuss.

4. In Exercise 10 of Section 2, find the payback period under the assumption that the machine will have a salvage value of $2000 regardless of when it is retired. Under the same assumption about the salvage value, find the internal rate of return.

5. In Exercise 11 of Section 2, find the payback period and the internal rate of return. Compare the ranking of the machines in Exercises 10 and 11 of that section when one ranks according to (a) net present value; (b) net present value per dollar invested; (c) payback period; (d) internal rate of return.   [*Partial Ans.* (a) B better; (b) A; (c) A; (d) A.]

6. A person may borrow $500 from the New York Finance Company and repay the loan in 24 equal monthly installments of $26.19. What monthly compounded monthly interest rate is the finance company implicitly charging?

7. Consider the following two problems:
   (a) From a fund with initial balance of $100,000, five annual payments of $10,000 each are to be made. What rate of interest must be earned on the balance in the fund in order for its balance at the end of the fifth year to be $20,000?
   (b) Ten annual payments of $10,000 per year are made into a fund whose initial balance is $50,000. What rate of interest must be earned on the balance in the fund in order for its balance at the end of the tenth year to be $120,000?
   In both problems, show that there is no $r \geq 0$ which satisfies the required conditions.

8. Show that for given P, S, n, and p, there can be a solution for $r \geq 0$ in (10) only if $S \geq P + np$. Did the problems of Exercise 7 satisfy this condition?

9. Show that the following flow diagram describes a computational process for finding the payback period.

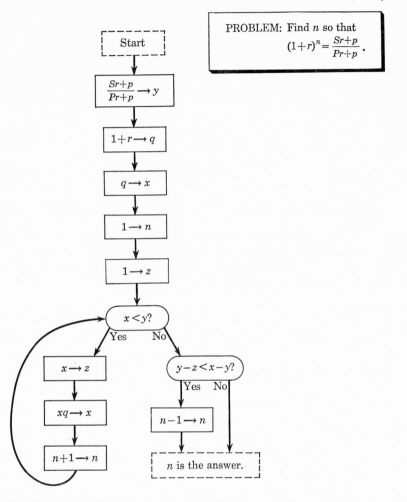

PROBLEM: Find n so that
$$(1+r)^n = \frac{Sr+p}{Pr+p}.$$

10. Construct a flow diagram for computing the rate of return r if P, n, and p are given, and if $S = 0$. Assume that a subroutine for computing $(1 + r)^i$ exists.

4. Nominal and effective interest rates

So far we have assumed that the payment period coincides with the compounding period. This assumption is not at all necessary; we can easily establish a relationship among interest rates subject to different periods of compounding. When we talk of an interest rate of 6% per year compounded quarterly, we really mean an interest rate of $\frac{1}{4} \cdot 6\% = 1.5\%$

compounded four times per year. The 6% is called the *nominal* interest rate; there is in fact an *effective* annually compounded interest rate greater than 6% which is equivalent to the nominal 6% compounded quarterly.

Let r' be a *nominal* interest rate which is compounded m times a year. What is the equivalent *effective* rate r compounded annually? Consider the compound amount S of a deposit P after N years at an interest rate r'/m compounded every $1/m$ years. We may then ask the equivalent question, what annually compounded effective interest rate r will produce from the same initial deposit the same compound amount? In the first case there are mN periods, so that

$$S = P\left(1 + \frac{r'}{m}\right)^{mN};$$

in the second, there are N periods, and

$$S = P(1 + r)^N.$$

Thus we want to find the r for which

$$P(1 + r)^N = P\left(1 + \frac{r'}{m}\right)^{mN}.$$

Dividing both sides of the equation above by P, taking the Nth root, and then subtracting 1 from both sides, we obtain

$$(13) \qquad r = \left(1 + \frac{r'}{m}\right)^m - 1.$$

Observe that this result is independent of N and P. Table III can be used directly to obtain the effective interest rate for a given nominal rate. It can be used inversely to obtain the nominal rate corresponding to a given effective rate.

Example 1. Suppose that 6% annual interest is to be compounded monthly. Then 6% is the nominal rate r', and $m = 12$. Thus the effective annual rate is

$$r = \left(1 + \frac{.06}{12}\right)^{12} - 1 = (1 + .005)^{12} - 1.$$

From Table III we find that $(1.005)^{12} = 1.0617$, hence $r = .0617$, or about $6\frac{1}{6}\%$.

A good approximate answer for the effective rate r may be obtained by applying the binomial theorem (see Chapter III, Section 8) to (13). We obtain

$$r = 1 + \binom{m}{1}\left(\frac{r'}{m}\right)^1 + \binom{m}{2}\left(\frac{r'}{m}\right)^2 + \ldots - 1 = r' + \left(\frac{m-1}{2m}\right)r'^2 + \ldots.$$

Hence

$$(14) \qquad r \approx r' + \frac{m-1}{2m}r'^2.$$

(For a discussion of the accuracy of this approximation see Exercises 6–7.) Note that the estimate given in (14) is always *less* than the true value of r, since the approximation was obtained by ignoring positive terms in the binomial expansion.

Example 1 (continued) If we use (14) instead of (13), we obtain

$$r \approx .06 + (\tfrac{11}{24})(.0036) = .06165,$$

whereas the correct answer to the same number of decimal places is .06168, an excellent agreement.

Example 2. A bank pays 4% interest compounded quarterly. What is the equivalent (effective) annual compounding interest rate?

Here $r' = .04$ and $m = 4$. Hence $r = (1.01)^4 - 1 = .0406$, from Table III. Therefore the effective rate is 4.06%. The approximate formula (14) yields $.04 + (\tfrac{3}{8})(.0016) = .0406$, which is correct to four decimal places.

Example 3. A mortgage of $50,000 is to be liquidated over 12 years in 48 equal quarterly installments. If interest is charged on the unpaid balance at the annual rate of 8.2% compounded annually, how large should the payments be?

Using equation (13) and Table III, we see that

$$.082 = \left(1 + \frac{.08}{4}\right)^4 - 1$$

so that $r' = .08$ and $r'/m = .02$. Now treating the problem in terms of quarter years, we apply the capital recovery formula. From Table IV, the uniform payment present value factor for 48 payments with interest of 2% is 30.67. Hence, from Figure 2,

$$p = \frac{1}{30.67}\,(-50,000) = -1630.$$

Thus payments of $1630 per quarter will liquidate the mortgage in 12 years.

Example 4. An investor can purchase a bond for $846.63. At maturity 24 years later, the investor will receive the face value of $1000. The "coupon rate" of the bond is 3% payable semi-annually; i.e., the investor receives "interest" on the bond of $15 twice each year. What is the yield to maturity?

We take as our standard time period a half year; we will determine the semi-annually compounded yield, and then translate this into an annually compounded yield. Thus $P = 846.63$, $S = 1000$, $p = -15$, and $n = mN = 2 \cdot 24 = 48$. There is a solution since

$$S = 1000 > P + np = 846.63 + (48)(-15) = 126.63$$

and $S > P$ (see Exercise 8, Section 3). After trying various values of r in (10), we find that

$$(1 + .02)^{48} = \frac{(1000)(.02) - 15}{(846.63)(.02) - 15},$$

hence $r'/m = r'/2 = .02$. Then

$$r = (1 + .02)^2 - 1 = .0404 = 4.04\%.$$

EXERCISES

1. In Example 3 of Section 3, find the effective annually compounded annual interest rate.   [*Ans.* $r \approx .108$.]

2. In Exercise 6 of Section 3, find the effective interest rate.

3. Find the effective interest rate equivalent to 12% compounded (a) monthly, (b) quarterly, (c) semi-annually.

   [*Ans.* (a) 12.68%; (b) 12.55%; (c) 12.36%.]

4. Find the effective interest rate equivalent to 100% compounded (a) twice per year, (b) five times per year, (c) ten times per year, (d) 20 times per year, (e) 100 times per year. Does the effective interest rate appear to increase without limit as the period of compounding becomes smaller and smaller? (It can be shown that as the period of compounding decreases, the effective interest rate approaches $e^{r'} - 1$, where r' is the nominal interest rate and $e = 2.718 \ldots$ is the number previously encountered in Chapter IV, Section 5. Thus, with $r' = 1.00$, r approaches $1.718 \ldots$.) [*Partial Ans.* (e) $r = 1.01^{100} - 1 = 1.01^{96} \cdot 1.01^4 - 1 = (2.5993)(1.0406) - 1 = 1.7048$.]

5. Find the nominal quarterly compounded interest rates equivalent to the following effective rates: (a) 4.06%, (b) 6.14%, (c) 8.24%, (d) 10.38%.

6. Use the binomial theorem to obtain a better approximation for r than (14). [*Hint:* Carry out the expansion to one more term.]

7. What is the maximum size of improvement obtained in Exercise 6 if r' is at most 10%?

8. Use the binomial theorem to show that if $n\epsilon$ is small, then

   (vi) $[(1 + r) + \epsilon]^n \approx (1 + r)^{n-1}[1 + r + n\epsilon]$.

9. Find an approximate value for $(1.0617)^{20}$, using Table III and formula (vi).

10. Use the result of Example 1 and of Exercise 9 to find the compound amount of \$1 compounded monthly at a nominal annual rate of 6% for 20 years. Compare your answer with that obtained by compounding \$1 at 0.5% interest per period for 240 periods.

11. Use (14) and the result of Exercise 8 to find the value of an annuity at the end of 24 years if \$100 per quarter is paid into a fund which bears interest at a nominal rate of 6% compounded quarterly.

*5. Tax offsets on depreciation

We have seen (see Exercise 4, Section 2) that under certain circumstances it is a rational policy to make investment decisions so as to maximize the net present value of future earnings. Reported corporate earnings are, of course, subject to tax, and it is the businessman's right, and frequently his objective, to act so as to maximize the present value of future earnings *after taxes*, subject to the legal constraints of the tax code. To evaluate different courses of action, therefore, we must know how to compute the ways in which taxes affect earnings.

Corporations are subject to a tax on their profits. At the time of this writing, the corporate tax rate on profits in excess of $25,000 in a year is 52%. The tax rate has occasionally been changed by act of Congress. It has generally been the policy of Congress—with the exception of wartime excess profits taxes—to levy taxes at a rate which is independent of the size of a company's profits for all profits in excess of some nominal amount (such as $25,000 a year). We shall call this tax rate t, $0 \leq t < 1$. For example, in 1962 we have $t = .52$.

Tax is charged on *reported* earnings. Reported earnings do not usually coincide with *cash* earnings. For example, an investment in a $10,000 machine reduces cash earnings by $10,000 but has no immediate effect on earnings reported for tax purposes. A $10,000 asset may, however, be *depreciated* over a period of years. The depreciation charges do not affect cash earnings, but they do reduce earnings reported for tax purposes, and therefore reduce the amount of income tax paid.

For a company which is currently operating profitably, earnings reported before tax are taxed at the rate t. Because this rate is independent of the size of the reported earnings, any increase in reported earnings causes a proportional increase in the tax paid. In contrast, any decrease in reported earnings is offset in part by a corresponding decrease in taxes. Thus, if $t = .52$ and earnings (both reported and actual) are decreased by $100,000 per year, then after-tax earnings are decreased by only $100,000(1 - t) = $48,000$. Also, if *reported* earnings are decreased (e.g., by charges to depreciation) by $100,000 while actual *cash* earnings are unchanged, then after-tax cash earnings are *increased* by $100,000t = $52,000$.

For tax purposes an asset purchased for an amount C can be *depreciated* over D years. The sum of the D amounts reported as depreciation will equal the original asset value C less anticipated salvage value S, if any. We shall assume in the remainder of the text of this section and of Section 6 that there will be no salvage value. (See Exercise 4 for a discussion of the effects of salvage value on depreciation rates.)

For assets with lives of three or more years, the Internal Revenue Service permits three principal methods of depreciation: straight-line, sum-of-the years'-digits, and double declining balance. A variety of other methods are permitted provided they meet certain requirements (see Exercise 3).

Under straight-line depreciation, an amount C/D is charged to depreciation each year.

In the sum-of-the-years'-digits method, the sum

$$1 + 2 + \ldots + (D - 1) + D = \tfrac{1}{2}D(D + 1)$$

(see Exercise 15, Section 1) is first computed. Then in the first year an amount $\dfrac{D}{\frac{1}{2}D(D + 1)} C$ is charged to depreciation, in the second year an amount $\dfrac{D - 1}{\frac{1}{2}D(D + 1)} C$, and so on. In the jth year, therefore, an amount $\dfrac{D - j + 1}{\frac{1}{2}D(D + 1)} C$ is charged to depreciation, where $1 \leq j \leq D$.

In the double declining balance method, a rate twice that of the straight-line method is applied each year to the undepreciated balance. Thus in the first year the depreciation charge is $2C/D$, after which the undepreciated balance is

$$C - \frac{2C}{D} = C\left(1 - \frac{2}{D}\right).$$

In the second year the depreciation charge is

$$\frac{2}{D} C\left(1 - \frac{2}{D}\right)$$

and the undepreciated balance then becomes

$$C\left(1 - \frac{2}{D}\right) - \frac{2}{D} C\left(1 - \frac{2}{D}\right) = C\left(1 - \frac{2}{D}\right)^2$$

and so forth. In the jth year the depreciation charge is

$$\frac{2}{D} C\left(1 - \frac{2}{D}\right)^{j-1}$$

and the undepreciated balance at the end of the year is $C\left(1 - \dfrac{2}{D}\right)^{j}$. Since the undepreciated balance never becomes 0 by this method, the company is permitted at any time before the end of the Dth year to switch to straight-line depreciation. Thus, if the switch is made at the beginning of the kth year, $1 \leq k \leq D$, there will be an undepreciated balance of $C\left(1 - \dfrac{2}{D}\right)^{k-1}$ which will be charged to depreciation in equal amounts over the remaining

$D - k + 1$ years. Thus, using the double declining balance method with a switch to straight-line depreciation at the beginning of the kth year, the depreciation charged in the jth year is

(14)
$$\frac{2}{D} C\left(1 - \frac{2}{D}\right)^{j-1} \quad \text{where} \quad 1 \leq j < k \leq D,$$
$$\frac{C(1 - 2/D)^{k-1}}{D - k + 1} \quad \text{where} \quad k \leq j \leq D.$$

Example. Consider the purchase of an asset costing $C = \$15,000$ which can be depreciated in $D = 5$ years. In Figure 7 are shown the amounts which can be charged to depreciation under (1) the straight-line method; (2) the sum-of-the-years'-digits method; (3) the double declining balance method, where the switch to straight-line is made at the beginning of (a) the third year, (b) the fourth year, (c) the fifth year. Verify all the figures. Observe that in every case the sum of the 5 years' depreciation charges is the $15,000 cost of the asset.

Year	(1) Straight-Line	(2) Sum-of-the-Years'-Digits	(3) Double Declining Balance (a) $k = 3$	(b) $k = 4$	(c) $k = 5$
1	$3,000	$5,000	$6,000	$6,000	$6,000
2	3,000	4,000	3,600	3,600	3,600
3	3,000	3,000	1,800	2,160	2,160
4	3,000	2,000	1,800	1,620	1,296
5	3,000	1,000	1,800	1,620	1,944
	$15,000	$15,000	$15,000	$15,000	$15,000

Figure 7

The tax offset on each of these methods in a given year is t times the amount of the depreciation in that year. We shall assume that the tax rate t is expected to remain the same for at least D more years. Then to calculate the present value of the future tax offsets from depreciation, we can first calculate the present value of the future depreciation charges and then multiply the result by t.

The present value of the depreciation charges in Figure 7 can always be calculated by computing the single payment present value for each year and adding the present values for years 1 through 5 so computed. Of course for straight-line depreciation it would be easier to use the uniform payment present value formula, but for consistency we shall use the single payment method for all calculations. In Figure 8, the present value factor $1/(1 + r)^j$ is shown for $r = .1$, for j from 1 to 5. The present value of each year's depreciation charge under each of the methods is shown, and the sum of the present values is computed in each case.

Year	Present Value Factor	(1) Straight-Line	(2) Sum-of-the Years'-Digits	(3) Double Declining Balance (a) $k = 3$	(b) $k = 4$	(c) $k = 5$
1	.9091	$2,727	$4,546	$5,455	$5,455	$5,455
2	.8264	2,479	3,306	2,975	2,975	2,975
3	.7513	2,254	2,254	1,352	1,623	1,623
4	.6830	2,049	1,366	1,229	1,106	885
5	.6209	1,863	621	1,118	1,006	1,207
		$11,372	$12,093	$12,129	$12,165	$12,145

Figure 8

Since the sums in Figure 8 will all be multiplied by t, it suffices to look at the sums themselves to see which method yields the largest tax offset. We observe that (a) of the three methods using the double declining balance method, the one with $k = 4$ is best; (b) the best double declining balance method is better than the sum-of-the-years'-digits method, which is better, in turn, than the straight-line method.

In this example the double declining balance method, with $k = 4$, is optimal. We will show in the next section that the straight-line method is *never* optimal. Examples in the Exercises will show that sometimes the sum-of-the-years'-digits method is superior to the double declining balance method, whereas in other cases the latter is preferable.

To show how the numbers in Figure 8 can be used in making an investment decision, suppose that for $15,000 a company can purchase a machine which will increase its earnings by $3500 per year for the next 8 years. Suppose that the machine can be depreciated over 5 years, that the tax rate $t = .52$, and that the company can earn 10% after taxes on alternative investments of its capital. Then if the present value of earnings after taxes plus the tax offset on depreciation exceeds $15,000, the company should purchase the asset; otherwise it should not.

The $3500 per year increase in earnings is subject to tax; after tax, it is $3500 $(1 - t) = 1680 per year. Because this amount will be earned each year, we may use the uniform series present value factor to obtain

$$P = (5.335)(\$1680) = \$8963.$$

The tax offset on depreciation will be t times the present value of the depreciation charges which have already been calculated for five different depreciation methods in Figure 8. Under the optimal method, 3(b), the tax offset is

$$(.52)(\$12,165) = \$6,326$$

and the total present value is

$$\$8,963 + \$6,326 = \$15,289 > \$15,000$$

so that the machine *should* be purchased. However, if the company (mistakenly) planned to use the straight-line method, the total present value would be only

$$\$8,963 + (.52)(\$11,372) = \$14,876$$

and they would not buy the machine.

EXERCISES

1. If a 20% return after taxes can be earned on other investment opportunities, calculate the present value of the depreciation charges on a $55,000 asset which is depreciable over 10 years
   (a) using straight-line depreciation;   [*Ans.* $23,056.]
   (b) using sum-of-the-years'-digits depreciation;   [*Ans.* $29,038.]
   (c) using double declining balance depreciation with (i) $k = 5$, (ii) $k = 6$, (iii) $k = 7$, (iv) $k = 8$.
                [*Ans.* (i) $28,090; (ii) and (iii) $28,211; (iv) $28,150.]
   What is the best value of k? What is the best method of depreciation? Compare your results with the results of the example.

2. In Exercise 1, suppose that the $55,000 asset will increase earnings before taxes by $20,000 per year, and that its anticipated physical life is 20 years. Should the investment be made if the tax rate is 52% and if sum-of-the-years'-digits depreciation is used? What is the net present value?

3. The actual internal revenue code permits other depreciation methods besides straight-line, sum-of-the-years'-digits, and double declining balance. It stipulates, however, that for any other method the undepreciated balance must be at least as high as it is under the double declining balance method during each of the years constituting the first two-thirds of the life of the asset. General Motors Corporation, for example, uses the following method. The depreciable life D of an asset whose original cost is C is divided into three equal periods. In each of the years constituting the first one-third of the life of the asset, an amount $1.5(C/D)$ is charged to depreciation. In the middle one-third of the asset's life an amount C/D is charged each year, whereas in the last one-third of its life the depreciation charge is $.5(C/D)$ each year. Calculate the present value of depreciation charges if $C = \$21,000$, $D = 6$ years, and $r = .10$:
   (a) using the General Motors method;   [*Ans.* $16,207.]
   (b) using the sum-of-the-years'-digits method;
   (c) using the double declining balance method with $k = 4$.
   Show that in this case the General Motors method satisfies the internal revenue code.

4. If an asset has an anticipated salvage value S at the end of its life, then the depreciation base for straight-line and sum-of-the-years'-digits depreciation is $C - S$. Thus, with straight-line depreciation one depreciates an amount

$(C - S)/D$ per year, whereas with sum-of-the-years'-digits one depreciates an amount $\dfrac{D - j + 1}{\frac{1}{2}D(D + 1)}\,(C - S)$ in the jth year. With double declining balance depreciation, however, one may depreciate at the same rate as one would if there were no salvage value, with the proviso that the sum of the depreciation charges cannot exceed $C - S$. The option to switch to straight-line depreciation also remains. In the example of this section, suppose the asset has an anticipated salvage value of $1000 at the end of the 5-year period. Calculate the present value of the depreciation charges using the methods of depreciation of Figure 7. What is the best value of k? [Ans. (1) $10,614; (2) $11,287; (3a) $11,444; (3b) $11,513; (3c) $11,524. Best $k = 5$.]

5. In Exercise 4, calculate the net present value after taxes of the investment using each of the depreciation methods. Assume that the asset will be salvaged after the fifth year. Under which methods should the investment be made?

6. In Exercise 1, suppose there is a $5000 salvage value anticipated at the end of 10 years. Referring to Exercise 4, calculate the present value of the depreciation charges under the methods of depreciation used in Exercise 1. Can you find a better value of k than those which you were asked to try in the exercise? What is the best method of depreciation? Compare your result with that of Exercise 1.

7. In Exercise 6, assume the asset will be salvaged after the tenth year. Calculate the net present value of the investment using the best depreciation method. Referring to Exercise 2, should the investment be made?

8. Given an asset costing C with depreciable life D and no salvage value, draw a flow chart for calculating the present value of the depreciation charges:
   (a) using sum-of-the-years'-digits depreciation;
   (b) using double declining balance depreciation with specified k.
   Assume that a subroutine for computing $(1 + r)^n$ exists.

9. Referring to Exercises 4 and 8, draw flow charts for computing the present value of the depreciation charges under the two methods of depreciation if there is a salvage value S at the end of the D years.

*6. Formulas for present value of depreciation charges

The present value of depreciation charges can always be calculated by the method of the last section; that is, by calculating the single payment present value for each year and adding the results. It is much more convenient, however, to derive a single formula for each of the three permissible methods of depreciation discussed in Section 5. In this section we shall derive these formulas. We shall also find the best value of k for double declining balance depreciation, and show that the double declining

balance and sum-of-the-years'-digits methods both have greater present
values than the straight-line method. Throughout this section we shall
assume that $D \geq 3$.

Straight-line depreciation. We have already observed that the present
value of a stream of depreciation charges of C/D per year for D years is
g'ven by the uniform series present value formula

$$(15) \qquad P_{s1} = \frac{C}{D}\left[\frac{(1+r)^D - 1}{r(1+r)^D}\right].$$

This is the present value of depreciation charges, by the straight-line
method, for an asset costing C dollars, depreciable over D years, with an interest rate r.

We also observe, for future use, that if we let b_j be the undepreciated
balance under straight-line depreciation after j years, we may write b_{j+1} in
terms of b_j in one of two ways:

$$(16a) \qquad b_{j+1} = b_j - \frac{C}{D}$$

$$(16b) \qquad b_{j+1} = b_j \frac{D - j - 1}{D - j}.$$

Formula (16b) follows from the fact that

$$b_j = C\frac{D - j}{D}.$$

For example, if $C = \$10,000$, $D = 10$, then after the sixth year,
$b_6 = \$4000$. By (16a),

$$b_7 = \$4000 - \frac{\$10,000}{10} = \$3000.$$

By (16b),

$$b_7 = \$4000 \frac{10 - 6 - 1}{10 - 6} = \$3000,$$

as before. We shall use these results in determining the optimal value of k
with double declining balance depreciation.

Double declining balance depreciation. We first show that the best time
to switch from double declining balance to straight-line depreciation is in
the year k, where

$$(17) \qquad k = \tfrac{1}{2}(D + 3) \quad \text{if } D \text{ is odd}$$

$$= \text{ either } \quad \tfrac{1}{2}(D + 2) \quad \text{or} \quad \tfrac{1}{2}(D + 4) \quad \text{if } D \text{ is even.}$$

It is immaterial whether the switch is made in year $\frac{1}{2}(D + 2)$ or in year
$\frac{1}{2}(D + 4)$ if D is even. It follows as a trivial consequence that this method
is better than straight-line depreciation for all D years since, if this were
not so, the optimal k would be $k = 1$.

We start with the observation that, given any undepreciated balance, the better method of depreciation in a given year is the one which depreciates more in that year. This observation follows from the facts that (a) the sum of the depreciation charges under any method will be C; (b) the earlier one has an opportunity to claim a depreciation charge, the higher will be its present value. In the double declining balance method of depreciation, if we let b'_j be the undepreciated balance in the jth period, then

$$(18) \qquad b'_{j+1} = \left(1 - \frac{2}{D}\right)b'_j.$$

In the straight-line method, we have, by (16b),

$$b_{j+1} = b_j\left[\frac{D - j - 1}{D - j}\right] = b_j\left[1 - \frac{1}{D - j}\right].$$

Now suppose that in year $j - 1$ we have an undepreciated balance b_{j-1} and, regardless of the depreciation method used previously, suppose (contrary to fact) that the law permits us to make a choice in year j between the double declining balance and straight-line methods. Then the straight-line method will be better if the balance in the jth year is less than it would be under double declining balance depreciation, i.e., if

$$b_j = b_{j-1}\left[1 - \frac{1}{D - j + 1}\right] < b'_j = \left(1 - \frac{2}{D}\right)b_{j-1}.$$

This condition will be met if

$$\frac{2}{D} < \frac{1}{D - j + 1},$$

i.e., if

$$j > \tfrac{1}{2}(D + 2).$$

The two methods will be equally good, of course, if

$$j = \tfrac{1}{2}(D + 2),$$

which can occur only if D is even. Straight-line depreciation will be worse if

$$j < \tfrac{1}{2}(D + 2).$$

Thus, even though one is not permitted to choose a depreciation method each year, an optimal system would use double declining balance for $j < \tfrac{1}{2}(D + 2)$ and straight-line for $j \geq \tfrac{1}{2}(D + 2)$, and *this* method *is* permitted by law. Hence the year k in which the switch to straight-line depreciation should be made is given by (17).

We turn next to the derivation of the formula for the present value of double declining balance depreciation, given that a switch to straight-line depreciation is made at the beginning of some year k (not necessarily optimal), where $1 \leq k \leq D$. Recall that this number multiplied by $(1 - t)$

is the present value of the tax offsets due to depreciation generated by the purchase of an asset.

Rather than calculate the present value directly, we shall calculate the balance each year in a certain hypothetical fund. The fund earns interest r each year on the balance at the end of the previous year. Payments equal in value to the depreciation charges are paid *out* of the fund at the end of each year. After D years the balance of the fund is 0. Then the value of the fund in year 0 is the present value of the depreciation charges. That this is so can be seen by recognizing that a person would be indifferent between receiving payments each year equal to the depreciation charges and receiving the fund itself. In the latter case, he could pay himself each year exactly what he would receive in the former case and finish with zero balance in the fund at the end of the depreciable life of the asset.

Let x_j be the balance in the fund at the end of the jth year, let b_j be the undepreciated balance at the end of the jth year, and let d_j be the depreciation charge in the jth year. Then

(19a) $$d_j = b_{j-1} - b_j$$

and, for $j < k$,

(19b) $$b_j = \left(1 - \frac{2}{D}\right)b_{j-1}$$

and

(20) $$x_j = (1 + r)x_{j-1} - d_j.$$

Let us look first at the difference equation (19b). This has a unique solution provided we can specify the value of some b_j. However, we know that the undepreciated balance at year 0 is C, the cost of the asset. Hence we can specify an *initial condition*

$$b_0 = C.$$

It is now easy to verify that the formula

(21) $$b_j = \left(1 - \frac{2}{D}\right)^j C$$

satisfies both (19b) and the initial condition. This is the same result which we obtained inductively in Section 5. Substituting (21) in (19a), we find, as in Section 5,

(22) $$d_j = \left(1 - \frac{2}{D}\right)^{j-1} \frac{2C}{D}.$$

We next turn to the difference equation (20). Substituting (22) in (20), we obtain

(23) $$x_j = (1 + r)x_{j-1} - \left(1 - \frac{2}{D}\right)^{j-1} \frac{2C}{D}.$$

We would like to know the balance in the fund at year 0; i.e., we would like to know x_0. We shall first obtain a general formula for x_j and then find the value of x_j when $j = 0$.

As with the difference equation (19b), equation (23) has a unique solution provided we can specify the value of x_j for some particular j. Unlike (19b), however, we cannot specify an initial condition, since this is the unknown of the problem. But we can specify the value of the fund at the end of year $k - 1$, i.e., just before the switch to straight-line depreciation. At that time, the fund must have a balance which is sufficient to make $D - k + 1$ equal annual payments of an amount such that the sum of these payments will be equal to the undepreciated balance b_{k-1} at the end of year $k - 1$. Also, the balance of the fund after the $D - k + 1$ payments have been made must be 0. However, the present value of a fund out of which a series of uniform payments is to be made until its balance is zero is given by the negative of the uniform series present value formula of Figure 1.

By (21),

$$b_{k-1} = \left(1 - \frac{2}{D}\right)^{k-1} C.$$

Since $D - k + 1$ equal payments are to be made from the fund, the amount of each payment will be

$$\left(1 - \frac{2}{D}\right)^{k-1} \frac{C}{D - k + 1}.$$

The value of a series of $D - k + 1$ such payments at the end of year $k - 1$, which is identical with the balance of our hypothetical fund at the end of year $k - 1$, is therefore

$$(24) \qquad x_{k-1} = \frac{(1 + r)^{D-k+1} - 1}{r(1 + r)^{D-k+1}} \frac{(1 - 2/D)^{k-1} C}{D - k + 1}.$$

Equation (24) then provides the value of x_j for some particular j, namely, $j = k - 1$. The unique solution to (23) subject to the condition (24) is given by

$$(25) \qquad x_j = C\left(1 - \frac{2}{D}\right)^j \times$$

$$\left\{\left[\frac{1 - 2/D}{1 + r}\right]^{k-j-1}\left[\frac{(1 + r)^{D-k+1} - 1}{(D - k + 1)r(1 + r)^{D-k+1}} - \frac{2}{rD + 2}\right] + \frac{2}{rD + 2}\right\}$$

as can be verified by direct substitution (see Exercise 4). Now, setting $j = 0$, we obtain the present value of double declining balance depreciation as

$$(26) \qquad P_{ddb} = x_0 =$$

$$C\left\{\left[\frac{1 - 2/D}{1 + r}\right]^{k-1}\left[\frac{(1 + r)^{D-k+1} - 1}{(D - k + 1)r(1 + r)^{D-k+1}} - \frac{2}{rD + 2}\right] + \frac{2}{rD + 2}\right\}.$$

Example 1. In the example of Section 5, $D = 5$, $r = .1$, and $C = \$15,000$. Since D is odd, the optimal value of k is

$$k = \tfrac{1}{2}(D + 3) = \tfrac{1}{2}(5 + 3) = 4,$$

as we saw previously. With $k = 4$,

$$P_{ddb} = \$15,000 \left\{ \left(\frac{1 - \tfrac{2}{5}}{1 + .1} \right)^3 \left[\frac{(1 + .1)^2 - 1}{(2)(.1)(1 + .1)^2} - \frac{2}{(.1)(5) + 2} \right] + \frac{2}{(.1)(5) + 2} \right\}$$

$$= \$12,165$$

as we saw previously.

Sum-of-the-years'-digits depreciation. It can again be shown (see Exercise 1) that this method of depreciation is superior to straight-line depreciation.

The formula for the present value of sum-of-the-years'-digits depreciation is easier to derive than was that for the double declining balance method. As before, we start with a hypothetical fund whose balance at the end of year j is given by x_j. The fund is exactly like the one we used previously except that payments equal to the value of the sum-of-the-years'-digits depreciation charges are made from the fund each year. Thus, the balance in the fund must satisfy the difference equation

$$(27) \qquad x_{j+1} = (1 + r)x_j - 2C \frac{D - j}{D(D + 1)}, \qquad 0 \le j \le D.$$

Equation (27) has a unique solution provided we can specify the value of x_j for some j. However, this is very easy to do: the balance in the fund at the end of year D must be zero. Hence,

$$(28) \qquad\qquad\qquad x_D = 0.$$

The solution to (27) subject to (28) is

$$(29) \qquad x_j = \frac{2C}{r^2 D(D + 1)} [rD - 1 - rj + (1 + r)^{-(D-j)}]$$

as can be verified by direct substitution (see Exercise 5). Setting $j = 0$ in (29), we obtain the present value of sum-of-the-years'-digits depreciation as

$$(30) \qquad P_{sd} = x_0 = \frac{2C}{r^2 D(D + 1)} [rD - 1 + (1 + r)^{-D}].$$

Example 2. In the Example of Section 5, $D = 5$, $C = \$15,000$, and $r = .1$. Then, from Table III, $(1 + .1)^5 = 1.6105$, and

$$P_{sd} = \frac{(2)(15,000)}{(.1)^2(5)(6)} \left[(.1)(5) - 1 + \frac{1}{1.6105} \right]$$

$$= 100,000[.5 - 1 + .6209]$$

$$= (100,000)(.1209) = 12,090$$

which agrees with the results of Figure 8 to four significant figures.

EXERCISES

1. Show that the total amount depreciated in the first j years is greater in the sum-of-the-years'-digits method than in the straight-line method, for all $j < D$. Use this result to prove that the former method is always preferable to the latter.

2. Use the formulas of this section to obtain answers to the questions of Exercise 1 of Section 5.

3. Show that (21) solves the difference equation (19b) and the initial condition $b_0 = C$.

4. Show that (25) solves the difference equation (23) subject to (24).

5. Show that (29) solves the difference equation (27) subject to (28).

6. Using sum-of-the-years'-digits depreciation, what is the present value of the depreciation charge in the jth year? Use the results of Exercises 14 and 16 of Section 1 to obtain the sum of the present values of the depreciation charges for $j = 1, 2, \ldots, D$, and show that this sum is equal to P_{sd} as given by (30).

7. Using double declining balance depreciation with a switch to straight-line in year k, what is the present value of the depreciation charge in the jth year? Use the result of Exercise 14 of Section 1 to obtain the sum of the present values of the depreciation charges for $j = 1, 2, \ldots, D$, and show that this sum is equal to P_{ddb} as given by (26).

8. For assets acquired before January 1, 1954, or for used property, whenever acquired, the declining balance method may be used but the rate may not exceed 1.5 times the rate of straight-line depreciation. Under this method of depreciation using the maximum permissible rate, in what year should a switch to straight-line depreciation be made?
[*Ans.* Switch after year $\frac{1}{3}D + 1$.]

9. Draw a flow diagram to compute P_{sd} as given by (30), given C, D, and r. You may assume that a subroutine for computing $(1 + r)^i$ exists.

10. Draw a flow diagram to compute P_{ddb} as given by (26), with arbitrary k. Assume the same quantities are given as in the previous exercise.

11. Draw a flow diagram to obtain the optimal value of k. Combine your diagram with that of the previous exercise to obtain the present value of double declining balance depreciation when an optimal switch to straight-line is made.

12. Referring to Exercise 4 of Section 5, modify the formulas for P_{sl} and P_{sd} given that an asset has an anticipated salvage value S at the end of its depreciable life.

13. Determine the optimal condition for switching from double declining balance to straight-line depreciation when an asset has an anticipated salvage value S at the end of its depreciable life. (See Exercise 4 of Section 5.) [*Ans.* If double declining balance depreciation has been used for the first $j - 1$ years, a switch to straight-line should be made in year j if

$$(b_{j-1} - S)\left[1 - \frac{1}{D - j + 1}\right] < \left(1 - \frac{2}{D}\right)b_{j-1} - S.]$$

14. Let $x_{j+1} = ax_j + bj + c$, and let $x_0 = d$. Then show that

$$x_1 = ad + c$$
$$x_2 = a^2 d + (a + 1)c + b$$
$$x_3 = a^3 d + (a^2 + a + 1)c + (a + 2)b$$
$$x_4 = a^4 d + (a^3 + a^2 + a + 1)c + (a^2 + 2a + 3)b$$

and, by induction, that

$$x_j = a^j d + (a^{j-1} + a^{j-2} + \ldots + a + 1)c$$
$$+ [a^{j-2} + 2a^{j-3} + \ldots + (j - 2)a + (j - 1)]b$$

Use the results of Exercises 14 and 16 of Section 1 to obtain the sums of the series. Then show that this difference equation is essentially the same as (27) by making appropriate substitutions for the values of a, b, and c. Finally, by setting $j = D$ and using (28), find P_{sd} by determining the value of d.

15. Let $x_j = ax_{j-1} + bc^{j-1}$, and let $x_0 = d$. Then show that

$$x_1 = ad + b$$
$$x_2 = a^2 d + b(a + c)$$
$$x_3 = a^3 d + b(a^2 + ac + c^2)$$
$$x_4 = a^4 d + b(a^3 + a^2 c + ac^2 + c^3)$$

and, by induction, that

$$x_j = a^j d + b(a^{j-1} + a^{j-2}c + a^{j-3}c^2 + \ldots + a^2 c^{j-3} + ac^{j-2} + c^{j-1}).$$

Use the results of Exercise 17 of Section 1 to obtain the sum of the series. Then show that the difference equation is essentially the same as (23) by making appropriate substitutions for the values of a, b, and c. Finally, by setting $j = k - 1$ and using (24), find P_{ddb} by determining the value of d.

7. Double classification bookkeeping

In a commonly used method of bookkeeping, called *double entry* bookkeeping, a single transaction is recorded twice: once as a *debit* and once as a *credit*. A debit is recorded on the left-hand side of an account. A credit of equal amount is recorded on the right-hand side of some other account. Since it is relatively easy to omit a debit or a credit, or to record two credits or two debits rather than one of each, a checking method called a trial balance is frequently used to verify that the sum of the debits equals the sum of the credits. The fact that these sums balance (i.e., are equal) is a necessary, but not a sufficient, condition that the transactions have been properly recorded.

A little reflection shows that the important point about double entry bookkeeping is not that each transaction is *recorded* twice but rather that each transaction is *classified* twice—once as a debit and once as a credit. Another way to doubly classify a number is to record it in a matrix. The number then is classified once according to the row in which it appears and once according to its column. Since this can be done by recording the number just once, the common errors of double entry bookkeeping mentioned above cannot be made, and the need for trial balances to detect these kinds of errors is eliminated.

In this section we shall describe the double classification method and illustrate it with a simple example. In the next section we show how to use the method to prepare the two most common financial reports: the income statement and the balance sheet. Also, in the final section of the chapter we show how to describe double classification bookkeeping using flow diagrams.

Example. Morrissey, the owner of a small household appliance repair business, has his business telephone in his house and keeps his tools and spare parts inventory on his truck which he leases. At the completion of a repair job he presents a bill to the householder who may pay cash or to whom Morrissey may extend credit. Morrissey buys spare parts partly for cash and partly on credit. The only other expenses he has are the rental fees and operating expenses on his truck. At the end of the month, Morrissey, by totalling his sales book, his invoices, and his check stubs, determines that the following (total) transactions have taken place during the month of January.

(a)	Cash sales	$400
(b)	Charge sales	600
(c)	Cost of goods sold (spare parts)	150
(d)	Cash purchases (spare parts)	80
(e)	Charge purchases (spare parts)	40
(f)	Rent on truck	150
(g)	Operating expense on truck	50
(h)	Collections on credit sales	450
(i)	Withdrawals	500
(j)	Payments on accounts payable	100

In order to determine the status of his business, Morrissey wants to prepare an income statement and a balance sheet for January. For this purpose he must record each of the (total) transactions above in various accounts. He has set up the following accounts:

    (1)   Cash
    (2)   Accounts receivable
    (3)   Inventory
    (4)   Accounts payable
    (5)   Equity (proprietorship)
    (6)   Profit or loss
    (7)   Sales
    (8)   Cost of goods sold
    (9)   Rent
  (10)   Operating expense
  (11)   Proprietor's withdrawals

These accounts are arranged so that (1)–(5) are the accounts that appear on the balance sheet, whereas accounts (6)–(11) appear in a somewhat modified form on the income statement.

Morrissey must now doubly classify each of the transactions (a)–(j) by determining to which of the accounts (1)–(11) it should be debited and to which credited. Some of the classifications are obvious, but some depend upon accounting conventions. For instance, (a), Cash sales, obviously affect (1), Cash, whereas (b), Charge sales, affect (2), Accounts receivable. The accounting convention is to record these transactions as debits to the accounts affected. The corresponding credits are to (7), Sales, an account set up to cumulate sales for the month. Transaction (c), Cost of goods sold, is recorded as a debit to account (8), Cost of goods sold, and a credit to (3), Inventory. The only other transaction that is difficult to classify is (i), Withdrawals, which represents the amount Morrissey takes from the business for his own personal use. It is doubly classified as a debit to (11), Proprietor's withdrawals and a credit to (1), Cash.

In order to doubly classify these transactions we set up the 11×11 matrix shown in Figure 9. Note that on the left we mark the rows Credit, and at the top we mark the columns Debit. To record a transaction we merely find the column number of the account which is debited and the row number of the account which is credited, and record the amount of the transaction in the cell which is at the intersection of the two. (More generally, if there were a number already in that cell of the matrix, we would add the new transaction to the number there.) Each of the transactions (a)–(j) above is recorded in Figure 9. The reader should verify that the transactions have been properly classified in the matrix. Note that solid lines separate balance sheet from income (profit and loss) accounts; the numbers in the resulting four submatrices will be treated differently in subsequent calculations.

A matrix that is subdivided into different submatrices is called a *partitioned matrix*.

We call the partitioned matrix in Figure 9 a *transaction matrix* and denote it by T. Let us now prove the remark made earlier that the sum of the debits is equal to the sum of the credits or, in other words, that a trial balance will always balance.

ACCOUNT DEBITED

		Balance Sheet Accounts				Income Statement Accounts					
	1	2	3	4	5	6	7	8	9	10	11
1			80	100					150	50	500
2	450										
3								150			
4			40								
5											
6											
7	400	600									
8											
9											
10											
11											

ACCOUNT CREDITED (labels for rows 6, 7)

Figure 9

Suppose that there are n accounts and T is the transaction matrix representing one or more transactions. In order to get the sum of the debits and credits we define the following vectors:

$$e = \underbrace{(1, 1, \ldots, 1)}_{n \text{ components}} \quad \text{and} \quad f = \left.\begin{pmatrix} 1 \\ 1 \\ \vdots \\ \vdots \\ 1 \end{pmatrix}\right\} n \text{ components.}$$

Then it is easy to see that the components of eT give the sum of the debits in each account, whereas the components of Tf give the sum of the credits in each of the accounts. To get a trial balance we total all the debits and compare that sum with the total of all credits. Since the components of eT give the debit balances, $(eT)f$ gives the total of the debit balances. Also, since the components of Tf give the credit balances, it is obvious that $e(Tf)$ gives the total of all credit balances. However, by the associative law for multiplication of matrices (see Section 4 of Chapter V) we know that

$$(eT)f = e(Tf).$$

This is also intuitively clear since the two expressions $(eT)f$ and $e(Tf)$ are simply two different ways of computing the total sum of all entries in T. We have then the following result.

THEOREM. In the double classification bookkeeping system, trial balances always balance.

This result means that, using this system, trial balances need never be taken to prove the equality of debits and credits. It should be emphasized that eliminating the need for trial balances does *not* eliminate the possibility of errors in the system. However, the kinds of errors which a trial balance was designed to reveal cannot occur. It is still possible to omit a transaction, to record it more than once, to classify it incorrectly, or to record the wrong amount. Various other checks must be employed to find such errors.

If bookkeeping is to be done solely with pencil and paper, it is obvious that the matrix method of doubly classifying transactions is extremely unwieldy. Several transactions may have to be recorded in a single cell in the square array of Figure 9. Also, in many businesses there may be hundreds of accounts, so that the physical size of the transaction matrix would exceed reasonable limits. Of course, each doubly classified cell of the matrix could be represented by a page or a series of pages in a "ledger," just as in traditional double entry bookkeeping, each *account* is represented in a ledger. If a business classifies its transactions in n different accounts, then the double entry system requires only n different "pages" in the ledger. However, if any two different accounts may be involved in a single transaction, the double classification system would require $n(n - 1)$ "pages." Also, as we shall see in the next section, it is often necessary to find the sum of the debits and the sum of the credits in a given account. If each cell in the transaction matrix became a "page" in a ledger, the simple task of adding the entries in a row or in a column of the matrix would become the forbidding task of looking up and adding the numbers recorded on many different pages of the ledger. For these reasons, the double entry system, in spite of its shortcomings and the necessity for trial balances, is usually preferable for a large "pencil and paper" bookkeeping system.

Equipment which has the capacity to store the information contained in a large number of cells and which permits rapid retrieval of the information in any one or a whole series of cells, however, is ideally suited to handle the double classification system of bookkeeping which we have described. There are many such devices. For example, punched card equipment using a key punch, sorter, and printer would perform the necessary mechanical functions. Even simpler, non-mechanized equipment would involve the use of "key sort" cards (see Chapter III, Section 1, Example 3, and also Exercise 5 of Section 9 of this chapter). Most important, the memory cells of electronic computers provide an excellent way of storing the information contained in a large number of cells. In addition, a computer provides an extremely fast and accurate means of performing the calculations required to update transactions and to derive the standard financial reports from them. It is in conjunction with devices of this kind that double classification bookkeeping should prove its usefulness. In the next two sections we will show in more detail how this can be done.

An additional kind of advantage of double classification bookkeeping is that when the numbers are displayed in matrix form, it is easy to analyze the use of each number in the matrix in preparing financial reports, to trace the effects of errors in such numbers, etc. Some of these ideas are developed in the exercises.

EXERCISES

1. Let T be the transaction matrix for one set of transactions and let S be the transaction matrix for a different set of transactions. Show that the entries of the matrix $T + S$ give the totals of both sets of transactions.

2. Morrissey, upon checking his records, found that he had omitted the following items:

    (k)   Additional charge sales.................................. $35
    (l)   Inventory loss (missing item)........................... 10
    (m)   Bad check returned from bank, which had been
          received in payment for a charge sale................... 22

    Add these items to the matrix of Figure 9 in the following two ways:
    (a) Use items (k), (l), and (m) to modify items (a)-(j) and record these numbers in a new transaction matrix.
    (b) Construct a new transaction matrix S that records items (k), (l), and (m) and form the sum $T + S$ as suggested in Exercise 1.
    (c) Are the two answers you obtained in (a) and (b) the same? (This will depend on how you handled (l) and (m), see Exercise 3.)

3. (a) What is the interpretation of a negative entry in a transaction matrix?
    (b) Show that a negative credit to account i and a negative debit to account j can always be replaced by a positive credit to account j and a positive debit to account i.
    (c) Work Exercise 2 in two different ways, once recording items (l) and (m) as negative amounts in the matrix, and once as positive amounts.
    (d) Is it more natural to treat items (l) and (m) as negative or as positive amounts?

4. The *transpose* of a matrix is obtained by interchanging rows and columns. Interpret the transpose of a transaction matrix T.

5. Let T and S be transaction matrices and let e and f be the vectors defined in the text. Interpret the following matrix equations in terms of accounting procedures:

(a) $\qquad\qquad\qquad e(T + S) = eT + eS$
(b) $\qquad\qquad\qquad (T + S)f = Tf + Sf$
(c) $\qquad\qquad\qquad e(T + S)f = eTf + eSf.$

6. At the end of February, Morrissey determines that the following transactions have taken place during the month:

(a)	Cash sales	$355
(b)	Charge sales	725
(c)	Cost of goods sold	165
(d)	Cash purchases	30
(e)	Charge purchases	90
(f)	Rent on truck	150
(g)	Operating expense on truck	60
(h)	Collections on credit sales	500
(i)	Withdrawals	750
(j)	Payments on accounts payable	30

Set up the transaction matrix for February.

7. Some other examples of double-classification systems are listed below. For each such example, list some typical "transactions" and set up "accounts." Record your transactions in a transaction matrix.
(a) The imports and exports of all countries in the world.
(b) Students transferring from one course to another in a university.
(c) A car rental agency which has cars located at various rental offices.
(d) Mail deliveries among cities.
(e) Interactions among workers in a department.

8. Financial reports

Financial reports are summaries made at the end of a given time period of the transactions of a business during that period and of the status of a business at the end of the period. The two most common financial reports are the *income* (or *profit and loss*) *statement* and the *balance sheet*. They are constructed by performing certain operations on the transaction matrix. We shall describe how to derive these statements from the balance sheet of the preceding period and the (total) transaction matrix for the current period.

In the preceding section we classified each account as either a balance sheet account or an income statement account. This classification partitioned the matrix into four submatrices so that the numbers in each submatrix were classified according to whether they would be used to carry out the balance sheet calculations only, the profit and loss calculations only, or both calculations. Figure 10 shows how these classifications apply to the various submatrices. In the Exercises, an analysis is made of how errors in the various parts of the matrix affect financial reports.

Used in balance sheet calculations only	Used in both calculations
Used in both calculations	Used in income statement calculations only

Figure 10

In order to carry out the calculations we will need the balance sheet from the previous period. We record it in a new row and column that we adjoin to the transaction matrix. Then we sum rows and columns of the enlarged matrix and obtain the sum of the debits and the sum of the credits for each account. From the sums in the income statement accounts we calculate the income statement and determine the net profit or loss. This number is recorded in the transaction matrix, whose row and column sums are then adjusted. Then from the debit and credit sums of the balance sheet accounts we prepare the balance sheet for the period in question. The example of the Morrissey Appliance Repair Company will illustrate the procedure.

Example (continued). At the end of December, Morrissey's balance sheet is shown in Figure 11.

MORRISSEY APPLIANCE REPAIR COMPANY
Balance Sheet, December 31, 196–

Assets (Debit Balances)		*Liabilities and Equity (Credit Balances)*	
Cash.................	$ 600	Accounts payable....	$ 100
Accounts receivable....	1500	Equity.............	2900
Inventory............	900		$3000
	$3000		

Figure 11

In order to combine these figures with the transaction matrix obtained in the previous section and have space to calculate row and column sums, we add three more rows and three more columns to the transaction matrix (see Figure 12). These rows are labelled Old Balance Sheet Assets, Total Debits, and New Balance Sheet Assets. The new columns are labelled Old Balance Sheet Liabilities, Total Credits, and New Balance Sheet Liabilities. (Accountants distinguish carefully between liability and equity accounts. Although these accounts are entirely different conceptually, they are treated similarly mathematically. Hence, we shall consider both liability and equity accounts under the heading "Liabilities.") Two dotted lines have been added to separate the

Asset accounts from the Liability accounts in the matrix. Observe that the December balance sheet figures have been properly recorded in Figure 12.

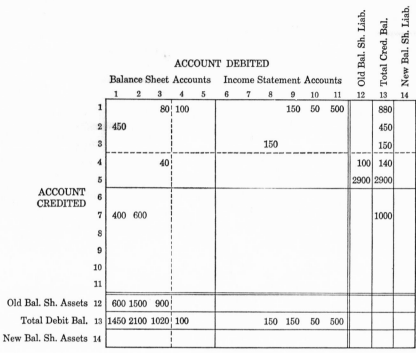

Figure 12

The next step is to calculate for each of the first 11 columns the sums of the entries in the first 12 rows and record these sums in the 13th row labelled Total Debits. We also calculate for each of the first 11 rows the sums of the first 12 columns and enter these in the 13th column, Total Credits.

From the sums just computed it is now possible to prepare the January income statement for Morrissey's company. There are several forms that such a statement can take, and we adopt a convenient, though unconventional, one here. It is shown in Figure 13.

MORRISSEY APPLIANCE REPAIR COMPANY

Income Statement, January, 196–

Sales..		$1000
Cost of goods sold..........	$150	
Rent.....................	150	
Expense.................	50	350
Profit before withdrawal....................		650
Withdrawal..............................		500
Net profit.................................		$ 150

Figure 13

The Sales and the Expense items on the income statement are determined by transactions of the business during the month of January. The item Withdrawals, however, depends upon a transaction between Morrissey and the business.

The reader may have wondered why we have not yet entered any number in either row 6 or column 6. These spaces have been saved for the net profit figure that was computed in preparing the income statement. Since the net profit is retained by the firm, it should be debited to the profit or loss account (6) and credited to the equity account (5) to indicate that Morrissey's ownership of the company has increased in value. Thus $150 is recorded in the fifth row and sixth column of the matrix in Figure 14. The fifth row sum and the sixth column sum have been correspondingly adjusted. (The traditional bookkeeping method proceeds somewhat differently on this point, but the net effect is the same.)

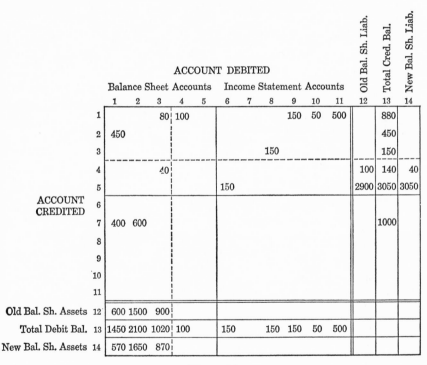

		ACCOUNT DEBITED										Old Bal. Sh. Liab.	Total Cred. Bal.	New Bal. Sh. Liab.
		Balance Sheet Accounts					Income Statement Accounts							
		1	2	3	4	5	6	7	8	9	10	11	12	13	14
ACCOUNT CREDITED	1			80	100					150	50	500		880	
	2	450												450	
	3								150					150	
	4			40									100	140	40
	5						150						2900	3050	3050
	6														
	7	400	600											1000	
	8														
	9														
	10														
	11														
Old Bal. Sh. Assets	12	600	1500	900											
Total Debit Bal.	13	1450	2100	1020	100		150		150	150	50	500			
New Bal. Sh. Assets	14	570	1650	870											

Figure 14

The only problem remaining is to calculate the balance sheet for January. This is done in the last row and last column of the matrix in Figure 14. For each balance sheet account, the total debits are *balanced* against the total credits. That is, we subtract a given total credits entry from the corresponding total debits entry and record the absolute value of the result next to whichever entry is larger. To illustrate this calculation for account (1), Cash, we see that the total debits are $1450 and the total credits are $880 so that 1450 − 880 = 570 is the difference which is then recorded as the new balance sheet debit (asset) in column 1, row 14. To illustrate a liability balance sheet calculation we consider (4), Accounts payable. Here there are $100 of debits and $140 credits so that we enter 140 − 100 = 40 as the new balance sheet credit (liability). The other balancing computations are similar.

From the last row and last column of Figure 14 we can now write the January balance sheet for the company, which is shown in Figure 15.

MORRISSEY APPLIANCE REPAIR COMPANY
Balance Sheet, January 31, 196–

Assets (*Debit Balances*)		*Liabilities and Equity* (*Credit Balances*)	
Cash.................	$ 570	Accounts payable....	$ 40
Accounts receivable....	1650	Equity.............	3050
Inventory............	870		$3090
	$3090		

Figure 15

The example above is quite simple and does not include all the ramifications possible in a full-fledged accounting system. For instance, we have ignored the problems of adjusting and reversing transactions, computing tax deductions, and preparing other kinds of financial statements. Some of these are considered in the exercises which follow. The techniques discussed in this section can easily be extended to handle these refinements.

EXERCISES

1. Let us consider errors in the transaction matrix as partitioned in Figure 10.
   (a) If an error occurs in the upper left-hand part of the matrix, show that only the balance sheet calculations will be affected.
   (b) If an error occurs in the lower right-hand part of the matrix, show that only the income statement calculations are affected. [*Hint*: Prove first that the profit or loss must be unchanged by such an error.]
   (c) Indicate how errors in the other two parts of the matrix affect each calculation.

2. In the example, suppose that Morrissey deducts 20% of his net profits to keep as a reserve for income taxes. Prepare a new income statement and balance sheet for January for him.

3. Use the data of Exercise 6 of the previous section to prepare financial reports for Morrissey's business at the end of February.

[*Partial Ans.* The net loss is $45.]

4. Use the data of Exercise 2 of the previous section to correct the financial reports of Morrissey's company for January. How do these changes affect the reports for February?

[*Partial Ans.* Only the balance sheet is affected.]

5. Let S and T be the (total) transaction matrices for two consecutive periods of a company's history. Let us compare the financial reports prepared from the matrices S, T, and $S + T$.
   (a) Show that the income statement for $S + T$ can be obtained by summing corresponding entries in S and T.
   (b) Show that the profit or loss for $S + T$ is the algebraic sum of the profits or losses for S and T.
   (c) Show that the balance sheet for $S + T$ can be obtained by summing corresponding entries in the balance sheets for S and T, and then balancing, if necessary.

6. Before preparing financial reports it is frequently necessary to record certain artificial transactions called *adjusting* transactions. These record amounts accrued for depreciation, interest, or rent, write-offs of bad debts, corrections of errors, etc. Adjusting transactions are like ordinary transactions, and can be represented by a matrix A, the *adjusting matrix*. If T is the transaction matrix for the period, then $T + A$ is the matrix actually used in preparing the financial reports. However, as soon as the reports are prepared, it is sometimes useful to reverse some of the adjusting transactions. This can be done by recording counter-transactions, called *reversing* transactions, which are also artificial. Let R be the *reversing matrix*, and let A' be a matrix which contains those transactions of the adjusting matrix which are to be reversed, and zeros elsewhere. There are two ways of recording the reversing transactions.
   (a) Show that the matrix $-A'$ can be used as the reversing matrix R.
   (b) Let C^{TR} be the transpose of C; i.e., the matrix obtained by interchanging the rows and columns of a matrix C. Show that $R = (A')^{TR}$ can be used as the reversing matrix.

7. For each of the examples of double classification systems mentioned in Exercise 7 of the preceding section, discuss what kinds of "financial" reports would be desirable. Devise matrix methods for preparing these reports.

8. (a) Show that the financial reports of Morrissey's company can be prepared knowing only row 13 and column 13 of the matrix of Figure 12.
   (b) Show, in general, that if we know the previous balance sheet together with the sum of the debits and the sum of the credits for each account for a given period, then we can prepare the financial reports for the period.

*9. Flow diagrams for double classification bookkeeping

Traditional double entry bookkeeping proceeds as follows: Daily transactions are recorded in books of original entry or journals. They are doubly classified, being recorded once as a debit and once as a credit. Periodically, the journal entries are transferred (posted) to the accounts or ledgers. Financial statements are then prepared from the ledgers. With the use of certain kinds of bookkeeping machines, the recordings in journals and the posting of ledgers is done automatically. However, even with these machines, a considerable amount of human labor is involved in the bookkeeping system.

We wish to describe, using flow diagrams, a double classification bookkeeping method which can be easily programmed for a digital computer. In order to save memory space we shall make use of the result of Exercise 8 of the preceding section and work from the sum of the debits and the sum of the credits of the accounts, without computing the entire transaction matrix. All arithmetic and transferring operations will be done by the computer.

The inputs to the program will be all the individual transactions (doubly classified) during a given period of time. Each such transaction can, for example, be recorded on a punched card, with the amount of the transaction, the number of the account to be credited and the number of the account to be debited. Included among these transactions are any made by management decision or policy, such as: dividends, bonuses, write-offs of intangibles, and extraordinary losses. (Additional adjusting transactions of various kinds, described in Exercise 6 of the preceding section, may also be made.) The computer program will then sum the debits in each account and the credits in each account, add in the balance sheet figures of the preceding period, and then prepare the income statement and balance sheet for the new period.

Note that human intervention is required only in doubly classifying and recording the transactions. This reduces the possibility of human error.

In order to describe the flow diagrams we will need to set up some notation. Let t_i represent a transaction. Each transaction can be summarized by three numbers: an amount a_i, the number $d(i)$ of an account to be debited, and the number $c(i)$ of an account to be credited. Thus we can represent t_i by the three-component vector

$$t_i = [a_i, d(i), c(i)].$$

We shall assume that the accounts have been numbered so that they follow the pattern of the Morrissey Appliance Repair Company. That is, first we list balance sheet accounts, then the profit or loss account, then revenue accounts, then expense accounts, and then withdrawal accounts. Specifically, the ranges of indices are assumed to be as follows:

$$\underbrace{1\ 2\ \ldots\ k}_{} \quad \underbrace{k+1}_{} \quad \underbrace{k+2\ \ldots\ h}_{} \quad \underbrace{h+1\ \ldots\ l}_{} \quad \underbrace{l+1\ \ldots\ n}_{}$$

| Balance Sheet accounts | Profit or loss | Revenue accounts | Expense accounts | Withdrawal accounts |

In particular, Account k is the "equity" or "earned surplus" or "net worth" account. Next, we let $D_1, \ldots, D_n$ and $C_1, \ldots, C_n$ be respectively the debit totals and credit totals of the various accounts for the period in question. Finally, we let $BD_1, \ldots, BD_k$, and $BC_1, \ldots, BC_k$ be the balance sheet assets and liabilities.

We now describe the computations by a series of three flow diagrams. Figure 16 shows the computation of the debit and credit balances of each

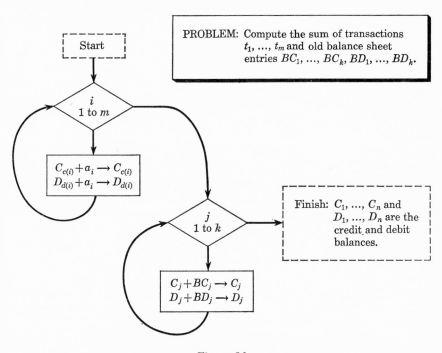

Figure 16

account. The first loop sums the individual transactions and the second loop adds in the previous balance sheet entries. Figure 17 shows the income statement calculations. The first loop sums the revenue accounts, the second loop sums the expense accounts, and the third loop sums the with-

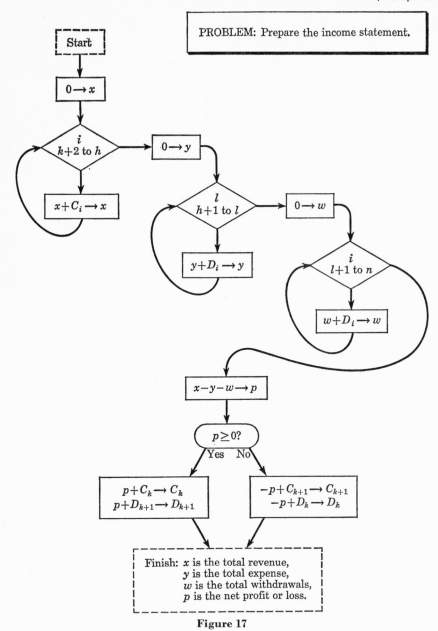

Figure 17

drawal accounts. Next, the net profit or loss, p, is computed and entered as a credit to equity if it is a profit, or as a debit to equity if it is a loss. Figure 18 shows the balance sheet calculations. Essentially, the only operation that remains to be done is to balance the first k accounts. The

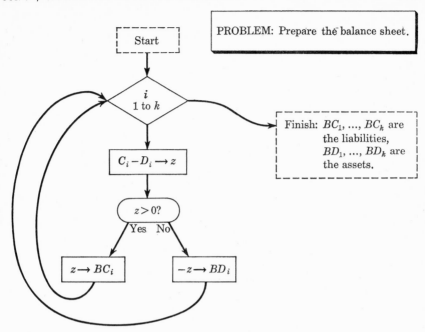

Figure 18

reader should convince himself that the fork in the diagram accomplishes the balancing operation.

Example. Let us illustrate the use of the flow diagrams by using them to compute again the Morrissey Appliance Repair Company financial reports for January. We have $k = 5$, $h = 7$, $l = 10$, and $n = 11$. In the tables of Figure 19 we list how the debit and credit vectors change during the course of

	D_1	D_2	D_3	D_4	D_5	D_6	D_7	D_8	D_9	D_{10}	D_{11}
(1)	850	600	120	100				150	150	50	500
(1′)	600	1500	900								
(2)	1450	2100	1020	100				150	150	50	500
(2′)						150					
(3)	1450	2100	1020	100		150		150	150	50	500
(4)	570	1650	870								

	C_1	C_2	C_3	C_4	C_5	C_6	C_7	C_8	C_9	C_{10}	C_{11}
(1)	880	450	150	40			1000				
(1′)				100	2900						
(2)	880	450	150	140	2900		1000				
(2′)					150						
(3)	880	450	150	140	3050		1000				
(4)				40	3050						

Figure 19

the computation. In the tables, line (1) gives the sums of the individual transactions and (1') gives the old balance sheet figures. Then (2) gives the values of the debit and credit vectors after these two are added together by the flow diagram of Figure 16. Then the income calculations are made as in the flow diagram of Figure 17. In the course of the calculation the quantities

$$x = 1000, \quad y = 350, \quad w = 500, \quad \text{and} \quad p = 150$$

will be found. The profit figure is recorded in line (2') of Figure 19. The final operation of balancing the balance sheet accounts is made according to the flow diagram of Figure 18, and yields the debit and credit vectors displayed on line (4) of the tables of Figure 19. (Note that we have also set the income statement account debit and credit balances back to zero to get ready for the next month's calculations.)

Briefly, after the operations of Figure 16 are made, the debit and credit vectors are given in line (2); after the income statement calculations are made they are given in line (3); and after the balance sheet calculations are made, they are given in line (4). It is instructive to carry out these computations following step by step the instructions of the flow diagrams.

EXERCISES

1. Modify the flow diagram of Figure 17 to permit the automatic deduction of 20% of net profit (*not* loss) for income taxes.

2. Consider as additional transactions the corrections given in Exercise 2 of Section 7 and recalculate the financial reports for Morrissey's company for January, using the flow diagrams of the present section.

3. Calculate the financial reports of Morrissey's company for February (see Exercise 6 of Section 7), using the flow diagrams of the present section.

4. Modify the flow diagrams to permit adjusting and reversing transactions to be recorded.

5. Devise a double-classification bookkeeping system for a small to medium sized company using the keysort system described in Chapter III, Section 1, Example 3. Write instructions for an operator to prepare financial reports manually, using the flow diagrams of the present section as a guide.

SUGGESTED READING

Bierman, H. and S. Smidt, *The Capital Budgeting Decision*, Macmillan, New York, 1960, Chapters III, VIII.

Goldberg, S., *Introduction to Difference Equations*, Wiley, New York, 1958, Chapter II.

Grant, E. L. and W. G. Ireson, *Principles of Engineering Economy* 4th ed., Ronald, New York, 1960, Chapters IV, XV, XVI.

Mattesich, R., "Towards a General and Axiomatic Foundation of Accountancy," *Accounting Research*, 8 (1957), pp. 328–353.

Morrissey, L.E., "The Many Sides of Depreciation," Tuck Bulletin 23, (1960), The Amos Tuck School of Business Administration, Dartmouth College, Hanover, New Hampshire.

VII

Linear Programming

---

1. Polyhedral convex sets

An equation containing one or more variables will be called an *open statement*. For instance,

(a) $$-2x_1 + 3x_2 = 6$$

is an example of an open statement. If we let $A = (-2, 3)$, $x = \begin{pmatrix} x_1 \\ x_2 \end{pmatrix}$, and $b = 6$ we can write (a) in matrix form as

$$Ax = (-2, 3)\begin{pmatrix} x_1 \\ x_2 \end{pmatrix} = -2x_1 + 3x_2 = 6 = b.$$

For some two-component vectors x the statement $Ax = b$ is true and for others it is false. For instance, if $x = \begin{pmatrix} 3 \\ 4 \end{pmatrix}$ it is true since $-2 \cdot 3 + 3 \cdot 4 = 6$, and if $x = \begin{pmatrix} 2 \\ 4 \end{pmatrix}$ it is false since $-2 \cdot 2 + 3 \cdot 4 = 8$. The set of all two-component vectors x that make the open statement $Ax = b$ true is defined to be the *truth set* of the open statement.

364

Example 1. In plane geometry it is usual to picture in the plane the truth sets of open statements such as (a). Thus we can regard each two-component vector x as being the components of a point in the plane in the usual way. Then the truth set or *locus* (which is the geometric term for truth set) of (a) is the straight line plotted in Figure 1. Points on this line may be obtained by assum-

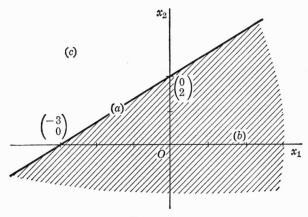

Figure 1

ing values for one of the variables and computing the corresponding values for the other variable. Thus, setting $x_1 = 0$, we find $x_2 = 2$, so that the point $x = \begin{pmatrix} 0 \\ 2 \end{pmatrix}$ lies on the locus; similarly, setting $x_2 = 0$, we find $x_1 = -3$, so that the point $\begin{pmatrix} -3 \\ 0 \end{pmatrix}$ lies on the locus, etc.

In the same way inequalities of the form $Ax \le b$ or $Ax < b$ or $Ax \ge b$ or $Ax > b$ are open statements and possess truth sets. And in the case that x is a two-component vector, these can be plotted in the plane.

Example 2. Consider the inequalities (b) $Ax < b$, (c) $Ax > b$, (d) $Ax \le b$, and (e) $Ax \ge b$, where A, x, and b are as in Example 1. They may be written as
(b) $-2x_1 + 3x_2 < 6$
(c) $-2x_1 + 3x_2 > 6$
(d) $-2x_1 + 3x_2 \le 6$
(e) $-2x_1 + 3x_2 \ge 6.$

Consider (b) first. What points $\begin{pmatrix} x_1 \\ x_2 \end{pmatrix}$ satisfy this inequality? By trial and error we can find many points on the locus. Thus the point $\begin{pmatrix} 1 \\ 2 \end{pmatrix}$ is on it since $-2\cdot 1 + 3\cdot 2 = 4 < 6$; on the other hand the point $\begin{pmatrix} 1 \\ 3 \end{pmatrix}$ is not on the locus because $-2\cdot 1 + 3\cdot 3 = -2 + 9 = 7$, which is not less than 6. In between these two points we find $\begin{pmatrix} 1 \\ \frac{8}{3} \end{pmatrix}$ which lies on the boundary, i.e., on the locus of (a).

We note that, starting with $\begin{pmatrix} 1 \\ \frac{8}{3} \end{pmatrix}$ on locus (a), by increasing x_2 we went outside the locus (b); by decreasing x_2 we came into the locus (b) again. This holds in general. Given a point on the locus of (a), by increasing its second coordinate we get more than 6, but by decreasing the second coordinate we get less than 6, and hence the latter gives a point in the truth set of (b). Thus we find that the locus of (b) consists of all points of the plane *below* the line (a), in other words, the shaded area in Figure 1. The area on one side of a straight line is called an *open half plane*.

We can apply exactly the same analysis to show that the locus of (c) is the open half plane above the line (a). This can also be deduced from the fact that the truth sets of statements (a), (b), and (c) are disjoint and have as union the entire plane.

Since (d) is the disjunction of (a) and (b), the truth set of (d) is the union of the truth sets of (a) and (b). Such a set, which consists of an open half plane together with the points on the line that define the half plane, is called a *closed half plane*. Obviously, the truth set of (e) consists of the union of (a) and (c) and therefore is also a closed half plane.

Frequently we want to assert several different open statements at once, that is, we want to assert the conjunction of several such statements. The easy way to do this is to let A be an $m \times n$ matrix, x an n-component column vector, and b an m-component column vector. Then the statement $Ax \leq b$ is the conjunction of the i statements $A_i x \leq b_i$ where A_i is the ith row of A and b_i is the ith entry of b.

Example 3. Consider the following example: $Ax \leq b$ where

$$A = \begin{pmatrix} -1 & 0 \\ 0 & -1 \\ 2 & 3 \end{pmatrix}, \quad x = \begin{pmatrix} x_1 \\ x_2 \end{pmatrix}, \quad b = \begin{pmatrix} 0 \\ 0 \\ 6 \end{pmatrix}.$$

If we write the components of the equations $Ax \leq b$, we obtain

(f) $-x_1 \leq 0$ which is equivalent to $x_1 \geq 0$
(g) $-x_2 \leq 0$ which is equivalent to $x_2 \geq 0$
(h) $2x_1 + 3x_2 \leq 6.$

Here we are simultaneously asserting three different statements; i.e., we assert their conjunction. Therefore the truth set of $Ax \leq b$ is the intersection of the three individual truth sets. The truth set of (f) is the right half plane; the truth set of (g) is the upper half plane; and the truth set of (h) is the half plane below the line $2x_1 + 3x_2 = 6$. The intersection of these is the triangle (including the sides) shaded in Figure 2. The area shaded in Figure 2 contains those points which simultaneously satisfy (f), (g), and (h).

In the examples so far we have restricted ourselves to open statements with two variables. Such statements have truth sets that can be sketched in the plane. In the same way open statements with three variables have truth sets that can be visualized in three-dimensional space. Open statements with four or more variables have truth sets in four or more dimensions, which we can no longer visualize. However, applied problems frequently lead to such statements. Fortunately, we will develop methods (in Section 4) for handling them without having to visualize the truth sets geometrically.

In order to have a notation that will enable us to talk in general about conjunctions of several open statements in any number of dimensions, we shall, for the remainder of this chapter, consider b to be an m-component column vector, x an n-component column vector, and A an $m \times n$ matrix. The ith row of A will be denoted by A_i. Similarly, the ith component of b will be denoted by b_i. Of course, A_i is an n-component row vector and b_i is a number. We shall let $\mathfrak{X}_n$ denote the set of all n-component column vectors x. Thus in Example 3 we had $m = 3$ and $n = 2$. A was a 3×2 matrix, x a two-component column vector, and b a three-component column vector. The set of all two-component column vectors x is denoted by $\mathfrak{X}_2$.

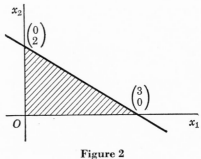

Figure 2

We now set up some definitions that will be used in the later exposition.

DEFINITION. The truth set of $A_i x = b_i$ is called a *hyperplane* in $\mathfrak{X}_n$. The truth sets of inequalities of the form $A_i x < b_i$ or $A_i x > b_i$ are called *open half spaces*, while the truth sets of the inequalities $A_i x \leq b_i$ or $A_i x \geq b_i$ are called *closed half spaces* in $\mathfrak{X}_n$.

When we assert the conjunction of several open statements the resulting truth set is the intersection of the truth sets of the individual open statements. Thus in Example 3 we have the conjunction of $m = 3$ open statements in $\mathfrak{X}_2$. In Figure 2 we show this geometrically as the intersection of $m = 3$ closed half spaces (planes) in $n = 2$ dimensions. Such intersections of closed half spaces are of special importance.

DEFINITION. The intersection of a finite number of closed half spaces is a *polyhedral convex set*.

THEOREM. Any polyhedral convex set is the truth set of an inequality statement of the form $Ax \leq b$.

Proof. A closed half space is the truth set of an inequality of the form $A_i x \leq b_i$. (An inequality of the form $A_i x \geq b_i$ can be converted into one of this form by multiplying by -1.) Now a polyhedral convex set is the truth set of the conjunction of several such statements. Since A is the matrix whose ith row is A_i and b is the column vector with components b_i, then the inequality statement $Ax \leq b$ is a succinct way of stating the conjunction of the inequalities $A_1x \leq b_1, \ldots, A_mx \leq b_m$. This completes the proof.

The terminology polyhedral *convex* sets is used because these sets are special examples of convex sets. A convex set C is a set such that whenever u and v are points of C, the entire line segment between u and v also belongs to C. This is equivalent to saying that all points of the form $z = au + (1 - a)v$ for $0 \leq a \leq 1$ belong to C whenever u and v do. We shall be concerned primarily with polyhedral convex sets in this chapter.

E X E R C I S E S

1. Draw pictures of the truth sets of $Ax \leq b$, where A and b are as given below. (Construct the truth sets of the individual statements first and then take their intersection.)

(a) $A = \begin{pmatrix} 1 & 0 \\ 0 & 1 \\ -2 & -3 \end{pmatrix}$, $b = \begin{pmatrix} 3 \\ 2 \\ 0 \end{pmatrix}$.

(b) $A = \begin{pmatrix} -2 & -3 \\ -1 & 1 \\ 1 & 1 \end{pmatrix}$, $b = \begin{pmatrix} -6 \\ 2 \\ 3 \end{pmatrix}$.

(c) $A = \begin{pmatrix} 2 & 3 \\ -1 & 1 \\ 1 & 1 \end{pmatrix}$, $b = \begin{pmatrix} 6 \\ 2 \\ 3 \end{pmatrix}$.

(d) $A = \begin{pmatrix} 0 & -1 \\ -1 & 0 \\ 1 & 0 \end{pmatrix}$, $b = \begin{pmatrix} 0 \\ 0 \\ 2 \end{pmatrix}$.

(e) $A = \begin{pmatrix} 1 & 0 \\ -1 & 0 \\ 0 & 1 \\ 0 & -1 \end{pmatrix}$, $b = \begin{pmatrix} 2 \\ 2 \\ 3 \\ 3 \end{pmatrix}$.

(f) $A = \begin{pmatrix} 3 & 2 \\ 3 & 2 \end{pmatrix}$, $b = \begin{pmatrix} -6 \\ 6 \end{pmatrix}$.

(g) $A = \begin{pmatrix} -3 & -2 \\ 3 & 2 \end{pmatrix}$, $b = \begin{pmatrix} -6 \\ 6 \end{pmatrix}$.

(h) $A = \begin{pmatrix} -1 & 1 \\ 1 & 1 \end{pmatrix}$, $b = \begin{pmatrix} 0 \\ 0 \end{pmatrix}$.

(i) $A = \begin{pmatrix} 1 & 0 \\ -1 & 0 \end{pmatrix}$, $b = \begin{pmatrix} 2 \\ -5 \end{pmatrix}$.

(j) $A = \begin{pmatrix} -3 & -2 \\ -2 & -3 \\ -1 & 0 \\ 0 & -1 \end{pmatrix}$, $b = \begin{pmatrix} -6 \\ -6 \\ 0 \\ 0 \end{pmatrix}$.

(k) $A = \begin{pmatrix} -2 & -1 \\ 1 & 0 \\ 0 & 1 \end{pmatrix}$, $b = \begin{pmatrix} -7 \\ 0 \\ 0 \end{pmatrix}$.

2. Consider the following sets:
   $\mathfrak{u}$ is the whole plane;
   A is the half plane which is the locus of $-2x_1 + x_2 < 3$.
   B is the half plane which is the locus of $-2x_1 + x_2 > 3$.
   C is the half plane which is the locus of $-2x_1 + x_2 \leq 3$.
   D is the half plane which is the locus of $-2x_1 + x_2 \geq 3$.
   L is the line which is the locus of $\qquad -2x_1 + x_2 = 3$.
   $\mathcal{E}$ is the empty set.
   Show that the following relationships hold among these sets: $\tilde{A} = D$, $\tilde{B} = C$, $\tilde{L} = A \cup B$, $C \cap D = L$, $A \cap B = \mathcal{E}$, $A \cap C = A$, $B \cap D = B$, $A \cup D = \mathfrak{u}$, $B \cup C = \mathfrak{u}$, $A \cup C = C$, $B \cup D = D$, $A \cup L = C$, $B \cup L = D$. Can you find other relationships?

3. Of the polyhedral convex sets constructed in Exercise 1, which have a finite area and which have infinite area?
   [*Partial Ans.* (c), (d), (f), (h), and (j) are of infinite area; (g) is a line; (i) and (k) are empty.]

4. For each of the following half planes give an inequality of which it is the truth set.
   (a) The open half plane above the x_1-axis.   [*Ans.* $x_2 > 0$.]
   (b) The closed half plane on and above the straight line making angles of 45° with the positive x_1- and x_2-axis.

Exercises 5–9 refer to a situation in which a retailer is trying to decide how many units of items A and B he should keep in stock. Let x be the number of units of A and y be the number of units of B. A costs \$4 per unit and B costs \$3 per unit.

5. One cannot stock a negative number of units of either A or B. Write these conditions as inequalities and draw their truth sets.

6. The maximum demand over the period for which the retailer is contemplating holding inventory will not exceed 600 units of A or 600 units of B. Modify the set found in Exercise 5 to take this into account.

7. The retailer is not willing to tie up more than \$2400 in inventory altogether. Modify the set found in Exercise 6.

8. The retailer decides to invest at least twice as much in inventory of item A as he does in inventory of item B. Modify the set of Exercise 7.

9. Finally, the retailer decides that he wants to invest \$900 in inventory of item B. What possibilities are left?   [*Ans.* None.]

10. Assume that the minimal nutritional requirements of human beings are given by the following table:

	Phosphorus	Calcium
Adult	.02	.01
Child	.03	.03
Infant	.01	.02

Plot the amount of phosphorus on the vertical axis and the amount of calcium on the horizontal. Then draw in the convex sets of minimal diet requirements for adults, children (noninfants), and infants. State whether or not the following assertions are true.

(a) If a child's needs are satisfied, so are an adult's.

(b) An infant's needs are satisfied only if a child's needs are.

(c) An adult's needs are satisfied only if an infant's needs are.

(d) Both an adult's and an infant's needs are satisfied only if a child's needs are.

(e) It is possible to satisfy adult needs without satisfying the needs of an infant.

11. Prove that the following sets are convex. Which are polyhedral convex sets?

(a) The interior plus the edges of a triangle.

(b) The interior of a circle.

(c) The interior of a rectangle.

(d) A rectangle surmounted by a semicircle.

12. Consider the plane with a cartesian coordinate system. A rectangle with sides of length a_1 and a_2 ($a_1 \neq a_2$) is placed with one corner at the origin and two of its sides along the axes. Prove that the interior of the rectangle plus its edges forms a polyhedral convex set and find the statement of the form $Ax \leq b$ of which it is the truth set.

13. The following polygons are placed in a plane with a cartesian coordinate system with one corner at the origin and one side along an axis. Find the statements $Ax \leq b$ of which they are the truth sets.

(a) A regular pentagon.

(b) A regular hexagon.

2. Extreme points; maxima and minima of linear functions

In the present section we first discuss the problem of finding the extreme points of a bounded convex polyhedral set. Then we find out how to compute the maximum and minimum values of a linear function defined on such a set.

We use the following notation: The polyhedral convex set C is the truth set of the statement $Ax \leq b$ where A is an $m \times n$ matrix, x is an n-component column vector, and b is an m-component column vector. We let $A_1, A_2, \ldots, A_m$ denote the rows of A. Hence A_i is an n-component row vector and

$$A = \begin{pmatrix} A_1 \\ A_2 \\ \cdot \\ \cdot \\ \cdot \\ A_m \end{pmatrix}.$$

The statement $Ax \leq b$ is then the conjunction of the statements

$$A_1x \leq b_1, \quad A_2x \leq b_2, \quad \ldots, \quad A_mx \leq b_m.$$

DEFINITION. We shall call the truth set of the statement $A_ix = b_i$ the *bounding hyperplane* of the half space $A_ix \leq b_i$.

Thus, in Figure 1 of the preceding section the slanting line (a) is the bounding hyperplane of the half space (b).

Sometimes it happens that one of the inequality statements defining a polyhedral convex set is unnecessary. We shall say that the inequality $A_ix \leq b_i$ is *superfluous* if the truth set of the conjunction of all the statements $A_1x \leq b_1, \ldots, A_mx \leq b_m$ is the same as the conjunction of all these statements except for $A_ix \leq b_i$. For instance, in Example 3 of Section 1, if we add the statement $x_1 \geq -1$ to the statements defining the polyhedral convex set there, it is superfluous, since the statement $x_1 \geq 0$ implies $x_1 \geq -1$. Other examples of superfluous statements are given in Exercise 1. Obviously, the elimination of superfluous inequalities does not change the polyhedral convex set C, and we shall assume that all such superfluous inequalities have been removed.

If the inequality $A_ix \leq b_i$ is not superfluous then its bounding hyperplane $A_ix = b_i$ must contain a point of the polyhedral convex set C.

DEFINITION. Let C be the polyhedral convex set defined by $Ax \leq b$. Then the *bounding hyperplanes* of C are the bounding hyperplanes of the (nonsuperfluous) half spaces of which C is the intersection.

In Example 3 of Section 1 the bounding hyperplanes of the polyhedral convex set given there are the three boundary lines of the triangle shaded in Figure 2. Note that these lines intersect in pairs in three points, the vertices of the triangle.

DEFINITION. Let C be the polyhedral convex set defined by $Ax \leq b$, where x is an n-component vector. Then a point T is an *extreme* (or *corner*) *point* of C if it

(a) belongs to C, and

(b) is the intersection of n bounding hyperplanes of C.

Example 1. Find the extreme points of the polyhedral convex set $Ax \leq b$ where

$$A = \begin{pmatrix} -2 & -1 \\ 1 & -3 \\ 1 & 2 \end{pmatrix}, \quad b = \begin{pmatrix} 9 \\ 6 \\ 3 \end{pmatrix}.$$

A sketch of the three half planes, Figure 3, shows that the set is a triangle.

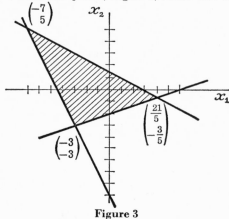

Figure 3

Hence we can find the extreme points by changing the inequalities to equalities in pairs and solving three sets of simultaneous equations. We obtain in this way the points

$$\begin{pmatrix} -3 \\ -3 \end{pmatrix}, \quad \begin{pmatrix} -7 \\ 5 \end{pmatrix}, \quad \text{and} \quad \begin{pmatrix} \frac{21}{5} \\ -\frac{3}{5} \end{pmatrix},$$

which are the extreme points of the set.

We can now give an interpretation for the various points of the polyhedral convex set in terms of the system of inequalities. An extreme point lies on two boundaries, which means that two of the inequalities are actually equalities. A point on a side, other than an extreme point, lies on one boundary and hence one inequality is an equality. An interior point of the polygon must, by a process of elimination, correspond to the case where the inequalities are all strict inequalities, i.e., not only $\leq$ but $<$ holds.

There is a mechanical (but lengthy) method for finding all the extreme points of a polyhedral convex set C defined by $Ax \leq b$. Consider the bounding hyperplanes $A_1x = b_1, \ldots, A_mx = b_m$ of the half spaces that determine C. Select a subset of n of these hyperplanes and solve their equations simultaneously. If the result is a unique point x^0 (and only then) check to see whether or not x^0 belongs to C. If it does, by the above definition, x^0 is an extreme point of C. Moreover, all extreme points of C can be found in this manner.

Example 2. Let

$$A = \begin{pmatrix} -1 & 0 \\ 0 & -1 \end{pmatrix} \quad \text{and} \quad b = \begin{pmatrix} 0 \\ 0 \end{pmatrix}.$$

Then the polyhedral convex set C defined by $Ax \leq b$ is the first quadrant of the x_1, x_2 plane, shaded in Figure 4. The only extreme point is the origin, which

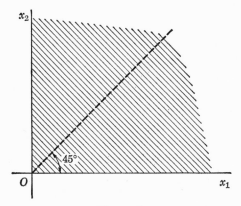

Figure 4

is the intersection of the lines $x_1 = 0$ and $x_2 = 0$. This is an example of an *unbounded* polyhedral convex set.

Notice that the set C contains the *ray* or half line that starts at the origin of coordinates and extends upward to the right making a 45° angle with the axes. This ray is dotted in Figure 4. Of course, this set also contains many other rays.

We shall say that a polyhedral convex set is *bounded* if it does not contain a ray. A set, such as the one in Figure 4, that does contain rays will be called *unbounded*. For simplicity we shall restrict our discussion to bounded convex sets in most of this chapter. In particular this means that necessarily $m > n$, that is, the convex set must be the intersection of at least $n + 1$ half spaces. This is a necessary but not sufficient condition that the convex set is bounded (see Exercise 23).

Example 3. Let us suppose that in a business problem x_1 and x_2 are quantities we can control, except that there are limitations imposed which can be stated as inequalities. We shall assume that the system of inequalities given in Example 1 limits our choice of x_1 and x_2. Let us assume that a given choice of x_1 and x_2 results in a profit of $x_1 + 2x_2$ dollars. What is the most and the least profit we can make? We must find the maximum and the minimum value of

$x_1 + 2x_2$ for points (x_1, x_2) in the triangle. Let us first try the extreme points. At $(-3, -3)$ we would have a profit of -9, i.e., a loss of \$9. At $(-7, 5)$ we have a profit of \$3, and at $(\frac{21}{5}, -\frac{3}{5})$ also a profit of \$3. What can we say about the remainder of the triangle? The last inequality tells that $x_1 + 2x_2 \leq 3$, hence our profit cannot be more than \$3. If we multiply the first inequality by $\frac{5}{7}$ and the second by $\frac{3}{7}$ and add them, we find that $x_1 + 2x_2 \geq -9$; hence, we cannot lose more than \$9. We have thus shown that both the greatest profit and the greatest loss occur at an extreme point. We will show that this is true in general.

Given a convex polyhedral set C and a linear function

$$cx = c_1x_1 + c_2x_2 + \ldots + c_nx_n$$

where $c = (c_1, c_2, \ldots, c_n)$, we want to show in general that the maximum and minimum values of the function cx always occur at extreme points of C. We shall carry out the proof for the planar case in which $n = 2$, but our results are true in general.

First, we will show that the values of the linear function $c_1x_1 + c_2x_2$ on any line segment lie *between* the values the function has at the two end points (possibly equal to the value at one end point). We represent the points as column vectors $\begin{pmatrix} x_1 \\ x_2 \end{pmatrix}$ and then we see that our linear function is represented by the row vector (c_1, c_2). Let the end points of the segment be

$$p = \begin{pmatrix} x_1' \\ x_2' \end{pmatrix} \quad \text{and} \quad q = \begin{pmatrix} x_1'' \\ x_2'' \end{pmatrix}.$$

We have seen in Chapter V (see Figure 4) that the points in between p and q can be represented as $tp + (1 - t)q$, with $0 \leq t \leq 1$. If the values of the function at the points p and q are P and Q, respectively (assume that $P \geq Q$), then at a point in between the value will be $tP + (1 - t)Q$, since the function is linear. This value can also be written as

$$tP + (1 - t)Q = Q + (P - Q)t$$

which (for $0 \leq t \leq 1$) is at least Q and at most P.

We are now in a position to prove the result illustrated in Example 3.

THEOREM. A linear function cx defined over a convex polyhedral set C takes on its maximum (and minimum) value at an extreme point of C.

The proof of the theorem is illustrated in Figure 5. We shall suppose that at the extreme point p the function takes on a value P greater than or equal to the value at any other extreme point, and at the extreme point q it takes on its smallest extreme point value, Q. Let r be any point of the polygon. Draw a straight line between p and r and continue it until it cuts the polygon again at a point u lying on an edge of the polygon, say the edge between the corner points s and t. (The line may even cut the edge at one of the points s and t; the analysis remains unchanged.) By hypothesis the value of the function at any corner point must lie between Q and P. By the above result the value of the function at u must lie between its values at s and t, and hence must also lie between Q and P. Again by the above

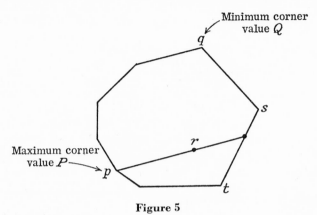

Figure 5

result the value of the function at r must lie between its values at p and u, and hence must also lie between Q and P. Since r was any point of the polygon our theorem is proved.

Suppose that in place of the linear function $c_1x_1 + c_2x_2$ we had considered the function $c_1x_1 + c_2x_2 + k$. The addition of the constant k merely changes every value of the function, including the maximum and minimum values of the function, by that amount. Hence the analysis of where the maximum and minimum values of the function are taken on is unchanged. Therefore, we have the following theorem.

THEOREM. The function $cx + k$ defined over a convex polyhedral set C takes on its maximum (and minimum) value at an extreme point of C.

A method of finding the maximum or minimum of the function $cx + k$ defined over a convex set C is then the following: find the extreme points of the set; there will be a finite number of them; substitute the coordinates of each into the function; the largest of the values so obtained will be the maximum of the function and the smallest value will be the minimum of the function. The method is illustrated in Example 3 above.

In Section 4 we will describe the so-called *simplex method*, which is a considerably more efficient method for solving the above problem.

EXERCISES

1. In the following sets of inequalities at least one is superfluous. In each case find the superfluous ones.

(a) $x_1 + x_2 \leq 3$ (b) $x_1 + x_2 \geq 0$
    $-x_1 - x_2 \geq 0$ $x_1 - x_2 \leq 0$
        $x_1 \geq -1$ $x_1 \leq 4$
    $-x_2 \leq 2.$ $x_2 \geq -4.$

(c) $-1 \leq x_1 \leq 1$
    $-2 \leq x_2 \leq 2$
    $x_1 + x_2 \geq -10$
    $2x_1 - x_2 \leq 2.$ [*Ans.* (a) $x_1 + x_2 \leq 3.$]

2. (a) Draw a picture of the convex set defined by the inequalities

$$2x_1 + x_2 + 9 \leq 0$$
$$-x_1 + 3x_2 + 6 \leq 0$$
$$x_1 + 2x_2 - 3 \leq 0.$$

(b) What is the relationship between this and Figure 3?

3. Find the corner points of the convex polygons given in parts (a), (b), and (e) of Exercise 1 of Section 1.

$$\left[\textit{Ans. (a)} \ \binom{3}{-2}, \binom{3}{2}, \binom{-3}{2}; \text{(e)} \ \binom{2}{3}, \binom{-2}{3}, \binom{2}{-3}, \binom{-2}{-3}.\right]$$

4. (a) Show that the three lines whose equations are

$$2x_1 + x_2 + 9 = 0$$
$$-x_1 + 3x_2 + 6 = 0$$
$$x_1 + 2x_2 - 3 = 0$$

divide the plane into seven convex regions. Mark these regions with Roman numerals I–VII.

(b) For each of the seven regions found in part (a), write a set of three inequalities, having the region as its locus. [*Hint:* Two of these sets of inequalities are considered in Exercise 2.]

(c) There is one more way of putting inequality signs into the three equations given in (a). What is the locus of this last set of inequalities?
[*Ans.* The empty set $\mathcal{E}$.]

5. A convex polygon has the points $(-1, 0)$, $(3, 4)$, $(0, -3)$, and $(1, 6)$ as extreme points. Find a set of inequalities which defines the convex polygon having these extreme points.

6. Find the extreme points of the convex polygon given by the equations

$$2x_1 + x_2 + 9 \geq 0$$
$$-x_1 + 3x_2 + 6 \geq 0$$
$$x_1 + 2x_2 - 3 \leq 0$$
$$x_1 + x_2 \leq 0.$$

[*Hint:* Use some of the results of Example 1 in the text.]

7. Find the extreme values of the function **G** defined by

$$\mathbf{G}(x) = 7x_1 + 5x_2 - 3$$

over the convex polygon of Exercise 6.

8. Find the maximum and minimum of the function

$$G(x) = -2x_1 + 5x_2 + 17$$

over each of the convex polygons given in parts (a), (b), and (e) of Exercise 1 of Section 1. [*Ans.* (a) 33, 1 (e) 36, −2.]

9. Find the maximum and minimum, when they exist, of the function

$$G(x) = 5x_1 + 3x_2 - 6$$

over each of the polyhedral convex sets given in parts (h) and (j) of Exercise 1 of Section 1.

[*Ans.* (h) Neither maximum nor minimum; (j)minimum is 3.]

10. The owner of an oil truck with a capacity of 500 gallons hauls gasoline and oil products from city to city. On any given trip he wishes to load his truck with at least 200 gallons of regular test gasoline, at least 100 gallons of high test gasoline, and at most 150 gallons of kerosene. Assuming that he always fills his truck to capacity, find the convex set of ways that he can load his truck. Interpret the extreme points of the set. [*Hint:* There are four extreme points.]

11. An advertiser wishes to sponsor a half hour television comedy and must decide on the composition of the show. The advertiser insists that there be at least three minutes of commercials, while the television network requires that the commercial time be limited to at most 15 minutes. The comedian refuses to work more than 22 minutes each half hour show. If a band is added to the show to play during the time that neither the comedian nor the commercials are on, construct the convex set C of possible assignments of time to the comedian, the commercials, and the band that use up the 30 minutes. Find the extreme points of C.

[*Ans.* If x_1 is the comedian time, x_2 the commercial time, and $30 - x_1 - x_2$ the band time, the extreme points are

$$\begin{pmatrix} 0 \\ 3 \end{pmatrix}, \begin{pmatrix} 22 \\ 3 \end{pmatrix}, \begin{pmatrix} 22 \\ 8 \end{pmatrix}, \begin{pmatrix} 15 \\ 15 \end{pmatrix} \text{ and } \begin{pmatrix} 0 \\ 15 \end{pmatrix}.]$$

12. In Exercise 10 suppose that the oil truck operator gets 3 cents per gallon for delivering regular gasoline, 2 cents per gallon for high test, and 1 cent per gallon for kerosene. Write the expression that gives the total amount he will get paid for each possible load that he carries. How should he load his truck in order to earn the maximum amount?

[*Ans.* He should carry 400 gallons of regular gasoline, 100 gallons of high test, and no kerosene.]

13. In Exercise 12, if he gets 3 cents per gallon of regular and 2 cents per gallon of high test gasoline, how high must his payment for kerosene become before he will load it on his truck in order to make a maximum profit?

[*Ans.* He must get paid at least 3 cents per gallon of kerosene.]

14. In Exercise 11 let x_1 be the number of minutes the comedian is on, and x_2 be the number of minutes the commercial is on the program. Suppose the comedian costs \$200 per minute, the commercials cost \$50 per minute, and the band is free. How should the advertiser choose the composition of the show in order that its cost be a minimum?

15. Consider the polyhedral convex set P defined by the inequalities

$$-1 \leq x_1 \leq 4$$
$$0 \leq x_2 \leq 6.$$

Find four different sets of conditions on the constants a and b that the function $\mathbf{F}(x) = ax_1 + bx_2$ should have its maximum at one and only one of the four corner points of P. Find conditions that $\mathbf{F}$ should have its minimum at each of these points.

[*Ans.* For example, the maximum is at $\begin{pmatrix} 4 \\ 6 \end{pmatrix}$ if $a > 0$ and $b > 0$.]

16. Let $\mathbf{H}$ be the quadratic function defined by $\mathbf{H}(x) = (x_1 - \tfrac{1}{4})^2 + (x_2 - \tfrac{1}{4})^2$ on the convex set C which is the truth set of the inequalities

$$x_1 + x_2 \leq 1, \qquad x_1 \geq 0, \qquad x_2 \geq 0.$$

Are the maximum and minimum values of $\mathbf{H}$ taken on at the extreme points of C? Discuss reasons why this problem is essentially harder than that of finding the extreme values of a linear function on a polyhedral convex set.

17. A set of points is said to be convex if whenever it contains two points it also contains the line segment connecting them. Show that:
   (a) If two points are in the truth set of an inequality, then any point on the connecting segment is also in the truth set.
   (b) Every polygonal convex set is a convex set in the above-mentioned sense.

18. Give an example of a quadrilateral that is not a convex set.

19. Prove that for any three vectors u, v, w, the set of all points $au + bv + cw$ ($a \geq 0$, $b \geq 0$, $c \geq 0$, $a + b + c = 1$) is a convex set. What geometric figure is this locus? [*Ans.* In general, the locus is a triangle.]

20. Let C be any plane polyhedral convex set. Show that if x is a point that lies on three bounding lines of C, then one of the inequalities defining C is superfluous.

21. Let x and y be two distinct points of a polyhedral convex set C, let t be a number such that $0 < t < 1$, and define $z = tx + (1 - t)y$. Show that z is not an extreme point of C.

22. Prove that the intersection of two half planes is a bounded convex set only if it is empty.

23. Construct examples that show that the intersection of three half planes either may or may not be a bounded convex set.

3. Linear programming problems

An important class of practical problems are those which require the determination of the maximum or the minimum of a linear function $cx + k$ defined over a polyhedral convex set of points C. We illustrate these so-called *linear programming problems* by means of the following examples. In the next section we shall discuss the simplex method for solving these examples.

Example 1. An automobile manufacturer makes automobiles and trucks in a factory that is divided into two shops. Shop 1, which performs the basic assembly operation, must work 5 man-days on each truck but only 2 man-days on each automobile. Shop 2, which performs finishing operations, must work 3 man-days for each automobile or truck that it produces. Because of men and machine limitations Shop 1 has 180 man-days per week available while Shop 2 has 135 man-days per week. If the manufacturer makes a profit of $300 on each truck and $200 on each automobile, how many of each should he produce to maximize his profit?

To state the problem mathematically we set up the following notation: Let x_1 be the number of trucks and x_2 the number of automobiles to be produced per week. Then these quantities must satisfy the following restrictions:

$$5x_1 + 2x_2 \le 180$$
$$3x_1 + 3x_2 \le 135.$$

We want to maximize the linear function $300x_1 + 200x_2$, subject to these inequality constraints, together with the obviously necessary constraints that $x_1 \ge 0$ and $x_2 \ge 0$.

To further simplify notation we define the quantities

$$A = \begin{pmatrix} 5 & 2 \\ 3 & 3 \end{pmatrix}, \quad b = \begin{pmatrix} 180 \\ 135 \end{pmatrix} \quad \text{and} \quad c = (300, 200).$$

Then we can state this linear programming problem as follows.

Maximum problem: Determine the vector x so that the weekly profit, given by the quantity cx, is a maximum subject to the inequality constraints $Ax \le b$ and $x \ge 0$. The inequality constraints insure that the weekly number of available man-hours is not exceeded and that nonnegative quantities of automobiles and trucks are produced.

The graph of the convex set of possible x vectors is pictured in Figure 6. Clearly this is a problem of the kind discussed in the previous section.

The extreme points of the convex set C are

$$T_1 = \begin{pmatrix} 0 \\ 0 \end{pmatrix}, \quad T_2 = \begin{pmatrix} 36 \\ 0 \end{pmatrix}, \quad T_3 = \begin{pmatrix} 0 \\ 45 \end{pmatrix} \quad \text{and} \quad T_4 = \begin{pmatrix} 30 \\ 15 \end{pmatrix}.$$

Following the solution procedure outlined in the previous section we test the function $cx = 300x_1 + 200x_2$ at each of these extreme points. The values taken on are 0, 10800, 9000, and 12000. Thus the maximum weekly profit is $12,000 and is achieved by producing 30 trucks and 15 automobiles per week.

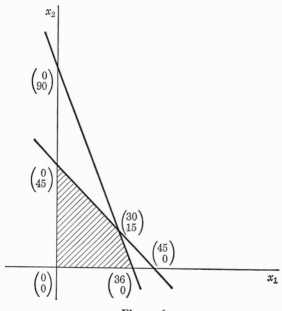

Figure 6

Example 2. A mining company owns two different mines that produce a given kind of ore. The mines are located in different parts of the country and hence have different production capacities. After crushing, the ore is graded into three classes: high-grade, medium-grade, and low-grade ores. There is some demand for each grade of ore. The mining company has contracted to provide a smelting plant with 12 tons of high-grade, 8 tons of medium-grade, and 24 tons of low-grade ore per week. It costs the company $200 per day to run the first mine and $160 per day to run the second. However, in a day's operation the first mine produces 6 tons of high-grade, 2 tons of medium-grade, and 4 tons of low-grade ore, while the second mine produces daily 2 tons of high-grade, 2 tons of medium-grade, and 12 tons of low-grade ore. How many days a week should each mine be operated in order to fulfill the company's orders most economically?

Before solving the problem it is convenient to summarize the above information as in the tableau of Figure 7. The numbers in the tableau form a 2-by-3 matrix, the requirements form a row vector c, and the costs form a column vector b. The entries in the matrix indicate the production of each kind of ore by the mines, the entries in the requirements vector c indicate the quantities that must be produced, and the entries in the cost vector b indicate the daily costs of running each mine.

	High Grade Ore	Medium Grade Ore	Low Grade Ore	
Mine 1	6	2	4	$200 ⎫
Mine 2	2	2	12	$160 ⎭ b
	12	8	24	

c

Figure 7

Let $w = (w_1, w_2)$ be the 2-component row vector whose component w_1 gives the number of days per week that mine 1 operates and w_2 gives the number of days per week that mine 2 operates. If we define the quantities

$$A = \begin{pmatrix} 6 & 2 & 4 \\ 2 & 2 & 12 \end{pmatrix}, \quad c = (12, 8, 24), \quad \text{and} \quad b = \begin{pmatrix} 200 \\ 160 \end{pmatrix},$$

we can state the above problem as a minimum problem.

Minimum problem: Determine the vector w so that the weekly operating cost, given by the quantity wb, is a minimum subject to the inequality restraints $wA \geq c$ and $w \geq 0$. The inequality restraints insure that the weekly output requirements are met and the limits on the components of w are not exceeded.

It is clear that this is a minimum problem of the type discussed in detail in the preceding section. In Figure 8 we have graphed the convex polyhedral set C defined by the inequalities $wA \geq c$.

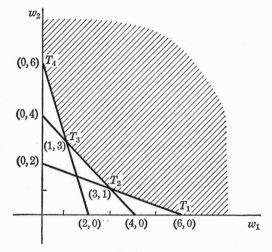

Figure 8

The extreme points of the convex set C are

$$T_1 = (6, 0), \quad T_2 = (3, 1), \quad T_3 = (1, 3), \quad T_4 = (0, 6).$$

Testing the function $wb = 200w_1 + 160w_2$ at each of these extreme points we see that it takes on the values 1200, 760, 680, and 960, respectively. We see that the minimum operating cost is $680 per week and it is achieved at T_3, i.e., by operating the first mine one day per week and the second mine three days a week.

Observe that if the mines are operated as indicated, then the combined weekly production will be 12 tons of high-grade ore, 8 tons of medium-grade ore, and 40 tons of low-grade ore. In other words, for this solution low-grade ore is overproduced. If the company has no other demand for the low-grade ore, then it must discard 16 tons of it per week in this minimum-cost solution of its production problem. We shall discuss this point further in Section 5.

Example 3. As a variant of Example 2, assume that the cost vector is $b = \begin{pmatrix} 160 \\ 200 \end{pmatrix}$; in other words the first mine now has a lower daily cost than the second. By the same procedure as above we find that the minimum cost level is again $680 and is achieved by operating the first mine three days a week and the second mine one day per week. In this solution 20 tons of high-grade ore, instead of the required 12 tons, are produced, while the requirements of medium- and low-grade ores are exactly met. Thus eight tons of high-grade ore must be discarded per week.

Example 4. As another variant of Example 2, assume that the cost vector is $b = \begin{pmatrix} 200 \\ 200 \end{pmatrix}$; in other words, both mines have the same production costs. Evaluating the cost function wb at the extreme points of the convex set we find costs of $1200 on two of the extreme points (T_1 and T_4) and costs of $800 on the other two extreme points (T_2 and T_3). Thus the minimum cost is attained by operating either one of the mines three days a week and the other one one day a week. But there are other solutions, since if the minimum is taken on at two distinct extreme points it is also taken on at each of the points on the line segment between. Thus any vector w where $1 \le w_1 \le 3$, $1 \le w_2 \le 3$, and $w_1 + w_2 = 4$ also gives a minimum-cost solution. For example, each mine could operate two days a week.

It can be shown (see Exercise 2) that for any solution w with $1 < w_1 < 3$, $1 < w_2 < 3$, and $w_1 + w_2 = 4$, both high-grade and low-grade ore are overproduced.

EXERCISES

1. In Example 1, assume that profits are $200 per truck and $300 per automobile. What should the factory now produce for maximum profit?

2. In Example 4, show that both high- and low-grade ore are overproduced for solution vectors w with $1 < w_1 < 3$, $1 < w_2 < 3$, and $w_1 + w_2 = 4$.

3. A well-known nursery rhyme says "Jack Sprat could eat no fat. His wife (call her Jill) could eat no lean. . . ." Suppose Jack wishes to have at least one pound of lean meat per day, while Jill needs at least .4 pound of fat per day. Assume they buy only beef having 10 per cent fat and 90 per cent lean, and pork having 40 per cent fat and 60 per cent lean. Jack and Jill want to fulfill their minimal diet requirements at the lowest possible cost.

(a) Let x be the amount of beef and y the amount of pork which they purchase per day. Construct the convex set of points in the plane representing purchases that fulfill both persons' minimum diet requirements.

(b) Suggest necessary restrictions on the purchases, that will change this set into a convex polygon.

(c) If beef costs \$1 per pound, and pork costs 50 cents per pound, show that the diet of least cost has only pork, and find the minimum cost.
[*Ans.* \$.83.]

(d) If beef costs 75 cents and pork costs 50 cents per pound, show that there is a whole line segment of solution points and find the minimum cost.
[*Ans.* \$.83.]

(e) If beef and pork each cost \$1 a pound, show that the unique minimal cost diet has both beef and pork. Find the minimum cost.
[*Ans.* \$1.40.]

(f) Show that the restriction made in part (b) did not alter the answer given in (c)–(e).

4. In Exercise 3(d) show that for all but one of the minimal cost diets Jill has more than her minimum requirement of fat, while Jack always gets exactly his minimal requirement of lean. Show that all but one of the minimal cost diets contains some beef.

5. In Exercise 3(e) show that Jack and Jill each get exactly their minimal requirements.

6. In Exercise 3, if the price of pork is fixed at \$1 a pound, how low must the price of beef fall before Jack and Jill will eat only beef? [*Ans.* \$.25.]

7. In Exercise 3, suppose that Jack decides to reduce his minimal requirement to .6 pound of lean meat per day. How does the convex set change? How do the solutions in 3(c), (d), and (e) change?

8. A poultry farmer raises chickens, ducks, and turkeys and has room for 500 birds on his farm. While he is willing to have a total of 500 birds, he does not want more than 300 ducks on his farm at any one time. Suppose that a chicken costs \$1.50, a duck \$1.00, and a turkey \$4.00 to raise to maturity. Assume that the farmer can sell chickens for \$3.00, ducks for \$2.00, and turkeys for T dollars each. He wants to decide which kind of poultry to raise in order to maximize his profit.

(a) Let x be the number of chickens and y be the number of ducks he will raise. Then $500 - x - y$ is the number of turkeys he raises. What is the convex set of possible values of x and y which satisfy the above restrictions?

(b) Find the expression for the cost of raising x chickens, y ducks, and $(500 - x - y)$ turkeys. Find the expression for the total amount he gets for these birds. Compute the profit which he would make under these circumstances.

(c) If $T = \$6.00$, show that to obtain maximal profit the farmer should raise only turkeys. What is the maximum profit?   [*Ans.* \$1000.]

(d) If $T = \$5.00$, show that he should raise only chickens and find his maximum profit.   [*Ans.* \$750.]

(e) If $T = \$5.50$, show that he can raise any combination of chickens and turkeys and find his maximum profit.   [*Ans.* \$750.]

9. Rework Exercise 8 if the price of chickens drops to \$2.00 and T is (a) \$6.00, (b) \$5.00, (c) \$4.50, and (d) \$4.00.

10. In Exercise 8 show that if the price of turkeys drops below \$5.50, the farmer should raise only chickens. Also show that if the price is above \$5.50, he should raise only turkeys.

11. In Exercise 10 of Section 2, assume that the truck operator gets p cents a gallon for regular gasoline, q cents a gallon for high-test gasoline, and r cents a gallon for kerosene. Show that he will carry kerosene for maximum profit only if $r \geq p$ and $r \geq q$.

12. In Exercise 11 of Section 2, suppose that for each minute the comedian is on the program 70,000 more people will tune in, for each minute the band is on 10,000 more people will tune in, and for each minute the commercial is on 1 more person will tune in. Let $\mathbf{N}$ be the function that gives the number of persons that tune in for each point in C. How should the times be allotted in order that $\mathbf{N}$ be a maximum?

[*Ans.* There should be 3 minutes of commercials, 22 minutes of the comedian, and 5 minutes of band music.]

13. In Exercise 11 of Section 2, assume that the band and comedian each cost \$200 per minute while the commercials cost \$50 per minute. Write the function that gives the cost of the program. Show that there is a whole line segment of minimum cost solutions.

[*Ans.* The commercials are on for 15 minutes while the band and comedian can share the remaining 15 minutes in any manner.]

4. The simplex method for solving linear programming problems

In Chapter V we developed an algorithm for finding solutions to simultaneous equations in many unknowns of the form

(1) $$Ax = b.$$

The reader will recall that when the solution was unique what we did was by row transformations to

(2)   transform $(A \mid b)$ into $(I \mid x)$.

We now know that geometrically this procedure is equivalent to finding the intersection of n hyperplanes in n-dimensional space. Fortunately, the algorithm (2) does not require us to be able to visualize geometrically the solution technique for the problem.

In Section 3 we solved simple linear programming problems having two variables by sketching convex sets in the plane. To solve such problems in more than two variables by the same method would require visualizing convex sets in more than two dimensions, which is extremely difficult. But fortunately there is an algorithm, called the *simplex algorithm*, that permits us to solve such large-scale linear programming problems without such visualization, in much the same way that (2) permits the solution of (1) without geometric visualization.

Although the simplex method can be shown to be applicable to any linear programming problem, we shall make two assumptions in order to simplify the description of the method. They are:

I. *The positivity assumption.* We shall assume that $b \geq 0$, i.e., every component of b is nonnegative.

II. *The nondegeneracy assumption.* If r is the number of linearly independent rows of A then it is not possible to write c as a linear combination of fewer than r rows of A, and it is not possible to write b as a linear combination of fewer than r columns of A.

The reason for the nondegeneracy assumption is that, without it, the simplex method may fail unless suitable precautions are taken. Actually (see Exercise 2) the simplex method works almost always even when this assumption is not satisfied. Both of these assumptions can be removed, and we refer the interested reader to the suggested reading at the end of the chapter for discussions of how this can be accomplished.

First, we recall that every linear programming problem can be put into one of the two following forms:

(3)
$$\left.\begin{array}{c} \text{Max } cx \\ \text{subject to} \\ Ax \leq b \\ x \geq 0 \end{array}\right\} \quad \text{the MAXIMUM problem}$$

or

(4)
$$\left.\begin{array}{c} \text{Min } wb \\ \text{subject to} \\ wA \geq c \\ w \geq 0 \end{array}\right\} \quad \text{the MINIMUM problem}$$

If the components of A, b, c are the same, then the two problems (3) and (4) are called *dual linear programming problems*. Every linear programming problem, whether of the maximum or minimum type, has a dual that can be formally stated as above. The dual of a given problem frequently has important economic meaning and always has mathematical significance—see the discussion in the next section.

To set up a MAXIMUM problem proceed as follows: Let the variables to be determined be $x_1, \ldots, x_n$ arranged as a column vector

$$x = \begin{pmatrix} x_1 \\ \cdot \\ \cdot \\ \cdot \\ x_n \end{pmatrix}.$$

Write the inequality constraints as $Ax \leq b$, where A is $m \times n$ and b is an m-component column vector. Write the objective function that is to be maximized as cx, where c is an n-component row vector.

To set up a MINIMUM problem proceed as follows: Let the variables to be determined be $w_1, \ldots, w_m$ arranged as a row vector

$$w = (w_1, \ldots, w_m).$$

Write the inequality constraints as $wA \geq c$, where A is $m \times n$ and c is an n-component row vector. Write the objective function to be minimized as wb, where b is an m-component column vector.

Note that for either problem we end up with the matrix A which is $m \times n$, the m-component column vector b which is $m \times 1$, and the n-component row vector c which is $1 \times n$. From these three matrices we form the *initial simplex tableau* shown in Figure 9. There the subscripts indicate the dimensions, I is an identity matrix, and 0 is a zero matrix.

$A_{m \times n}$	$I_{m \times m}$	$b_{m \times 1}$
$-c_{1 \times n}$	$0_{1 \times m}$	$0_{1 \times 1}$

Figure 9

Let us write this initial simplex tableau in more expanded form adding some labels to columns and rows and marking what we shall call *indicators* in the tableau. The result is shown in Figure 10.

The label A_j stands for the jth column of the matrix A, while the label E_j stands for the jth column of the identity matrix I. The labels of the columns will always remain the same. The labels of the rows are initially all E's, but the rows will change labels as the algorithm proceeds. The indicators consist of the entries of the last row of the simplex tableau, with the

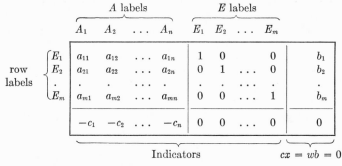

Figure 10

exception of the final entry. To fix these ideas let us set up the initial simplex tableaus for the auto-truck and the mining company examples of Section 3.

Example 1. The initial simplex tableau for Example 1 in Section 3 is shown in Figure 11.

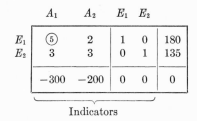

Figure 11

Example 2. The initial simplex tableau for Example 2 in Section 3 is shown in Figure 12.

	A_1	A_2	A_3	E_1	E_2	
E_1	⑥	2	4	1	0	200
E_2	2	2	12	0	1	160
	-12	-8	-24	0	0	0

Indicators

Figure 12

The reader should set up the initial simplex tableaus for Examples 3 and 4 of the same section.

The reader will note that in every case some of the initial indicators are negative. The simplex algorithm will change the initial tableau into a second one, that into a third, etc., until finally a tableau is obtained in which none of the indicators is negative. The required answer will be displayed in the final tableau. To describe how the simplex algorithm works we refer to the flow chart in Figure 13.

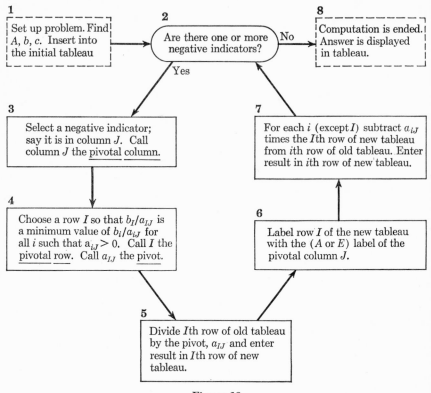

Figure 13

The flow chart describes how to carry out the computation. Look at box 1 of the chart which appears in the upper left-hand corner of Figure 13. We see that in Examples 1 and 2 we have already carried out the directives there; namely, the problems are set up and the initial tableaus formed. We now discuss in detail the rest of the computation for these two examples.

Example 1 (continued). We now look at box 2 of the flow chart, and we see that in the initial simplex tableau of Figure 11 there are negative indicators, so that the answer to the question in box 2 is "yes." Hence we proceed to box 3, which says "select a negative indicator." Suppose we select -300, which makes column 1 the pivotal column and $J = 1$. We now go to box 4 and proceed to find the pivotal row. For this we examine the ratios b_i/a_{i1} for $i = 1$ and 2.

These ratios are $180/5 = 36$ and $135/3 = 45$. Since the smaller ratio occurs in the first row we see that the 5 entry in the first column of Figure 11 is the pivot and $I = 1$, so that the pivotal row is the first one. The pivot is circled in Figure 11.

Next we construct the new simplex tableau shown in Figure 14. In box 5 of the flow chart we see that to get the first row of the new tableau of Figure 14 we divide the old first row by the pivot, 5. Then, as directed in box 6, we

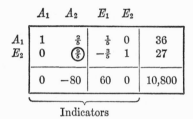

$$A_1 \quad A_2 \quad E_1 \quad E_2$$

	A_1	A_2	E_1	E_2	
A_1	1	$\frac{2}{5}$	$\frac{1}{5}$	0	36
E_2	0	$\textcircled{\frac{9}{5}}$	$-\frac{3}{5}$	1	27
	0	-80	60	0	10,800

Indicators

Figure 14

label the new first row with A_1, the label of the pivotal column. To construct the rest of Figure 14 we carry out the instructions in box 7. For instance, the second row of the new tableau is obtained by subtracting 3 times the first row of the new tableau from the old tableau. In vector form, this computation is

$$-3(1 \quad \tfrac{2}{5} \quad \tfrac{1}{5} \quad 0 \quad 36) + (3 \quad 3 \quad 0 \quad 1 \quad 135) = (0 \quad \tfrac{9}{5} \quad -\tfrac{3}{5} \quad 1 \quad 27).$$

And the last row of the new tableau is -300 times the first row of the new tableau subtracted from the last row of the old tableau. The reader should repeat these calculations for himself.

We now find ourselves back at box 2 of the flow chart. The answer to the question is still "yes" since there is one negative indicator, -80, in the second column of the second tableau of Figure 14. Hence we go around the loop of the flow chart again and construct a third tableau. In choosing the pivotal element, the two ratios are $36/\tfrac{2}{5} = 90$ and $27/\tfrac{9}{5} = 15$ so that the second row is pivotal and $\tfrac{9}{5}$ (circled in Figure 14) is the new pivot. Finishing the calculations indicated in the flow diagram we obtain the third simplex tableau of Figure 15.

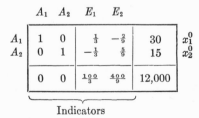

$$A_1 \quad A_2 \quad E_1 \quad E_2$$

	A_1	A_2	E_1	E_2		
A_1	1	0	$\frac{1}{3}$	$-\frac{2}{9}$	30	x_1^0
A_2	0	1	$-\frac{1}{3}$	$\frac{5}{9}$	15	x_2^0
	0	0	$\frac{100}{3}$	$\frac{400}{9}$	12,000	

Indicators

Figure 15

We again find ourselves at box 2 of the flow diagram. But this time we find no negative indicators for the tableau of Figure 15. Hence the answer to the question is "no" and we go to box 8, which says that the computation is ended and that the answers are displayed. In fact we see them in the last column, namely, $x_1 = 30$ in the first row labeled A_1, and $x_2 = 15$ in the second row labeled A_2. Also the maximum value of the objective function is \$12,000 and appears in the lower right-hand corner.

We must now describe how to interpret a final simplex tableau, obtained when all indicators become nonnegative. Figure 16 shows such a

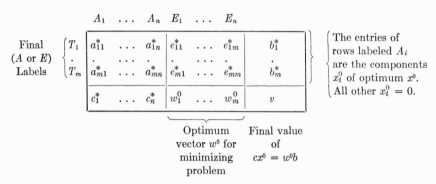

Figure 16

final tableau. The final optimum value of the objective function, whether maximizing or minimizing, appears in the lower right-hand corner of the final tableau. The optimum vector w^0 for a minimizing problem appears under the columns labeled with E's. And the entries in the last column opposite rows labeled with A_i's are the nonzero entries x_i^0 of the optimum solution x^0 to a maximizing problem. Note that it is always true that $cx^0 = w^0 b$ at an optimum solution. The reason for this will be discussed in the next section.

Example 2. (continued). Let us solve the second example using the simplex method. The initial tableau is in Figure 12, and the first indicator -12 was selected so that the first column is pivotal. The pivot is 6, which is circled in the first row and first column of Figure 12. This was chosen because the two ratios involved are $\frac{100}{3}$, which is smaller than $\frac{280}{2} = 80$, hence the first row is pivotal and 6 the pivot. Carrying out steps 5, 6, and 7 of the flow diagram, we construct the second tableau shown in Figure 17. There are still two

	A_1	A_2	A_3	E_1	E_2	
A_1	1	$\frac{1}{3}$	$\frac{2}{3}$	$\frac{1}{6}$	0	$\frac{100}{3}$
E_2	0	$\textcircled{\scriptsize $\frac{4}{3}$}$	$\frac{3}{2}$	$-\frac{1}{3}$	1	$\frac{280}{3}$
	0	-4	-16	2	0	400

Figure 17

negative indicators, and we choose the first one, -4, so that the second column is now pivotal. The new pivot is $\frac{4}{3}$ which is circled in the second (pivotal) row. Carrying out steps 5, 6, and 7 of the flow diagram we obtain the final tableau, shown in Figure 18. All indicators are nonnegative in Figure 18 so that the computation is complete. We read off the optimum answer $w_1^0 = 1$ and $w_2^0 = 3$, and the final minimum operating cost for the mines is \$680. Of course, these are the same answers that were obtained by the method of Section 3.

	A_1	A_2	A_3	E_1	E_2	
A_1	1	0	-2	$\frac{1}{4}$	$-\frac{1}{4}$	10
A_2	0	1	8	$-\frac{1}{4}$	$\frac{3}{4}$	70
	0	0	16	1	3	680

$$w_1^0 \qquad w_2^0$$

Figure 18

Example 3. Our last example illustrates a case in which some of the w_j indicators become negative. Figures 19 through 22 give the necessary tableaus, and the pivots are circled there. There is another way of working this problem that requires only two tableaus. It starts with a pivot in the first column instead of the second (see Exercise 2). This illustrates the rule that it is frequently (but not invariably) best to start the simplex method with a column having the most negative indicator.

	A_1	A_2	E_1	E_2	
E_1	2	①	1	0	3
E_2	3	1	0	1	4
	-17	-5	0	0	0

Figure 19

	A_1	A_2	E_1	E_2	
A_2	2	1	1	0	3
E_2	①	0	-1	1	1
	-7	0	5	0	15

Figure 20

	A_1	A_2	E_1	E_2	
A_2	0	1	③	-2	1
A_1	1	0	-1	1	1
	0	0	-2	7	22

Figure 21

E_1	0	$\frac{1}{3}$	1	$-\frac{2}{3}$	$\frac{1}{3}$
A_1	1	$\frac{1}{3}$	0	$\frac{1}{3}$	$\frac{4}{3}$
	0	$\frac{2}{3}$	0	$\frac{17}{3}$	$22\frac{2}{3}$

Figure 22

EXERCISES

1. Use the simplex method to solve Example 3 of Section 3.

2. Use the simplex method to solve Example 4 of Section 3 even though the nondegeneracy hypothesis is not satisfied. Show that there are two ways to proceed, each one leading to a different solution of the minimum problem.

3. In the tableau of Figure 12 make the pivot be the 2 entry in the first column rather than the circled 6 entry shown. Show that this leads to a negative value of x_1, and hence explain the reasons in box 4 for the special choice of the pivot.

4. Solve the problem in Example 3 by choosing the first pivot in the first column. Show that the answer can be obtained in one step.

5. Use the simplex method to solve the linear programming problem with data given as

$$A = \begin{pmatrix} 3 & 0 \\ -2 & 1 \end{pmatrix}, \quad b = \begin{pmatrix} 1 \\ 0 \end{pmatrix}, \quad c = (-1 \quad 1)$$

6. Try the simplex method on the problem with the following data:

$$A = \begin{pmatrix} -3 & 0 \\ -2 & 1 \end{pmatrix}, \quad b = \begin{pmatrix} 1 \\ 0 \end{pmatrix}, \quad c = (-1 \quad 1)$$

Show that the simplex method breaks down and then prove independently that the problem has no solution.

Set up each of the remaining problems as a linear programming problem and solve it by means of the simplex algorithm.

7. A caterer knows that he will need 40 napkins on a given day and 70 napkins the day after. He can purchase napkins at 20 cents each and, after they are purchased, he can have dirty napkins laundered at 5 cents each for use the next day. In order to minimize his costs, how many napkins should he purchase initially and how many dirty napkins should he have laundered?

[*Ans.* Let w_1 be the number purchased and w_2 the number laundered. Then the data of the problem are given by the following quantities:

$$A = \begin{pmatrix} 0 & 1 \\ -1 & 1 \end{pmatrix}, \quad b = \begin{pmatrix} 20 \\ 5 \end{pmatrix} \quad \text{and} \quad c = (-40, 110).$$

The caterer should buy 70 napkins and have 40 laundered after the first day.]

8. A more complicated version of Exercise 7 is the following: A caterer knows he will need 40, 70, and 60 napkins on three successive days. He can purchase napkins at 20 cents each, after which he can have dirty napkins laundered by a fast one-day laundry service at 15 cents each and by a slow two-day laundry service at 8 cents each. How many napkins should he purchase initially and how many dirty napkins should he have laundered on each of the days in order to minimize his costs?

[*Ans.* Let w_1 be the number purchased, w_2 the number of dirty napkins from the first day laundered by the fast service, w_3 the number of dirty napkins from the first day laundered by the slow service, and w_4 the number of dirty napkins from the second day laundered by the fast service. The data of the problem are given by

$$A = \begin{pmatrix} 0 & 1 & 0 & 1 \\ -1 & 1 & -1 & 1 \\ -1 & 0 & -1 & 1 \\ 0 & 0 & -1 & 1 \end{pmatrix}, \quad b = \begin{pmatrix} 20 \\ 15 \\ 8 \\ 15 \end{pmatrix} \quad \text{and} \quad c = (-40, 110, -110, 170).$$

The caterer should purchase 110 napkins, have 40 laundered by the slow service after the first day, and have 20 laundered by the fast service after the second day.]

9. A nut manufacturer has on hand 121 pounds of peanuts and 49 pounds of cashews. He can sell two kinds of mixtures of these nuts: a cheap mix that has 80 per cent peanuts and 20 per cent cashews; or a party mix that has 30 per cent peanuts and 70 per cent cashews. If he can sell the party mix at 80 cents a pound and the cheap mix at 50 cents a pound, how many pounds of each mix should he make in order to maximize the amount he can obtain?

[*Ans.* Let x_1 be the number of pounds of party mix and x_2 the number of pounds of the cheap mix. Then the data are

$$A = \begin{pmatrix} .3 & .8 \\ .7 & .2 \end{pmatrix}, \quad b = \begin{pmatrix} 121 \\ 49 \end{pmatrix} \quad \text{and} \quad c = (80, 50).$$

The manufacturer should make 30 pounds of the party mix and 140 pounds of the cheap mix. His income is $94.]

10. We consider another example of a maximizing problem. An oil refinery changes crude oil into gasoline, kerosene, and low-grade motor oil. The refinery processes 20,000 barrels of crude oil per day, and from this a total of at most 16,000 barrels of gasoline and kerosene can be produced each day. Moreover the process is such that there is always at least as much kerosene as gasoline produced, and all the remaining crude oil is converted into low-grade motor oil. If the wholesale prices of kerosene, gasoline, and motor oil are $9, $16, and $3 per barrel, respectively, what quantities of each should the manufacturer produce in order to maximize his income?

11. Two very small countries, call them P and Q, decide to join together in their production of food and clothing. Country P has 28,000 man-hours of labor available per month, and for each man-hour applied to food manufacture, produces 1 unit of food, while for each man-hour applied to clothing manufacture it produces 3 units of clothing. Country Q has 15,000 man-hours of labor available and for each man-hour applied to food manufacture produces 2 units of food while for each man-hour applied to clothing manufacture produces $\frac{1}{2}$ unit of clothing. Country P pays its food workers $2 per hour and its clothing workers $3 per hour, while country Q pays its food workers $5 an hour and its clothing workers $4 an hour. How should the countries divide up the labor if in all they need 10,000 units of food and 15,000 units of clothing and want to minimize total labor cost?

[*Partial Ans.* All the laborers of country Q rest.]

12. In Exercise 11 suppose country P raises the wages of its food workers to $4 per hour. What is the new solution?

[*Partial Ans.* The food workers of country P and the clothing workers of country Q rest.]

13. A manufacturer of a certain good owns two warehouses and supplies two markets. The first warehouse contains 90 tons of the good and the second contains 120 tons. The first market needs 60 tons of the good while the second market needs 150 tons. From the first warehouse it costs $6 per ton to ship to the first market and $10 per ton to ship to the second market. From the second warehouse it costs $8 per ton to ship to the first market and $12 per ton to ship to the second market. What quantities should the manufacturer ship from each warehouse to each market in order to minimize shipping costs? [*Ans.* The simplex method gives two solutions; in each solution one of the warehouses supplies the entire needs of market 1.]

5. Dual linear programming problems

The reader undoubtedly noticed that the simplex method described in the previous section was the same for both maximizing and minimizing problems. The only difference in setting up the two problems is the choice of row or column vectors for the various quantities involved. In each case we end up with a matrix A, a column vector b, and a row vector c. Using these data we can state both a maximizing and a minimizing problem—only one of which is the problem in which we were initially interested. The other problem is called the *dual* linear programming problem. The dual of a maximizing problem is a minimizing problem, and the dual of a minimizing problem is a maximizing problem. And the dual of the dual problem is, in either case, the original problem.

It is important to observe that the simplex method we have described solves both the original problem and its dual simultaneously. It is therefore of interest to see what interpretation if any can be given to the dual of a linear programming problem. We shall see that it is always possible to give a mathematical interpretation to the dual, and it is also possible to give an economic interpretation to the dual which may be of considerable interest. These ideas are best introduced by means of examples.

Example 1. Let us consider the automobile-truck example of Example 1, Section 3 again. Suppose that the management of the firm wishes to attach a value to a man-day's work in each of the two shops. The answer to such a question might be of interest in management-labor negotiations. The values that we shall compute will depend not upon the worker's salary but upon the imputed worth of his labor.

For this purpose let w_1 be the value (dollars per man-day) of a worker in Shop 1, and let w_2 be the value of a worker in Shop 2. Then since a truck is constructed with 5 man-days of labor of Shop 1 and 3 man-days labor of Shop 2, and since the profit obtained is $300, we will want $5w_1 + 3w_2 \geq 300$. Similarly, since an automobile is constructed with 2 man-days of labor from Shop 1 and 3 man-days of labor from Shop 2 and since it yields a profit of $200, we will want $2w_1 + 3w_2 \geq 200$. If we let $w = (w_1, w_2)$ and let A and c be as before, we see that these two inequalities may be written together as $wA \geq c$. These inequalities imply that the imputed values should be at least as great as the profits obtainable.

On the other hand, management wants to keep the total weekly imputed labor costs as small as possible. This quantity is $180w_1 + 135w_2 = wb$. Hence we see that the present problem is a minimizing linear programming problem: to minimize wb subject to $wA \geq c$. Since labor values are inherently nonnegative we can add the additional inequalities $w \geq 0$.

It may seem strange to impute value to workers' efforts in this manner. The strangeness arises in part because it is an unfamiliar operation, but also because the *imputed* or *shadow* value of a worker may be quite different from his actual wage. However, the mechanism for setting wages is quite different from the method described above for computing inferred values. The real use of shadow values is for management's evaluation of the manufacturing process.

Example 2. Let us consider a problem related to that mentioned in Example 2 of Section 3. Suppose that the accounting department of the mining company wishes to assign a value to each of the grades of ore that the company produces. Such an assignment might help it in determining retail prices. These prices will assign, in effect, a share of the cost of running the mine to each product produced.

Economists call these *shadow* prices—they are inferred prices and have no necessary relation to market prices. As we shall see, any product that is produced in surplus will be assigned zero shadow price even though part of it may be sold at a positive market price. Such a product may conveniently be interpreted as a *by-product* of the mine. And we shall see that if the demand for the various products changes, some by-products may change into principal products and vice versa.

To return to the mine example, let x_1 be the shadow price assigned to high-grade ore, x_2 the shadow price of medium-grade ore, and x_3 the shadow price assigned to low-grade ore. We let x be a three-component column vector with these components. Then with these shadow prices, the shadow value of weekly sales is simply $cx = 12x_1 + 8x_2 + 24x_3$. Clearly it is desirable for the company to make this amount as large as possible. However, if the shadow value is to have meaning, the total shadow value of ore produced by a mine must not add up to more than it costs to run the mine for a day. We write two inequalities that express this fact: for Mine 1 the inequality is

$$6x_1 + 2x_2 + 4x_3 \leq 200$$

and for Mine 2 it is

$$2x_1 + 2x_2 + 12x_3 \leq 160.$$

In matrix notation these can be more simply written as: $Ax \leq b$. Since prices are naturally nonnegative we can also add the obvious inequality $x \geq 0$.

The linear programming problems we have just defined are the dual problems to the original ones we formulated in Section 3. They use the same data as the original problems, and we can state the pair of dual linear programming problems as follows:

The MAXIMUM Problem	*The MINIMUM Problem*
Find:	Find:
Max cx	Min wb
Subject to:	Subject to:
(1) $Ax \leq b$	(3) $wA \geq c$
(2) $x \geq 0$	(4) $w \geq 0$.

Vectors x that satisfy (1) and (2) and vectors w that satisfy (3) and (4) will be called *feasible* vectors.

Let us try to give general interpretations to the pair of dual linear programming problems. For either problem the matrix A will be called the matrix of *technological coefficients*, since it indicates how activity vectors are combined into the constraining inequalities. Then we can give different interpretations to the vectors c, b, x, and w depending on whether our original problem is a maximizing or a minimizing problem.

If the original problem is maximizing, we interpret x as the *activity vector*. Then the vector b is interpreted as the *capacity constraint* vector which limits the amount of "raw materials" that can be demanded by a given activity vector. The vector c is the *profit* vector whose entries give the amount of profit for each component of the activity vector x. Finally, the vector w is the *imputed value* vector whose entries give the imputed value of the labor or raw materials that enter into the process.

On the other hand, if the original problem is minimizing, we interpret w as the *activity* vector. Then the vector c is interpreted as the *requirements* vector whose entries give the minimum amounts of each good that must be produced. The vector b is the *cost* vector whose entries give the costs of each component of the activity vector w. Finally, the vector x is the *imputed value* of the raw materials that enter into the process.

As previously remarked, we have already solved both of the dual problems of Examples 1 and 2 of Section 3. For all we have to do is go back to the simplex calculations of the previous section, and reinterpret our work properly.

Example 1 (continued from Section 3). From Figures 11, 14, and 15 we see that if we had set up and solved a labor value problem as a minimizing problem our calculations would have been just as before for the maximizing problem. From Figure 15 we read off $w_1^0 = \frac{100}{3}$ and $w_2^0 = \frac{400}{9}$. Hence the workers in the finishing shop, Shop 2, have imputed value somewhat more than that of workers in the assembly shop, Shop 1. Note also that the total weekly imputed value is \$12,000, which is the same as the total weekly maximum profit.

Example 2 (continued from Section 3). Again we can interpret Figures 12, 17, and 18 as being the calculations for the accounting prices for the mining problem. The accounting price solution is

$$x^0 = \begin{pmatrix} 10 \\ 70 \\ 0 \end{pmatrix}.$$

Thus, high-grade ore has a shadow value of \$10 per ton, medium-grade ore has a shadow value of \$70 per ton, and low-grade ore is valued as \$0 per ton! Observe that the accounting or shadow price of the ore depends more upon the cost of producing it than upon its quality. (Selling prices *would* reflect quality.) Observe also that the overproduced low-grade ore has shadow price zero, i.e., it is a by-product. Actually, *any* overproduced quantity has zero shadow price. A final important observation is that max cx = min wb = \$680.

It is no accident that the dual problems share common values. The next theorem, which is the principal theorem of linear programming, shows that this will always happen whenever the problems have solutions.

THE DUALITY THEOREM. The maximum problem has as a solution a feasible vector x^0, such that $cx^0 = $ max cx, if and only if the minimum problem has a solution that is a feasible vector w^0, such that $w^0b = $ min wb. Moreover, the equality $cx^0 = w^0b$ holds if and only if x^0 and w^0 are solutions to their respective problems.

The duality theorem is extremely powerful, for it says that if one of the problems has a solution, then the other one necessarily also has a solution, and both problems share a common value. Another consequence of the theorem is that if one of the problems does *not* have a solution, then neither does the other one.

The proof of the duality theorem is beyond the scope of this book but some parts of it are indicated in Exercise 5. An example of a linear programming problem that has no solution is given in Exercise 6.

As a final consideration let us investigate more fully the simplex method. Before we can describe how the simplex method works we must make a change in the formulation of the dual programs. What we shall do is to add *dummy* variables to the inequalities stated in expressions (1) and (4) of this section in such a way as to make them into equations. To see how this is done, consider as an example the system of inequalities

$$-u + 2v \leq 5, \quad u \geq 0 \quad \text{and} \quad v \geq 0.$$

We now add a new dummy variable w and obtain a new system of expressions,

$$-u + 2v + w = 5, \quad u \geq 0, \quad v \geq 0 \quad \text{and} \quad w \geq 0.$$

Thus we obtain the equation

$$-u + 2v + w = 5$$

in nonnegative variables. Notice that the new system of expressions is equivalent to the old system, since any solution of the new system that has $w = 0$ represents a case for which $-u + 2v = 5$, and a solution of the new system for which $w > 0$ represents a case for which $-u + 2v < 5$. Moreover, it is obvious that any solution of the old system can be written as a solution of the new system by properly choosing a nonnegative value of w. Thus the truth sets of the two systems are identical.

In order to change expressions (1) and (4) into equalities we must add $m + n$ dummy variables to the system. For this purpose we define the following vectors of dummy variables: y is an m-component column vector of dummy variables y_i, and z is an n-component row vector of dummy variables z_j. We then restate the dual linear programming problems:

The MAXIMUM Problem	*The MINIMUM Problem*
Max cx	Min wb
Subject to:	Subject to:
(1') $Ax + y = b$	(3') $wA - z = c$
(2') $x \geq 0, y \geq 0$	(4') $w \geq 0, z \geq 0.$

Vectors x and y that satisfy (1') and (2') and vectors w and z that satisfy (3') and (4') will be called *feasible vectors*. We shall identify this form of the problem by saying the constraints are in *equality* form.

The proof that the solutions of a linear programming problem stated in equality form are the same as the solutions of the problem stated in inequality form, follows from the facts that the sets of x and w vectors in each case are the same and that the dummy variables do not affect the functions being maximized or minimized.

Since we have assumed that $b \geq 0$, the following vectors will solve equations (1'), (2'), and (3'):

(5) $$x = 0, \quad y = b, \quad w = 0 \quad \text{and} \quad z = -c.$$

Note that x, y, and w are nonnegative, but that z is nonnegative only if we already have a solution to the problem. Note also that $cx = wb = 0$, initially.

We can now explain the reasons for the various steps in the flow diagram of Figure 13. The initial diagram is set up with the values (5) entered in it (see Exercise 3). The simplex method systematically changes the tableau in order to make z into a nonnegative vector without destroying the nonnegativeness of x, y, or w, and also keeping $cx = wb$ at all times. In step 4 of the figure the pivot was chosen in order to have the smallest ratio b_i/a_{ij} in order that no current x_i or y_i variable should become negative. The reader may verify that if the pivot is chosen not to have this property, then some such variable is made negative (see Exercise 3 of the preceding section). The reason that the algorithm was finished when all the indicators were positive is also clear. For we moved from step to step with equations (1'), (2'), and (3') and $cx = wb$ continuously satisfied. And when all the indicators are nonnegative we have also that $w \geq 0$ and $z \geq 0$, which means that (4') is also satisfied (see Exercise 4). By the duality theorem if x^0, y, w^0, and z satisfy (1')–(4') and also $cx^0 = w^0b$, then a solution to the programming problem has been obtained.

EXERCISES

1. Interpret the dual problems for each of the Exercises 7–13 at the end of the preceding section. Find the solution to each problem in the simplex tableau already computed for the original problem.

2. A nutritionist in a large institution wishes to serve foods that provide the necessary vitamins for the people who eat them. Upon testing three different foods F_1, F_2, and F_3, he finds they contain the following amounts of vitamins A and B:

	F_1	F_2	F_3
Vitamin A	2	4	3
Vitamin B	5	2	5

The units of the numbers express the quantity of each vitamin per pound of food eaten. Suppose the nutritionist must provide at least 80 units of vitamin A and at least 60 units of vitamin B. If the costs of the three foods are $1 per pound for food F_1, 80 cents per pound for F_2, and $1.50 per pound for F_3, how should he place his orders for the various foods to meet the minimum diet requirements while also minimizing the total cost of the foods purchased? Interpret and solve the dual maximizing problem.

[*Ans.* 5 units of F_1 and $17\frac{1}{2}$ units of F_2 at a cost of $19. The imputed values per unit are $12\frac{1}{2}\cent$ for vitamin A and $15\cent$ for vitamin B.]

3. Consider the initial simplex tableau in Figure 10 and the initial solution of Equation (5).

(a) Show that $cx = wb = 0$ appear in the lower right-hand corner of Figure 10.

(b) Show that $z = -c$ and $w = 0$ appear along the bottom of the initial tableau in that order.

(c) Show that $y = b$ appears in the rightmost column of the initial tableau, since the first m rows are labeled with the E_i labels initially.

(d) Show that $x = 0$ initially, although no component of it appears in the initial tableau since none of the rows have A labels initially.

4. Consider the final simplex tableau of Figure 16.

(a) Show that $cx^0 = w^0b$ appears in the lower right-hand corner of the tableau.

(b) Show that the entries in the first n columns of the last row give the final values of the dummy variables $z_1, \ldots, z_n$. Show that the next m entries in the last row give the final values of the answer $w_1^0, \ldots, w_m^0$.

(c) Show that the entries in the last column whose rows are labeled with A labels are the nonzero entries of the answer $x_1^0, \ldots, x_n^0$, while the entries in the last column whose rows are labeled with E labels are the nonzero entries of $y_1, \ldots, y_m$. All other components of x and y are 0's.

5. Let x^0 and w^0 be nonnegative vectors such that $cx^0 = w^0b$, $Ax^0 \leq b$, and $w^0A \geq c$.

(a) Show that if x is any other feasible vector, then

$$cx \leq w^0Ax \leq w^0b = cx^0$$

so that x^0 solves the maximum problem.

(b) Similarly, show that w^0 solves the minimum problem.

(c) Show that $cx^0 = w^0b = w^0Ax^0$.

6. Consider the following problem: minimize $-w_1 + w_2$ subject to the inequalites $w_1 \geq 0$, $w_2 \geq 0$, and $w_1 - w_2 \geq 1$.

(a) Sketch the convex set of feasible vectors and show that it is unbounded.

(b) What is the convex set of vectors for the dual problem?

(c) Prove that the dual problems have no solution using the duality theorem.

(d) Prove directly that the minimizing problem has no solution.

SUGGESTED READING

Charnes, A., and W. W. Cooper, "Linear Programming," *Scientific American*, **191** (1954), pp. 21–23.

Charnes, A., and W. W. Cooper, *Management Models and Industrial Applications of Linear Programming*, 2 volumes, Wiley, New York, 1961.

Dartmouth College Writing Group, *Modern Mathematical Methods and Models*, Mathematical Association of America.

Dorfman, R., P. A. Samuelson, and R. M. Solow, *Linear Programming and Economic Analysis*, McGraw-Hill, New York, 1957.

Ficken, F. A., *The Simplex Method of Linear Programming*, Holt, Rinehart and Winston, New York, 1961.

Koopmans, T. C., editor, *Activity Analysis of Production and Allocation* (Cowles Commission Monograph No. 13), Wiley, New York, 1951.

Kuhn, H. W., and A. W. Tucker, editors, *Linear Inequalities and Related Systems*, Annals of Mathematics Study No. 38, Princeton University Press, Princeton, 1956.

Vajda, S., *The Theory of Games and Linear Programming*, Methuen and Co., London, and Wiley, New York, 1956.

VIII

The Theory of Games

1. Introduction: strictly determined games

The first eight and the tenth sections of this chapter are written so that the reader can follow them if he has covered the first five chapters of the book. However, Section 9 depends upon the simplex method of linear programming, which is discussed in Chapter VII.

Game theory considers situations in which there are two (or more) persons, each of whose actions influence, but do not completely determine, the outcome of a certain event. Depending on which event actually occurs, the players receive various payments. If for each possible event the algebraic sum of payments to all players is zero, the game is called *zero-sum;* otherwise it is *nonzero-sum*. Usually the players will not agree as to which event should occur, so that their objectives in the game are different. In the case of a matrix game, which is a two-person game in which one player loses what the other wins (i.e., a two person zero-sum game), game theory provides a solution, based on the principle that each player tries to choose his course of action so that, regardless of what his opponent does, he can assure himself of a certain amount. Matrix games are discussed in Sections

1–9. For many-person, nonzero-sum games, several solution concepts have been proposed, of which we discuss only a few in Section 10.

Most recreational games such as tick-tack-toe, checkers, backgammon, chess, poker, bridge, and other card games can be viewed as games of strategy. On the other hand, gambling games such as dice, roulette, etc., are *not* (as usually formulated) games of strategy, since a person playing one of these games is merely "betting against the odds."

The actual games of strategy mentioned above are too complicated, as they stand, to be analyzed completely. We shall instead construct simple examples which, although uninteresting from a player's point of view, do illustrate the theory and are amenable to computation.

In this section and the next we shall discuss some simple examples of games. The general definition of a matrix game will be given in Section 3.

Example. Consider the following card game: Suppose there are two players, call them R and C (the reason for the use of these letters will be explained later); player R is given a hand consisting of a red 5 and a black 5, while player C is given a black 5 and a red 3. The game that they are to play is the following: At a given signal the players *simultaneously* expose one of their two cards; if the cards *match* in color, player R wins the (positive) difference between the numbers on the cards; while if the cards do *not match* in color, player C wins the (positive) difference between the numbers on the cards played. Obviously the strategical decision that each player must make is which of his two cards to play.

A convenient way of representing the game is by means of the matrix shown in Figure 1. (In game theory it is customary to present matrices in this "table" form.) The rows represent the possible choices of player R, and the columns the possible choices of C; hence our use of R and C. The number in position a_{ij} represents the gain of R if R chooses row i and C chooses column j. A positive entry is a payment from C to R, while a negative "gain" for R is a payment from R to C. For example, if R chooses row 1 (plays bk 5) and C chooses column 1 (plays bk 5), then R wins the difference of the two numbers, which is 0. If R chooses row 1 but C chooses column 2 (plays rd 3), then C wins the difference of 5 minus 3, which is indicated by the -2 entry in the matrix. The strategic characteristics of the game are completely described by the matrix.

The game shown in Figure 1 is called a *matrix game*. Any 2×2 matrix

Player C

		bk 5	rd 3
	bk 5	0	-2
Player R	rd 5	0	2

Figure 1

can be considered a two-person matrix game by allowing one player to control the rows, the other the columns, and defining the payoffs of the game to be the various matrix entries. In Section 3 we shall see that a matrix of *any* size can in the same way also be considered a matrix game.

How should the players play the matrix game of Figure 1? Player C would like to get the −2 entry in the matrix; however, the only way he could get it would be to play the second column of the matrix, in which case player R would surely choose the second row and C would lose 2 rather than gain 2. On the other hand, if C chooses the first column (i.e., plays bk 5), he assures himself that he will break even regardless of what R does. It is clear that R has nothing to lose and may possibly gain by choosing the second row, hence he should do so. The knowledge that he will do so reinforces C in his choice of the first column. The optimal procedure for the players is then: R should play rd 5 and C should play bk 5. If they play this way, neither player wins from the other, that is, the game is *fair*.

A command of the form: "Play rd 5," or "Play bk 3," will be called a *strategy*. If player R uses the strategy "Play rd 5" in the game of Figure 1, then, regardless of what C does, R assures himself that he will get at *least* a payoff of zero. Similarly, if C uses the strategy "Play bk 5," then, regardless of what R does, C assures himself of obtaining a payoff of *at most zero*, i.e., a loss of at most zero. Since R cannot, by his own efforts, assure himself of gaining more than zero, and C cannot, by his own efforts, assure himself of losing less than zero, and since these two numbers are the same, we call these *optimal strategies* for the game. Also we call zero the *value* of the game, since it is the outcome of the game if each player uses his optimal strategy.

DEFINITION. We shall say that a 2 × 2 matrix game is *strictly determined* if the matrix contains an entry, call it v, which is *simultaneously* the *minimum* of the row in which it occurs and the *maximum* of the column in which it occurs. *Optimal strategies* for the players are then the following:

For player R: "Choose a row that contains v."
For player C: "Choose a column that contains v."

The *value* of the game is v. The game is *fair* if its value is zero.

In Section 3 it will be shown that the strategies here defined are optimal in the sense indicated above, and that v has the property of being the best either player can assure for himself. The game of Figure 1 is strictly determined, since the 0 entry in the lower left-hand corner of the matrix is the minimum of the second row and the maximum of the first column of that matrix. Observe that the optimal strategies given in the definition above agree with those found in the Example. The value of that game, according to the above definition, is zero; hence it is fair.

The solution of a strictly determined game is particularly easy to find since each player can calculate the other's optimal strategy and hence know what he will do. Not all 2 × 2 matrix games are so easy to solve, as we shall see in the next section.

In Figure 2 we show three matrix games. The game in Figure 2(a) is

0	1
−3	10

(a)

5	2
−7	−4

(b)

0	1
2	0

(c)

Figure 2

strictly determined and fair, and its optimal strategies are for R to choose the first row and C to choose the first column. The game in Figure 2 (b) is strictly determined but not fair, since its value is 2. What are its optimal strategies? Finally, the game in Figure 2 (c) is not strictly determined, and the solution of games such as this one will be the subject of the next section.

EXERCISES

1. Determine which of the games given below are strictly determined and which are fair. When the game is strictly determined find optimal strategies for each player.

(a)

0	2
−1	4

(b)

5	0
0	2

(c)

3	1
4	0

(d)

1	−1
−1	1

(e)

3	1
−4	0

(f)

0	4
0	2

(g)

7	0
0	0

(h)

0	0
0	−7

(i)

0	0
0	0

(j)

1	1
1	1

[*Ans.* (a) Strictly determined and fair; R play row 1, C play column 1; (b) nonstrictly determined; (e) strictly determined but not fair; R play row 1, C play column 2; (j) strictly determined but not fair; both players can use any strategy.]

2. In the Example suppose that R is given rd 5 and bk 3, and C is given bk 3 and rd 3. Set up the matrix game corresponding to it. Is it strictly determined? Is it fair? Find optimal strategies for each player.

[*Ans.* Yes. Yes. Both play bk 3.]

3. Each of two players shows one or two fingers (simultaneously) and C pays to R a sum equal to the total number of fingers shown. Write the game matrix. Show that the game is strictly determined, and find the value and optimal strategies.

4. Each of two players shows one or two fingers (simultaneously) and C pays to R an amount equal to the total number of fingers shown, while R pays to C an amount equal to the product of the numbers of fingers shown. Construct the game matrix (the entries will be the net gain of R), and find the value and the optimal strategies.

[*Ans.* $v = 1$, R must show one finger, C may show one or two.]

5. Show that a strictly determined game is fair if and only if there is a zero entry such that both entries in its row are nonnegative and both entries in its column are nonpositive.

6. Consider the game

$$G = \begin{array}{|c|c|} \hline 2 & 5 \\ \hline -1 & a \\ \hline \end{array}.$$

(a) Show that G is strictly determined regardless of the value of a.
(b) Find the value of G.   [*Ans.* 2.]
(c) Find optimal strategies for each player.
(d) If $a = 1{,}000{,}000$, obviously R would like to get it as his payoff. Is there any way he can assure himself of obtaining it? What would happen to him if he tried to obtain it?
(e) Show that the value of the game is the most that R can assure for himself.

7. Consider the matrix game

$$G = \begin{array}{|c|c|} \hline a & a \\ \hline c & d \\ \hline \end{array}.$$

Show that G is strictly determined for every set of values for a, c, and d. Show that the same result is true if two entries in a given column are always equal.

8. Find necessary and sufficient conditions that the game

$$G = \begin{array}{|c|c|} \hline a & 0 \\ \hline 0 & b \\ \hline \end{array}$$

should be strictly determined. [*Hint:* These will be expressed in terms of relations among the numbers a and b and the number zero.]

9. Suppose that in the example discussed in the text, player R is given a hand consisting of bk x and rd y, and player C is given bk u and rd v, where x, y, u, and v are real numbers. Suppose that the matrix game which they play is the following:

Player C

	bk u	rd v
bk x	$x - u$	$v - x$
rd y	$u - y$	$y - v$

Player R (rows bk x, rd y)

(a) Show that if $x = u$, $v \geq x$, and $y \geq x$, the game is strictly determined and fair.

(b) Show that if $y = v$, $y \leq x$, and $y \leq u$, the game is strictly determined and fair.

10. Consider a strictly determined 2 × 2 matrix game G. Suppose u and v are two entries of the matrix such that each is the minimum of the row and the maximum of the column in which it occurs. Show that $u = v$.

2. Nonstrictly determined games

As we saw in the numerical examples of the last section, some matrix games are nonstrictly determined, that is, they have no entry which is simultaneously a row minimum and a column maximum. We can characterize nonstrictly determined 2 × 2 matrix games as follows:

THEOREM. The matrix game

$$G = \begin{array}{|c|c|} \hline a & b \\ \hline c & d \\ \hline \end{array}$$

is nonstrictly determined if and only if one of the following two conditions is satisfied:

(i) $a < b$, $a < c$, $d < b$, and $d < c$.

(ii) $a > b$, $a > c$, $d > b$, and $d > c$.

(These equations mean that the two entries on one diagonal of the matrix must each be greater than each of the two entries on the other diagonal.)

Proof. If either of the conditions (i) or (ii) holds, it is easy to check that no entry of the matrix is simultaneously the minimum of the row and the maximum of the column in which it occurs; hence the game is not strictly determined.

To prove the other half of the theorem, recall that, by Exercise 7 of the last section, if two of the entries in the same row or the same column of G are equal, the game is strictly determined; hence we can assume that no two entries in the same row or the same column are equal. Suppose now that $a < b$; then $a < c$ or else a is a row minimum and a column maximum; then also $c > d$ or else c is a row minimum and a column maximum; then also $d < b$ or else d is a row minimum and a column maximum. Hence the assumption $a < b$ leads to case (i) above.

In a similar manner the assumption $a > b$ leads to case (ii). This completes the proof of the theorem.

Example 1. Consider the card game of the Example in the last section and assume that player R has bk 5 and rd 3 while player C has bk 3 and rd 5. The rules of play are as before. The corresponding matrix game is

Player C

		bk 3	rd 5
Player R	bk 5	2	0
	rd 3	0	2

which clearly is nonstrictly determined.

Example 2. Consider again Chapter III, Section 2, Example 1. Recall that Jones conceals either a $1 or a $2 bill in his hand; Smith guesses 1 or 2, and wins the bill if he guesses its number. The matrix of this game is

Smith guesses

		1	2
Jones chooses	$1 bill	-1	0
	$2 bill	0	-2

Again the game is nonstrictly determined.

How should one play a nonstrictly determined game? We must first convince ourselves that no one choice is clearly optimal for either player. In Example 1, R would like to win 2. But if he definitely chooses bk 5, and

C finds this out, C can bring about a zero by playing rd 5. If R chooses rd 3, C can bring about a zero by playing bk 3. Similarly, if C's choice is found out by R, then R can win 2. So our first result is that each player must, in some way, prevent the other player from finding out which card he is going to play.

We also note that for a single play of the game there is no difference be- tween the two strategies, as long as one's strategy is not guessed by the opponent. Let us now consider the game being played several times. What should R do? Clearly, he should not play the same card all the time, or C will be able to notice what R is doing, and profit by it. Rather, R should sometimes play one card, and sometimes the other! Our key question then is, "How often should R play each of his cards?" From the symmetry of the problem we can guess that he should play each card as often as the other, hence each one-half the time. (We will see later that this is, indeed, opti- mal.) In what order should he do this? For example, should he alternate bk 5 and rd 3? That is dangerous, because if C notices the pattern, he will gain by knowing just what R will do next. Thus we see that R should play bk 5 half the time, but according to some unguessable pattern. The only safe way of doing this is to play it half the time at random. He could, for example, toss a coin (without letting C see it) and play bk 5 if it comes up heads, rd 3 if it comes up tails. Then his opponent cannot guess his decision, since he himself won't know what the decision is. Thus we conclude that a rational way of playing is for each player to *mix* his strategies, selecting sometimes one, sometimes the other; and these strategies should be selected at random, according to certain fixed ratios (probabilities) of selecting each.

By a *mixed strategy* for player R we shall mean a command of the form, "Play row 1 with probability p_1 and play row 2 with probability p_2," where we assume that $p_1 \geq 0$ and $p_2 \geq 0$ and $p_1 + p_2 = 1$. Similarly, a mixed strategy for player C is a command of the form, "Play column 1 with prob- ability q_1 and play column 2 with probability q_2," where $q_1 \geq 0$, $q_2 \geq 0$, and $q_1 + q_2 = 1$. A mixed strategy vector for player R is the probability row vector (p_1, p_2), and a mixed strategy vector for player C is the proba- bility column vector $\begin{pmatrix} q_1 \\ q_2 \end{pmatrix}$.

Examples of mixed strategies are $(\frac{1}{2}, \frac{1}{2})$ and $\begin{pmatrix} \frac{1}{5} \\ \frac{4}{5} \end{pmatrix}$. The reader may won- der how a player could actually play one of these strategies. The mixed strategy $(\frac{1}{2}, \frac{1}{2})$ is easy to realize since it is simply the coin-flipping strategy described above. The mixed strategy $\begin{pmatrix} \frac{1}{5} \\ \frac{4}{5} \end{pmatrix}$ is more difficult to realize since there is no chance device in common use that gives these probabilities. However, suppose that a pointer is constructed with a card that is $\frac{4}{5}$ shaded and $\frac{1}{5}$ unshaded, as in Figure 3, and C simply spins the pointer (without letting R see it, of course!). Then, if the pointer stops on the unshaded part he plays the first column, and if it stops on the shaded part he plays the second column, and thus realizes the desired strategy. By varying the proportion of shaded area on the card, other mixed strategies can conveniently be realized. An equally effective and less mechanical device for realizing a given mixed strategy is to use a table of random digits (see Table II). For the strategy $\begin{pmatrix} \frac{1}{5} \\ \frac{4}{5} \end{pmatrix}$, for example, we could let the digits 0 and 1 represent a play of column 1, and the remaining digits a play of column 2.

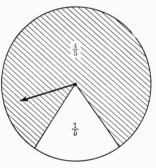

Figure 3.

Consider the nonstrictly determined game

$$G = \begin{array}{|c|c|} \hline a & b \\ \hline c & d \\ \hline \end{array}.$$

Having argued, as above, that the players should use mixed strategies in playing a nonstrictly determined game, it is still necessary to decide how to choose an optimal mixed strategy.

DEFINITION. For the nonstrictly determined game G, the number v is its value and $p^0 = (p_1^0, p_2^0)$ and $q^0 = (q_1^0, q_2^0)$ are optimal strategies for R and C, respectively, if the following inequalities are satisfied:

(1) $$p^0 G = (p_1^0, p_2^0)\begin{pmatrix} a & b \\ c & d \end{pmatrix} \geq (v, v)$$

(2) $$G q^0 = \begin{pmatrix} a & b \\ c & d \end{pmatrix}\begin{pmatrix} q_1^0 \\ q_2^0 \end{pmatrix} \leq \begin{pmatrix} v \\ v \end{pmatrix}.$$

(If z and w are vectors, the inequality $z \geq w$ means that each component of z is greater than or equal to the corresponding component of w.) The game is *fair* if $v = 0$.

If R chooses a mixed strategy $p = (p_1, p_2)$ and (independently) C chooses a mixed strategy $q = \begin{pmatrix} q_1 \\ q_2 \end{pmatrix}$, then player R obtains the payoff a with probability $p_1 q_1$; he obtains the payoff b with probability $p_1 q_2$; he obtains c with probability $p_2 q_1$; and he obtains d with probability $p_2 q_2$; hence his mathematical expectation (see Chapter IV, Section 11) is given by the expression

$$a p_1 q_1 + b p_1 q_2 + c p_2 q_1 + d p_2 q_2 = pGq.$$

By a similar computation, one can show that player C's expectation is the negative of this expression.

To justify this definition we must show that if v, p^0, q^0 exist for G, each player can guarantee himself an expectation of v. Let q be any strategy for C. Multiplying (1) on the right by q, we get $p^0 G q \geq (v, v)q = v$, which shows that, regardless of how C plays, R can assure himself of an expectation of at least v. Similarly, let p be any strategy vector for R. Multiplying (2) on the left by p, we obtain $p G q^0 \leq p \begin{pmatrix} v \\ v \end{pmatrix} = v$ which shows that, regardless of how R plays, C can assure himself of an expectation of at most v. It is in this sense that p^0 and q^0 are optimal. It follows further that, if both players play optimally, then R's expectation is exactly v and C's expectation is exactly v. (See Exercise 11.) Hence we call v the (expected) *value* of the game.

We must now see whether there are strategies p^0 and q^0 for the game G. For complicated games the finding of optimal strategies will be discussed in Section 9. For a 2×2 nonstrictly determined game the following formulas provide the solution:

$$(3) \qquad p_1^0 = \frac{d - c}{a + d - b - c}$$

$$(4) \qquad p_2^0 = \frac{a - b}{a + d - b - c}$$

$$(5) \qquad q_1^0 = \frac{d - b}{a + d - b - c}$$

$$(6) \qquad q_2^0 = \frac{a - c}{a + d - b - c}$$

$$(7) \qquad v = \frac{ad - bc}{a + d - b - c}.$$

It is an easy matter to verify (see Exercise 12) that formulas (3)–(7) satisfy conditions (1)–(2). Actually, the inequalities in (1) and (2) become equalities in this simple case, a fact that is not true in general for nonstrictly determined games of larger size.

The denominator in each formula is the difference between the sums of the entries on the two diagonals. Since, for a nonstrictly determined game, the entries on one diagonal must be larger than those on the other, the denominator cannot be zero.

Let us use these formulas to solve the examples mentioned earlier.

Example 1 (continued). The solution is easily found by substituting into the above formulas. We obtain $(\frac{1}{2}, \frac{1}{2})$ as the optimal strategy for R and $\begin{pmatrix} \frac{1}{2} \\ \frac{1}{2} \end{pmatrix}$ as the optimal strategy for C. Hence each player should use the coin-flipping strategy for optimal results. The value of the game is plus 1, which means that it is biased in R's favor, and R has an expected gain of 1 per game.

Example 2 (continued). Substitution into the formulas gives $(\frac{2}{3}, \frac{1}{3})$ as the optimal strategy for R and $\begin{pmatrix} \frac{2}{3} \\ \frac{1}{3} \end{pmatrix}$ as the optimal strategy for C. The value of the game is $-\frac{2}{3}$, which means that the game is biased in Smith's favor. Smith should then pay $66\frac{2}{3}$ cents to play the game, which answers the question raised in Chapter III.

EXERCISES

1. Find the optimal strategies for each player and the values of the following games:

(a)

1	2
3	4

(b)

1	0
−1	2

(c)

2	3
1	4

(d)

15	3
−1	2

(e)

7	−6
5	8

(f)

3	15
−1	10

[*Ans.* (a) $v = 3$; $(0, 1)$; $\begin{pmatrix} 1 \\ 0 \end{pmatrix}$.   (b) $v = \frac{1}{2}$; $(\frac{3}{4}, \frac{1}{4})$; $\begin{pmatrix} \frac{1}{2} \\ \frac{1}{2} \end{pmatrix}$.

(d) $v = 3$; $(1, 0)$; $\begin{pmatrix} 0 \\ 1 \end{pmatrix}$.   (e) $v = \frac{43}{8}$; $(\frac{3}{16}, \frac{13}{16})$; $\begin{pmatrix} \frac{7}{8} \\ \frac{1}{8} \end{pmatrix}$.]

2. Set up the ordinary game of matching pennies as a matrix game. Find its value and optimal strategies. How are the optimal strategies realized in practice by players of this game?

3. A version of two-finger Morra is played as follows: Each player holds up either one or two fingers; if the sum of the number of fingers shown is even, player R gets the sum, and if the sum is odd, player C gets it.
(a) Show that the game matrix is

Player C

		1	2
Player R	1	2	−3
	2	−3	4

.

(b) Find optimal strategies for each player and the value of the game.

$$[Ans. \ (\tfrac{7}{12}, \tfrac{5}{12}); \ \begin{pmatrix} \tfrac{7}{12} \\ \tfrac{5}{12} \end{pmatrix}; v = -\tfrac{1}{12}.]$$

4. Rework Exercise 3 if player C gets the even sum and player R gets the odd sum.

5. Consider the following "war" problem: Some attacking bombers are attempting to bomb a city that is protected by fighters. The bombers can each day attack either "high" or "low," the low attack making the bombing more accurate. Similarly, the fighters can each day look for the bombers either "high" or "low." Credit the bombers with six points if they avoid the fighters, and zero if the fighters find them. Also credit the bombers with three extra points for accurate bombing if they fly low.
   (a) Set up the game matrix.
   (b) Find optimal strategies for each player.
   (c) Give instructions to the bomber and fighter commanders so that by flipping coins they can decide what to do.
      [Ans. (c) The bomber commander should flip one coin to decide whether to go high or low. The fighter commander should flip two coins and then go high if both turn up heads.]

6. Generalize the problem in Exercise 5 by crediting the bombers with x points for avoiding the fighters and y points for flying low. (Assume that x and y are positive.)
   (a) Set up the matrix.
   (b) If $y \geq x$ show that the game is strictly determined, and find optimal strategies.
   (c) If $y < x$ show that the game is nonstrictly determined and find optimal strategies.
   (d) Comment on these results, with special attention to the bombers' strategies.

7. If

$$G = \begin{array}{|c|c|} \hline a & b \\ \hline c & d \\ \hline \end{array}$$

is nonstrictly determined, prove that it is fair if and only if $ad = bc$.

8. In formulas (3)–(7) prove that $p_1 > 0$, $p_2 > 0$, $q_1 > 0$, and $q_2 > 0$. Must v be greater than zero?

9. Utilizing the results of Exercise 8 of the last section, find necessary and sufficient conditions that the game

$$G = \begin{array}{|c|c|} \hline a & 0 \\ \hline 0 & b \\ \hline \end{array}$$

be nonstrictly determined. Find optimal strategies for each player and the value of G, if it is nonstrictly determined.

[*Ans.* a and b must be both positive or both negative. $p_1 = b/(a + b)$; $p_2 = a/(a + b)$; $q_1 = b/(a + b)$; $q_2 = a/(a + b)$; $v = ab/(a + b)$.]

10. Suppose that R is given bk x and rd y while C is given bk u and rd v (where x, y, u, and v stand for positive integers). Let them play the matrix game

	bk u	rd v
bk x	xu	$-xv$
rd y	$-yu$	yv

Show that the game is always nonstrictly determined, and always fair.

11. If G, p^0, q^0, and v are as in the definition, show that $v = p^0 G q^0$.

12. Verify that (3)–(7) satisfy the conditions (1) and (2).

3. Matrix games

We shall consider a large class of games in this section, and discuss them in considerable generality. Our games are played between two players, according to strictly specified rules. Each player performs certain actions, as specified by the rules of the game, and then, at the end of the play of the game, one of the players may have to make a payment to the other player. The game may be repeated many times.

During such a game a player may have to make many strategic decisions. By a (pure) *strategy* for one of the players we mean a complete set of rules as to how he should make his decisions. We shall illustrate this in terms of the game of tick-tack-toe (and nearly the same remarks would apply to any game in which the players take turns moving). Let us construct a strategy for the player who moves first. His first decision concerns the opening move. He may choose any one of nine squares, and the strategy must tell him which choice to make. Let us say we tell him to move into the upper left-hand corner. His opponent may answer this in one of eight ways, and the strategy must be prepared for each alternative. It must have eight rules, such as "If he moves into the middle, move into the lower right-hand corner." For every such move the opponent may respond with one of several alternatives, and the strategy must again have an answering move ready for each of them, etc. Hence the strategy takes into account every conceivable position of the first player, and instructs what move to make in each one.

A strategy may be thought of as a set of instructions to be given to a machine, so that the machine will play the game exactly the way we would have.

We number the strategies of the first player $1, 2, \ldots, m$, and those of the second player $1, 2, \ldots, n$. Since each of the players must play according to one of his strategies, the game may proceed in any one of mn ways, and if each player chooses a definite strategy, the outcome is determined. We may think of giving the two strategies to two machines, and let them work out what happens. Let us suppose that, when the first player chooses strategy i and the second strategy j, the former wins an amount g_{ij}. We arrange these numbers g_{ij} into an $m \times n$ matrix, the *game matrix*. We may then think of the game as consisting of a choice of a row by the first player, and a column by the second player. Hence we see that any two-person zero-sum game specified by rules may be thought of as a matrix game.

Conversely, every matrix can be considered as a game. An $m \times n$ matrix may be thought of as a game between two players, in which player R chooses one of the m rows and player C simultaneously chooses one of the n columns. The outcome of the game is that C pays to R an amount equal to the entry of the matrix in the chosen row and column. (A negative entry represents a payment from R to C, as usual.)

In an $m \times n$ matrix game, the player R has m pure strategies, and the player C has n. We have seen in the last section that, in addition, we must consider the mixed strategies of the two players. We extend this concept to $m \times n$ games.

DEFINITION. An m-component row vector p is a *mixed-strategy vector* for R if it is a probability vector; similarly, an n-component column vector q is a mixed-strategy vector for C if it is a probability vector. (Recall from Chapter V that a probability vector is one with nonnegative entries whose sum is 1.) Let V and V' be the vectors

$$V = \underbrace{(v, v, \ldots, v)}_{m \text{ components}} \quad \text{and} \quad V' = \left.\begin{pmatrix} v \\ v \\ \cdot \\ \cdot \\ \cdot \\ v \end{pmatrix}\right\} n \text{ components}$$

where v is a number. Then v is the *value of the game* and p^0 and q^0 are *optimal strategies* for the players if and only if the following inequalities hold:

$$p^0 G \geq V$$
$$G q^0 \leq V'.$$

In Sections 1 and 2 we have given several examples of such matrix games together with their solutions. Notice that we have *not* proved that an arbitrary matrix game has a value and optimal strategies for each player; that question will be discussed in the next section.

THEOREM. If G is a matrix game which has a value and optimal strategies, then the value of the game is unique.

Proof. Suppose that v and w are two different values for the game G. Let $V = (v, v, \ldots, v)$ and $W = (w, w, \ldots, w)$ be m-component row vectors, and let

$$V' = \begin{pmatrix} v \\ v \\ \cdot \\ \cdot \\ \cdot \\ v \end{pmatrix} \quad \text{and} \quad W' = \begin{pmatrix} w \\ w \\ \cdot \\ \cdot \\ \cdot \\ w \end{pmatrix}$$

be n-component column vectors. Then let p^0 and q^0 be optimal mixed-strategy vectors associated with the value v such that

(a) $\qquad\qquad\qquad\qquad p^0 G \geq V$

(b) $\qquad\qquad\qquad\qquad G q^0 \leq V'.$

Similarly, let p^1 and q^1 be optimal mixed-strategy vectors associated with the value w such that

(c) $\qquad\qquad\qquad\qquad p^1 G \geq W$

(d) $\qquad\qquad\qquad\qquad G q^1 \leq W'.$

If we now multiply (a) on the right by q^1, we get $p^0 G q^1 \geq V q^1 = v$. In the same way, multiplying (d) on the left by p^0 gives $p^0 G q^1 \leq w$. The two inequalities just obtained show that $w \geq v$.

Next we multiply (b) on the left by p^1 and (c) on the right by q^0, obtaining $v \geq p^1 G q^0$ and $p^1 G q^0 \geq w$, which together imply that $v \geq w$.

Finally we see that $v \leq w$ and $v \geq w$ imply together that $v = w$, that is, the value of the game is unique.

THEOREM. If G is a matrix game with value v and optimal strategies p^0 and q^0, then $v = p^0 G q^0$.

Proof. By definition v, p^0, and q^0 satisfy

$$p^0 G \geq V \quad \text{and} \quad G q^0 \leq V'.$$

Multiplying the first of these inequalities on the right by q^0, we get $p^0 G q^0 \geq v$. Similarly, multiplying the second inequality on the left by p^0, we obtain $p^0 G q^0 \leq v$. These two inequalities together imply that $v = p^0 G q^0$, concluding the proof.

The theorems just proved are important because they permit us to give an interpretation of the *value* of a game as an *expected value* (see Chapter IV, Section 11). Briefly the interpretation is the following: If the game G is played repeatedly and if each time it is played player R uses the mixed strategy p^0 and player C uses the mixed strategy q^0, then the value v of G is the expected value of the game for R. The law of large numbers implies that, if the number of plays of G is sufficiently large, then the average value of R's winnings will (with high probability) be arbitrarily close to the value v of the game G.

As an example, let G be the matrix of the game of matching pennies, i.e.,

$$G = \begin{array}{|c|c|} \hline 1 & -1 \\ \hline -1 & 1 \\ \hline \end{array}.$$

As was found in Exercise 2 of the last section, optimal strategies in this game are for R to choose each row with probability $\frac{1}{2}$ and for C to choose each column with probability $\frac{1}{2}$. The value of G is zero. Notice that the only two payoffs that result from a single play of the game are $+1$ and -1, neither of which is equal to the value of the game. However, if the game is played repeatedly, the average value of R's payoffs will approach zero, which is the value of the game.

THEOREM. If G is a game with value v and optimal strategies p^0 and q^0, then v is the largest expectation that R can assure for himself. Similarly, v is the smallest expectation that C can assure for himself.

Proof. Let p be any mixed strategy vector of R and let q^0 be an optimal strategy for C; then multiply the equation $Gq^0 \le V'$ on the left by p, obtaining $pGq^0 \le v$. The latter equation shows that, if C plays optimally, the most that R can assure for himself is v. Now let p^0 be optimal for R; then, for every q, $p^0Gq \ge v$, so that R can actually assure himself of an expectation of v. The proof of the other statement of the theorem is similar.

The above theorem gives an intuitive justification to the definition of value and optimal strategies for a game. Thus the value is the "best" that a player can do and optimal strategies are the means of assuring this "best."

DEFINITION. A matrix game G is *strictly determined* if there is an entry g_{ij} in G that is the minimum entry in the ith row and the maximum entry in the jth column. (By rearranging and renumbering the rows and columns of a strictly determined matrix game G we can assume that g_{11} is an entry that is the minimum of row 1 and the maximum of column 1.)

THEOREM. If G is a strictly determined matrix game, arranged as indicated in the definition, the value of the game is $v = g_{11}$. Moreover, optimal strategies for the players are

$$p^0 = (1, 0, 0, \ldots, 0) \quad \text{and} \quad q^0 = \begin{pmatrix} 1 \\ 0 \\ 0 \\ . \\ . \\ . \\ 0 \end{pmatrix}.$$

(These optimal strategies simply say that R should choose the row that contains the entry g_{11} (the first row) and C should choose the column that contains the entry g_{11} (the first column). Compare these optimal strategies with those found in Section 1 for strictly determined 2 × 2 games.)

Proof. Suppose that G is strictly determined and the rows and columns of G are so arranged and numbered that g_{11} is an entry of G that is the minimum of row 1 and the maximum of column 1. Then we set $v = g_{11}$ and let p^0 and q^0 be the strategies as defined in the statement of the theorem. We have

$$p^0 G = (g_{11}, g_{12}, \ldots, g_{1n})$$
$$\geq (g_{11}, g_{11}, \ldots, g_{11}) = V,$$

where we have used the fact that g_{11} was the minimum of the first row. Similarly, using the fact that g_{11} is the maximum of the first column, we have

$$G q^0 = \begin{pmatrix} g_{11} \\ g_{21} \\ \cdot \\ \cdot \\ \cdot \\ g_{m1} \end{pmatrix} \leq \begin{pmatrix} g_{11} \\ g_{11} \\ \cdot \\ \cdot \\ \cdot \\ g_{11} \end{pmatrix} = V'.$$

From these two inequalities and the definition of a matrix game given above, we conclude that v is the value of the game and p^0 and q^0 are optimal strategies.

THEOREM. If g_{11} and g_{ij} are two entries of G that are the minima of the rows and the maxima of the columns in which they occur, then $v = g_{11} = g_{1j} = g_{i1} = g_{ij}$.

Proof. Using the facts that g_{11} and g_{ij} are the minima of the rows and the maxima of the columns in which they occur we see that

$$g_{ij} \geq g_{1j} \geq g_{11}, \qquad g_{ij} \leq g_{i1} \leq g_{11}.$$

(These inequalities are redundant but still true if either $i = 1$ or $j = 1$.) These two sets of inequalities imply that $g_{ij} = g_{1j} = g_{i1} = g_{11} = v$, completing the proof of the theorem.

Example 1. Although we have proved that the value of a game is unique, it may happen that a game has more than one pair of optimal strategies. For example, let G be the game

$$G = \begin{array}{|c|c|c|c|}
\hline
1 & 5 & 1 & 7 \\
\hline
-2 & 8 & 0 & -9 \\
\hline
1 & 12 & 1 & 3 \\
\hline
\end{array}.$$

Then we see that G is strictly determined with value 1, and the optimal strategies are $(1, 0, 0)$ and $(0, 0, 1)$ for player R and

$$\begin{pmatrix} 1 \\ 0 \\ 0 \\ 0 \end{pmatrix} \text{ and } \begin{pmatrix} 0 \\ 0 \\ 1 \\ 0 \end{pmatrix}$$

for player C. In the next theorem we shall see that there are still other optimal strategies for this game.

THEOREM. If p^0 and p^1 are two optimal strategies for R in a matrix G then the strategy

$$p = ap^0 + (1 - a)p^1,$$

where a is any number satisfying $0 \le a \le 1$, is also an optimal strategy for R.

Similarly, if q^0 and q^1 are optimal strategies for C in G, then the strategy

$$q = aq^0 + (1 - a)q^1,$$

where a is any number satisfying $0 \le a \le 1$, is also an optimal strategy for C.

Proof. We shall prove the first statement only and leave the second as an exercise (see Exercise 3). It is easy to show that p is a probability vector. By hypothesis we have $p^0G \ge V$ and $p^1G \ge V$. Hence we see that

$$\begin{aligned} pG &= [ap^0 + (1 - a)p^1]G \\ &= ap^0G + (1 - a)p^1G \\ &\ge aV + (1 - a)V = V, \end{aligned}$$

which shows that p is also an optimal strategy, completing the proof of the theorem.

This theorem implies that, in Example 1, the strategies of the form $a(1, 0, 0) + (1 - a)(0, 0, 1) = (a, 0, 1 - a)$ are optimal for R. It is easy to check that $(\frac{1}{2}, 0, \frac{1}{2})$ and $(\frac{1}{4}, 0, \frac{3}{4})$ are optimal and of this form.

EXERCISES

1. Find the value and all optimal strategies for the following games.

(a)

15	2	−3
6	5	7
−7	4	0

$[Ans.\ v = 5;\ (0, 1, 0);\ \begin{pmatrix} 0 \\ 1 \\ 0 \end{pmatrix}.]$

(b)

5	2	−1	−1
1	1	0	1
3	0	−3	7

(c)

0	5	6	−3
1	−1	2	3
1	2	3	4
−1	0	7	5

2. Find the values of and all optimal strategies for the following games.

(a)

5	10	6	5
5	7	8	5
0	5	6	5

(b)

−2	0	−1
−5	7	8

(c)

0	0	1	0
1	0	0	0
1	0	1	0

(d)

3	2	3
6	2	7
5	1	4

[*Ans.* (a) $v = 5$; $(a, 1 - a, 0)$; $\begin{pmatrix} a \\ 0 \\ 0 \\ 1 - a \end{pmatrix}$. (d) $v = 2$; $(a, 1 - a, 0)$; $\begin{pmatrix} 0 \\ 1 \\ 0 \end{pmatrix}$.]

3. If q^0 and q^1 are optimal strategies for C in the matrix game G, show that the strategy

$$q = aq^0 + (1 - a)q^1,$$

where a is a constant with $0 \le a \le 1$, is also optimal in the game G.

4. Verify that the strategies $p^0 = (\tfrac{1}{3}, \tfrac{1}{3}, \tfrac{1}{3})$ and

$$q^0 = \begin{pmatrix} \tfrac{1}{3} \\ \tfrac{1}{3} \\ \tfrac{1}{3} \end{pmatrix}$$

are optimal in the game G whose matrix is

$$G = \begin{array}{|c|c|c|} \hline 1 & 0 & 0 \\ \hline 0 & 1 & 0 \\ \hline 0 & 0 & 1 \\ \hline \end{array}.$$

What is the value of the game?

5. Generalize the result of Exercise 4 to the game G whose matrix is the $n \times n$ identity matrix.

6. Suppose that player R tries to find C in one of three towns X, Y, and Z. The distance between X and Y is five miles, the distance between Y and Z is five miles, and the distance between Z and X is ten miles. Assume that R and C can go to one and only one of the three towns and that if they both go to the same town, R "catches" C and otherwise C "escapes." Credit R with ten points if he catches C, and credit C with a number of points equal to the number of miles he is away from R if he escapes.
(a) Set up the game matrix.
(b) Show that both players have the same optimal strategy, namely, to go to towns X and Z with equal probabilities and to go to town Y with probability $\frac{1}{4}$.
(c) Find the value of the game.

7. A version of five-finger Morra is played as follows: Each player shows from one to five fingers, and the sum is divided by three. If the sum is exactly divisible by three, there is no exchange of payoffs. If there is a remainder of one, player R wins a sum equal to the total number of fingers, while if the remainder is two, player C wins the sum.
(a) Set up the game matrix. [*Hint:* It is 5 × 5.]
(b) Verify that an optimal strategy for either player is to show one or five fingers with probability $\frac{1}{9}$, to show two or four fingers with probability $\frac{2}{9}$, and to show three fingers with probability $\frac{1}{3}$.
(c) Is the game fair? [*Ans.* Yes.]

8. Consider the following game:

$$G = \begin{array}{|c|c|c|}
\hline
a & 0 & 0 \\
\hline
0 & b & 0 \\
\hline
0 & 0 & c \\
\hline
\end{array}.$$

(a) If a, b, and c are not all of the same sign, show that the game is strictly determined with value zero.
(b) If a, b, and c are all of the same sign, show that the vector

$$\left(\frac{bc}{ab + bc + ca}, \frac{ca}{ab + bc + ca}, \frac{ab}{ab + bc + ca} \right)$$

is an optimal strategy for player R.
(c) Find player C's optimal strategy for case (b).
(d) Find the value of the game for case (b) and show that it is positive if a, b, and c are all positive, and negative if they are all negative.

9. Two players agree to play the following game. The first player will show 1, 2, or 4 fingers. The second player will show 2, 3, or 5 fingers, simultaneously. If the sum of the fingers shown is 3, 5, or 9, the first player receives this sum. Otherwise no payment is made.
(a) Set up the game matrix.
(b) Use the results of Exercise 8 to solve the game.

(c) How much should the first player be willing to pay to play the game? [*Ans.* $\frac{45}{29}$.]

10. Consider the (symmetric) game whose matrix is

$$
G = \begin{array}{|c|c|c|}
\hline
0 & -a & -b \\
\hline
a & 0 & -c \\
\hline
b & c & 0 \\
\hline
\end{array}
$$

(a) If a and b are both positive or both negative, show that G is strictly determined.

(b) If b and c are both positive or both negative, show that G is strictly determined.

(c) If $a > 0$, $b < 0$, and $c > 0$, show that an optimal strategy for player R is given by

$$
\left(\frac{c}{a-b+c}, \quad \frac{-b}{a-b+c}, \quad \frac{a}{a-b+c} \right).
$$

(d) In part (c) find an optimal strategy for player C.

(e) If $a < 0$, $b > 0$, and $c < 0$, show that the strategy given in (c) is optimal for R. What is an optimal strategy for player C?

(f) Prove that the value of the game is always zero.

11. In a well-known children's game each player says "stone" or "scissors" or "paper." If one says "stone" and the other "scissors," then the former wins a penny. Similarly, "scissors" beats "paper," and "paper" beats "stone." If the two players name the same item, then the game is a tie.

(a) Set up the game matrix.

(b) Use the results of Exercise 10 to solve the game.

12. In Exercise 11 let us suppose that the payments are different in different cases. Suppose that when "stone breaks scissors," the payment is one cent; when "scissors cut paper," the payment is two cents; and when "paper covers stone," the payment is three cents.

(a) Set up the game matrix.

(b) Use the results of Exercise 10 to solve the game.

[*Ans.* $\frac{1}{3}$ "stone," $\frac{1}{2}$ "scissors," $\frac{1}{6}$ "paper"; $v = 0$.]

4. More on matrix games: the fundamental theorem

Here we continue the discussion of the basic properties of matrix games. First we show what happens to the game if each entry in the matrix is multiplied by a nonnegative constant or if the same constant is added to each entry in the matrix. Then we discuss the fundamental existence theorem for matrix games.

THEOREM. If k is a nonnegative number, i.e., $k \geq 0$, and G is a matrix game with value v, then the game kG is a matrix game with value kv, and every strategy optimal in G is also optimal in kG. (Recall that the matrix kG is obtained from G by multiplying every entry of G by the number k.)

Proof. Let p^0 be an optimal strategy for R in the game G, that is, $p^0 G \geq V$. Then we have

$$p^0(kG) = k(p^0G) \geq kV.$$

Similarly, if q^0 is optimal for C in the game G, then

$$(kG)q^0 = k(Gq^0) \leq kV'.$$

These two inequalities show that kv is the value of kG and that optimal strategies in G are also optimal in the game kG.

It should be observed that it was essential for the proof of this theorem that k be nonnegative, since multiplying an inequality by a *negative* number has the effect of reversing the direction of the inequality sign. The following example shows that the above theorem is false for negative k's.

Example 1. Let $k = -1$ and let G and $(-1)G$ be the matrices

$$G = \begin{array}{|c|c|} \hline 2 & 3 \\ \hline -1 & 0 \\ \hline \end{array} \qquad \text{and} \qquad (-1)G = \begin{array}{|c|c|} \hline -2 & -3 \\ \hline 1 & 0 \\ \hline \end{array}.$$

Observe that each of these games is strictly determined but that the value of the first game is 2, while the value of the second is 0 (which is not equal to $(-1)2 = -2$). Moreover, optimal strategies in G are for R to play the first row with probability 1, and for C to play the first column with probability 1, but neither of these strategies is optimal in the game $(-1)G$.

THEOREM. Let G be an $m \times n$ matrix game with value v; let E be the $m \times n$ matrix each of whose entries is 1; and let k be *any* constant. Then the game $G + kE$ has value $v + k$, and every strategy optimal in the game G is also optimal in the game $G + kE$. (The game $G + kE$ is obtained from the game G by adding the number k to each entry in G.)

Proof. Let p^0 and q^0 be optimal strategies in G; then $p^0 G \geq V$ and $Gq^0 \leq V'$. We have

$$\begin{aligned} p^0(G + kE) &= p^0G + p^0(kE) \\ &= p^0G + k(p^0E) \\ &\geq (v, v, \ldots, v) + (k, k, \ldots, k) \\ &= (v + k, v + k, \ldots, v + k). \end{aligned}$$

Similarly, we have

$(G + kE)q^0 = Gq^0 + k(Eq^0)$

$$\leq \begin{pmatrix} v \\ v \\ \cdot \\ \cdot \\ \cdot \\ v \end{pmatrix} + \begin{pmatrix} k \\ k \\ \cdot \\ \cdot \\ \cdot \\ k \end{pmatrix} = \begin{pmatrix} v + k \\ v + k \\ \cdot \\ \cdot \\ \cdot \\ v + k \end{pmatrix}.$$

These inequalities show that the value of the game $G + kE$ is $v + k$ and also show that each strategy optimal in G is optimal in $G + kE$.

Matrix game theory would not be of very great interest unless we knew under what conditions such a game has a solution. The fundamental theorem of game theory is that every matrix game has a solution.

FUNDAMENTAL THEOREM. Let G be any $m \times n$ matrix game; then there exists a value v for G and optimal strategies p^0 for player R and q^0 for player C. In other words, every matrix game possesses a solution.

Proof for 2×2 *matrices.* If G is strictly determined, the value and optimal strategies were found in Section 1. If G is not strictly determined, formulas (3) through (7) of Section 2 give the optimal strategies and value for G. Since G must be either strictly determined or nonstrictly determined we have covered all cases.

In Section 9 we discuss a proof of the general theorem, based on the duality theorem of linear programming.

EXERCISES

1. Find the values of the games kG and $G + kE$ for each of the games G whose matrices are given in Exercise 1 of Section 3, if k takes on the values 3, 0, and -2.

2. If G is any matrix game and $k = 0$ find all optimal strategies for each player in the game kG.   [*Ans.* Any strategy is optimal.]

3. If G is any matrix game and $k > 0$, show that every strategy optimal in kG is also optimal in G. [*Hint:* Multiply by $1/k$.]

4. If G is any matrix game and k is any constant, show that every strategy optimal in the game $G + kE$ is also optimal in the game G.

5. Suppose that before C and R play a matrix game G, player C gives to player R a payment of k dollars. In this case we shall say C has made a *side payment* of k to R. (If k is negative, then, as usual, this will be a side payment from R to C.)
   (a) If C has made a side payment of k to R before playing the game G, show that the game they actually play is $G + kE$.
   (b) If v is the value of the game G, find the value of the game $G - vE$.

(c) Using the results of (a) and (b), show that any matrix game G with value v can be made into a fair matrix game by requiring that C make a side payment of $-v$ to R before they play the game G.

6. Show that any matrix game G can be made into a fair matrix game, with each entry in the matrix lying between -1 and 1, by adding the same number to each entry in the matrix and by multiplying each entry by a positive number.

7. Show that the sets of optimal strategies for each player are unchanged by the transformation suggested in Exercise 6. How does the value of the game change?

8. Consider the matrix game:

a	b	b
b	a	b
b	b	a

where $a > b$.

(a) Show that this can be obtained from the identity matrix by multiplying it by a suitable number, and then adding bE.
(b) Use the results of Section 3, Exercise 10, to solve the game.

$$[Ans.\ v = a/3 + 2b/3.]$$

9. Suppose that the entries of a matrix game are rewritten in new units (e.g., dollars instead of cents). Show that the monetary value of the game has not changed.

10. Consider the game of matching pennies whose matrix is

1	-1
-1	1

If the entries of the matrix represent gains or losses of one penny, would you be willing to play the game at least once? If the entries represent gains or losses of one dollar would you be willing to play the game at least once? If they represent gains or losses of one million dollars would you play the game at least once? In each of these cases show that the value is zero and optimal strategies are the same. Discuss the practical application of the theory of games in the light of this example.

5. Two-row and two-column matrix games

After the 2×2 games, the simplest matrix games are the $2 \times n$ and $m \times 2$ games, i.e., where one player has only two strategies. Here we discuss the solution of such games.

Example 1. Suppose that Jones conceals one of the following 4 bills in his hand: a \$1 or a \$2 United States bill or a \$1 or a \$2 Canadian bill. Smith guesses either "United States" or "Canadian" and gets the bill if his guess is correct. We assume that a Canadian dollar has the same real value as a United States dollar. The matrix of the game is the following:

		Smith guesses U.S.	Smith guesses Can.
U.S.	\$1	−1	0
	\$2	−2	0
Can.	\$1	0	−1
	\$2	0	−2

Jones chooses (labels at left)

It is obvious that Jones should always choose the \$1 bill of either country rather than the \$2 bill, since by doing so he may cut his losses and will never increase them. This can be observed in the matrix above, since every entry in the second row is less than or equal to the corresponding entry in the first row, and every entry in the fourth row is less than or equal to the corresponding entry in the third row. In effect we can eliminate the second and fourth rows and reduce the game to the following 2 × 2 matrix game:

		Smith guesses U.S.	Smith guesses Can.
Jones chooses	U.S. \$1	−1	0
	Can. \$1	0	−1

The new matrix game is nonstrictly determined with optimal strategies $(\frac{1}{2}, \frac{1}{2})$ for Jones and $\begin{pmatrix} \frac{1}{2} \\ \frac{1}{2} \end{pmatrix}$ for Smith. The value of the game is $-\frac{1}{2}$, which means that Smith should pay 50 cents to play it.

DEFINITION. Let A be an $m \times n$ matrix game. We shall say that row i *dominates* row h if every entry in row i is as large as or larger than the corresponding entry in row h. Similarly, we shall say that column j *dominates* column k if every entry in column j is as small as or smaller than the corresponding entry in column k.

Any dominated row or column can be omitted from the matrix game without materially affecting its solution. In the original matrix of Example 1 above, we see that row 1 dominates row 2, and also that row 3 dominates row 4.

Example 2. Consider again the card game of Section 1, this time giving R a bk 5 and rd 3, while C receives a bk 6 and a bk 5 and a rd 4 and a rd 5. The matrix of the game is

	bk 6	bk 5	rd 4	rd 5
bk 5	1	0	−1	0
rd 3	−3	−2	1	2

Observe that column 2 (and also 3) dominates column 4; that is, C should never play rd 5. Thus our game can be reduced to the following 2 × 3 game:

	bk 6	bk 5	rd 4
bk 5	1	0	−1
rd 3	−3	−2	1

No further rows or columns can be omitted; hence we must introduce a new technique for the solution of this game.

It can be shown (though we will not attempt to do so) that, in any 2 × n game, the column player C has an optimal mixed strategy that uses only two pure strategies. Hence he may consider the game matrix two columns at a time, and select the 2 × 2 game he likes best. That is, he solves each of the 2 × 2 games consisting of two columns of the matrix, and selects the one having smallest value.

In the above 2 × 3 game we have three derived games:

	bk 6	bk 5
bk 5	1	0
rd 3	−3	−2

	bk 6	rd 4
bk 5	1	−1
rd 3	−3	1

	bk 5	rd 4
bk 5	0	−1
rd 3	−2	1

The first game is fair, the second has value $-\frac{1}{3}$, and third $-\frac{1}{2}$. Hence player C selects the third game, i.e., he decides to use only strategies bk 5 and rd 4. The optimal strategy for the given game is to play each card one-half of the time, hence his strategy for the 2 × 4 game should be

$$\begin{pmatrix} 0 \\ \frac{1}{2} \\ \frac{1}{2} \\ 0 \end{pmatrix}.$$

Since R knows that C will select this particular 2 × 2 game, R's optimal strategy is his strategy in this 2 × 2 game, which is $(\frac{3}{4}, \frac{1}{4})$.

Example 3. A numerical example of a 3 × 2 game is

6	−1
0	4
4	3

No dominations are possible in this game, hence we look at the three possible 2×2 subgames. The one that yields the largest value is the game composed of the last two rows. Its value is $\frac{6}{5}$ and optimal strategies for the original game are $(0, \frac{1}{5}, \frac{4}{5})$ and $\begin{pmatrix} \frac{1}{5} \\ \frac{4}{5} \end{pmatrix}$ for R and C, respectively.

Example 4. Another numerical example is

1	−1	2	−3
−1	1	0	1

Here the fourth column dominates the second, and the first column dominates the third. The game is then reduced to

1	−3
−1	1

whose value is $-\frac{1}{3}$, and optimal strategies are $p^0 = (\frac{1}{3}, \frac{2}{3})$ and $q^0 = \begin{pmatrix} \frac{2}{3} \\ \frac{1}{3} \end{pmatrix}$; the latter strategy extends to the strategy

$$\begin{pmatrix} \frac{2}{3} \\ 0 \\ 0 \\ \frac{1}{3} \end{pmatrix}$$

which is optimal in the original game.

EXERCISES

1. Solve the following games:

(a)

3	0
−2	3
7	5

$[Ans. \ v = 5; (0, 0, 1); \begin{pmatrix} 0 \\ 1 \end{pmatrix}.]$

(b)

10	5	4	6
18	3	3	4

(c)

1	0	2
0	3	2

$[Ans. \ v = \frac{3}{4}; (\frac{3}{4}, \frac{1}{4}); \begin{pmatrix} \frac{3}{4} \\ \frac{1}{4} \\ 0 \end{pmatrix}.]$

(d)

0	2
1	3
−1	0
2	0

(e)

1	2	3
4	2	1

$[An\ Ans.\ v = 2;\ (\frac{3}{5}, \frac{2}{5});\ \begin{pmatrix} 0 \\ 1 \\ 0 \end{pmatrix}.]$

(f)

1	0	1	1	2
0	−1	−2	−3	−10

2. Solve the following games:

(a)

0	15
8	0
−10	20
10	12

(b)

−1	−2	0	−3	−4
−2	1	0	2	5

(c)

−1	5	−1	−2	8	10
3	−6	0	8	−9	−8

$[An\ Ans.\ v = -\frac{1}{2};\ (\frac{1}{2}, \frac{1}{2});\ \begin{pmatrix} 0 \\ \frac{1}{12} \\ \frac{11}{12} \\ 0 \\ 0 \\ 0 \end{pmatrix}.]$

3. Solve the game

1	2	3
3	2	1

.

Since there is more than one optimal strategy for C, find a range of optimal strategies for him. (See Section 3, Exercise 3.)

4. In the card game of Example 2 suppose that R has bk 9, bk 5, rd 7 and rd 3, while C has bk 8 and rd 4. Set up and solve the corresponding matrix game.

[*Ans.* $v = 1$; R shows bk 5 and rd 7 each with probability $\frac{1}{2}$; C shows each of his cards with probability $\frac{1}{2}$.]

5. Suppose that Jones conceals in his hand one, two, three, or four silver dollars and Smith guesses "even" or "odd." If Smith's guess is correct, he wins the amount which Jones holds, otherwise he must pay Jones this amount. Set up the corresponding matrix game and find an optimal strategy for each player in which he puts positive weight on all his (pure) strategies. Is the game fair?

6. Consider the following game: Player R announces "one" or "two"; then, independently of each other, both players write down one of these two numbers. If the sum of the three numbers so obtained is odd, C pays R the odd sum in dollars; if the sum of the three numbers is even, R pays C the even sum in dollars.
   (a) What are the strategies of R? [*Hint:* He has four strategies.]
   (b) What are the strategies of C? [*Hint:* We must consider what C does after "one" is announced or after a "two." Hence he has four strategies.]
   (c) Write down the matrix for the game.
   (d) Restrict player R to announcing "two," and allow for C only those strategies where his number does not depend on the announced number. Solve the resulting 2 × 2 game.
   (e) Extend the above mixed strategies to the original game, and show that they are optimal.
   (f) Is the game favorable to R? If so, by how much?

7. Answer the same questions as in Exercise 6 if R gets the even sum and C gets the odd sum (except that, in part (d) restrict R to announce "one"). Which game is more favorable for R? Could you have predicted this without the use of game theory?

8. Rework the five-finger Morra game of Section 3, Exercise 7, with the following payoffs: If the sum of the number of fingers is even, R gets one, while if the sum is odd, C gets one. Suppose that each player shows only one or two fingers. Show that the resulting game is like matching pennies. Show that the optimal strategies for this game, when extended, are optimal in the whole game.

9. A version of three-finger Morra is played as follows: Each player shows from one to three fingers; R always pays C an amount equal to the number of fingers that C shows; if C shows exactly one more or two fewer fingers than R, then C pays R a positive amount x (where x is independent of the number of fingers shown).

(a) Set up the game matrix for arbitrary x's.

(b) If $x = \frac{1}{2}$, show that the game is strictly determined. Find the value.
[*Ans.* $v = -\frac{5}{2}$.]

(c) If $x = 2$, show that there is a pair of optimal strategies in which the first player shows one or two fingers and the second player shows two or three fingers. [*Hint:* Solve a 2 × 2 derived game.] Find the value.
[*Ans.* $v = -\frac{3}{2}$.]

(d) If $x = 6$, show that an optimal strategy for R is to use the mixed strategy, $(\frac{1}{3}, \frac{1}{2}, \frac{1}{6})$. Show that the optimal mixed strategy for C is to choose his three strategies each with probability $\frac{1}{3}$. Find the value of the game.

10. Another version of three-finger Morra goes as follows: Each player shows from one to three fingers; if the sum of the number of fingers is even, then R gets an amount equal to the number of fingers that C shows: if the sum is odd, C gets an amount equal to the number of fingers that R shows.

(a) Set up the game matrix.

(b) Reduce the game to a 2 × 2 matrix game.

(c) Find optimal strategies for each player and show that the game is fair.

11. Two companies, one large and one small, manufacturing the same product, wish to build a new store in one of four towns located on a given highway. If we regard the total population of the four towns as 100 per cent, the distribution of population and distances between towns are as shown:

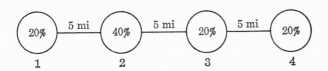

Assume that if the large company's store is nearer a town it will capture 80 per cent of the business, if both stores are equally distant, then the large company will capture 60 per cent of the business, and if the small store is nearer, then the large company will capture 40 per cent of the business.

(a) Set up the matrix of the game.

(b) Test for dominated rows and columns.

(c) Find optimal strategies and the value of the game and interpret your results.
[*Ans.* Both companies should locate in town 2; the large company captures 60 per cent of the business.]

12. Rework Exercise 11 if the per cent of business captured by the large company is 90, 75, and 60, respectively.

13. We have stated without proof that any 2 × n game can be solved by considering only its 2 × 2 derived games. Verify that this is the case for a game of the form

C

a	0	1
R		
0	b	1

(a) Show that if $a \leq 1$ or $b \leq 1$, then column 3 is dominated. Hence solve the game.

(b) If $a > 1$ and $b > 1$, solve the three 2×2 derived games. [*Hint:* Two of them are strictly determined.]

(c) If $a > 1$, $b > 1$, but $ab < a + b$, then show that the strategies of the nonstrictly determined derived game are optimal for both players.

(d) If $ab \geq a + b$, then show that R has as optimal strategy the same strategy as in part (c), but C has a pure strategy as optimal strategy.

(e) Using the previous results, show that the value of the game is always the smallest of the values of the three derived games.

6. Simplified poker

In order to illustrate the procedure of translating a game specified by rules into a matrix game, we shall carry it out for a simplification of a well-known game. The example that we are about to discuss is a simplification (by A. W. Tucker) of the poker game discussed on pp. 211–219 in the book *The Theory of Games and Economic Behavior*, by John von Neumann and Oskar Morgenstern.

The deck that is used in simplified poker has only two types of cards, in equal numbers, which we shall call "high" and "low." For example, an ordinary bridge deck could be used with red cards high and black cards low. Each player "antes" an amount a of money and is dealt a single card which is his "hand." By a "deal" we shall mean a pair of cards, the first being given to player R and the second to player C. Thus the deal (H, H) means that each player obtains a high card. There are then four possible deals, namely,

$$(H, H), \qquad (H, L), \qquad (L, H), \qquad (L, L).$$

Ignoring minor errors (see Exercise 1), if the number of cards in the deck is large, each of these deals is "equally likely," that is, the probability of getting a specific one of these deals is $\frac{1}{4}$.

After the deal, player R has the first move and has two alternatives, namely, to "see," or to "raise" by adding an amount b to the pot. If R elects to see, the higher hand wins the pot or equal hands split the pot equally. If R elects to raise, then C has two alternatives, to "fold," or to "call" by adding the amount b to the pot. If C folds, player R wins the pot (without revealing his hand). If C calls, then the higher hand wins the pot or equal hands split the pot equally. These are all the rules.

A pure strategy for a player is a command that tells him exactly what to do in every conceivable situation that can arise in the game. An example of a pure strategy for R is the following: "Raise if you get a high card, and see if you get a low card." We can abbreviate this strategy to simply raise-see. It is easy to see that R has four pure strategies, namely, raise-raise, raise-see, see-raise, and see-see. In the same manner, C has four pure strategies, fold-fold, fold-call, call-fold, call-call.

Given a choice of a pure strategy for each player, there are exactly four ways the play of the game can proceed, depending on which of the four deals occurs. For example, suppose that R has chosen the see-raise strategy, and C has chosen the fold-fold strategy. If the deal is (H, H), then R sees, and they split the pot, so neither wins; if the deal is (H, L), then R sees and wins the pot, giving him a; if the deal is (L, H), then R raises and C folds, so that R wins a; and if the deal is (L, L), then R raises and C folds, so that R wins a. Since the probabilities of each of these deals is $\frac{1}{4}$, the expected value of R's gain is $3a/4$. Let us compute another expected value, namely, suppose that R uses see-raise and C uses call-fold. Then, if the deal is (H, H), R sees and wins nothing; if the deal is (H, L), then R sees and wins a; if the deal is (L, H), then R raises, C calls, and C wins $a + b$; and if the deal is (L, L), then R raises, C folds, and R wins a. The expected value for R here is $(a - b)/4$.

Continuing in this manner we can compute the expected outcome for each of the 16 possible choice of pairs of strategies. The payoff matrix so obtained is given in Figure 4.

High		fold	fold	call	call
	Low	fold	call	fold	call
see	see	0	0	0	0
see	raise	$\dfrac{3a}{4}$	$\dfrac{2a}{4}$	$\dfrac{a - b}{4}$	$\dfrac{-b}{4}$
raise	see	$\dfrac{a}{4}$	$\dfrac{a + b}{4}$	0	$\dfrac{b}{4}$
raise	raise	$\dfrac{4a}{4}$	$\dfrac{3a + b}{4}$	$\dfrac{a - b}{4}$	0

Figure 4

The reader should observe that we have just completed the translation of a game specified by rules into a matrix game.

Since a and b are positive numbers, we see that, in the matrix above, the fourth row dominates the second, and the third row dominates the first. Similarly, the third column dominates the first and second columns. We can reduce the 4 × 4 matrix to the 2 × 2 matrix in Figure 5.

		Conservative	Calling
High		call	call
Low		fold	call
Conservative raise	see	0	$\frac{b}{4}$
Bluffing raise	raise	$\frac{a-b}{4}$	0

Figure 5

Notice that we have labeled the raise-see strategy as "conservative" for R, since it seems sensible to raise when he has a high card and to see when he has a low one. The strategy raise-raise which says, raise even if you have a low card, we have labeled "bluffing," since it corresponds to the ordinary notion of bluffing. In the same manner we have labeled the call-fold strategy "conservative." The call-call (or "calling") strategy is designed to call an opponent's possible bluff, thus discouraging him from too frequent use of his bluffing strategy.

Example 1. Suppose $a = 4$ and $b = 8$. Then the matrix becomes

	Conservative	Calling
Conservative	0	2
Bluffing	−1	0

Here the game is strictly determined and fair, and optimal strategies are for each player to play conservatively.

Example 2. Suppose $a = 8$ and $b = 4$. Then the matrix becomes

	Conservative	Calling
Conservative	0	1
Bluffing	1	0

Here the value of the game is $\frac{1}{2}$, meaning that it is biased in favor of R. Optimal strategies are for each player to bluff (or call a bluff) with probability $\frac{1}{2}$ and to play conservatively with probability $\frac{1}{2}$.

Here we have one of the most interesting results of game theory, since it turns out that, as part of an optimal strategy, one *should* actually bluff part of the time. The solution for arbitrary a and b is found in Exercises 3–6.

EXERCISES

1. Suppose that the simplified poker game is played with an ordinary bridge deck where red is "high" and black is "low." Compute to four decimal places the conditional probability of drawing a red card, given that one red card has already been drawn. From this, discuss the accuracy of the assumption that the four deals are equally likely. How could the accuracy of the assumption be improved?

2. Substitute $a = 4$ and $b = 8$ into the 4×4 matrix above, and reduce it by dominations to a 2×2 matrix game. Is it the one considered in Example 1 above? Do the same for $a = 8$ and $b = 4$ and Example 2.

3. If $a \leq b$, show that the simplified poker game is strictly determined and fair. Show that both players' optimal strategy is to play conservatively.

4. If $a > b$, show that the simplified poker game is biased in favor of R. Show that, to play optimally, each player must bluff (or call a bluff) with positive probability, and find the optimal strategies.

5. If $a > b$, discuss ways of making the game fair.

6. When $b \geq a$, show that the optimal strategy of player R is not unique. Show that although he has two "optimal" strategies, the raise-see strategy is in a sense better than the other.

7. Show that in the case $a = 8$, $b = 4$, the strategy of R can be interpreted as follows: "On a high card always raise, on a low card raise with probability $\frac{1}{2}$." Reinterpret C's mixed strategy similarly.

The remaining exercises concern a variant of the simplified poker game. Real poker is characterized by the fact that there are very many poor hands, and very few good ones. We can make the above model of poker more realistic by making the draw of a low card more probable than that of a high card. Let us say that the probability of drawing a high card is only $\frac{1}{5}$. The rules of the game remain as in the text.

8. Calculate the probabilities of (H, H), (H, L), and (L, L) deals.

9. The strategies of the two players are as in the text, hence we will get a similar 4×4 game matrix. Calculate the see-raise *vs.* fold-fold entry of the matrix, just as in the text, but using the results of Exercise 8. Do the same for the see-raise *vs.* call-fold entry.   [*Ans.* $24a/25$; $(16a - 4b)/25$.]

10. Fill in the remaining matrix entries.

11. Show that two rows and two columns are dominated.

12. Show that the resulting 2×2 game is strictly determined if and only if $b \geq 4a$. What is the value of the game in these cases?

13. Let $a = 4$, $b = 8$, as in the text, and solve the game. Compare your solution with that in the text.

[*Ans.* Each player should bluff (or call a bluff) half the time; $v = \frac{16}{25}$; in the previous version there was no bluffing in this case, and the game was fair.]

14. Let $a = 8$, $b = 4$, as in the text, and solve the game. Compare your solution with that in the text.

[*Ans.* Each player plays more conservatively; game is slightly more favorable to R than in the previous version.]

15. The players have agreed that the ante will be $4. They are debating the size of the raise. What value of b should player R argue for? [*Hint:* He does not want the game to be fair. Then what are the possible values of b? Find the value of the 2 × 2 game for any such b, and find its maximum value by trying several values of b.]

*7. Model of an expanding economy

The following model is a modification of a model proposed by John von Neumann. It is designed to study an economy which is expanding at a fixed rate, but which is otherwise in equilibrium. The model makes certain assumptions about how an economy behaves in equilibrium. These assumptions are idealizations, and it is to be expected that the model will eventually be replaced by a better model. For the present many economists consider the von Neumann model to be a reasonable approximation of reality. Our interest in the model is purely to illustrate how finite mathematics is used in an economic problem.

The economy is described by n *goods* and m *processes*. A good may be steel, coal, houses, shoes, etc. Goods are the materials of production in the economy. Each good may be measured in any convenient units, as long as the units are fixed once and for all. It is convenient to be able to talk of arbitrary multiples of these units; e.g., we will consider not only 2.75 tons of steel but also 2.75 houses. The latter may be interpreted as an average.

A manufacturing process needs certain goods as raw materials (the *inputs*) and produces one or more of our goods (the *outputs*). As a process we may, for example, consider the conversion of steel, wood, glass, etc. into a house. Of course this process may be used to manufacture more than one house, and hence we have the concept of the *intensity* with which a process is used. One of the basic assumptions is one of linearity, i.e., that k houses will require k times as much of each raw material. Thus we choose an arbitrary "unit intensity" for each process, and the process is completely described if we know the inputs necessary for this unit operation and the outputs produced.

Process i when operating at unit intensity will require a certain amount of good j as an input. This amount will be called a_{ij}. (In particular, if good j is not needed for process i, then $a_{ij} = 0$.) We will call b_{ij} the amount of good j produced by process i. Here we allow a process to produce several different goods (e.g., a principal output and by-products). But we allow processes that produce only one good, in which case all the b_{ij} for this i will be 0, except for one. The a_{ij} and b_{ij} are nonnegative numbers.

We define the matrix A to be the $m \times n$ matrix having components a_{ij}, and B to be the $m \times n$ matrix with components b_{ij}. Then the entire economy is described by these two matrices.

We must still consider the element of time. It is customary to think of the economy as working in stages or cycles. In one such stage there is just time enough for process i to convert the inputs a_{ij} to outputs b_{ij}. Then in the next stage, these outputs may in turn be used as inputs. The length of this cycle may be any time interval convenient for the study of the particular economy. It may be a month, a year, or a number of years.

Example. Let us take as our economy a chicken farm. Our goods are chickens and eggs, with one chicken and one egg being the natural units. Our two processes consist of laying eggs and hatching them. Let us assume that in a given month a chicken lays an average of 12 eggs if we use it for laying eggs. If used for hatching, it will hatch an average of four eggs per month. From this information we can construct A and B.

Our cycle is of length one month. Good 1 is "chicken," good 2 is "egg," process 1 is "laying," and process 2 is "hatching." The unit of intensity of a process will be what one chicken can do on the average in a month. The input of process 1 is one chicken, i.e., one unit of good 1. The output will consist of a dozen eggs *plus* the original chicken. (We must not forget this, since the original chicken can be used again in the next cycle.) Hence the output is one unit of good 1 and 12 units of good 2. In process 2 the inputs are one chicken and four eggs, while the output consists of five chickens (the original one plus the four hatched). Hence our matrices are

	Chicken	Egg			Chicken	Egg	
Laying eggs:							
Hatching eggs:							

$$A = \begin{pmatrix} 1 & 0 \\ 1 & 4 \end{pmatrix}, \qquad B = \begin{pmatrix} 1 & 12 \\ 5 & 0 \end{pmatrix}.$$

Suppose that our farmer starts with three chickens and eight eggs ready for hatching. He will need two chickens for hatching the eight eggs, and this leaves him one for laying eggs. Hence he uses process 1 with intensity 1, process 2 with intensity 2. We symbolize this by the vector $x = (1, 2)$. Note that his inputs are the components of xA. His one laying chicken will lay 12 eggs. He will end up with his original three chickens plus eight new ones. Hence he will have an output of 11 units of good 1 and 12 units of good 2. These are the components of xB. Of his 11 chickens only three can be used for hatching, hence he will employ intensities $(8, 3)$. The outputs will be $(8, 3)B$

$= (23, 96)$, as can easily be checked (see Exercise 1). He now has 96 eggs and only 23 chickens, so that some eggs must go unhatched.

On the other hand, suppose that he starts with only two chickens and four eggs. He will then use intensity $(1, 1)$. His laying chicken lays 12 eggs, and with four newly hatched chickens he has a total of six chickens. This result is also given by $(1, 1)B = (6, 12)$. He now has tripled both his chickens and his eggs. He can use intensity $(3, 3)$ on the next cycle, yielding $(3, 3)B = (18, 36)$, which again triples both the chickens and the eggs. Thus he can continue to use the same proportion of the processes, and will continue to triple his output on every cycle. This economy operates in *equilibrium*.

As was seen in the example, the natural way to represent the intensities of our processes is by means of a row vector. Let x_i be the intensity with which process i is operated; then the *intensity vector* x is $(x_1, \ldots, x_m)$. Matrix multiplication is then an easy way of finding the total amount of each good needed, and the totals produced. Component j of xA is the sum $x_1 a_{1j} + \ldots + x_m a_{mj}$; where $x_1 a_{1j}$ is the amount of good j we are using in process 1, $x_2 a_{2j}$ the amount we use in process 2, etc. Hence the jth component of xA is the total amount of good j needed in the inputs. Similarly, xB gives the total amounts of the various goods in the outputs.

We must now introduce prices for the various goods. Let y_j be the price of a unit of good j; this must be nonnegative, but it may be zero. (The latter represents a good that is so cheap as to be "practically free.") It is assumed that k units of good j will cost ky_j. The *price vector* y is the column vector

Let us consider the products Ay and By. In Ay the ith element is $a_{i1}y_1 + \ldots + a_{in}y_n$; the product $a_{i1}y_1$ is the amount of good 1 needed for unit operation of process i multiplied by the per unit price of good 1, hence this is the cost of good 1 used in the process, $a_{i2}y_2$ is the cost of good 2 used, etc. Hence the ith component of Ay is the total cost of inputs for a unit intensity operation of process i. Similarly, By gives the cost (value) of the outputs.

Finally, we consider the products xAy and xBy. Since x is $1 \times m$, the matrices $m \times n$, and y is $n \times 1$, each product is 1×1—or a number. An analysis similar to those above shows that xAy is the total cost of inputs if the economy is operated at intensity x, with prices y, and xBy is the total value of all goods produced. (See Exercise 2.)

Example (continued). Suppose that a chicken costs 10 monetary units, while an egg costs 1 unit; then $y = \begin{pmatrix} 10 \\ 1 \end{pmatrix}$. Here

$$Ay = \begin{pmatrix} 10 \\ 14 \end{pmatrix} \quad \text{and} \quad By = \begin{pmatrix} 22 \\ 50 \end{pmatrix}.$$

This means that process 1, laying eggs, multiplies our investment by a factor of 2.2; while process 2, hatching, brings in over \$3.50 for every \$1.00 invested. There will be pressure to use the hens just for hatching—which will create a shortage of eggs, bringing about a change in prices. Suppose now that a chicken costs only six times as much as an egg, i.e., $y = \begin{pmatrix} 6 \\ 1 \end{pmatrix}$. Then

$$Ay = \begin{pmatrix} 6 \\ 10 \end{pmatrix} \quad \text{and} \quad By = \begin{pmatrix} 18 \\ 30 \end{pmatrix}.$$

In this case each process triples our investment, and there will be no undue monetary pressure. Hence the farmer can set up his processes so as to be in equilibrium, and the price structure will be stable.

The remaining factor to be considered is the expansion of the economy. We assume that everything expands at a constant rate, i.e., that there is a fixed *expansion factor* α such that if the processes operate at intensity x in this cycle, they operate at intensity αx during the next cycle, $\alpha^2 x$ after that, etc. There is also something similar to expansion for the money of the economy, namely, that through bearing interest, y units of money in this cycle will be worth βy units after the cycle. We again assume that the *interest factor* β is fixed once and for all in equilibrium. Usually these factors will be greater than 1, but this does not have to be the case. Thus $\alpha = 1$ represents a stationary economy, and $\alpha < 1$ represents a contracting economy.

This completes the survey of the basic concepts. We must now lay down our assumptions concerning the behavior of an economy which is in equilibrium. These assumptions serve as axioms for the system.

First of all, we must assure that we produce enough of each good in each cycle to furnish the inputs of the next cycle. If in a given cycle the economy functions at intensity x, it will function at αx next time. The outputs this time will be xB, while the inputs next time will be $\alpha x A$; hence we must require

AXIOM 1 $\qquad\qquad\qquad xB \geq \alpha x A.$

(When we write a vector inequality, we mean that the inequality holds for every component.) We will of course have to require similar conditions for the future. For example, in the second cycle the outputs are $\alpha x B$, and the inputs needed for the third cycle are $\alpha^2 x A$. But when we write the condition that the former be greater than the latter, an α cancels, and we have again the same condition as in Axiom 1. Hence this axiom serves for all cycles.

The first condition assures that it is possible for the economy to expand at the constant rate α. We must also assure that the economy is financially in equilibrium. Suppose that the output of some process was worth more than β times the input. Then we would be prepared to pay interest at a larger rate to some one willing to invest in our process. Hence β would increase. Thus, in equilibrium this must not be possible; no process can produce profits at a rate greater than that given by investment. If we operate processes at a unit intensity, then Ay gives the costs of inputs, while By gives the cost of outputs. The latter cannot exceed the former by more than a factor β for any process

AXIOM 2 $By \leq \beta Ay.$

The next assumption concerns surplus production. If we produce more of a given good than can be used by the total economy, the price drops sharply as merchants try to get rid of their produce. It is customary to assume that such goods are free, i.e., to give them price zero. The vector difference $xB - \alpha xA = x(B - \alpha A)$ gives the amounts of overproduction, i.e., the jth component is positive if and only if good j is overproduced. If we assign price zero to these goods, then in the product of the above vector with y every nonzero factor of the former is multiplied by zero; hence the product of the two vectors will be 0.

AXIOM 3 $x(B - \alpha A)y = 0.$

Now we turn to the question of whether a given process is worth undertaking. From Axiom 2 we know that no process can yield more profit than investment can. But if it yields any less, it is better not to use it, but rather to invest our money. Hence in Axiom 2 we form the difference $By - \beta Ay$; if the ith component of this is negative, process i should not be used; it must be assigned intensity 0. Similar to the argument used for Axiom 3, this shows that multiplying this vector difference by x must yield zero.

AXIOM 4 $x(B - \beta A)y = 0.$

Our final assumption is that something worth while is produced in the economy, i.e., that the value of all goods produced is a positive amount.

AXIOM 5 $xBy > 0.$

If for a given economy (given A and B) we find vectors x and y and numbers α and β which satisfy these five axioms, we say that we have found a *possible equilibrium solution* for the economy.

> **Example** (continued). We have already seen that if $x = (1, 1)$, the economy expands at the fixed rate $\alpha = 3$. We can now check that Axiom 1 is satisfied. Actually, xB turns out to equal αxA. Similarly, we have noted a monetary equilibrium if $y = \begin{pmatrix} 6 \\ 1 \end{pmatrix}$, and each process multiplies the money put

into it by a factor of $\beta = 3$. We can check that Axiom 2 holds. Actually By is equal to βAy in this case. From these two equations we also know that $x(B - \alpha A)$ and $(B - \beta A)y$ are identically 0; hence Axioms 3 and 4 hold. Finally, $xBy = 48$; the total value of goods produced is positive, so that Axiom 5 holds. Therefore these values of x, y, α, and β represent an equilibrium for the economy. It can also be shown that these are the only possible values of α and β, and that x and y must be multiples of the vectors shown here (this may be thought of simply as a change in the units).

In our example we found one and only one equilibrium for the economy, and we found that $\alpha = \beta$. This raises several very natural questions: (1) Is there a possible equilibrium for every economy? (2) If yes, then is there only one? (3) Must the expansion factor always be the same as the interest factor? In the next section we will establish the following answers: (1) For every economy satisfying a certain restriction (which is certainly satisfied for all real economies) there is a possible equilibrium. (2) There may be more than one equilibrium, though the number of different possible expansion factors is finite. (In the example there is essentially only one possibility for x and y; however this is not true in general.) (3) The interest and expansion factors are always equal in equilibrium.

EXERCISES

1. In the Example, for $x = (1, 2)$, verify for three cycles that xA and xB give the correct inputs and outputs.

2. Give an interpretation of xAy and xBy:
   (a) Using the interpretations of xA and xB given above.
   (b) Using the interpretations of Ay and By given above.
   (c) Show that the results in (a) and (b) are the same.

3. In the Example, suppose that two chickens lay eggs and three hatch eggs. Find x, xA, and xB. Substitute these quantities into Axiom 1, and find the largest possible expansion factor.　　　　　　　　[$Ans.\ \alpha = 2.$]

4. In the Example, suppose that chickens cost 80 cents and eggs cost five cents. Find y, Ay, and By. Substitute these quantities into Axiom 2, and find the smallest possible interest factor.　　　　　　　　[$Ans.\ \beta = 4.$]

5. Show that the x, y, α, and β found in the two previous Exercises do *not* lead to equilibrium, by showing that Axioms 3 and 4 fail to hold.

6. Show that if $\alpha = \beta = 3$, then the only possible x's and y's are proportional to those given above. [*Hint:* Show that the axioms force us to choose $x_1 = x_2$ and $y_1 = 6y_2$.]

The remaining problems refer to the following economy: On a chicken farm there is a breed of chicken that lays an average of 16 eggs a month and can hatch an average of $3\frac{1}{5} = \frac{16}{5}$ eggs.

7. Set up the matrices A and B.

8. Suppose that three chickens lay and five chickens hatch. Find x, xA, and xB. What is the largest possible α?

[*Ans.* $x = (3, 5); xA = (8, 16); xB = (24, 48); \alpha = 3$.]

9. Suppose that chickens cost 40 cents and eggs five cents. Find y, Ay, and By. What is the smallest possible β?

10. Verify that the x, y, α, and β found in the previous Exercises represent an equilibrium for the economy, by substituting these into the five axioms.

11. Suppose that we start with 16 chickens and 32 eggs. Choose the intensities so that the economy will be in equilibrium, and find what happens in the the first three months. [*Ans.* $x = (6, 10)$; 432 chickens, and 864 eggs.]

12. Suppose that with 16 chickens and 32 eggs (see Exercise 11) we start out by having only five hatching, the others laying. Show that we cannot have as many chickens after three months as we would have in the equilibrium solution.

*8. Existence of an economic equilibrium

We must ask whether the axioms can always be satisfied, i.e., whether the model of the economy allows such an equilibrium.

Of course we are interested only in an economy that could really occur. That means that these goods must be goods that are somehow produced, and that they cannot be produced out of nothing. Hence every process must require at least one raw material and every good has at least one process that produces it. We summarize this:

RESTRICTION. Every row of A and every column of B has at least one positive component.

THEOREM. If A and B satisfy the restriction, then an equilibrium is possible.

We will sketch the proof of this theorem. From Axiom 3 we have that $xBy = \alpha xAy$, while from Axiom 4, $xBy = \beta xAy$. Hence $\alpha xAy = \beta xAy$. Furthermore, from Axiom 5 we know that xBy is not zero, hence xAy is not zero. Then $\alpha = \beta$. Hence *in equilibrium the rate of expansion equals the interest rate.*

If $\alpha = \beta$, then Axioms 3 and 4 are equivalent. We can also rewrite the first two axioms (using our result):

AXIOM 1′ $x(B - \alpha A) \geq 0$.

AXIOM 2′ $(B - \alpha A)y \leq 0$.

If we multiply the first inequality by y on the right, and the second by x on the left, we see that Axiom 3 (and hence 4) follows from these two axioms. Hence we need only worry about Axioms 1', 2', and 5.

The key to the proof is to reinterpret the problem as a game-theoretic one. This is done in spite of the fact that no game is involved in the model. We simply use the mathematical results of the theory of games as tools.

Axioms 1' and 2' suggest that we think of the matrix $B - \alpha A$ as a matrix game. We would then like to think of the vectors x and y as mixed strategies for the two players. The vectors are nonnegative, but the sum of their components need not be 1. However, we know that multiplying x by a constant can be thought of as a change in the units of intensities, and multiplying y by a constant is equivalent to a change in the units of the various goods. Hence, without loss of generality, we may assume that x and y have component sum 1, and think of them as mixed strategies. If we do this, the two axioms state precisely that the game has value zero, and that x and y form a pair of optimal strategies for the two players. Thus our first problem is to choose α so that the "game" $B - \alpha A$ has value zero.

Example 1. Let us set up the Example of the last section as a game.

$$M = B - \alpha A = \begin{pmatrix} 1 - \alpha & 12 \\ 5 - \alpha & -4\alpha \end{pmatrix}.$$

If we choose $x = (\frac{1}{2}, \frac{1}{2})$ as a mixed strategy for the row player, then

$$xM = [3 - \alpha, 2(3 - \alpha)].$$

If $\alpha < 3$, the components are both positive; hence the game has value greater than zero. If we choose $y = \begin{pmatrix} \frac{6}{7} \\ \frac{1}{7} \end{pmatrix}$ as a mixed strategy for the column player, then

$$My = \begin{bmatrix} \frac{6}{7}(3 - \alpha) \\ \frac{10}{7}(3 - \alpha) \end{bmatrix}.$$

If $\alpha > 3$, both components are negative, and hence the game has negative value. We thus see that the only value of α that could possibly give us a zero value of the game is $\alpha = 3$, and we see from the above that in this case the value really is zero, and x and y are optimal strategies. (See Exercise 1.)

We must now show that the above example is typical in that we can always find an α making the value of $B - \alpha A$ equal to zero. We may write this matrix as the sum $B + \alpha(-A)$, and think of our game as a combination of game B and game $(-A)$.

By our restriction, every column of B has a positive entry. The strategy vector y for the column player must have at least one positive component. Hence in the product By, one of the components at least must be positive. Hence the value of the game B is positive. Since every row of A has a positive entry, every row of the game $-A$ must have a negative entry. Hence at least one component of $x(-A)$ must be negative, and hence $(-A)$ has a negative value.

In the combination $B + \alpha(-A)$ the second term is negligible for very small α; hence for these the game has positive value. As α increases, we keep adding larger negative quantities to some of the entries of the game, i.e., we keep decreasing some of these entries. Hence the value of the game decreases steadily. For very large α the first term is negligible, and hence the combined game has negative value. For some intermediate value of α the game must have value zero.

Example 1 (continued). The value of the combined game M is plotted for various α in Figure 6. Since B has value $\frac{15}{4}$ and $-A$ has value -1 (see Exercise 2), for α near 0 the game M has value nearly $\frac{15}{4}$, and for large α it has value nearly $2 - \alpha$, which is well below zero (see Exercise 3).

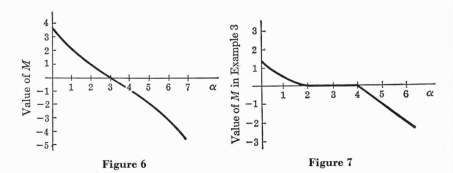

Figure 6   **Figure 7**

We know that there is at least one α for which the game $B - \alpha A$ has value zero. By choosing such an α together with a pair x, y of optimal strategies, we arrive at a set of quantities satisfying Axioms 1′ and 2′. This still leaves the question of Axiom 5.

If there are two values of α, say $p < q$, for which the game has value zero, every value between p and q also has this property. This is because the value of the game cannot increase as α increases, as we saw above. Hence we must have a situation such as that shown in Figure 7. It can be shown, however, that most of these values represent methods of procedure where nothing worth while is produced, i.e., where Axiom 5 fails. For Axiom 5 to hold, different values of α can be achieved only by using at least one new process. Since there are only a finite number of processes, we can have only a finite number of different possible α's on the interval between p and q. If p is the smallest possible expansion rate and q the largest, then p and q are such that Axiom 5 can be satisfied, and there may be a limited number of additional values in between.

Example 2. In the chemical industry we are interested in manufacturing compounds P, Q, and R. We assume that the basic chemicals are available in plentiful supply, and that their cost can be neglected for this analysis. But to manufacture compound P we must have a unit of both P and Q available, while to manufacture Q we must have P and R available. Compound R is a by-product of both manufacturing processes. The exact quantities are given by:

$$
\begin{array}{ll}
& \begin{array}{ccc} P & Q & R \end{array} \qquad\qquad \begin{array}{ccc} P & Q & R \end{array} \\
\begin{array}{l}\text{Manufacture of } P:\\ \text{Manufacture of } Q:\end{array} & A = \begin{pmatrix} 1 & 1 & 0 \\ 1 & 0 & 1 \end{pmatrix}, \quad B = \begin{pmatrix} 6 & 0 & 1 \\ 0 & 3 & 2 \end{pmatrix}.
\end{array}
$$

Then

$$
M = B - \alpha A = \begin{pmatrix} 6 - \alpha & -\alpha & 1 \\ -\alpha & 3 & 2 - \alpha \end{pmatrix}.
$$

Let us choose

$$
x = (\tfrac{1}{2}, \tfrac{1}{2}) \quad \text{and} \quad y = \begin{pmatrix} \tfrac{1}{6} \\ \tfrac{1}{3} \\ \tfrac{1}{2} \end{pmatrix}.
$$

Then

$$
xM = [3 - \alpha, \tfrac{1}{2}(3 - \alpha), \tfrac{1}{2}(3 - \alpha)] \quad \text{and} \quad My = \begin{bmatrix} \tfrac{1}{2}(3 - \alpha) \\ \tfrac{2}{3}(3 - \alpha) \end{bmatrix}.
$$

From this we see that if $\alpha < 3$, then the row player has a guaranteed profit, while if $\alpha > 3$, the column player does. Thus $\alpha = 3$ is the only possibility, and for this case the value of the game is zero, and the vectors x and y are optimal strategies, as can be seen from the fact that xM and My have all components zero. Thus there is a unique equilibrium, with $\alpha = \beta = 3$.

We also find that the mixed strategy x is unique, which means that the two processes must be used with the same intensity. However, the strategy y is not unique. We may instead use

$$
y' = \begin{pmatrix} \tfrac{1}{2} \\ \tfrac{1}{2} \\ 0 \end{pmatrix} \quad \text{or} \quad y'' = \begin{pmatrix} 0 \\ \tfrac{1}{4} \\ \tfrac{3}{4} \end{pmatrix}
$$

or any mixture $ty' + (1 - t)y''$, $0 \le t \le 1$. Our y is the case $t = \tfrac{1}{3}$. Hence we see that different price structures are possible, each leading to the same expansion rate.

Example 3. This "economy" is a schematic representation of the production of essentials and inessentials in a society. Goods are lumped together into two types, E (essential goods) and I (inessential goods or luxury items). For the manufacture of E we need only essential goods (since anything so needed is essential). For the manufacture of I we may need both types of raw materials. Let us suppose that our economy functions as follows.

$$
\begin{array}{ll}
& \begin{array}{cc} E & I \end{array} \qquad\qquad \begin{array}{cc} E & I \end{array} \\
\begin{array}{l}\text{Manufacture of essentials:}\\ \text{Manufacture of luxuries:}\end{array} & A = \begin{pmatrix} 1 & 0 \\ 1 & 1 \end{pmatrix}, \quad B = \begin{pmatrix} 4 & 0 \\ 0 & 2 \end{pmatrix}.
\end{array}
$$

Then

$$M = B - \alpha A = \begin{pmatrix} 4 - \alpha & 0 \\ -\alpha & 2 - \alpha \end{pmatrix}.$$

With a little patience we can determine the values of M for various values of α, and we arrive at the curve in Figure 7. (See Exercise 4.) Hence α must be between 2 and 4. For $\alpha = 4$, we have the optimal strategies

$$x = (1, 0) \quad \text{and} \quad y = \begin{pmatrix} 1 \\ 0 \end{pmatrix}$$

which satisfy all our axioms; while for $\alpha = 2$ we have

$$x = (\tfrac{1}{2}, \tfrac{1}{2}) \quad \text{and} \quad y = \begin{pmatrix} 0 \\ 1 \end{pmatrix}.$$

For in-between values of α we cannot satisfy Axiom 5. (See Exercises 5–7.) Hence there are two possible equilibria: (1) The society can decide to manufacture only essentials, in which case the production of these will increase rapidly. (2) By putting a high enough value on inessentials, it will arrive at an equilibrium in which both essentials and inessentials are produced, but then the rate of expansion is considerably decreased.

We have now completely answered the three questions raised at the end of the last section, providing a mathematical solution to a series of economic problems.

EXERCISES

1. In Example 1, verify that for $\alpha = 3$ the game M has value 0, and that the x and y given are optimal strategies.

2. In Example 1, solve the 2×2 games B and $-A$, finding their values and pairs of optimal strategies.

3. In Example 1:
   (a) Show that the game M is nonstrictly determined for every α.
   (b) Find the value of M for any α.   [*Ans.* $(5 + \alpha)(3 - \alpha)/(4 + \alpha)$.]
   (c) Show that the value for $\alpha = .01$ is very near $\tfrac{15}{4}$.
   (d) Show that the value for $\alpha = 100$ is very near -98.
   (e) Show that the value is 0 if and only if $\alpha = 3$.

4. Find the value of M in Example 3 for $\alpha = 0, 1, 2, 3, 4, 5,$ and 6. [*Hint:* Some of these games are strictly determined.]
   [*Ans.* 1.33; .60; 0; 0; 0; -1.00; -2.00.]

5. In Example 3, for $\alpha = 4$, verify that the strategies given are optimal, and that Axiom 5 is satisfied.

6. In Example 3, for $\alpha = 2$, verify that the strategies given are optimal, and that Axiom 5 is satisfied.

7. In Example 3, for $\alpha = 3$, find the unique optimal x and y, and show that Axiom 5 is *not* satisfied. Prove that the same happens for every α if $2 < \alpha < 4$.

The remaining problems refer to the following economy: There are four goods and five processes, and the economy is given by

$$A = \begin{pmatrix} 0 & 0 & 1 & 1 \\ 0 & 0 & 2 & 2 \\ 0 & 4 & 0 & 2 \\ 2 & 1 & 1 & 0 \\ 0 & 1 & 0 & 2 \end{pmatrix}, \quad B = \begin{pmatrix} 0 & 0 & 4 & 2 \\ 0 & 0 & 5 & 7 \\ 6 & 5 & 4 & 0 \\ 0 & 4 & 0 & 3 \\ 3 & 0 & 6 & 0 \end{pmatrix}.$$

Also let $x = (\tfrac{1}{2}, \tfrac{1}{2}, 0, 0, 0), \quad x' = (0, 0, \tfrac{2}{5}, \tfrac{3}{5}, 0),$

$$y = \begin{pmatrix} \tfrac{1}{3} \\ \tfrac{2}{3} \\ 0 \\ 0 \end{pmatrix}, \quad y' = \begin{pmatrix} 0 \\ 0 \\ \tfrac{1}{2} \\ \tfrac{1}{2} \end{pmatrix}.$$

8. Verify that A and B satisfy the restriction.

9. Compute $M = B - \alpha A$.

10. Compute xM, $x'M$, My, and My'.

11. When will $x'M$ have all positive entries? When will My' have all negative entries? What possibilities does this leave for α?
[*Ans.* $\alpha < 2$; $\alpha > 3$; $2 \le \alpha \le 3$.]

12. Show that for the remaining possible values of α the game M has value zero, and x and y are optimal strategies.

13. Show that for the largest possible α the vectors x and y' provide optimal strategies which satisfy Axiom 5.

14. Show that for the smallest possible α the vectors x' and y provide optimal strategies which satisfy Axiom 5.

15. If α is in between its two extreme values, show that:
(a) xM is positive in its last two components, and hence the second player can use only his first two strategies.
(b) My is negative in its last three components, and hence the first player can use only his first two strategies.
(c) For these cases it is impossible to satisfy Axiom 5.

16. Process number five is in a special position. Why?   [*Ans.* Never used.]

17. Use the results of Exercises 8–16 to show that there are exactly two possible equilibriums for this economy. Interpret each equilibrium, and point out the differences between the two methods of operating the economy.
        [*Ans.* At the price of reducing the expansion rate, the economy can produce a larger variety of goods. To achieve this, the additional types of goods must be valued (relatively) very high.]

*9. The simplex method for solving matrix games

We have so far restricted our attention to examples of matrix games that were simple enough to be solved by unformalized computations. However, games of realistic size frequently lead to very large matrices for which these simple techniques are not adequate. A clue to a general technique may be found in the fact that the row player is a maximizing player while the column player is a minimizing player. Hence, the problems they are trying to solve sound somewhat like the dual linear programming problems of Chapter VII. So if a matrix game can be formulated as a linear programming problem, it can be solved by the simplex method discussed in the previous chapter.

There are several ways of showing that a matrix game is equivalent to a linear program. We choose a very simple approach here, based on the fact, proved in Section 4, that every matrix game is equivalent to one in which all entries are positive and hence whose value is positive.

Besides finding an equivalent linear programming problem, we shall give a proof, based on the duality theorem of linear programming, that every matrix game has a solution. And we will present a simplex format suitable for the solution of any matrix game.

Let G be an $m \times n$ matrix game and let E be the $m \times n$ matrix all of whose entries are 1's. The second theorem of Section 4 states that G and $G + kE$ have the same optimal strategies, and the value of the second game is k plus the value of the first game. Hence if we start with any game G we can replace it by a game G' all of whose entries are positive, and which has the same optimal strategies. For instance, to get G' we could add 1 minus the most negative entry in G to every entry in G.

Thus without loss of generality we let G be a positive matrix game. We also let e be the n-component row vector all of whose entries are 1's, and let f be the m-component column vector all of whose entries are 1's. Let x be an m-component row vector and y an n-component column vector. We now consider the following dual linear programming problems:

$$
(1) \quad \left\{ \begin{array}{ll}
\text{Min } xf & \text{Max } ey \\
\text{subject to:} & \text{subject to:} \\
xG \geq e & Gy \leq f \\
x \geq 0 & y \geq 0.
\end{array} \right.
$$

Note that $y = 0$ satisfies the constraints of the maximizing problem, and also, because the entries of G and f are positive, there is at least one nonzero y vector that will satisfy these constraints. Moreover, the set of feasible y vectors is bounded. Because of these facts, and because e has all positive entries, the maximizing problem has solution y^0 such that $ey^0 > 0$. Hence, by the duality theorem, the minimum problem has a solution x^0 and

$$t = x^0 G y^0 = x^0 f = e y^0 > 0.$$

We now set

$$p^0 = \frac{x^0}{t}, \qquad q^0 = \frac{y^0}{t}, \quad \text{and} \quad v = \frac{1}{t},$$

and observe that p^0 and q^0 are probability vectors.

It is easy to see that p^0 is an optimal strategy for player R in G since x^0 satisfies the constraints of the minimizing problem, and hence

$$p^0 G = \frac{x^0 G}{t} \geq \frac{e}{t} = V$$

(where V is defined in Section 3 as the row vector all of whose entries are v). In Exercise 1 the reader is asked to show similarly that $G q^0 \leq V'$.

We summarize these results in the following theorem.

THEOREM. (a) Solving the matrix game G with positive entries can be accomplished by solving the dual linear programming problems (1).

(b) Every matrix game has at least one solution; solutions to such games can be found by the simplex method.

Actually, it is not necessary that the matrix game be positive in order that the simplex method work. It is enough that its value be positive. However, in Exercise 3 the reader is asked to work a specific example for which the linear programming problem as described above has no solution if applied to a game with zero value.

Before proceeding to specific examples let us outline the procedure to be followed in setting up a matrix game for solution by the simplex method.

1. Set up the matrix of the game.
2. Check to see whether the game is strictly determined; if so the solution is already obtained.
3. Check for row and column dominance and remove dominated rows and columns.
4. Make certain that the value of the game is positive. It is sufficient for this to add 1 minus the most negative matrix entry to every entry of the matrix. Let k be the amount added, if any, to each matrix entry.
5. Let G be the matrix of the resulting game; suppose it is $m \times n$. Let I be the $m \times n$ identity matrix and let e and f be as defined above. Put these quantities into the following matrix tableau:

G	I	f
$-e$	0	0

6. Carry out the steps of the simplex algorithm until all indicators are nonnegative. Determine the solutions x^0 and y^0 to the dual linear programming problems, and let $t = x^0 f = e y^0$. We know $t > 0$.

7. The solutions to the original matrix game are given by

$$p^0 = \frac{x^0}{t}, \qquad q^0 = \frac{y^0}{t} \quad \text{and} \quad v = \frac{1}{t} - k.$$

(If dominated rows or columns were removed from the game, the strategy vectors may have to be extended by the addition of some zero components.)

Example 1. We know that the matching pennies game is fair, i.e., it has value zero. To make its value positive, we add $k = 2$ to each matrix entry, yielding the following game:

3	1
1	3

Obviously this game is not strictly determined and it does not have dominated rows or columns. We set up the simplex tableau and solve it as shown in Figure 8(a)–(c). From the final tableau in Figure 8(c) we can see that the

$A_1 \qquad A_2$

③	1	1	0	1
1	3	0	1	1
-1	-1	0	0	0

(a)

$A_1 \qquad A_2$

A_1	1	$\frac{1}{3}$	$\frac{1}{3}$	0	$\frac{1}{3}$
	0	$\frac{8}{3}$	$-\frac{1}{3}$	1	$\frac{2}{3}$
	0	$-\frac{2}{3}$	$\frac{1}{3}$	0	$\frac{1}{3}$

(b)

$A_1 \qquad A_2$

A_1	1	0	$\frac{3}{8}$	$-\frac{1}{8}$	$\frac{1}{4}$
A_2	0	1	$-\frac{1}{8}$	$\frac{3}{8}$	$\frac{1}{4}$
	0	0	$\frac{1}{4}$	$\frac{1}{4}$	$\frac{1}{2}$

(c)

Figure 8

value of the game is 2 (the reciprocal of $t = \frac{1}{2}$) so that the value of the matching pennies game is 0, which we know already. Also optimal strategies are

$$p^0 = \frac{x^0}{t} = (\tfrac{1}{2}, \tfrac{1}{2}) \quad \text{and} \quad q^0 = \frac{y^0}{t} = \begin{pmatrix} \frac{1}{2} \\ \frac{1}{2} \end{pmatrix},$$

which we had discovered earlier.

Example 2. Let us solve the two-finger Morra game of Exercise 3 of Section 2. To convert the game into one with positive value let us add 3 to each entry of the matrix, noting that this will give two zeros in the resulting game matrix. These zeros will simplify the simplex calculations. The game matrix now is

5	0
0	7

In Figure 9(a)–(c) the initial and two subsequent simplex tableaus are shown.

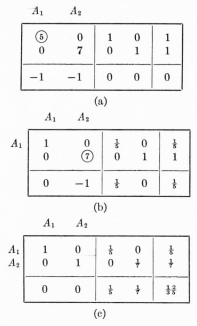

(a)

(b)

(c)

Figure 9

The value of the game, from Figure 9(c) is $\frac{35}{12}$, which means that the value of the original game is $\frac{35}{12} - 3 = -\frac{1}{12}$. Optimal strategies agree with the answer stated in the Exercise.

Example 3. Consider the following game: R and C simultaneously display 1, 2, or 3 pennies. If both show the same number of pennies, no money is exchanged; but if they show different numbers of pennies, R gets odd sums and C gets even sums. The matrix of the game is

		\multicolumn{3}{c}{C shows}		
		1	2	3
	1	0	3	-4
R shows	2	3	0	5
	3	-4	5	0

Since the second row has all nonnegative entries, the game is, if anything, in R's favor. And if R plays the first two rows with equal weight, his expectation is positive. Hence the value of the game is positive and we do not have to add anything to the matrix entries. The simplex calculations needed to solve the game are shown in Figure 10(a)–(d).

	A_1	A_2	A_3				
	0	3	-4	1	0	0	1
	③	0	5	0	1	0	1
	-4	5	0	0	0	1	1
	-1	-1	-1	0	0	0	0

(a)

	A_1	A_2	A_3				
A_1	0	③	-4	1	0	0	1
	1	0	$\frac{5}{3}$	0	$\frac{1}{3}$	0	$\frac{1}{3}$
	0	5	$\frac{20}{3}$	0	$\frac{4}{3}$	1	$\frac{7}{3}$
	0	-1	$\frac{2}{3}$	0	$\frac{1}{3}$	0	$\frac{1}{3}$

(b)

	A_1	A_2	A_3				
A_2	0	1	$-\frac{4}{3}$	$\frac{1}{3}$	0	0	$\frac{1}{3}$
A_1	1	0	$\frac{5}{3}$	0	$\frac{1}{3}$	0	$\frac{1}{3}$
	0	0	㊵/3	$-\frac{5}{3}$	$\frac{4}{3}$	1	$\frac{2}{3}$
	0	0	$-\frac{2}{3}$	$\frac{1}{3}$	$\frac{1}{3}$	0	$\frac{2}{3}$

(c)

	A_1	A_2	A_3				
A_2	0	1	0	$\frac{1}{6}$	$\frac{2}{15}$	$\frac{1}{10}$	$\frac{2}{5}$
A_1	1	0	0	$\frac{5}{24}$	$\frac{1}{6}$	$-\frac{1}{8}$	$\frac{1}{4}$
A_3	0	0	1	$-\frac{1}{8}$	$\frac{1}{10}$	$\frac{3}{40}$	$\frac{1}{20}$
	0	0	0	$\frac{1}{4}$	$\frac{2}{5}$	$\frac{1}{20}$	$\frac{7}{10}$

(d)

Figure 10

From this we see that the value of the game is $1/t = \frac{10}{7}$, and that optimal strategies are

$$p^0 = \frac{x^0}{t} = (\tfrac{5}{14}, \tfrac{4}{7}, \tfrac{1}{14}) \text{ and } q^0 = \frac{y^0}{t} = \begin{pmatrix} \frac{5}{14} \\ \frac{4}{7} \\ \frac{1}{14} \end{pmatrix}.$$

The reader should check that these strategies do solve the game.

The examples just solved could have been worked directly, without the use of the simplex method. However, the simplex method works just as well for much larger games for which there is no easy direct method.

EXERCISES

1. If $q^0 = y^0/t$ where y^0 solves the maximum problem stated in (1) and $t = ey^0$, show that q^0 is an optimal strategy for player C in the matrix game G.

2. Solve the following games by the simplex method.

(a)

1	0	3
-2	3	0
-4	5	-6

(b)

-2	3	0	5	-6
3	-4	5	0	7
-4	5	-6	7	0

3. Consider the matching pennies game with matrix

$$G = \begin{array}{|c|c|} \hline 1 & -1 \\ \hline -1 & 1 \\ \hline \end{array}.$$

(a) Substitute it directly into the simplex format described in rule (5) above, and show that the simplex method breaks down.

(b) Consider the linear programming problem defined in (1) with this G and show directly that it has no solution.

4. Use the simplex method to derive formulas (3)–(7) of Section 2 for optimal strategies in a nonstrictly determined 2×2 game.

5. Work Exercise 8 of Section 3 using the simplex method.

6. Work Exercise 10 of Section 3 using the simplex method.

7. A passenger on a Mississippi river boat was approached by a flashily dressed stranger (the gambler) who offered to play the following game: "You take a red ace and a black deuce and I'll take a red deuce and a black trey; we will simultaneously show one of the cards; if the colors don't match you pay me and if the colors match I'll pay you; moreover if you play the red ace we will exchange the difference of the numbers on

the cards; but if you play the black deuce we will exchange the sum of the numbers. Since you will pay me either $2 or $4 if you lose and I will pay you either $1 or $5 if I lose, the game is obviously fair." Set up and solve the matrix game using the simplex method. Show that the game is not fair. Find the optimal strategies.

[*Partial Ans.* The gambler will win an average of 25 cents per game.]

8. Consider the following game: R chooses 0 or 1 and reveals his choice to C; C chooses 0 or 1, but does not reveal his choice to R; R then chooses 0 or 1 a second time. The sum of the three numbers chosen is computed and R receives odd sums while C receives even sums.

(a) Show that R has four strategies: 00, 01, 10, 11.

(b) Show that C has four strategies: (1) always choose 0, (2) choose the same as R, (3) choose opposite to R, (4) always choose 1.

(c) Show that the payoff matrix is

	(1)	(2)	(3)	(4)
00	0	0	1	1
01	1	1	-2	-2
10	1	-2	1	-2
11	-2	3	-2	3

(d) Solve the game by the simplex method, finding its value and optimal strategies.

$$[Ans. \ p^0 = (\tfrac{3}{4}, \tfrac{1}{4}, 0, 0), \ q^0 = \begin{pmatrix} \tfrac{3}{10} \\ \tfrac{9}{20} \\ \tfrac{1}{4} \\ 0 \end{pmatrix}, \ v = \tfrac{1}{4}.]$$

9. Rework Exercise 8 assuming that the players choose 1 or 2 each time.

10. *The Silent Duel.* Two duelists each have a pistol which contains a single bullet and is equipped with a silencer. They advance toward each other in N steps, and each may fire at his opponent at the end of each step. Neither knows whether his opponent has fired, and each has but one shot in the game. The probability that a player will hit his opponent if he fires after moving k steps is k/N. A player gets 1 if he kills his opponent without being killed himself, -1 if he gets killed without killing his opponent, and 0 otherwise. Each player has N strategies corresponding to firing after steps $1, 2, \ldots, N$. Let i be the strategy chosen by R and j the strategy chosen by C.

(a) If $i < j$, show that the expected payoff to R is given by

$$\frac{N(i - j) + ij}{N^2}$$

(b) If $i > j$, show that the expected payoff to R is given by

$$\frac{N(i - j) - ij}{N^2}$$

(c) If $i = j$, show that the expected payoff to R is 0.

11. In Exercise 10, prove that the game is strictly determined and fair for $N = 2, 3$, and 4. Show that the optimal strategy for $N = 3, 4$ is to fire at the end of the second step in each case. For $N = 2$, show that any strategy is optimal.

12. In Exercise 10, show that the game is nonstrictly determined and fair for $N = 5$, and find the optimal strategies.
    [$Ans.$ $p^0 = (0, \frac{5}{11}, \frac{5}{11}, 0, \frac{1}{11})$, and q^0 is the column vector having the same components.]

13. A $symmetric$ $matrix$ $game$ G is one for which $g_{ij} = -g_{ji}$ for $i, j = 1, 2, \ldots, n$. In other words, for every payment from C to R there is an equal payment from R to C. Show that every symmetric game is fair. [$Hint:$ Show that if x^0 is optimal for R then the column vector y with $y_k = x_k^0$ for $k = 1, \ldots, n$ is optimal for C. From this deduce that the value of the game is zero.]

14. Use Exercise 13 to show that the silent duel is fair for every N.

15. Consider a matrix game G with positive value in which the first row strictly dominates the second row. Show that in the simplex algorithm, no entry in the second row will ever be chosen as a pivot in the first step.

16. Consider a matrix game G with positive value in which the first column dominates the second column. Show that if the pivot is chosen in the first column, after the end of the first simplex calculation the indicator for the second column will be nonnegative.

*10. Two-person nonzero-sum games

The two-person zero-sum games we have discussed so far in the present chapter represent the most orderly and well-developed part of game theory. Unfortunately, it is not always possible to formulate applications of game theory as two-person zero-sum games. Instead two- or more-person non-zero-sum games are frequently needed. For such games there are many solution concepts that have been proposed, and there are various arguments for and against each such concept. But no single solution concept is acceptable for all cases.

In the present section we shall discuss only two-person nonzero-sum games. For these we shall consider four proposed types of solutions: (a) maximin solutions, (b) equilibrium point solutions, (c) cooperative solutions, and (d) threat solutions. We shall indicate by examples circumstances under which each of these solutions might be applicable. In the exercises, other solution concepts are considered.

A two-person nonzero-sum game is defined as follows: There are two players R and C as before. Player R has m strategies $1, 2, \ldots, m$, while C has n strategies $1, 2, \ldots, n$. If R chooses strategy i and C chooses strategy j then the players receive the payoff vector (a_{ij}, b_{ij}), where a_{ij} is the amount R receives and b_{ij} is the amount C receives. Let A be the $m \times n$ matrix whose entries are a_{ij}, and let B be the $m \times n$ matrix whose entries are b_{ij}. It is convenient to arrange the payoffs (a_{ij}, b_{ij}) in rectangular form as the following examples illustrate. If $B = -A$, i.e., $b_{ij} = -a_{ij}$ for all i and j, then the game is zero-sum and reduces to an ordinary matrix game with matrix A.

Example 1. Suppose there are two firms R and C who are deciding whether or not to enter two different markets, 1 and 2. As the result of market surveys they decide that R is strong in the first market and C is strong in the second market. Their evaluation of the merits of entering these markets is as indicated in the table of Figure 11. The entries in these vectors represent estimated

		C Enters	
		Market 1	Market 2
R Enters	Market 1	(15, 10)	(22, 20)
	Market 2	(11, 13)	(10, 15)

Figure 11

yearly profit figures, where the first entry is R's profit and the second entry is C's profit. What strategies shall each player choose?

Here the solution is quite obvious since R, looking at his own profits, always prefers to enter Market 1 regardless of what C does, while C always prefers to enter Market 2. And if they make these choices, each one gets his highest possible profits. Here is a situation in which the players, each acting purely in his own self-interest, arrive at a mutually satisfactory solution.

Suppose now that the results of the survey revealed the payoffs shown in Figure 12. Note that Figure 12 is just like Figure 11 except that the two payoffs of 10 have been changed to 30.

		C Enters	
		Market 1	Market 2
R Enters	Market 1	(15, 30)	(22, 20)
	Market 2	(11, 13)	(30, 15)

Figure 12

Note that in Figure 12 there is no domination of the kind observed in Figure 11, and it is not immediately clear what the solution should be. Suppose that R makes the most pessimistic assumption, namely, that C is fully opposed to him and wants to minimize his payoff. Then R would solve the matrix game

$$
A = \begin{array}{|c|c|}
\hline
15 & 22 \\
\hline
11 & 30 \\
\hline
\end{array}
$$

which consists of his own payoffs. This is a strictly determined game for which his optimal strategy is "enter Market 1." Similarly, if C were pessimistic he would solve the game

$$
-B = \begin{array}{|c|c|}
\hline
-30 & -20 \\
\hline
-13 & -15 \\
\hline
\end{array}
$$

(remember that the b_{ij}'s are payments *to* C), which again is strictly determined and yields the optimal strategy, "enter Market 2." If the two players follow these strategies, which we call *maximin* strategies, then they will attain the payoff vector (22, 20) as before.

Before proceeding further with Example 1 we formulate the definition of a maximin strategy.

DEFINITION. Let G be a nonzero-sum game with payoffs (a_{ij}, b_{ij}) for $i = 1, \ldots, m$ and $j = 1, \ldots, n$. Let A be the matrix with entries a_{ij} and B be the matrix with entries b_{ij}. Then a *maximin strategy* for R in G is any optimal strategy for him in the matrix game A, while a *maximin strategy* for C is any optimal strategy for him in the matrix game $-B$.

Example 1 (continued). The maximin strategy for the game of Figure 11 is obtained by solving the matrix games

$$
A = \begin{array}{|c|c|}
\hline
15 & 22 \\
\hline
11 & 10 \\
\hline
\end{array}
\qquad \text{and} \qquad
-B = \begin{array}{|c|c|}
\hline
-10 & -20 \\
\hline
-13 & -15 \\
\hline
\end{array}
$$

which yield the optimal strategies "enter Market 1" for R and "enter Market 2" for C. Again this gives the payoff vector (22, 20).

Note that the answers obtained for the games of Figures 11 and 12 are the same and yield the same payoff vector, but they have different stability properties. In Figure 11 if the players are at (22, 20) there is no incentive for either of them to change the status quo. But in Figure 12, assume that the players are at the (22, 20) point; if R now makes the assumption that C will keep his choice of strategy fixed, he would prefer to change his strategy from the maximin strategy of "enter Market 1" to the more profitable strategy of "enter Market 2," since this would lead to the payoff vector of (30, 15) which is better for him (though worse for C). Similarly, if C makes the assumption that R will keep his choice "enter Market 1" fixed, C would prefer to switch from "enter Market 2" to "enter Market 1," since his payoff would be increased from 20 to 30. We see that the (22, 20) point is stable in Figure 11 but unstable in Figure 12.

In order to capture the idea of stability of solutions we define equilibrium point strategies.

DEFINITION. Let G be a nonzero-sum game and let A and B be the payoff matrices to R and C, respectively. Then the pair of mixed strategies p^0, q^0 are *equilibrium point strategies* for R and C, respectively, if the following conditions hold:

$$pAq^0 \leq p^0Aq^0 \qquad \text{for all strategies } p \text{ for R, and}$$
$$p^0Bq \leq p^0Bq^0 \qquad \text{for all strategies } q \text{ for C.}$$

The intuitive idea of an equilibrium point is that it is a pair of strategies having the property that neither player can increase his own payoff by changing his strategy, assuming that his opponent keeps his strategy fixed. It can be shown that every nonzero-sum game has equilibrium point solutions.

Example 1 (continued). In the game of Figure 11 there is a unique equilibrium point strategy given by the pair $p^0 = (1, 0)$ and $q^0 = \begin{pmatrix} 0 \\ 1 \end{pmatrix}$. The payoff vector for these two strategies is (22, 20). However, in the game of Figure 12 there are two equilibrium points:

(i) $p^0 = (1, 0)$, $q^0 = \begin{pmatrix} 1 \\ 0 \end{pmatrix}$ with payoff vector (15, 30),

(ii) $p^0 = (0, 1)$, $q^0 = \begin{pmatrix} 0 \\ 1 \end{pmatrix}$ with payoff vector (30, 15).

Thus for the game of Figure 12 we have discovered three possible "solutions" —one maximin solution and two equilibrium point solutions. And no one of these is clearly preferred by both players to any other one.

When solution concepts are not unique, there is nothing in the theory of games that tells how one of these should be chosen as the solution, or how players should behave so as to reach one of them. Recent experimental work has revealed some experimental conditions under which one or another kind of solution is likely to be reached when such games are played over and over again by the same pair of players. For such games, psychological, historical, legal, or moral factors may dictate which solution would actually be reached if the game were played.

Example 2. We illustrate next a case in which the maximin strategies are mixed and again are not equilibrium point strategies. Consider the market entry game whose payoffs are given in Figure 13. To get the maximin strategies

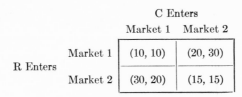

C Enters

Market 1   Market 2

	Market 1	Market 2
Market 1	(10, 10)	(20, 30)
Market 2	(30, 20)	(15, 15)

R Enters

Figure 13

we solve the games

$$A = \begin{array}{|c|c|} \hline 10 & 20 \\ \hline 30 & 15 \\ \hline \end{array} \quad \text{and} \quad -B = \begin{array}{|c|c|} \hline -10 & -30 \\ \hline -20 & -15 \\ \hline \end{array},$$

which yield optimal strategies $p^0 = (\frac{3}{5}, \frac{2}{5})$ for R and $q^0 = \begin{pmatrix} \frac{3}{5} \\ \frac{2}{5} \end{pmatrix}$ for C. The expected payoff vector for the players if they use these strategies is (18, 18), as the reader can easily compute. There are two equilibrium points, namely,

(a) $p^0 = (1, 0)$ and $q^0 = \begin{pmatrix} 0 \\ 1 \end{pmatrix}$ with payoff vector (20, 30),

(b) $p^0 = (0, 1)$ and $q^0 = \begin{pmatrix} 1 \\ 0 \end{pmatrix}$ with payoff vector (30, 20).

Note that either of the equilibrium point strategies yields certain payoffs that are better than the expected payoff for the maximin strategies. However, player R clearly prefers the equilibrium point (b) while player C clearly prefers the equilibrium point (a). We again have three possible solutions, and any one of them may occur depending on other factors.

In games such as those of Figures 12 and 13 there is a clear tendency for the two players to cooperate and choose strategies that will maximize the sum of their payoffs. This would be particularly desirable if there were some way that they could share the total proceeds. For instance, in Example 2, equilibrium point (a) might be satisfactory to both players if C could give a side payment of 5 to R. Or some other division of the proceeds might be agreed upon.

DEFINITION. Let G be a nonzero-sum game. A *cooperative solution* to G is a pair of strategies p^0, q^0 such that the quantity

$$p^0 A q^0 + p^0 B q^0 = p^0(A + B)q^0$$

is a maximum.

Note that nothing in the definition of a cooperative solution tells how the two players will divide their total gains. Various proposals have been made for making this division, but none of them is satisfactory in all cases. It should also be remarked that there may be legal or moral reasons (e.g., anti-trust laws, moral codes) that prevent certain kinds of cooperation in actual games.

Example 3. To point up further difficulties with these solution concepts, we consider the following example. R and C sit on opposite sides of a table. On the table are three one-dollar bills. If they agree on the division of the money (no change is provided) they may have it, otherwise they will get nothing.

We can enumerate the players' strategies as being the demands they make on the money. Each player can demand 0, 1, 2, or 3 dollars. The payoff table is given in Figure 14. In this game every strategy for each player

		C Demands			
		0	1	2	3
	0	(0, 0)	(0, 1)	(0, 2)	(0, 3)
	1	(1, 0)	(1, 1)	(1, 2)	(0, 0)
R Demands	2	(2, 0)	(2, 1)	(0, 0)	(0, 0)
	3	(3, 0)	(0, 0)	(0, 0)	(0, 0)

Figure 14

is a maximin strategy, so that solution concept does not limit action. There are four equilibrium points with payoffs (3, 0), (2, 1), (1, 2), and (0, 3). Each of these is also the payoff of a cooperative solution! How shall we choose among them?

If R and C are able to wait until the conclusion of the game to get change to make some division of their total payoffs, then any of these solutions might be acceptable. But suppose such cooperation is ruled out. It is reasonable then to rule out strategies 0 and 3 for each player since the first represents too small and the second too large a demand. If we do so, we can consider the reduced game in Figure 15. Here the unique maximin strategy yields the

		C Demands	
		1	2
	1	(1, 1)	(1, 2)
R Demands	2	(2, 1)	(0, 0)

Figure 15

payoffs (1, 1) while the equilibrium point strategies yield (2, 1) and (1, 2). Thus the maximin strategy, although unique, yields less to each player than either equilibrium point strategy. We see that the theory of games does not provide a unique answer for this situation.

Example 4. Jones and Smith own gasoline stations on opposite sides of the street. No other stations are nearby. There are only two prices they can charge, high and low, and each day they must decide which price they will use for the day. They are not permitted to change prices during the course of the day. Suppose their daily gross receipts are as in the table of Figure 16.

		Smith Charges	
		High	Low
Jones Charges	High	(10, 10)	(6, 16)
	Low	(16, 6)	(7, 7)

Figure 16

To interpret these numbers observe that if both charge the high price, each receives $10. If both charge the low price (the "gas war"), their income is cut to $7 for the day. Finally, if one charges the high price and the other low, the low-priced man can draw extra business so that his income is $16 while his opponent gets only $6. Let us assume that each station has fixed charges of $8 per day, so that either player will lose money if his opponent charges the low price.

The unique equilibrium and maximin strategies yield the payoff pair (7, 7), as the reader can easily check. Cooperative solutions will yield either the point (16, 6) or the point (6, 16). The total take for the cooperative solution is 22. This could be divided equally by means of side payments. It could also be divided as the game is played day by day, by having the players alternate between high and low prices each day so that their average income is $11.

Still one other solution that has been proposed for such a game is the following: Suppose that Jones is richer than Smith. If Jones charges the low price, Smith will certainly lose money. Hence Jones can make the following type of *threat:* "If you do not agree to a $13–$9 split, I shall lower my price and keep it down until you are bankrupt." Since Jones has more capital than Smith, the threat is effective and, if carried out, would result in the closing of Smith's business. On the other hand, if Smith tried to make a similar threat, he would simply ruin himself, and his threat is therefore suicidal. Here Jones is able to enforce the 13–9 division and has the dominant position in what otherwise appears to be a symmetric game, simply by being richer.

Although we have been deliberately skeptical about these various solution proposals, each has some merit. The fact that none of them fits every conceivable nonzero-sum game is perhaps an indication that such games do not reveal enough of the richness of real-world situations to provide universally satisfactory answers. It also provides avenues for future research.

EXERCISES

1. Consider the following nonzero-sum games:

G_1

(10, 10)	(5, 8)
(8, 5)	(3, 3)

,

G_2

(10, 10)	(12, 5)
(5, 12)	(7, 7)

,

G_3

(10, 10)	(18, 5)
(5, 18)	(7, 7)

,

G_4

(10, 10)	(25, 15)
(15, 25)	(5, 5)

,

G_5

(10, 10)	(20, −5)
(−5, 20)	(0, 0)

,

G_6

(0, −2)	(15, −5)
(−5, 15)	(10, 10)

.

Complete the following table by filling in the payoffs for each of the three types of solutions to these games.

	Maximin	Equilibrium Point	Cooperative
G_1	(10, 10)	(10, 10)	(10, 10)
G_2			
G_3			(5, 18) or (18, 5)
G_4	(13, 13)	(15, 25) or (25, 15)	
G_5			
G_6	(0, −2)		(10, 10)

2. In Exercise 1, assume that both players are equally rich and that it costs nothing for either of them to play any of the games. In which of the games, if any, might a threat solution be applicable? Why? [*Ans.* G_6.]

3. Consider the problem in Example 3 with $2 to be divided between R and C this time. Show that there are three equilibrium points, and that there is a strong argument for choosing one of them as the solution. Try an experimental version of the game in which two players play the game over and over again and see if they tend to the distinguished equilibrium point.

4. Consider a general version of the situation of Example 3 in which two players must divide N dollars. Show that if N is even there is a distinguished equilibrium point, but if N is odd this is not so.

5. By a *competitive solution* to a two-person nonzero-sum game we mean a solution in which R and C choose optimal strategies in the matrix game $A - B$. The rationale for this type of solution is that each player tries to maximize the difference between his own and his opponent's expected payoffs. Find competitive solutions to the six games in Exercise 1.

   [*Partial Ans.* In G_1 it yields the point $(3, 3)$; in G_4 and G_5 it yields $(10, 10)$.]

6. A matrix game can be considered a nonzero-sum game in which $b_{ij} = -a_{ij}$ for every i and j. With this interpretation show that a pair of optimal strategies p^0 and q^0 for a matrix game are equilibrium point solutions to the corresponding nonzero-sum game.

7. Show that for 2×2 nonzero-sum games, in the definition of a maximin strategy we can replace the phrase "C chooses an optimal strategy in the game $-B$" by "C chooses an optimal strategy in the game B," provided B is not strictly determined. Is the same result true when B is strictly determined? [*Ans.* No.]

8. By a *vindictive solution* to a two-person nonzero-sum game we mean a solution in which R chooses an optimal strategy in the game $-B$ and C chooses an optimal strategy in the game A. In other words each player tries to minimize his opponent's payoff, regardless of what it does to his own payoff. Find vindictive solutions to the games of Exercise 1.

   [*Partial Ans.* For G_1 it yields $(3, 3)$; for G_4 it yields $(13, 13)$.]

9. Prove that maximin strategies cannot be better for either player than equilibrium point strategies.

10. Prove that vindictive strategies cannot be better for either player than maximin strategies.

11. Use Exercises 9 and 10 to show that vindictive strategies cannot do better for either player than equilibrium point strategies.

12. Prove that if there are strategies for both players that are both maximin and vindictive, then they are both competitive.

13. Use the following example to show that a strategy can be both maximin and competitive without being vindictive:

(10, 10)	(9, 9)
(9, 9)	(8, 8)

14. Use the example of Exercise 13 to show that a strategy may be both competitive and vindictive without being maximin.

15. Prove that if there are strategies for both players that are both cooperative and competitive, then they are both maximin.

SUGGESTED READING

Von Neumann, J., and Oskar Morgenstern, *Theory of Games and Economic Behavior*, Princeton University Press, Princeton, 1944, 3d edition, 1953, Chapter I.

Williams, J. D., *The Compleat Strategyst*, McGraw-Hill, New York, 1950.

Luce, R. Duncan, and Howard Raiffa, *Games and Decisions: Introduction and Critical Survey*, Wiley, New York, 1957.

Shubik, Martin, *Strategy and Market Structure*, Wiley, New York, 1959.

Rapoport, Anatol, *Fights, Games, and Debates*, University of Michigan Press, Ann Arbor, 1960.

Kuhn, H. W., and A. W. Tucker, "Theory of Games," *Encyclopaedia Britannica*, 1956 edition.

Morgenstern, Oskar, "The Theory of Games," *Scientific American*, **180** (1950), pp. 294–308.

Gale, David, *The Theory of Linear Economic Models*, McGraw-Hill, New York, 1960.

McKinsey, J. C. C., *Introduction to the Theory of Games*, McGraw-Hill, New York, 1952.

Bellman, R., and D. Blackwell, "Red Dog, Blackjack, Poker," *Scientific American*, **184** (1951), pp. 44–47.

MacDonald, J., *Strategy in Poker, Business and War*, Norton, New York, 1950.

Kemeny, John G., Oskar Morgenstern, and Gerald L. Thompson, "A Generalization of the von Neumann Model of an Expanding Economy," *Econometrica*, **24** (1956), pp. 115–135.

Appendix Tables

$$\mathbf{b}(r;\, n,\, p) = \binom{n}{r} p^r (1 - p)^{n-r}$$

n	r	p = .01	.02	.05	.10	.15	.20	.25	.30	.40	.50
1	0	.990	.980	.950	.900	.850	.800	.750	.700	.600	.500
	1	.010	.020	.050	.100	.150	.200	.250	.300	.400	.500
2	0	.980	.960	.902	.810	.722	.640	.562	.490	.360	.250
	1	.020	.039	.095	.180	.255	.320	.375	.420	.480	.500
	2			.002	.010	.022	.040	.062	.090	.160	.250
3	0	.970	.941	.857	.729	.614	.512	.422	.343	.216	.125
	1	.029	.058	.135	.243	.325	.384	.422	.441	.432	.375
	2		.001	.007	.027	.057	.096	.141	.189	.288	.375
	3				.001	.003	.008	.016	.027	.064	.125
4	0	.961	.922	.815	.656	.522	.410	.316	.240	.130	.062
	1	.039	.075	.171	.292	.368	.410	.422	.412	.346	.250
	2	.001	.002	.014	.049	.098	.154	.211	.265	.346	.375
	3				.004	.011	.026	.047	.076	.154	.250
	4					.001	.002	.004	.008	.026	.062
5	0	.951	.904	.774	.590	.444	.328	.237	.168	.078	.031
	1	.048	.092	.204	.328	.392	.410	.396	.360	.259	.156
	2	.001	.004	.021	.073	.138	.205	.264	.309	.346	.312
	3			.001	.008	.024	.051	.088	.132	.230	.312
	4					002	.006	.015	.028	.077	.156
	5							.001	.002	.010	.031
6	0	.941	.886	.735	.531	.377	.262	.178	.118	.047	.016
	1	.057	.108	.232	.354	.399	.393	.356	.303	.187	.094
	2	.001	.006	.031	.098	.176	.246	.297	.324	.311	.234
	3			.002	.015	.041	.082	.132	.185	.276	.312
	4				.001	.005	.015	.033	.060	.138	.234
	5						.002	.004	.010	.037	.094
	6								.001	.004	.016
7	0	.932	.868	.698	.478	.321	.210	.133	.082	.028	.008
	1	.066	.124	.257	.372	.396	.367	.311	.247	.131	.055
	2	.002	.008	.041	.124	.210	.275	.311	.318	.261	.164
	3			.004	.023	.062	.115	.173	.227	.290	.273
	4				.003	.011	.029	.058	.097	.194	.273
	5					.001	.004	.012	.025	.077	.164
	6							.001	.004	.017	.055
	7									.002	.008
8	0	.923	.851	.663	.430	.272	.168	.100	.058	.017	.004
	1	.075	.139	.279	.383	.385	.336	.267	.198	.090	.031
	2	.003	.010	.051	.149	.238	.294	.311	.296	.209	.109
	3			.005	.033	.084	.147	.208	.254	.279	.219
	4				.005	.018	.046	.087	.136	.232	.273
	5					.003	.009	.023	.047	.124	.219
	6						.001	.004	.010	.041	.109
	7								.001	.008	.031
	8									.001	.004
9	0	.914	.834	.630	.387	.232	.134	.075	.040	.010	.002
	1	.083	.153	.299	.387	.368	.302	.225	.156	.060	.018
	2	.003	.013	.063	.172	.260	.302	.300	.267	.161	.070
	3		.001	.008	.045	.107	.176	.234	.267	.251	.164
	4			.001	.007	.028	.066	.117	.172	.251	.246
	5				.001	.005	.017	.039	.074	.167	.246
	6					.001	.003	.009	.021	.074	.164
	7							.001	.004	.021	.070
	8									.004	.018
	9										.002

Blank spaces mean $\mathbf{b}(r;\, n,\, p) < .0005$.

APPENDIX TABLE I (concluded)

$$b(r;\ n,\ p)$$

n	r	$p = .01$	.02	.05	.10	.15	.20	.25	.30	.40	.50
10	0	.904	.817	.599	.349	.197	.107	.056	.028	.006	.001
	1	.091	.167	.315	.387	.347	.268	.188	.121	.040	.010
	2	.004	.015	.075	.194	.276	.302	.282	.233	.121	.044
	3		.001	.010	.057	.130	.201	.250	.267	.215	.117
	4			.001	.011	.040	.088	.146	.200	.251	.205
	5				.001	.008	.026	.058	.103	.201	.246
	6					.001	.006	.016	.037	.111	.205
	7						.001	.003	.009	.042	.117
	8								.001	.011	.044
	9									.002	.010
	10										.001
15	0	.860	.739	.463	.206	.087	.035	.013	.005	.000	.000
	1	.130	.226	.366	.343	.231	.132	.067	.031	.005	.000
	2	.009	.032	.135	.267	.286	.231	.156	.092	.022	.003
	3		.003	.031	.129	.218	.250	.225	.170	.063	.014
	4			.005	.043	.116	.188	.225	.219	.127	.042
	5			.001	.010	.045	.103	.165	.206	.186	.092
	6				.002	.013	.043	.092	.147	.207	.153
	7					.003	.014	.039	.081	.177	.196
	8					.001	.003	.013	.035	.118	.196
	9						.001	.003	.012	.061	.153
	10							.001	.003	.024	.092
	11								.001	.007	.042
	12									.002	.014
	13										.003
	14										
	15										
20	0	.818	.668	.358	.122	.039	.012	.003	.001	.000	.000
	1	.165	.272	.377	.270	.137	.058	.021	.007	.000	.000
	2	.016	.053	.189	.285	.229	.137	.067	.028	.003	.000
	3	.001	.006	.060	.190	.243	.205	.134	.072	.012	.001
	4		.001	.013	.090	.182	.218	.190	.130	.035	.005
	5			.002	.032	.103	.175	.202	.179	.075	.015
	6				.009	.045	.109	.169	.192	.124	.037
	7				.002	.016	.055	.112	.164	.166	.074
	8					.005	.022	.061	.114	.180	.120
	9					.001	.007	.027	.065	.160	.160
	10						.002	.010	.031	.117	.176
	11							.003	.012	.071	.160
	12							001	.004	.035	.120
	13								.001	.015	.074
	14									.005	.037
	15									.001	.015
	16										.005
	17										.001
	18										
	19										
	20										

APPENDIX TABLE II
Random Numbers

62483	55445	80895	43055	29682
09255	67132	07454	77644	70903
49979	59207	95504	99022	18529
90249	57452	40864	18665	78138
77549	81759	54304	61250	66699
76179	79533	64104	29709	37190
28596	22223	60280	46786	58623
20770	24192	08705	80677	79847
92625	51170	26874	78382	26398
28415	13180	59307	27329	07272
99047	16485	88497	12806	36211
96473	34238	54870	15512	96324
34324	21563	57794	11107	04158
36276	19759	88914	82368	01203
34678	37106	28420	39276	19117
31979	49329	83742	05647	26962
66208	14507	05855	27500	47616
01494	41401	56658	60208	54181
44360	52562	83111	54031	27834
03894	47680	74577	77226	20716
07031	93942	96934	79554	44074
21059	54837	40761	55969	64622
45286	88209	61026	44535	44285
34927	79089	05330	22104	59632
36165	24164	58437	19923	80475
37608	94140	14585	80655	94850
46730	12214	11015	72134	03847
33971	68083	05917	27896	93466
81654	96364	91122	35741	26619
70159	43964	67805	31452	34039
88743	95788	64467	95939	13659
84439	96972	56996	69182	85423
70330	91241	86901	05901	62508
09705	18931	61236	24129	62162
29678	50391	13190	15092	89017
00918	92378	30580	75852	95352
65453	81851	08703	36098	01017
78806	57628	78931	82451	89663
51330	72244	42157	43455	63889
18281	56070	09232	93952	57834
64353	37648	00401	72530	14489
30499	32631	47076	39657	43078
02031	80276	70492	39758	65253
29492	25096	48338	91815	64806
54042	56695	06917	79628	70701
92154	74519	57381	66251	96197
45890	99918	89770	35212	87582
54853	04762	12154	09150	34920
33401	71486	42807	79008	74244
37345	81231	81516	17763	53698

28470	19220	15251	81185	80949
05763	73998	70518	30736	77140
46967	59492	81935	44627	84918
65361	73425	04969	03676	27486
79821	50363	08667	98500	42817
77019	03964	93346	88152	03833
00884	34387	15224	51234	39434
67676	93996	82687	50068	72664
03119	47252	21495	49173	75833
36641	96536	88110	52973	70006
94747	79548	47263	68535	95606
41779	46981	67109	48880	10904
41500	58247	31942	01343	98176
70479	65749	63606	34527	92341
85243	78316	49539	79128	00224
99998	77109	67495	75596	49799
62074	15227	52236	79174	56289
82992	54801	39132	45332	19371
79503	73188	56454	91756	66459
22710	90391	69403	28217	29460
61686	12118	32455	27147	43331
66868	86886	16048	06962	36381
12204	53778	51127	43422	87225
18893	57833	10340	80118	54645
38143	41971	14805	09795	05943
20827	09452	72782	82231	75340
14123	49864	58660	71595	00363
42316	49930	86439	99287	98624
78495	80189	14086	19743	93623
41292	37330	29993	27573	22481
99545	51902	72154	78368	08734
47168	58480	55103	70609	62239
51410	35094	04263	37717	96866
89509	17236	49840	86025	96416
89731	85785	36220	52879	04604
89918	90438	99982	58187	51539
72618	80754	21291	96433	09214
81530	13638	79720	52571	40507
08901	04808	25832	51404	68377
41388	94935	40894	29304	87665
32777	08201	32680	12876	72006
46754	47018	16225	81687	28647
42759	80483	35260	09318	36720
59376	12414	43204	30006	61461
92163	40927	89243	84735	26876
05968	73574	21954	09901	01159
18573	36121	81220	26043	52796
13380	74910	59169	20433	25333
13400	54167	90416	10325	66284
86166	10097	51518	10052	89113

75722	89176	80307	63131	87190
49212	34682	44641	82369	81519
95090	09765	65628	98729	68001
17768	68852	48428	68154	10053
41378	07937	62350	82051	61684
73373	43037	11991	87921	38622
38863	17327	93732	24181	76505
09372	51990	38141	38974	95696
18120	15814	54770	66557	27710
71357	11797	39062	32276	87037
08173	80204	46402	22043	38310
64736	99181	18771	61220	36062
78891	35239	40508	26934	58585
06826	07463	41653	11745	45947
34666	79532	69093	82296	05513
76588	40389	41867	18461	94237
28227	45664	64682	53229	65676
25692	62227	50386	78806	22102
84543	66728	53281	73306	19259
60751	38660	82292	89939	25992
52448	54178	85018	41958	14992
21933	95640	84120	86031	79793
65366	05401	50738	55701	36802
17149	09217	10663	80471	65572
29193	87336	31182	29963	17936
33971	62401	83210	62752	28165
12172	59935	57556	33795	41570
84948	95439	66849	87170	59861
55742	68345	74918	20733	49522
98479	59802	11015	74621	17321
87574	77012	69497	37400	02373
74299	56964	79566	16613	74702
85926	23880	28376	33938	39506
01629	12674	99526	46071	71653
64489	72447	86570	15709	94996
16695	55798	04605	56249	96625
86689	68192	76289	64144	75515
29640	00748	64256	31576	48882
45602	31186	58670	80988	93346
30102	54221	72477	02417	95440
54677	34916	64338	57901	24058
17610	95371	86682	63993	47947
30737	56574	26131	15817	73625
70920	38347	42717	69086	33901
09234	30789	21794	29397	71235
94148	02940	96255	69893	20415
44067	65060	18249	87803	25662
30815	41690	04630	70317	52740
77881	01796	78496	79806	44414
95254	38929	27324	40237	77323

40575	79339	59874	56320	61151
81968	53775	82368	68218	48016
87689	03896	20884	56709	30480
31228	10777	79488	57472	10959
63510	73019	18266	77263	16598
23651	78815	98791	35854	94772
49628	69773	10359	62152	04334
51211	03442	07060	48154	83052
00752	87877	00117	50449	08581
96370	84776	72822	12949	84844
71555	41764	93579	96082	35335
24276	88597	30626	31213	63751
85194	59692	01220	44923	85040
54700	86194	72751	91697	95782
09692	70582	05989	66620	95318
75873	24064	95514	29067	78134
68051	33729	67378	54609	48365
52151	34667	66402	76208	95307
96561	75175	09677	46147	07121
21916	97649	79441	63537	17219
35707	98838	25899	47716	49946
30575	18276	41443	10501	27998
50374	69340	97816	18812	89428
00347	13222	36546	98795	20132
86642	13038	23994	21604	52991
97019	50685	61161	88121	15959
32599	80442	14069	52853	34648
31442	33682	28978	63258	17212
37463	38728	04291	77354	71750
48312	56799	23047	21775	25114
50732	73577	37090	25567	49898
08742	00359	81816	87036	29986
45734	62166	07098	24142	86220
75917	60196	73294	08512	29384
50880	33109	84342	65725	10194
78906	94031	46346	87543	07827
12405	56648	78777	86456	70986
72884	78154	98615	55814	87076
64383	40305	82186	63302	10323
96740	93229	46308	97470	34214
20230	97803	49985	81833	87365
10730	60143	51446	83530	03657
36099	22521	53482	52322	27098
83634	88066	67394	72624	45344
46314	37551	82125	16293	35180
41825	39069	75375	27059	27732
95291	18681	95794	97366	84647
76548	57499	76221	49147	24140
76071	77716	87073	37591	60869
26495	12526	70314	58329	79129

APPENDIX TABLE III

Single Payment Compound Amount Factor

$$(1 + r)^n$$

$n \backslash r$	.0025	.0050	.0075	.010	.015	.020	.025	.030
4	1.0100	1.0202	1.0303	1.0406	1.0614	1.0824	1.1038	1.1255
8	1.0202	1.0407	1.0616	1.0829	1.1265	1.1717	1.2184	1.2668
12	1.0304	1.0617	1.0938	1.1268	1.1956	1.2682	1.3449	1.4258
16	1.0408	1.0831	1.1270	1.1726	1.2690	1.3728	1.4845	1.6047
20	1.0512	1.1049	1.1612	1.2202	1.3469	1.4859	1.6386	1.8061
24	1.0618	1.1272	1.1964	1.2697	1.4295	1.6084	1.8087	2.0328
30	1.0778	1.1614	1.2513	1.3478	1.5631	1.8114	2.0976	2.4273
36	1.0941	1.1967	1.3086	1.4308	1.7091	2.0399	2.4325	2.8983
42	1.1106	1.2330	1.3686	1.5188	1.8688	2.2972	2.8210	3.4607
48	1.1273	1.2705	1.4314	1.6122	2.0435	2.5871	3.2715	4.1323
54	1.1443	1.3091	1.4970	1.7114	2.2344	2.9135	3.7939	4.9341
60	1.1616	1.3489	1.5657	1.8167	2.4432	3.2810	4.3998	5.8916
72	1.1969	1.4320	1.7126	2.0471	2.9212	4.1611	5.9172	8.4000
84	1.2334	1.5204	1.8732	2.3067	3.4926	5.2773	7.9580	11.976
96	1.2709	1.6141	2.0489	2.5993	4.1758	6.6929	10.703	17.076
108	1.3095	1.7137	2.2411	2.9289	4.9927	8.4883	14.394	24.346
120	1.3494	1.8194	2.4514	3.3004	5.9693	10.765	19.358	34.711
180	1.5674	2.4541	3.8380	5.9958	14.584	35.321	85.172	204.50
240	1.8208	3.3102	6.0092	10.893	35.633	115.89	374.74	1204.9
300	2.1150	4.4650	9.4084	19.788	87.059	380.23	1648.8	7098.5
360	2.4568	6.0226	14.731	35.950	212.70	1247.6	7254.2	41822.

$n \backslash r$	.03	.04	.05	.06	.07	.08	.09
1	1.0300	1.0400	1.0500	1.0600	1.0700	1.0800	1.0900
2	1.0609	1.0816	1.1025	1.1236	1.1449	1.1664	1.1881
3	1.0927	1.1249	1.1576	1.1910	1.2250	1.2597	1.2950
4	1.1255	1.1699	1.2155	1.2625	1.3108	1.3605	1.4115
5	1.1593	1.2167	1.2763	1.3382	1.4026	1.4693	1.5386
6	1.1941	1.2653	1.3401	1.4185	1.5007	1.5869	1.6771
7	1.2299	1.3159	1.4071	1.5036	1.6058	1.7138	1.8280
8	1.2668	1.3686	1.4775	1.5938	1.7182	1.8509	1.9926
9	1.3048	1.4233	1.5513	1.6895	1.8385	1.9990	2.1719
10	1.3439	1.4802	1.6289	1.7908	1.9672	2.1589	2.3674
12	1.4258	1.6010	1.7959	2.0122	2.2522	2.5182	2.8127
14	1.5126	1.7317	1.9799	2.2609	2.5785	2.9372	3.3417
16	1.6047	1.8730	2.1829	2.5404	2.9522	3.4259	3.9703
18	1.7024	2.0258	2.4066	2.8543	3.3799	3.9960	4.7171
20	1.8061	2.1911	2.6533	3.2071	3.8697	4.6610	5.6044
25	2.0938	2.6658	3.3864	4.2919	5.4274	6.8485	8.6231
30	2.4273	3.2434	4.3219	5.7435	7.6123	10.063	13.268
35	2.8139	3.9461	5.5160	7.6861	10.677	14.785	20.414
40	3.2620	4.8010	7.0400	10.286	14.974	21.725	31.409
45	3.7816	5.8412	8.9850	13.765	21.002	31.920	48.327
50	4.3839	7.1067	11.467	18.420	29.457	46.902	74.358

APPENDIX TABLE III

Single Payment Compound Amount Factor (concluded)

$n\backslash r$	.10	.12	.14	.16	.18	.20
1	1.1000	1.1200	1.1400	1.1600	1.1800	1.2000
2	1.2100	1.2544	1.2996	1.3456	1.3924	1.4400
3	1.3310	1.4049	1.4815	1.5609	1.6430	1.7280
4	1.4641	1.5735	1.6890	1.8106	1.9388	2.0736
5	1.6105	1.7623	1.9254	2.1003	2.2878	2.4883
6	1.7716	1.9738	2.1950	2.4364	2.6996	2.9860
7	1.9487	2.2107	2.5023	2.8262	3.1855	3.5832
8	2.1436	2.4760	2.8526	3.2784	3.7589	4.2998
9	2.3579	2.7731	3.2519	3.8030	4.4355	5.1598
10	2.5937	3.1058	3.7072	4.4114	5.2338	6.1917
12	3.1384	3.8960	4.8179	5.9360	7.2876	8.9161
14	3.7975	4.8871	6.2613	7.9875	10.147	12.839
16	4.5950	6.1304	8.1372	10.748	14.129	18.488
18	5.5599	7.6900	10.575	14.463	19.673	26.623
20	6.7275	9.6463	13.743	19.461	27.393	38.337
25	10.835	17.000	26.462	40.874	62.669	95.396
30	17.449	29.960	50.950	85.850	143.37	237.38
35	28.102	52.800	98.100	180.31	328.00	590.67
40	45.259	93.051	188.88	378.72	750.38	1469.8
45	72.890	163.99	363.68	795.44	1716.7	3657.3
50	117.39	289.00	700.23	1670.7	3927.4	9100.4

$n\backslash r$	.25	.30	.35	.40	.45	.50
1	1.2500	1.3000	1.3500	1.4000	1.4500	1.5000
2	1.5625	1.6900	1.8225	1.9600	2.1025	2.2500
3	1.9531	2.1970	2.4604	2.7440	3.0486	3.3750
4	2.4414	2.8561	3.3215	3.8416	4.4205	5.0625
5	3.0518	3.7129	4.4840	5.3782	6.4097	7.5938
6	3.8147	4.8268	6.0534	7.5295	9.2941	11.391
7	4.7684	6.2749	8.1722	10.541	13.476	17.086
8	5.9605	8.1573	11.032	14.758	19.541	25.629
9	7.4506	10.604	14.894	20.661	28.334	38.443
10	9.3132	13.786	20.107	28.925	41.085	57.665
12	14.552	23.298	36.644	56.694	86.381	129.75
14	22.737	39.374	66.784	111.12	181.62	291.93
16	35.527	66.542	121.71	217.80	381.85	656.84
18	55.511	112.46	221.82	426.88	802.83	1477.9
20	86.736	190.05	404.27	836.68	1688.0	3325.3
25	264.70	705.64	1812.8	4499.9	10819.	25251.
30	807.79	2620.0	8128.5	24201.	69349.	191750.
35	2465.2	9727.9	36449.	130160.	444510.	1456100.
40	7523.2	36119.	163440.	700040.	2849200.	11057000.
45	22959.	134110.	732860.	3765000.	18262000.	83967000.
50	70065.	497930.	3286200.	20249000.	117060000.	637620000.

APPENDIX TABLE IV

Uniform Payment Present Value Factor

$$\frac{(1 + r)^n - 1}{r(1 + r)^n}$$

n/r	.0025	.0050	.0075	.010	.015	.020	.025	.030
4	3.9751	3.9505	3.9261	3.9020	3.8544	3.8077	3.7620	3.7171
8	7.9107	7.8230	7.7366	7.6517	7.4859	7.3255	7.1701	7.0197
12	11.807	11.619	11.435	11.255	10.908	10.575	10.258	9.9540
16	15.665	15.340	15.024	14.718	14.131	13.578	13.055	12.561
20	19.484	18.987	18.508	18.046	17.169	16.351	15.589	14.877
24	23.266	22.563	21.889	21.243	20.030	18.914	17.885	16.936
30	28.868	27.794	26.775	25.808	24.016	22.396	20.930	19.600
36	34.386	32.871	31.447	30.108	27.661	25.489	2.3556	21.832
42	39.823	37.798	35.914	34.158	30.994	28.235	25.821	23.701
48	45.179	42.580	40.185	37.974	34.043	30.673	27.773	25.267
54	50.455	47.221	44.269	41.569	36.831	32.838	29.457	26.578
60	55.652	51.726	48.173	44.955	39.380	34.761	30.909	27.676
72	65.817	60.340	55.477	51.150	43.845	37.984	33.240	29.365
84	75.681	68.453	62.154	56.648	47.579	40.526	34.974	30.550
96	85.255	76.095	68.258	61.528	50.702	42.529	36.263	31.381
108	94.545	83.293	73.839	65.858	53.314	44.110	37.221	31.964
120	103.56	90.073	78.942	69.701	55.498	45.355	37.934	32.373
180	144.81	118.50	98.593	83.322	62.096	48.584	39.530	33.170
240	180.31	139.58	111.14	90.819	64.796	49.569	39.893	33.306
300	210.88	155.21	119.16	94.947	65.901	49.869	39.976	33.329
360	237.19	166.79	124.28	97.218	66.353	49.960	39.994	33.333

n/r	.03	.04	.05	.06	.07	.08	.09
1	.9709	.9615	.9524	.9434	.9346	.9259	.9174
2	1.9135	1.8861	1.8594	1.8334	1.8080	1.7833	1.7591
3	2.8286	2.7751	2.7232	2.6730	2.6243	2.5771	2.5313
4	3.7171	3.6299	3.5460	3.4651	3.3872	3.3121	3.2397
5	4.5797	4.4518	4.3295	4.2124	4.1002	3.9927	3.8897
6	5.4172	5.2421	5.0757	4.9173	4.7665	4.6229	4.4859
7	6.2303	6.0021	5.7864	5.5824	5.3893	5.2064	5.0330
8	7.0197	6.7327	6.4632	6.2098	5.9713	5.7466	5.5348
9	7.7861	7.4353	7.1078	6.8017	6.5152	6.2469	5.9952
10	8.5302	8.1109	7.7217	7.3601	7.0236	6.7101	6.4177
12	9.9540	9.3851	8.8633	8.3838	7.9427	7.5361	7.1607
14	11.296	10.563	9.8986	9.2950	8.7455	8.2442	7.7862
16	12.561	11.652	10.838	10.106	9.4466	8.8514	8.3126
18	13.754	12.659	11.690	10.828	10.059	9.3719	8.7556
20	14.877	13.590	12.462	11.470	10.594	9.8181	9.1285
25	17.413	15.622	14.094	12.783	11.654	10.675	9.8226
30	19.600	17.292	15.372	13.765	12.409	11.258	10.274
35	21.487	18.665	16.374	14.498	12.948	11.655	10.567
40	23.115	19.793	17.159	15.046	13.332	11.925	10.757
45	24.519	20.720	17.774	15.456	13.606	12.108	10.881
50	25.730	21.482	18.256	15.762	13.801	12.233	10.962

APPENDIX TABLE IV

Uniform Payment Present Value Factor (concluded)

n/r	.10	.12	.14	.16	.18	.20
1	.9091	.8929	.8772	.8621	.8475	.8333
2	1.7355	1.6901	1.6467	1.6052	1.5656	1.5278
3	2.4869	2.4018	2.3216	2.2459	2.1743	2.1065
4	3.1699	3.0373	2.9137	2.7982	2.6901	2.5887
5	3.7908	3.6048	3.4331	3.2743	3.1272	2.9906
6	4.3553	4.1114	3.8887	3.6847	3.4976	3.3255
7	4.8683	4.5638	4.2883	4.0386	3.8115	3.6046
8	5.3349	4.9676	4.6389	4.3436	4.0776	3.8372
9	5.7590	5.3282	4.9464	4.6065	4.3030	4.0310
10	6.1446	5.6502	5.2161	4.8332	4.4941	4.1925
12	6.8137	6.1944	5.6603	5.1971	4.7932	4.4392
14	7.3667	6.6282	6.0021	5.4675	5.0081	4.6106
16	7.8237	6.9740	6.2651	5.6685	5.1624	4.7296
18	8.2014	7.2497	6.4674	5.8178	5.2732	4.8122
20	8.5136	7.4694	6.6231	5.9288	5.3527	4.8696
25	9.0770	7.8431	6.8729	6.0971	5.4669	4.9476
30	9.4269	8.0552	7.0027	6.1772	5.5168	4.9789
35	9.6442	8.1755	7.0700	6.2153	5.5386	4.9915
40	9.7791	8.2438	7.1050	6.2335	5.5482	4.9966
45	9.8628	8.2825	7.1232	6.2421	5.5523	4.9986
50	9.9148	8.3045	7.1327	6.2463	5.5541	4.9995

n/r	.25	.30	.35	.40	.45	.50
1	.8000	.7692	.7407	.7143	.6897	.6667
2	1.4400	1.3609	1.2894	1.2245	1.1653	1.1111
3	1.9520	1.8161	1.6959	1.5889	1.4933	1.4074
4	2.3616	2.1662	1.9969	1.8492	1.7195	1.6049
5	2.6893	2.4356	2.2200	2.0352	1.8755	1.7366
6	2.9514	2.6427	2.3852	2.1680	1.9831	1.8244
7	3.1611	2.8021	2.5075	2.2628	2.0573	1.8829
8	3.3289	2.9247	2.5982	2.3306	2.1085	1.9220
9	3.4631	3.0190	2.6653	2.3790	2.1438	1.9480
10	3.5705	3.0915	2.7150	2.4136	2.1681	1.9653
12	3.7251	3.1903	2.7792	2.4559	2.1965	1.9846
14	3.8241	3.2487	2.8144	2.4775	2.2100	1.9931
16	3.8874	3.2832	2.8337	2.4885	2.2164	1.9970
18	3.9279	3.3037	2.8443	2.4941	2.2195	1.9986
20	3.9539	3.3158	2.8501	2.4970	2.2209	1.9994
25	3.9849	3.3286	2.8556	2.4994	2.2216	1.9999
30	3.9950	3 3321	2.8568	2.4999	2.2219	2.0000
35	3.9984	3.3330	2.8571	2.5000	2.2222	2.0000
40	3.9995	3.3332	2.8571	2.5000	2.2222	2.0000
45	3.9998	3.3333	2.8571	2.5000	2.2222	2.0000
50	3.9999	3.3333	2.8571	2.5000	2.2222	2.0000

Index

A

Absorbing Markov chains, 282
  absorption probabilities, 286
  canonican form of, 283
  charge accounts, 295
  fundamental matrix of, 284
  random walk, 283
  work load model, 299
Associative law for product of matrices,
  250

B

Balance sheet, 352
Base, of number system, 44
Basic conjunctions, 37
Bayes' theorem, 152, 156
Binary numbers, 44
Binomial coefficients, 104
  computation of, 127
  properties of, 110
Binomial probability, 171, 466
Binomial theorem, 114, 115
Birthday problem, 148
Bond yield, 328, 332
Bookkeeping:
  double entry, 346
  double classification, 346
  flow diagrams for, 358
Boolean algebra, 67
Bounding hyperplane, 371
Business game, 211

C

Capital recovery factor, 320
Charge accounts, 295

Circuits, switching, 40
  basic series, 42
  computer, 47
Coalitions:
  blocking, 68
  dictator, 69
  losing, 68
  minimal winning, 69
  powerless, 70
  veto power of, 70
  voting, 68
  winning, 68
Commutative law of addition for vectors,
  230
Complement of a set, 58
Complete permutation, 149
Components of a vector, 229
Compound amount factor, 320, 472
Compound statement, 1
  simple parts of, 1
  truth set of, 62
Conditional, 9
Conjunction, 4
  basic, 37
Connectives, 4
  biconditional, 10
  conditional, 9
  conjunction, 4
  disjunction, 4
  negation, 5
Contradictories, 34
Convex set, 368
Critical path analysis, 72
Critical path, 76

D

Decision making:
  under certainty, 26, 306
  under uncertainty, 26, 306
Decision:
  problem, 244
  theory, 221
  trees, 25
Decision rules, 24, 175, 207, 211
  cyclical ordering, 212
  reorder quantity, 212
  trigger level, 212
Dependent statements, 33
Depreciation, 334
  double declining balance, 335, 340
  formulas for present value, 339
  straight-line, 335, 340
  sum-of-years'-digits, 335, 344
Detached coefficient tableau, 258
Dictator, 69
Difference equation, 312
  initial condition for, 314
Disjoint sets, 59
Disjunction, 4
  inclusive, 5
  exclusive, 5
Dominated rows and columns, 426
Double classification bookkeeping, 346,
    358
  adjusting transactions, 357
  balance sheet, 352
  balancing, 355
  income statement, 352
  reversing transactions, 357
  transaction matrix, 348
  trial balance, 349
Double declining balance depreciation,
    335, 340
Double entry bookkeeping, 346, 350
Dual linear programming problems, 386,
    394
Duality theorem of linear programming,
    397
Dummy variables, 398

E

Earnings:
  cash, 334
  reported, 334

Empty set, 54
Equilibrium, 438, 440, 442
Equivalence of statements, 11, 31
Expanding economy model, 436
  equilibrium solution of, 438, 440
  existence of equilibrium for, 442
Expansion factor, 439
Expected value, 179, 186, 222

F

Factor:
  capital recovery, 320
  compound amount, 320, 472
  expansion, 439
  interest, 439
  investment, 319
  present value, 320, 474
  sinking fund, 320
Feasible vectors, 396
Financial reports, 352
  balance sheet, 352
  flow diagrams for, 358
  income statement, 352
Flow diagrams, 120, 126
  for computing compound amount, 317
  for computing payback period, 330
  for computing present value of depreci-
    ation, 339, 345
  for financial reports, 358
  for simplex method, 388
  for simulation, 202, 208, 212

G

Games:
  expected value of, 416
  fair, 404
  matrix, 414
  nonzero-sum, 402, 455
  nonstrictly determined games, 407
  optimal strategies for, 404, 415
  poker, 432
  simplex method for, 448
  strictly determined, 404, 417
  symmetric, 455
  theory of, 402
  value of, 404, 415, 416
  zero sum, 402

H

Half line, 373
Half plane, 366
Half space, 367
Hat-check problem, 149
Hypergeometric probability, 146
Hyperplane, 367
  bounding, 371
  superfluous, 370

I

Implication, 29, 33
Income statement, 352
Inconsistency of statements, 31, 33
Independence of statements, 17, 33, 154
Independent trials process, 169
  with more than two outcomes, 183
Interest factor, 439
Interest rate, 325
Interest rates:
  effective, 330
  nominal, 330
Internal rate of return, 328
Intersection of two sets, 57
Inventory control, 211
Inverse of a square matrix, 262
  rule for, 265

J

Job, 72
  critical, 75
  early finish time, 74
  early start time, 74
  late finish time, 74
  slack time, 75

L

Law of large numbers, 177, 179
Linear equations:
  detached coefficient, tableau for, 258
  solution of, 254
Linear function, maximum and minimum
  of, 370
Linear programming, 364
  dual problems, 386, 394
  duality theorem of, 397

Linear programming (*Cont.*)
  problems, 379
  simplex method for, 384
Locus, 365
Logical possibilities, 2, 13
  main requirement of, 14
  tree diagrams for, 19
Logical relations, 29, 33
Logically true statement, 11, 15
Logically false statement, 15

M

Markov chains, 193, 274
  absorbing, 282
  application of matrix theory to, 274
  random walk, 283
  regular, 275
  transition matrix, 275
  transition probabilities, 194
Mathematics of accounting, 346
Mathematics of finance, 312
Matrices, 240
  addition of two, 248
  associative law for products, 250
  equality of two, 240
  fixed point of, 276
  powers of a square matrix, 252
  product of two, 249
  product with a number, 248
  product with a vector, 242
Matrix:
  adjusting, 357
  partitioned, 348
  reversing, 357
  transaction, 348
  transition, 194
  transpose of, 351
Matrix games, 414, 422
  dominated rows and columns, 426
  simplex method for solving, 448
  symmetric, 455
  two-row and two-column, 425
Max and min of vectors, 304
Maximum and minimum of a linear function, 370
Mean, 127
Measure, probability, 135
  equiprobable, 141
  properties of, 137
  tree, 161

Median, 127
Mixed strategy, 409, 410
  vector, 415
Mode, 128
Monte Carlo simulation, 199
  analysis of decision rules, 207
Morgenstern, O., 432
Morra, 421, 430, 431, 451
Morrissey, L. E., 347
Multinomial theorem, 116

N

Negation, 5
Nonstrictly determined games, 407
  optimal strategies for, 410
Nonzero-sum games, 455
  competitive strategy, 463
  cooperative strategy, 459
  equilibrium point strategy, 457
  maximin strategy, 457
  threat strategy, 461
  vindictive strategy, 463
Numbers:
  binary, 44
  decimal, 44
  octal, 47

O

Octal number system, 47
Open statement, 364
  truth set of, 364
Optimal strategies, 404, 410
Outcome:
  worth of, 244
  utility of, 244

P

Partition of a set, 84
  cells of, 84
  cross, 85
Partitioned matrix, 348
Partitions:
  counting of, 102
  number of, 103
  ordered, 102
  two-cell, 106
Parts requirements listing problem, 268

Payback period, 326
Permutations, 98
  complete, 149
Poker, 432
  bluffing in, 434
Polyhedral convex set, 364, 367
  bounded, 373
  bounding hyperplane of, 371
  extreme points of, 370, 371
  unbounded, 373
Posterior probability, 155
Predecessor:
  immediate, 73
  of a job, 72
Present value factor, 320, 474
Prior probability, 155
Probability measure, 135
  binomial, 171
  properties of, 137
Probability:
  binomial, 171
  conditional, 152
  hypergeometric, 146
  measure, 135
  Monte Carlo simulation, 199, 207
  posterior, 155
  prior, 155
  properties of, 138
  of a statement, 135
  of a sample, 145
  transition, 194
Probabilistic independent statements, 154
Probability vector, 275
Processes:
  independent trials, 169
  independent trials with more than two
    outcomes, 183
  Markov chains, 193, 274
  stochastic, 160
Project, 72
  dual, 80
  graph, 73
Proper subset, 54
Pure strategy, 414

Q

Queuing theory:
  by Markov change, 289
  by simulation, 202, 207

R

Random numbers, 200, 410, 468
Random walk, 283
Ray, 373
Regular Markov chain, 275
    fixed point for, 276
    investment problem, 302
    personnel problem, 301
    waiting line, 289
Relations, logical, 29
    equivalence, 11, 31
    implication, 29
    onefold, 33
    systematic analysis of, 33
    twofold, 33
Reliability, 215
Reorder quantity, 212
Rule for inverting a matrix, 265

S

Sample, probability of, 145
Set, 53
    complement of, 58
    description of, 53
    difference of two, 59
    disjoint, 59
    empty, 54
    intersection of two, 57
    laws of set operations, 66
    listing of, 53
    number of element in, 95
    polyhedral convex, 364
    proper, 54
    subset, 54
    truth set of a statement, 62
    union of two, 58
    unit, 54
    universal, 54
Set, partition of, 84
    cells of, 84
    cross-partition of, 85
Shadow prices, 395
    value, 395
Shapley, L. S., 117
Shubik, M., 117
Simple parts of a compound statement, 1
Simplex method:
    algorithm flow chart, 388

Simplex method (*Cont.*)
    for games, 448
    for linear programming, 384
Simplex tableau, 386
Single payment, compound amount, 320, 472
    present value, 320
Sinking fund factor, 320
Slack time:
    free, 82
    independent, 82
    of a project, 75
Solution of linear equations, 254
    detached coefficient tableau for, 258
Standard deviation, 179
Statements:
    compound, 1
    contradictories, 34
    dependent, 33
    equivalence of two, 11, 31
    having given truth tables, 37
    implication, 29, 33
    inconsistent, 31, 33
    independent, 17, 33
    logically false, 15
    logically true, 11, 13
    open, 364
    probabilistically independent, 154
    probability of, 138
    subcontraries, 33
Straight-line depreciation, 335, 340
Strategies, 404
    mixed, 419
    optimal, 404, 410
    pure, 414
Strictly determined games, 404, 417
    fair, 404
    optimal strategies for, 404
    value of, 404
Stochastic processes, 160
    independent trials, 169
    independent trials with more than two outcomes, 183
    Markov chains, 193, 274
Subcontraries, 33
Subroutine, 128
Subset, 53, 54, 57
    proper, 54
Sum-of-years'-digits depreciation, 335, 344
Switching circuits, 40

T

Tableau:
 detached coefficients, 258
 simplex, 386
Tax offsets on depreciation, 334
Technological coefficients, 396
Technological order, 269
Transaction matrix, 348
Transition probabilities, 194
Transpose of a matrix, 351
Tree diagrams, 19
 branches, 21
 decision trees, 25
 paths, 20
Tree measure, 161
Trigger level, 212
Truth set:
 of a compound statement, 62
 of an open statement, 364
Truth table, 4, 37
Truth value, 2
Tucker, A. W., 432

U

Uniform payment:
 capital recovery, 320
 compound amount, 320
 present value, 320, 474
 sinking fund, 320
Union of two sets, 58
Unit set, 54
Universal set, 54
Utility of an outcome, 244

V

Value:
 expected, 179, 186
 imputed or shadow, 395

Vector:
 activity, 396
 capacity constraint, 396
 column, 229
 commutative law of addition, 230
 cost, 397
 equality of two, 230
 feasible, 396
 fixed point of a matrix, 276
 imputed value, 397
 intensity, 438
 max and min operations on, 304
 multiplication by a number, 231
 price, 438
 probability, 275
 product of two, 234, 235
 product with a matrix, 242
 profit, 396
 requirements, 397
 row, 230
 zero, 232
von Neumann, John, 432, 436
Voting coalitions, 68
Voting power, 117

W

Waiting line, 201, 207, 289
 queue length, 293
 traffic intensity, 290
Winters, P. R., 80
Work load model, 299

Y

Yield, 328, 332

Z

Zero-sum games, 402